CONDENSED MATTER THEORIES
VOLUME 19

For permission to use material from this book please contact us:
Telephone 631-231-7269; Fax 631-231-8175
Web Site: http://www.novapublishers.com

ISBN 1-59454-308-9

Published by Nova Science Publishers, Inc. ✢ New York

Condensed Matter Theories
Volume 19

M. Belkacem and P. M. Dinh
(Editors)

Nova Science Publishers, Inc.
New York

Contents

Preface

The Twenty-Seventh International Workshop on Condensed Matter Theories (CMT-27) was held from Sep 15–20, 2004 in Toulouse, at the University Paul Sabatier. The Workshop on Condensed Matter Theories, founded in 1977 and held annually since then in various countries in the Americas, Europe, and Asia, was thus organized for the first time in France.

The orientation of the CMT Worshops has traditionally been highly interdisciplinary, emphasis being placed on the common concerns of theorists applying advanced many-particle methods in such diverse areas as Solid-State, Low-Temperature, Atomic, Nuclear, Particle, Statistical, Astronomical, Chemical, and Biological Physics. Adhering to this tradition, the XXVII International Workshop on Condensed Matter Theories has highlighted theoretical advances at the interface with nanosciences, which represent a stronghold in Toulouse area, both at the experimental and theoretical sides. With a particular focus on the potential interest of theoretical methods and numerical simulations dedicated to the description of various physical systems at the nanometer scale (molecules, clusters, nanomaterials, biomolecules, ...), the CMT27 Workshop has provided a forum at which specialists of various connex fields of physics have presented and fruitfully discussed the latest developments and newest techniques in these areas. The CMT Worshops also aim to give a unique opportunity of exchanging ideas to researchers from both developed and developing countries, and this goal was fully attained during the 27th edition.

The CMT27 Workshop has been sponsored by the University Paul Sabatier of Toulouse through the Laboratoire de Physique Théorique, the Laboratoire de Physique Quantique and the 'Institut de Recherche sur les Systèmes Atomiques et Moléculaires Complexes' (IRSAMC), by the Ministxere de la Jeunesse, de l'Education Nationale et de la Recherche, by the Conseil Régional Midi-Pyrénées, by the Conseil Général de Haute-Garonne and by the US Army Research Office. These various structures are warmly acknowledged for their support.

We also thank all the members of the various committees for their support and help, in particular Bary Malik and John W. Clark.

Phuong Mai Dinh
For the Organizing Committee

Atomic and Small Molecule Physics

MOMENTUM DISTRIBUTION IN LIQUID PARA-HYDROGEN

J. W. Kim

Semiconductor Research Center, Dongguk University
Seoul, Korea 100–715

F. J. Bermejo

Department of Electricity and Electronics
University of the Basque Country
P. O. 644, E–48080 Bilbao, Spain

M. L. Ristig

Institut für Theoretische Physik, Universität zu Köln
D–50937 Köln, Germany

J. W. Clark

Department of Physics, Washington University
St. Louis, Missouri 63130, USA

1. INTRODUCTION

Experimental and theoretical studies of hydrogen atoms and molecules laid the foundation of modern quantum physics. The hydrogen atom has provided an excellent laboratory for discovering basic quantum effects: Bohr's atomic model and space quantization, explanation of fine and hyperfine structure in atomic spectra, quantum-electrodynamic effects, etc. Quantum chemistry had its beginnings in investigations of the H_2 molecule and its vibrational and rotational excitations.

The coupling of the proton-spin states in the hydrogen molecule gives rise to two distinguishable isomers, para-hydrogen ($p\mathrm{H}_2$) with nuclear spins antiparallel (total spin $J = 0$) and ortho-hydrogen ($o\mathrm{H}_2$) with nuclear spins parallel ($J = 1$). Thus, under normal thermal conditions, bulk hydrogen matter is a mixture of these two species with concentrations determined by the intramolecular rotational excitations. This property is of course rooted in nuclear physics, since it must be ascribed to internal degrees of freedom of the constituent nucleons.

Moreover, in neutron scattering on hydrogen, internal excitations of the H_2 molecules are responsible for deviations from Y-scaling symmetry, just as internal excitations of nucleons are responsible for such violation in electron scattering on nuclei [1-3]. Until very recently, this complication has severely hindered attempts at precise measurement of the liquid-structure function $S(k)$ of para-hydrogen [4,5]. Under the impetus of continuing strong interest in the properties of hydrogen, concerted efforts have been successful in overcoming this experimental difficulty [6,7].

The existing scattering experiments reveal the presence of extremely strong spatial correlations in liquid $p\mathrm{H}_2$ in a temperature range near the triple point. At a temperature $T = 15.2\,\mathrm{K}$, the correlations are significantly stronger than in liquid $^4\mathrm{He}$. This rather surprising result demonstrates that even today, research on hydrogen may lead us to new and important physical effects that enrich the field of quantum many-body physics.

Currently, our primary interests lie in the properties and effects of spatial correlations in liquid $p\mathrm{H}_2$, as revealed both through high-precision neutron-scattering measurements and through quantitative *ab initio* theoretical investigations. As we shall see, these correlations exert a prominent influence on the behavior of the static liquid-structure function $S(k)$ under variation of the wave number k. Their effect is also visible in the k-dependence of the momentum distribution $n(k)$, the dispersion relation of collective excitations, and other physical quantities. In this paper we shall focus on the behavior of $n(k)$ while also presenting results for the structure function $S(k)$ and its Fourier partner, the radial distribution function $g(r)$.

To further illuminate the broad interest in properties of hydrogen systems in condensed matter physics and planetary science, we point out that the liquid and solid phases of hydrogen provide the dominant constituents of the giant planets [8], and that the realization of metallic hydrogen in the laboratory remains a Holy Grail of high-pressure physics [9]. A number of other questions of principle and practice in the basic quantum physics of hydrogen have attracted much interest over the years, and continue to do so.

Chief among these questions is the issue of the existence of a Bose-Einstein transition to a superfluid phase. Experimental efforts persist in the attempt to supercool liquid $p\mathrm{H}_2$ to temperatures low enough that the liquid undergoes such a transition [10,11]. To aid mapping out the relevant regions of the phase diagram of hydrogen matter, experiments have been performed on hydrogen films [12–14] and on hydrogen in confined geometries [15,16]. Refs. 17 and 18 report experimental results on cluster experiments indicating that transitions to a hydrogenic superfluid state in mesoscopic systems can indeed occur, but only at very low temperatures. To cite another example, it is well to recall that the quest for Bose-Einstein condensation in quantum gases first began with intensive efforts to observe this phenomenon in spin-polarized atomic-hydrogen gas brought to sufficiently high densities [19].

To demonstrate the presence of very strong spatial correlations in liquid $p\mathrm{H}_2$, we describe in Section 2 our recent experimental results on the liquid-structure function $S(k)$ of bulk para-hydrogen at $T = 15.2\,\mathrm{K}$, not far from the triple point of this substance. The data are extracted from neutron scattering cross-section measurements performed with high precision at the Institut Laue-Langevin (ILL) in Grenoble [6].

The results spur the exploration of spatial correlation effects in other physical quantities, notably the momentum distribution of H_2 molecules in liquid pH_2 and the corresponding reduced one-body density matrix. We summarize the results of a theoretical analysis of these quantities in Section 3. For correlated boson fluids and normal Fermi liquids at nonzero temperatures, one may decompose the one-body density matrix into three factors, which in turn characterize the strength of the spatial correlations, the renormalized exchange effects, and the dynamical correlation effects induced by the particle-particle interactions.

A numerical calculation of these factors appropriate to the problem of liquid pH_2 in the vicinity of its triple point may be carried out by specializing the chosen many-body formalism to the normal liquid phase of the Bose fluid and ignoring exchange correlation effects [20]. The method of choice for quantitative evaluation is the version of correlated density matrix (CDM) theory developed in Refs. 21–23. This treatment has been already applied to liquid pH_2 in a study of the liquid-structure function, the radial distribution function, and the exchange correlation function [20].

Correlated density matrix theory is based on a minimum principle for the Helmholtz free energy. The key steps of this *ab initio* approach are sketched briefly in Section 4. Numerical results on the momentum distribution and the one-body density matrix of liquid para-hydrogen at temperature $T = 16\,\mathrm{K}$ and particle number density $\varrho = 0.021\,\text{Å}^{-3}$ are presented and discussed in Section 5, which concludes the paper.

2. PRECISION MEASUREMENTS

Quantum zero-point motion in bulk matter composed of ^{4}He atoms prevents solidification at zero temperature. The helium system crystallizes only under sufficiently high pressure. Thus, its phase diagram does not possess a triple point where helium gas, liquid, and solid can coexist. In contrast, hydrogen matter, like a classical substance, exhibits a triple point (at temperature $T_3 = 13.8\,\mathrm{K}$), as well as a gas-liquid critical point (at $T_c = 33\,\mathrm{K}$) [24]. However, helium and hydrogen systems have in common the existence of strong spatial correlations in the liquid phase caused by the interactions between the constituents. Numerical estimates of the strength of these correlations as reflected in the radial distribution function $g(r)$ and in the corresponding static structure function $S(k)$ of liquid pH_2 have been made at a density $\varrho = 0.021\,\text{Å}^{-3}$ and at two different temperatures, $T = 16\,\mathrm{K}$ and $T = 7.5\,\mathrm{K}$. The results give clear evidence of a liquid having significant structure [20]. The calculations, based on the realistic H_2–H_2 potential of Silvera and Goldman [9], have been performed using CDM theory [21–23], making the specializations indicated above.

Figure 1 displays the results for the radial distribution function $g(r)$. Results for the corresponding liquid-structure function $S(k)$ and for other physical quantities are reported in Ref. 20. As seen in Fig. 1, the spatial correlations exhibit a pronounced shell structure with the main peak at $r_0 = 3.6$ Å and a height $g(r_0) \approx 1.5$. Since the calculation of $g(r)$ was performed in the HNC/0 hypernetted-chain approximation, which ignores elementary and triplet contributions, the predicted peak height is expected to be on the low side. Recent path-integral molecular dynamics simulations

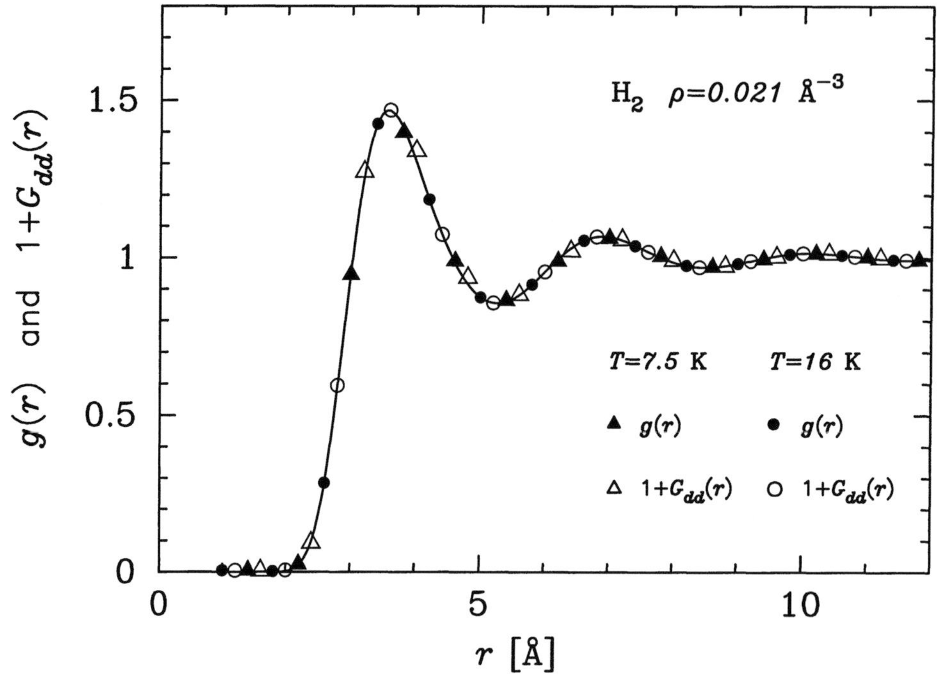

Figure 1. Numerical results for the optimal radial distribution function $g(r)$ of liquid $p\mathrm{H}_2$ at particle number density $\varrho = 0.021\,\mathrm{\AA}^{-3}$ and two different temperatures, $T = 16\,\mathrm{K}$ and $T = 7.5\,\mathrm{K}$. The function $1 + G_{dd}(r)$ represents the direct component of $g(r)$. The calculated radial distribution function is insensitive to exchange.

on liquid para-hydrogen [25,26] bear out this expectation and clearly improve upon the HNC/0 estimate for the peak height [6].

Further, we may infer from Fig. 1 that the spatial correlations as described by $g(r)$ are insensitive to changes in temperature and, in particular, that correlations associated with particle exchange can be ignored around $T = 16\,\mathrm{K}$, i.e., we may safely replace the function $g(r) - 1$ by its direct component $G_{dd}(r)$ (see Ref. 20 for details).

Major difficulties frustrated early attempts at experimental determination of the static structure function $S(k)$ of liquid para-H_2 in the vicinity of the triple point by measuring the cross section of the liquid for neutron scattering. At low temperatures, transitions between discrete molecular rotational energy levels occur, with the effect that liquid molecular hydrogen is a mixture of two different species, para- and ortho-hydrogen. If the incident neutron energy in such an experiment exceeds 80 meV, the ortho admixture becomes too large. The scattering is dominated by para-ortho transitions with a form factor quite different from the liquid-structure function $S(k)$ of pure $p\mathrm{H}_2$, preventing a precise measurement of the $p\mathrm{H}_2$ component [6].

This difficulty has been circumvented in a recent experiment performed at the D1B spectrometer at ILL. A cold neutron diffractometer was employed with an incident neutron wavelength of 2.52 Å. The incident energy of only 12.88 meV covers the relevant wave vector transfer range of $0 < k < 4\,\mathrm{\AA}^{-1}$. Under these conditions, the

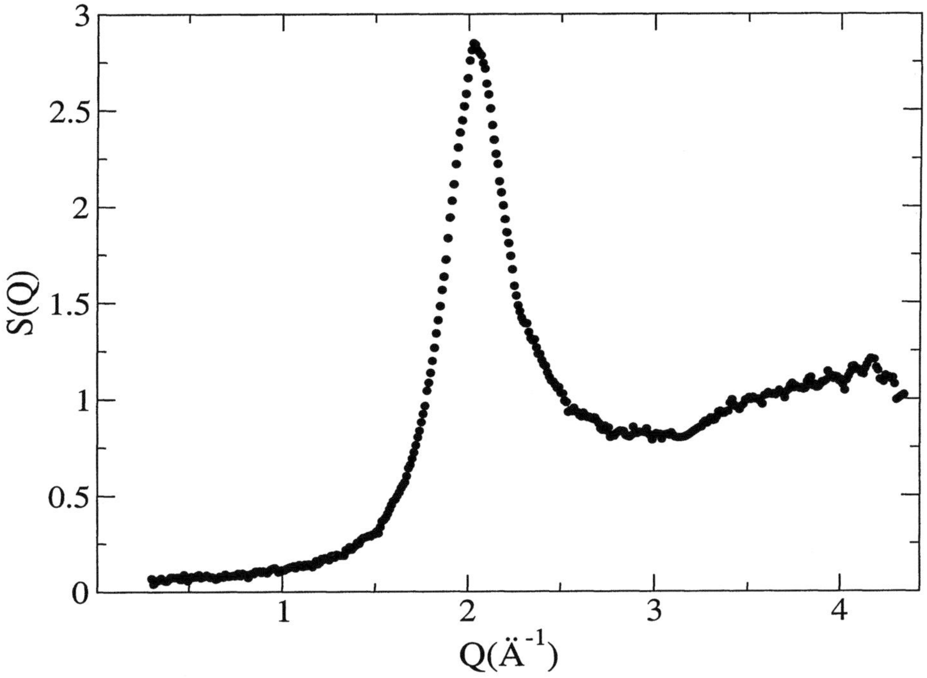

Figure 2. Experimental results for the static structure function $S(k)$ of liquid $p\mathrm{H}_2$ at temperature $T = 15.2\,\mathrm{K}$ as a function of wave number k (note $k = Q$; see also Ref. 6).

scattering arises from liquid-structure effects rather than from single-particle molecular rotations, the $o\mathrm{H}_2$ admixture in the sample then being below 2 %. To extract the liquid-structure function $S(k)$ from the raw experimental data, a number of corrections had to be made for multiple scattering, attenuation, inelasticity effects, ortho admixture, etc. Details of the data processing and a discussion of the experimental results may be found in Ref. 6.

In this paper, explicit consideration of the experimentally determined structure function of liquid $p\mathrm{H}_2$ will be limited to the results at temperature $T = 15.2\,\mathrm{K}$, shown in Fig. 2. We are immediately confronted with the fact that the spatial correlations are extremely strong, clearly in excess of those found in liquid helium. The experimental results are in good agreement with results from path-integral molecular dynamics simulations [20,25,26]. The origin of the large differences between the CDM results for $S(k)$ and both the experimental data and the simulations remains an open issue.

The above findings provide compelling motivation for exploring the effects of spatial correlations on other properties of liquid para-hydrogen, such as the one-body density matrix and the momentum distribution of the H_2 molecules.

3. MOMENTUM DISTRIBUTIONS

The momentum distribution $n(k)$ in a homogeneous fluid is defined as the thermal average of the number of particles with wave number k at given particle density ϱ and temperature T. We may evaluate this quantity by taking the dimensionless Fourier transform of the corresponding reduced one-body density matrix $n(r)$, where $r \geq 0$ is a spatial separation variable [1,22,27]. The formal structure of the function $n(r)$ for a quantum fluid has been extensively studied within correlated-basis-functions (CBF) theory at zero temperature [27–29] and within correlated-density-matrix (CDM) theory at nonzero temperatures [22,30]. The generic matrix element $n(r)$ may be written as a product of three irreducible quantities, namely a strength factor n_c, a renormalized exchange function $N_0(r)$, and an exponential factor whose exponent $Q(r)$ characterizes the dynamic correlations; thus

$$n(r) = n_c N_0(r) \exp\left[-Q(r)\right] . \tag{1}$$

The quantities n_c, $N_0(r)$, and $Q(r)$ have been analyzed theoretically for Bose fluids in the normal state and in the Bose-Einstein condensed phase [27,30], assuming respectively a correlated ground state of Jastrow type (at zero temperature) and an N-body density matrix of analogous form (at nonzero temperatures). The results may be generalized to a normal Fermi liquid without undue complications [22]. The structural decomposition (1) is valid for a much larger set of trial states or density matrices, such as correlated N-boson states of Feenberg type [31]. The quantities n_c, $N_0(r)$, and $Q(r)$ have been further analyzed within CDM theory using HNC techniques, to derive explicit formulas that permit their approximate numerical evaluation.

We now summarize a number of general and exact properties of Eq. (1) and its ingredients (see also Ref. 1). Conservation of the total number N of particles is expressed by the normalization of the one-body density matrix $n(r)$ at $r = 0$,

$$n(0) = \frac{1}{N} \sum_{\mathbf{k}} n(k) = 1 . \tag{2}$$

The strength factor n_c in Eq. (1), determined by $Q(r)$ through the relation

$$n_c = \exp\left[Q(r = 0)\right] , \tag{3}$$

provides a useful measure of the strength of the spatial correlations in a quantum fluid [1]. Consequently, at $r = 0$ we have

$$N_0(0) = \frac{1}{N} \sum_{\mathbf{k}} N_0(k) = 1 . \tag{4}$$

The direct correlation function $Q(r)$ is generated by the particle-particle interactions and vanishes at large separations r. For a system of non-interacting bosons or fermions, the function $Q(r)$ is therefore identically zero and the strength factor n_c is unity.

In the normal phase of a quantum fluid, the exchange function $N_0(r)$ is of short range, vanishing asymptotically, i.e.,

$$N_0(r) \longrightarrow 0\,, \quad \text{as } r \longrightarrow \infty\,. \tag{5}$$

At sufficiently low temperatures, however, particle exchange is no longer localized and the function $N_0(r)$ develops long-range order,

$$N_0(r) \longrightarrow N_0(\infty) > 0\,, \quad \text{as } r \longrightarrow \infty\,, \tag{6}$$

signaling the presence of a Bose-Einstein condensate [30,20]. In the ground state at zero temperature, $N_0(r) \equiv 1$ and the strength factor n_c coincides with the condensate fraction of the boson fluid.

For the normal phase of a homogeneous Bose or Fermi fluid, the statistical correlation factor $N_0(r)$ may be decomposed into two terms,

$$N_0(r) = n_{cc}(r) + N_c(r)\,. \tag{7}$$

The component $n_{cc}(r)$ is the one-body density matrix attributed in Ref. 22 to quasiparticles (quasiholes) within the context of CDM theory. At $r = 0$ the quasiparticles (quasiholes) obey the sum rule

$$n_{cc}(0) = \frac{1}{N} \sum_{\mathbf{k}} n_{cc}(k) = 1\,, \tag{8}$$

where $n_{cc}(k)$ is the thermal occupation number of a quasiparticle with wave vector $\mathbf{k}$. The second term $N_c(r)$ in Eq. (7) collects the renormalized contributions of statistical correlations that are not contained in the quasiparticle term. This component has the property

$$N_c(r = 0) = 0\,. \tag{9}$$

Explicit analysis of the functions $Q(r)$, $N_0(r)$, and $n_{cc}(r)$ for liquid para-hydrogen is readily performed within CDM theory, but will not be elaborated here.

Liquid pH_2 will presumably condense into a superfluid or Bose-Einstein phase, if, in practice, it can be supercooled down to sufficiently low temperatures. Should the H_2–H_2 interaction be somehow switched off, the condensation would occur at about 7 K. The intermolecular forces would act to lower the transition temperature from this fiducial value. Attempts to supercool liquid hydrogen down to this temperature range have not yet been successful. However, ongoing experiments with hydrogen clusters [18] may again enliven the quest for Bose-Einstein condensation in bulk hydrogen matter.

4. Pair-Density Functional Theory

We have applied CDM theory to carry out a numerical calculation of the one-body density matrix and the momentum distribution of liquid para-hydrogen close to the triple point. The CDM approach is a generalization of the highly successful CBF theory of the ground state of a strongly correlated quantum fluid [32,33] to nonzero temperatures. It may also be viewed as a pair-density functional approach [20,34], i.e., as a generalization of density-functional theory. The theory is non-perturbative and thus well suited to strongly correlated quantum many-body systems. It has been employed in Ref. 20 to evaluate, for liquid $p\mathrm{H}_2$, the static function $S(k)$, the exchange structure function $S_{cc}(k)$, the quasiparticle (quasihole) occupation number $n_{cc}(k)$, and various structural components associated with these quantities, at a density $\varrho = 0.021\,\text{Å}^{-3}$ and at two special temperatures, $T = 16\,\mathrm{K}$ and $T = 7.5\,\mathrm{K}$.

These several functions, discussed in detail in Ref. 20, are needed as input for a quantitative calculation of the momentum distribution of a boson liquid. Here, we merely indicate in broad terms how they are determined within CDM theory.

(i) Adopting the Silvera-Goldman two-body potential, an explicit expression is constructed for the Helmholtz free energy of liquid $p\mathrm{H}_2$ in the normal phase,

$$F = F\left[g(r), G_{cc}(r), n_{\mathrm{coll}}(k)\right]_{T,\varrho}\,, \tag{10}$$

as a functional of the radial distribution function $g(r)$, the exchange distribution function $G_{cc}(r)$, and the phonon/roton occupation number $n_{\mathrm{coll}}(k)$, all at given particle density and temperature. The construction is based on the N-body density matrix [20]

$$W\left(\mathbf{R},\mathbf{R}'\right) = \frac{1}{I}\Phi(\mathbf{R})Q\left(\mathbf{R},\mathbf{R}'\right)\Phi\left(\mathbf{R}'\right) \tag{11}$$

in the configuration-space representation, with $\mathbf{R} = (\mathbf{r}_1, \mathbf{r}_2, \cdots, \mathbf{r}_N)$. As a first approximation, the temperature-dependent wave function $\Phi(\mathbf{R})$ and the incoherence factor $Q\left(\mathbf{R},\mathbf{R}'\right)$ are each represented by a Jastrow-type trial ansatz.

(ii) A minimum principle for the Helmholtz free energy (10) is invoked to determine the best functions $g(r)$, $G_{cc}(r)$, and $n_{\mathrm{coll}}(k)$. Taking account of condition (8), which reflects conservation of the total number N of quasiparticles (quasiholes) in the normal liquid phase, variation of the functional (10) yields three Euler–Lagrange equations. These equations are solved numerically for the optimal quantities $g(r)$, $G_{cc}(r)$, and $n_{\mathrm{coll}}(k)$ at density $\varrho = 0.021\,\text{Å}^{-3}$ and temperature T. Results at two different temperatures are reported in Ref. 20.

At the temperature $T = 16\,\mathrm{K}$ close to the triple point, it is found that the optimal exchange correlation function is short-ranged and very small in magnitude. We may therefore ignore exchange correlations and set $G_{cc}(r)$ to zero. Moreover, the optimal momentum distribution $n_{cc}(k)$ of quasiparticles (quasiholes) is very well represented by a Gaussian fit,

$$n_{cc}(k) = \exp\left\{\beta\left[\mu_0 - \varepsilon_0(k)\right]\right\}\,, \tag{12}$$

where $\beta = 1/k_{\mathrm{B}}T$, $\varepsilon_0(k) = \hbar^2k^2/2m$ is the kinetic energy of a free H_2 molecule of mass m, and $\mu_0 \approx -7.8\,\mathrm{K}$ is the chemical potential at $T = 16\,\mathrm{K}$. Thus, within our approximate realization of CDM theory, the quasiparticles (quasiholes) present in the vicinity of the triple-point temperature T_3 are simply free H_2 molecules with a momentum distribution of classical Boltzmann form. It is consistent with this

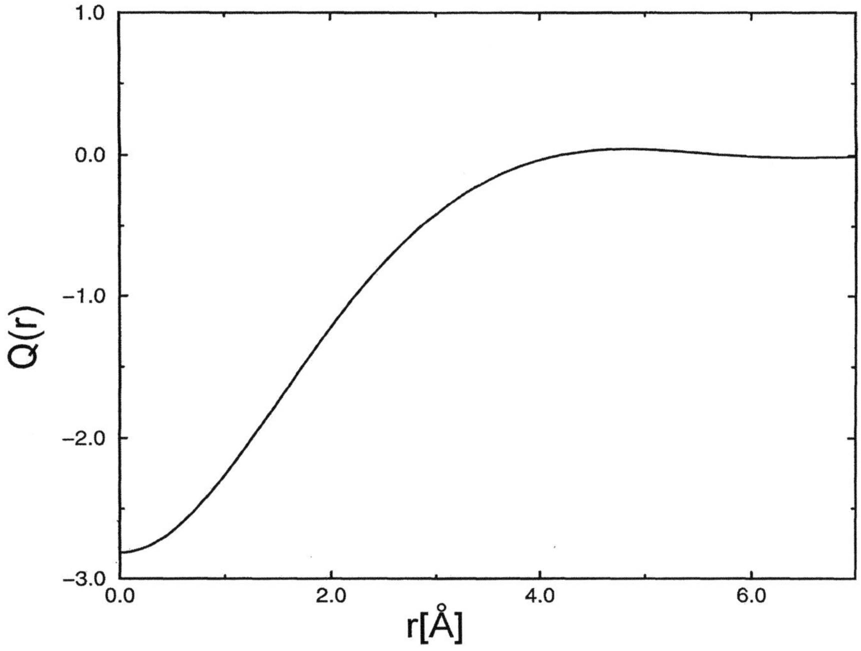

Figure 3. Numerical results for the correlation function $Q(r)$, calculated within CDM theory for liquid $p\mathrm{H}_2$ at temperature $T = 16\,\mathrm{K}$ and density $\varrho = 0.021\,\text{Å}^{-3}$ (see text).

result to neglect exchange contributions to the statistical function $N_0(r)$ and to the function $Q(r)$. Accordingly, Eq. (7) reduces to $N_0(r) = n_{cc}(r)$, with $n_{cc}(r)$ given by the Fourier inverse of expression (12).

We emphasize that although they are negligible near the triple point, exchange effects rapidly increase in importance as the temperature is lowered, with long-range order setting in at about $T \approx 7\,\mathrm{K}$ in the supercooled temperature regime (see Ref. 20).

5. NUMERICAL RESULTS AND DISCUSSION

Based on the formal and numerical procedures outlined in Section 4, we have completed optimal determinations of the function $Q(r)$, the strength-factor n_c, the one-body density matrix $n(r)$, and the momentum distribution for liquid $p\mathrm{H}_2$, all at density $\varrho = 0.021\,\text{Å}^{-3}$ and temperature $T = 16\,\mathrm{K}$. Technically, the calculations rest on a hypernetted-chain analysis [30]. Effects of (real) phonon excitations are not included in the trial density matrix; we also ignore effects of molecular vibrations. Due to the absence of exchange correlations, the nontrivial behavior of the function $Q(r)$, and hence of the one-body density matrix and the momentum distribution, is exclusively governed by dynamical effects arising from the intermolecular interactions as represented by the Silvera-Goldman potential. Diffusion and other possible effects

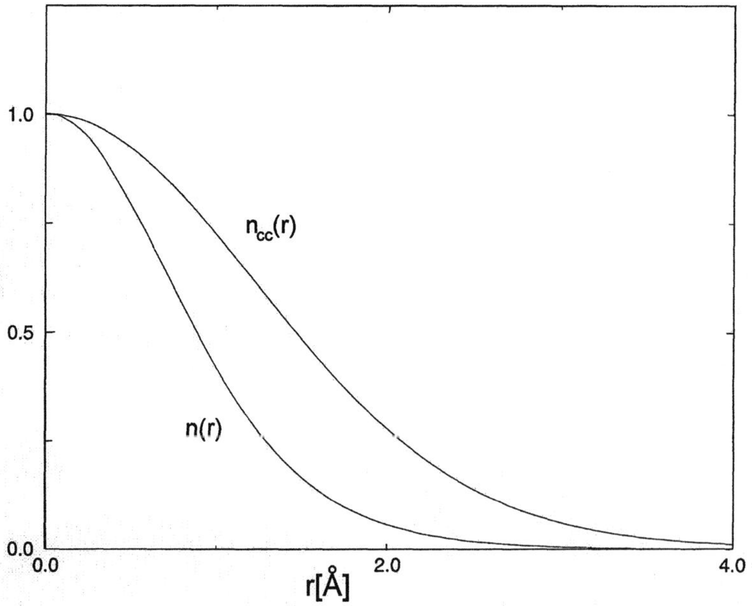

Figure 4. Same as Fig. 3 but for the reduced one-body density matrices $n(r)$ and $n_{cc}(r)$ of real particles (H_2 molecules in liquid pH_2) and quasiparticles (behaving like H_2 molecules in a free pH_2 gas), respectively.

that deform the shape of the distribution $n(k)$ are not considered.

The numerical results for the correlation function $Q(r)$ reflect the strong influence of the molecular interactions. Referring to Fig. 3, we see that at $T = 16\,\text{K}$, this function is negative for separations r in the range $0 \leq r < 4\,\text{Å}$ and vanishes at larger values, $r \geq 6\,\text{Å}$. We find numerically that $Q(r = 0) \approx -2.8$. The large absolute value of $Q(0)$ is a direct consequence of the strong spatial correlations, which lead, according to relation (3), to a strength factor n_c of only 0.06. This result is to be compared with the value $n_c = 1$ for the corresponding non-interacting gas and a value of about 0.10 for liquid ^{4}He in equilibrium at zero temperature. If liquid para-hydrogen could be supercooled down to zero temperature, the strength factor would coincide with the condensate fraction. The theoretical value of the condensate fraction is then even much smaller than 0.06 [35].

Figure 4 depicts the numerical results for the one-body density matrix $n(r)$ in comparison with the results for the quasiparticle one-body density matrix $n_{cc}(r)$. Due to the strong spatial correlations induced by the interactions, $n(r)$ departs very much from $n_{cc}(r)$, which we have found to be well represented by the classical Boltzmann form (12). This Gaussian distribution is conveniently rewritten as

$$n_{cc}(r) = \exp\left\{-\pi\left(\frac{r}{\lambda}\right)^2\right\} \tag{13}$$

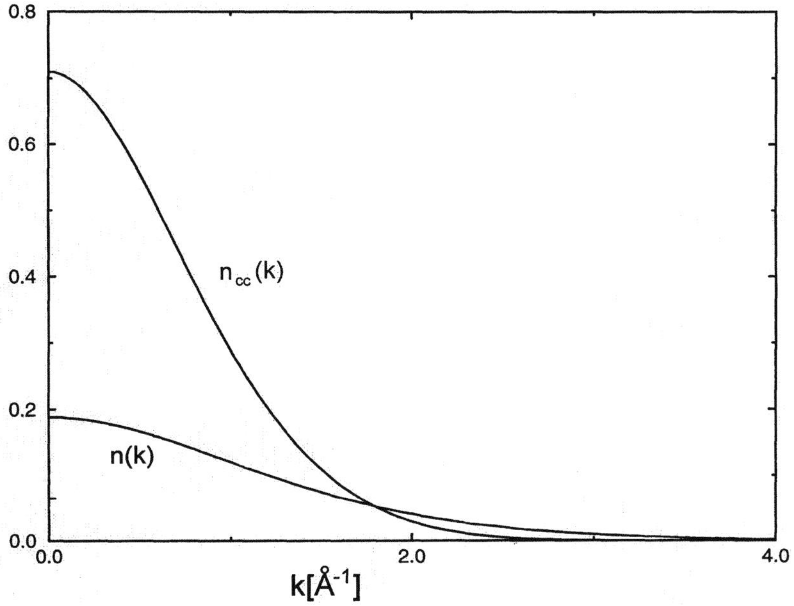

Figure 5. Same as Fig. 4 but for the momentum distribution $n(k)$ in liquid pH_2 and $n_{cc}(k)$ in a free pH_2 gas.

by introducting the thermal wavelength $\lambda = \sqrt{2\pi\beta\hbar^2/m}$, which has a value ≈ 3.09 Å at $T = 16$ K.

By contrast, the calculated one-body density matrix $n(r)$ is of significantly shorter range. Moreover, it evidently deviates from a Gaussian form, since

$$n(r) = n_c \exp\left\{-\pi\left(\frac{r}{\lambda}\right)^2 - Q(r)\right\} \tag{14}$$

and the function $Q(r)$ deviates significantly from quadratic behavior at separations $r \geq 3$ Å. However, we may still approximate this function rather well by a parabola at separations $0 \leq r < 3$ Å, appreciable differences arising only in the tail region, where the absolute values of $Q(r)$ are relatively small. In a simple first approximation, the one-body density matrix (14) may therefore be fitted rather well by a Gaussian function of the separation r. The resulting fit is characterized by an effective thermal wavelength λ^* of only ≈ 2 Å at $T = 16$ K. However, precision measurements of the molecular momentum distribution in liquid pH_2 should enable experimental detection of deviations from such a Gaussian approximation.

Our theoretical results for the momentum distributions $n_{cc}(k)$ of noninteracting Boltzmann H_2 molecules and $n(k)$ of H_2 molecules in the liquid are plotted in Fig. 5. The intermolecular interactions drastically reduce the number of real H_2 molecules in the liquid having small momenta (specifically, by a factor of about one-third at a given small wave number). The H_2–H_2 interaction promotes a large number of molecules in the liquid to the intermediate and tail regimes of momenta $\hbar\mathbf{k}$. To explore the fine structure of the momentum distribution, we have recently performed an inelastic neutron scattering experiment on liquid para-hydrogen with the MARI spectrometer at Rutherford Laboratory. Processing of the data is currently under way.

ACKNOWLEDGMENTS

The research described herein was supported by the U.S. National Science Foundation under Grant No. PHY-0140316. JWC is grateful to the US Army Research Office–Research Triangle Park for travel support through a grant to Southern Illinois University–Carbondale. MLR acknowledges financial support by the DAAD and the Department of Physics, University of Pretoria, where part of this work was done.

REFERENCES

[1] P. E. Sokol, R. N. Silver, J. W. Clark, in *Momentum Distributions*, eds. R. N. Silver and P. E. Sokol (Plenum Press, N.Y., 1989); J. W. Clark and M. L. Ristig, *ibid.*

[2] D. B. Day et al., Phys. Rev. Lett. **59**, 427 (1987).

[3] K. A. Gernoth and M. L. Ristig, in *Particle Scattering, X-Ray Diffraction, and Microstructure of Solids and Liquids*, eds. M. L. Ristig and K. A. Gernoth, LNP **610** (Springer-Verlag, Berlin, 2003).

[4] F. J. Bermejo et al., Phys. Rev. Lett. **84**, 5359 (2000).

[5] M. Zoppi et al., Phys. Rev. B **58**, 11905 (1998).

[6] I. Dawidowski et al., Phys. Rev. B (2004), in press.

[7] F. J. Bermejo et al., Phys. Rev. B **66**, 212202 (2002).

[8] M. Ross, Rep. Prog. Phys. **48**, 1 (1985).

[9] I. F. Silvera, Rev. Mod. Phys. **52**, 393 (1980).

[10] V. L. Ginzburg and A. A. Sobyanin, JETP Lett. **15**, 242 (1972).

[11] H. J. Maris et al., J. Low Temp. Phys. **51**, 471 (1983).

[12] H. Wiechert, Physica B **169**, 144 (1991).

[13] V. L. P. Frank et al., Phys. Rev. Lett. **61**, 436 (1988).

[14] F.C. Liu et al., Phys. Rev B **51**, 2848 (1995).

[15] D. F. Brewer et al., J. Low Temp. Phys. **101**, 317 (1995).

[16] M. Schindler et al., Phys. Rev. B **53**, 11451 (1996).

[17] S. Grebenev et al., Physica B **280**, 65 (2000).

[18] S. Grebenev et al., Science **289**, 1532 (2000).

[19] Physics Today, October 1998, Vol. 51, Number 10, p. 17.

[20] M. L. Ristig, T. Lindenau, and L. Szybisz, in *Condensed Matter Theories*, Vol. 17, eds. M. P. Das and F. Green (Nova Science Publishers, N.Y., 2003).

[21] C. E. Campbell, K. E. Kürten, M. L. Ristig, and G. Senger, Phys. Rev. B **30**, 3728 (1984).

[22] G. Senger et al., Ann. Phys. **218**, 160 (1992).

[23] M. L. Ristig et al., Ann. Phys. **243**, 247 (1995).

[24] P. C. Souers, *Cryogenic Hydrogen Data Pertinent to Magnetic Fusion Energy*, Lawrence Livermore Laboratory Report UCRL–52628 (1979).

[25] K. Kinugawa et al., Chem. Phys. Lett. **292**, 454 (1998).

[26] S. Miura et al., J. Chem. Phys. **110**, 4523 (1999).

[27] M. L. Ristig, in *From Nuclei to Particles*, Proceedings, International School of Physics, Enrico Fermi, Course LVII, Varenna, 1981, ed. A. Molinari (North-Holland, Amsterdam, 1982).

[28] P. M. Lam and M. L. Ristig, Phys. Rev. B **20**, 1960 (1979).

[29] M. L. Ristig and J. W. Clark, Phys. Rev. B **14**, 2875 (1976).

[30] R. Pantförder et al., J. Low Temp. Phys. **108**, 245 (1997).

[31] C. E. Campbell, Phys. Lett. A **44**, 471 (1973).

[32] E. Feenberg, *Theory of Quantum Fluids* (Academic Press, N.Y., 1969).

[33] J. W. Clark, in *Progress in Particle and Nuclear Physics*, Vol. 2, ed. D. Wilkinson (Pergamon, Oxford, 1979).

[34] W. Kohn and L. J. Sham, Phys. Rev. **140**, A1133 (1965); E. Krotscheck, Phys. Lett. A **190**, 201 (1994).

[35] M. L. Ristig, G. Senger, and K. E. Kürten, in *Recent Progress in Many-Body Theories*, Vol. 1, eds. A. J. Kallio, E. Pajanne, and R. F. Bishop (Plenum, N.Y., 1988).

BEHAVIOR OF THE SPHERICAL CELLULAR MODEL OF A PARTIALLY IONIZED GAS

George A. Baker, Jr.

Theoretical Division, Los Alamos National Laboratory
University of California, Los Alamos, NM 87545 USA

1. INTRODUCTION

The present purpose is to study a model of a partially to fully ionized, neutral gas of electrons and ions. This paper is a summary of further results, beyond those given in ref. [1]. In previous work[2,3] the numerical evaluations were confined to the simplest case, hydrogen. Here we also report on larger values of the ionic charge. The details have been submitted for publication elsewhere.[4] The basic philosophy is similar to the of Thomas-Fermi theory[5–7], but with a more fundamental approach to the inclusion of quantum statistical physics. The increasing speed of computing equipment makes it possible to envisage this project, which was not possible in previous times. Still, fairly drastic approximations have been required in its implementation.

In the next section I summarize the necessary statistical mechanics formulæ.[8] In the third section, I give the equations for Z electrons in a spherical cell. As this formulation is currently intractable, in the fourth section I apply the independent electron approximation. I have programed the spherical cellular model, so developed, for the computations of its predictions of the pressure and the energies. In the fifth section I report the results for various limiting values of the temperature and density. In the sixth section, I examine the results for intermediate values of the temperature and the density. I find various critical points, and their pendant phase boundaries, triple points, *etc.* These features either mark the limit of the one phase region or the limit of validity of the model.

In the last section I discuss the energies. This model has the feature that the thermodynamically consistent internal energy and the "physically reasonable" energy are different.

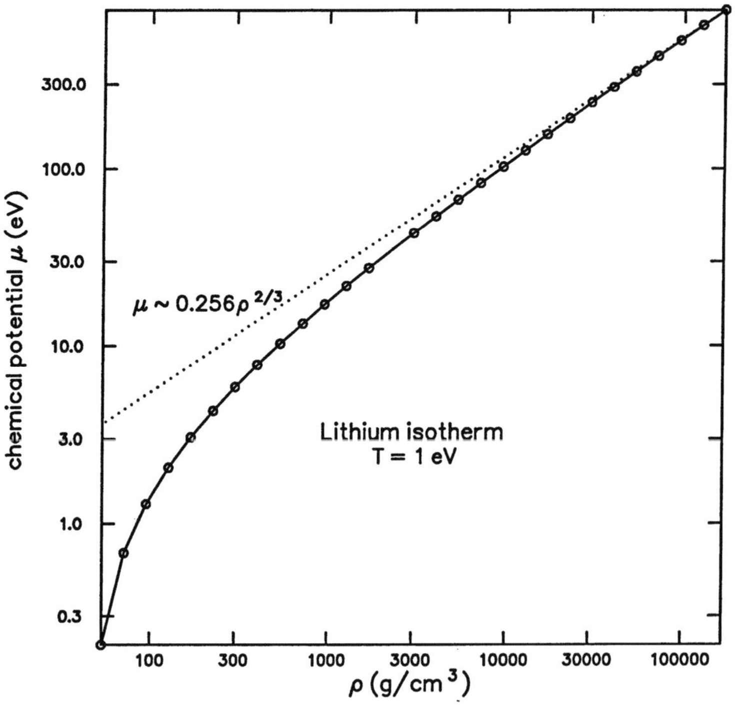

Fig. 1. The chemical potential μ of the spherical cellular model for lithium ($Z = 3$) vs. the density. These results are for the 1 electron volt isotherm. The dotted line shows the asymptote proportional to $\rho^{2/3}$.

2. THE STATISTICAL MECHANICS FORMULÆ

I treat the electrons as Fermions and the ions as Maxwell-Boltzmann particles. The grand canonical partition function is

$$\begin{aligned}\mathcal{Q}(\Omega, T) &= \sum_{\mathcal{N}=0} \exp\left[\mathcal{N}\mu(\Omega, T)/(kT)\right] Q_{\mathcal{N}}(\Omega, T) \\ &= \sum_{\mathcal{N}=0}^{\infty} \sum_{\substack{\{n_j\} \\ \sum n_j = \mathcal{N}}} \exp\left[(\mu(\Omega, T) - \epsilon_j) n_j/(kT)\right] \\ &= \prod_j \left\{1 + \exp\left[(\mu(\Omega, T) - \epsilon_j)/(kT)\right]\right\},\end{aligned} \tag{1}$$

for the case of Fermi statistics. By taking the partial derivative of $\log \mathcal{Q}$ with respect to the parameter μ, I obtain in the usual manner,

$$\mathcal{N} = \sum_j \frac{1}{\exp[(\epsilon_j - \mu)/kT] + 1}, \tag{2}$$

where $\mathcal{N}$ is the average number of occupied states of the system. Equation (2) fixes μ as a function of the temperature and the volume.

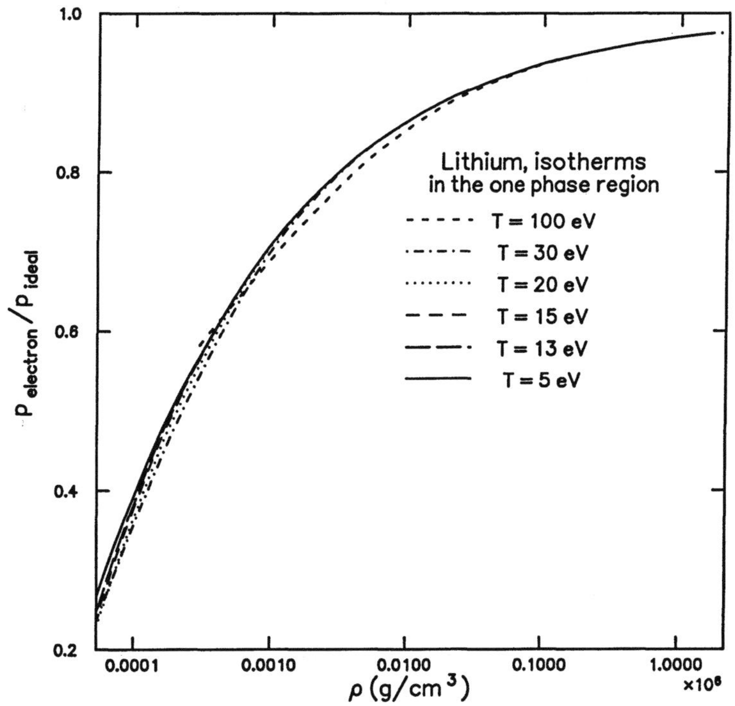

Fig. 2. The ratio of the electron pressure to the ideal gas pressure for several lithium ($Z = 3$) isotherms at high density. This figure illustrates temperature independence at high densities, as expected.

Since for the canonical partition function $Q_{\mathcal{N}}(\Omega, T)$, as usual I have $kT \log Q_{\mathcal{N}} = -A(\Omega, T)$. $A(\Omega, T)$ is the Helmholtz free energy. I deduce directly from (1) in the usual way by considering only the term in the sum corresponding to $\mathcal{N}$,

$$A(\Omega, T) = \mathcal{N}\mu(\Omega, T) - kT \sum_j \log\{1 + \exp[(\mu(\Omega, T) - \epsilon_j)/(kT)]\} \tag{3}$$

The internal energy is given from the Helmholtz free energy by the thermodynamic relation,

$$U = A - T\left.\frac{\partial A}{\partial T}\right|_{\Omega} = \sum_j \frac{\epsilon_j - T\left.\frac{\partial \epsilon_j}{\partial T}\right|_{\Omega}}{\exp[(\epsilon_j - \mu)/kT] + 1}. \tag{4}$$

Notice the $T\partial\epsilon_j/\partial T|_{\Omega}$ term. It doesn't occur in text books, but my treatment of the many-body effects induces a temperature dependence in energy eigenvalues in the cellular equations. That term is not always small and leads to some interesting behavior as will be discussed in the last section of this paper.

The pressure is also given from the Helmholtz free energy by the thermodynamic

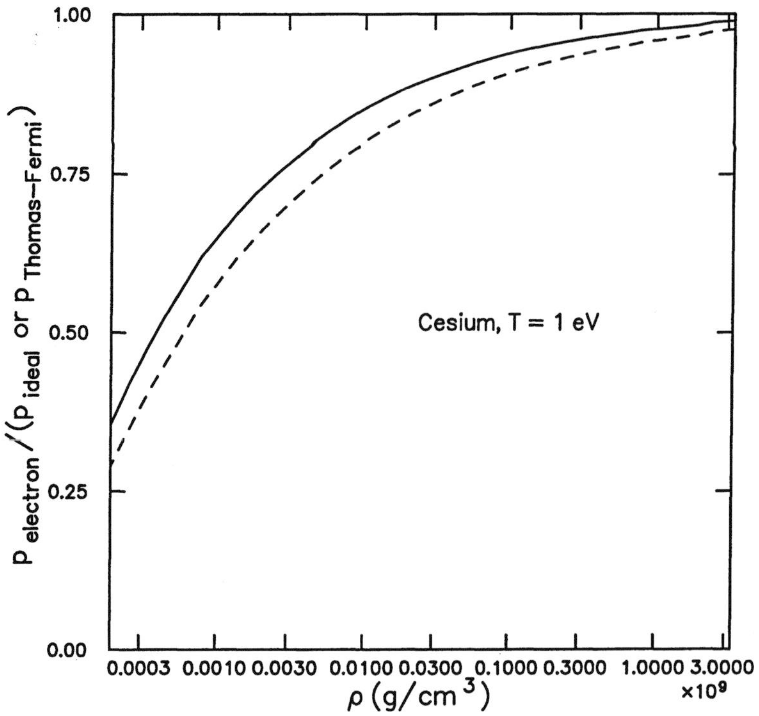

Fig. 3. The dashed line is the ratio of the electron pressure to the ideal Fermi gas pressure and the solid line is the ratio of the electron gas pressure to the $T = 0$ Thomas-Fermi theory pressure. The electron gas pressure is that computed from the spherical cellular model of cesium ($Z = 55$) at $T = 1$ eV.

relation

$$p\Omega = -\Omega \left.\frac{\partial A}{\partial \Omega}\right|_T = -\frac{1}{3}\sum_j \frac{r_b \left.\dfrac{\partial \epsilon_j}{\partial r_b}\right|_T}{\exp[(\epsilon_j - \mu)/kT] + 1}, \tag{5}$$

where r_b will be the radius of the spherical cell in the spherical cellular model.

3. THE EQUATIONS FOR Z ELECTRONS IN A SPHERICAL CELL

What is needed is the ϵ_j to put in the statistical mechanics formulæ. I have given the following generalization of my study of hydrogen to a cell with a central charge $+Ze$ and Z electrons.

First some notation,

$$f_n(z) = \frac{1}{\Gamma(n)}\int_0^\infty \frac{z\eta^{n-1}e^{-\eta}\,d\eta}{1+ze^{-\eta}}, \quad \frac{4\pi r_b^3}{3} = \frac{\Omega}{N}$$
$$\zeta = \frac{ZN}{2\Omega}\left(\frac{h^2}{2\pi mkT}\right)^{\frac{3}{2}} \quad y^2 = \frac{Ze^2}{r_b kT} \tag{6}$$

where ζ is the de Broglie density which measures the importance of quantum effects, ZN is the number of electrons, Ω is the volume, m is the electron mass, and $z =$

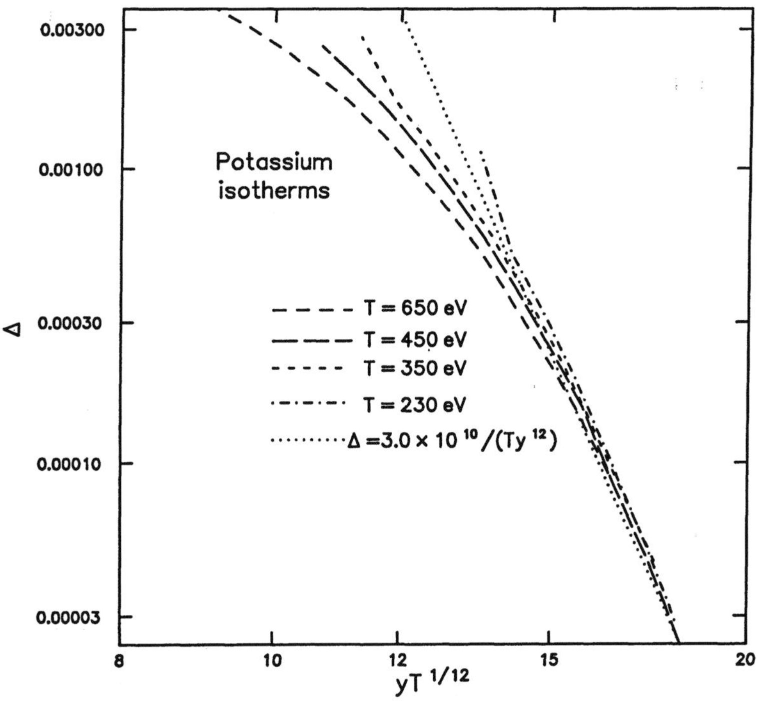

Fig. 4. The deviation $\Delta = 1 - [p_{\text{electron}}(\rho, T)p_{\text{ideal}}(\rho, 1\text{eV})]/[p_{\text{electron}}(\rho, 1\text{eV})p_{\text{ideal}}(\rho, T)]$ from the zero temperature limit (approximated here by the one electron volt curve) of the pressure for several potassium ($Z = 19$) isotherms at high density. In other variables, $\Delta \propto 1/(y^8\zeta^{2/3})$.

$\exp(\mu/kT)$ in the notation of (2). The quantity y measures the ratio of the Coulomb energy to the thermal energy. The leading order in y of the exchange energy is[9]

$$E_{\text{exch}} = -\frac{e^2}{2\pi r_b}\left(\frac{3}{\pi}\right)^{1/3}\zeta^{-4/3}X(\zeta) \tag{7}$$

where, to within about 0.1%,

$$X(\zeta) \approx \frac{\pi}{2}\zeta^2\left[\frac{1 + 0.088\,412\,769\zeta}{1 + 0.795\,519\,53\zeta + 0.193\,500\,34\zeta^2 + 0.013\,716\,390\zeta^3}\right]^{1/3} \tag{8}$$

The Schrödinger equation for this cellular model is,[3]

$$\begin{aligned}
&\sum_{j=1}^{Z}\left\{\frac{\hbar^2}{2m^*}\left[k^2 - 2i\vec{k}\cdot\vec{\nabla}_j - \nabla_j^2\right] - \frac{Ze^2}{r_j} + \frac{3Ze^2}{10r_b}g(y^2)\right\}\phi_\lambda(\vec{r}_1,\ldots,\vec{r}_Z) + \\
&\left\{\frac{1}{2}\sum_{j\neq l}^{Z}\frac{e^2}{|\vec{r}_l - \vec{r}_j|} + \frac{3e^2}{2r_b}F\left(\frac{y^2}{Z}\right)\left[Z - \frac{1}{3}\sum_{j=1}^{Z}\left(\frac{r_j}{r_b}\right)^2 - \frac{4}{3}Z\left(\frac{3Z}{\pi\zeta}\right)^{\frac{1}{3}} f_{\frac{1}{2}}(z(\zeta))\right]\right. \\
&\left.+\frac{6Z^2e^2}{5r_b}F(y^2Z)\right\}\phi_\lambda(\vec{r}_1,\ldots,\vec{r}_Z) = E_\lambda(\vec{k})\phi_\lambda(\vec{r}_1,\ldots,\vec{r}_Z),
\end{aligned} \tag{9}$$

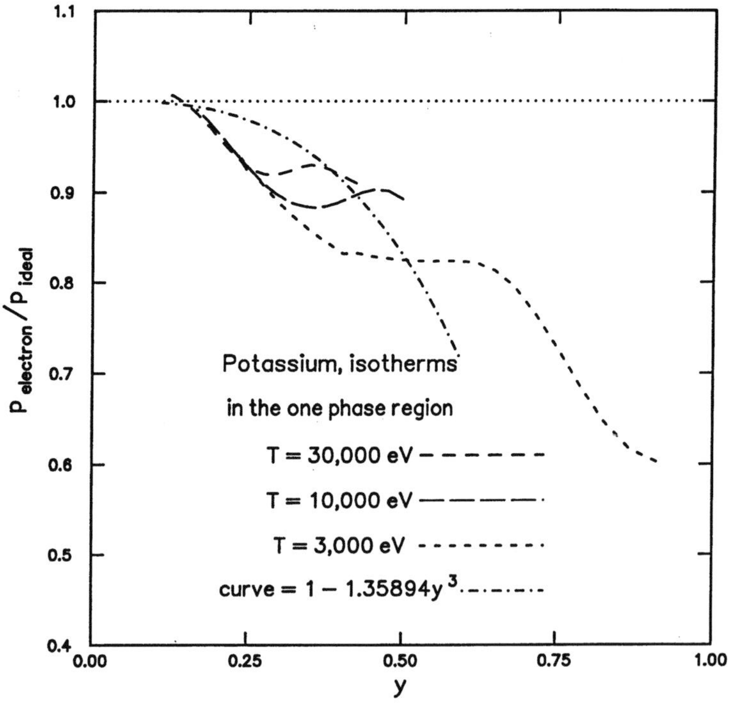

Fig. 5. The ratio of the electron pressure to the ideal gas pressure for several potassium ($Z = 19$) isotherms at low density. The dot-dashed curve is the result of Eq. (24).

where $m^*/m = 1$ and the $f_{\frac{1}{2}}$ term is dropped for the anti-parallel spin case. Here m^* is given by

$$\frac{m}{m^*} = 1 + A(\zeta)\frac{y^2}{Z}F\left(\frac{y^2}{Z}\right),$$
$$A(\zeta) = \frac{2}{3}\left(\frac{\zeta}{Z}\right)^{\frac{2}{3}}\left(\frac{3}{\pi}\right)^{\frac{1}{3}}\left\{\frac{2f_{\frac{1}{2}}(z(\zeta)) - X(\zeta)/(\pi\zeta)}{f_{\frac{5}{2}}(z(\zeta))}\right\}. \quad (10)$$

This result is arrived at by starting with the Heitler-London equation[10] which is valid in the cold, dilute limit and by adding corrections, proportional to F and g. In the cold dilute limit, $F = g = 0$. When $F = g = 1$, the equation is correct for the hot, ideal gas limit through order y^2. The functions are approximated as[3]

$$F(y^2) \approx e^{-y^2}\left(\frac{2 + 2y^2}{2 + 4y^2 + y^4}\right),$$
$$g(y^2) \approx \left[1 + \frac{41}{14}y^2 + \frac{2}{5}\left(\frac{3}{2\pi}\right)^{1/2} y^3\right]^{-1}, \quad (11)$$

and they were derived semi-classically.

When I separate out the state independent terms,

$$\mathcal{E}_{l,\lambda} = E_{l,\lambda} + \Delta E, \quad (12)$$

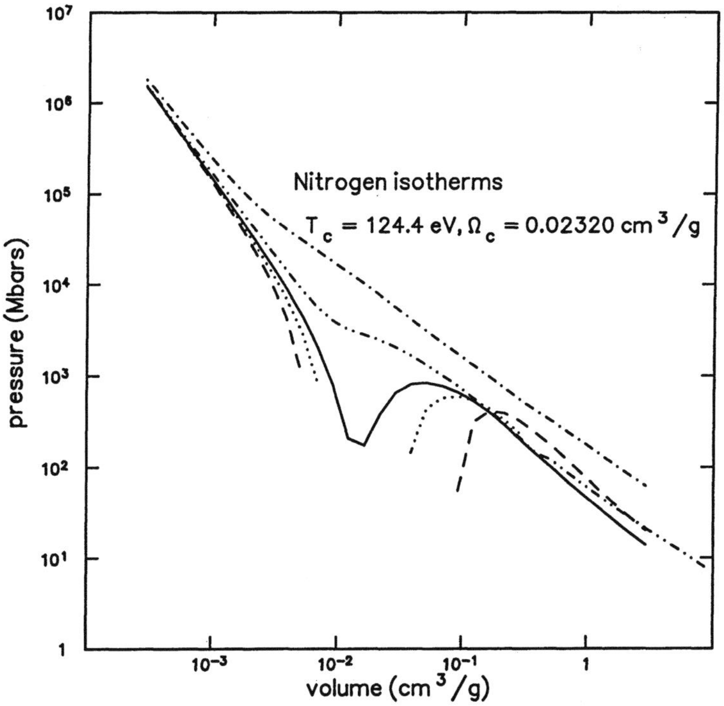

Fig. 6. Some isotherms for nitrogen ($Z = 7$). The breaks in the curves occur when the computed pressure is negative. This feature is interpreted as the low part of a "van der Waals loop" which is to be replaced by a flat line determined by the Maxwell construction.

where

$$
\begin{aligned}
\Delta E_{||} &= -\frac{3Ze^2}{10r_b}g(y^2) - \frac{3Ze^2}{2r_b}F\left(\frac{y^2}{Z}\right)\left[1 - \frac{4}{3}\left(\frac{3Z}{\pi\zeta}\right)^{\frac{1}{3}} f_{\frac{1}{2}}(z(\zeta))\right] \\
&\quad - \frac{6Z^2e^2}{5r_b}F(y^2 Z) \\
\Delta E_{\text{anti}-||} &= -\frac{3Ze^2}{10r_b}g(y^2) - \frac{3Ze^2}{2r_b}F\left(\frac{y^2}{Z}\right) - \frac{6Z^2e^2}{5r_b}F(y^2 Z)
\end{aligned}
\tag{13}
$$

equation (9) simplifies to

$$
\begin{aligned}
&\sum_{j=1}^{Z}\left\{\frac{\hbar^2}{2m^*}\left[k^2 - 2i\vec{k}\cdot\vec{\nabla}_j - \nabla_j^2\right] - \frac{Ze^2}{r_j}\right\}\phi_{l,\lambda}(\vec{r}_1,\ldots,\vec{r}_Z)+ \\
&\left\{\frac{1}{2}\sum_{j\neq l}^{Z}\frac{e^2}{|\vec{r}_l - \vec{r}_j|} - \frac{e^2}{2r_b}F\left(\frac{y^2}{Z}\right)\sum_{j=1}^{Z}\left(\frac{r_j}{r_b}\right)^2\right\}\phi_{l,\lambda}(\vec{r}_1,\ldots,\vec{r}_Z) \\
&= \mathcal{E}_{l,\lambda}(\vec{k})\phi_\lambda(\vec{r}_1,\ldots,\vec{r}_Z),
\end{aligned}
\tag{14}
$$

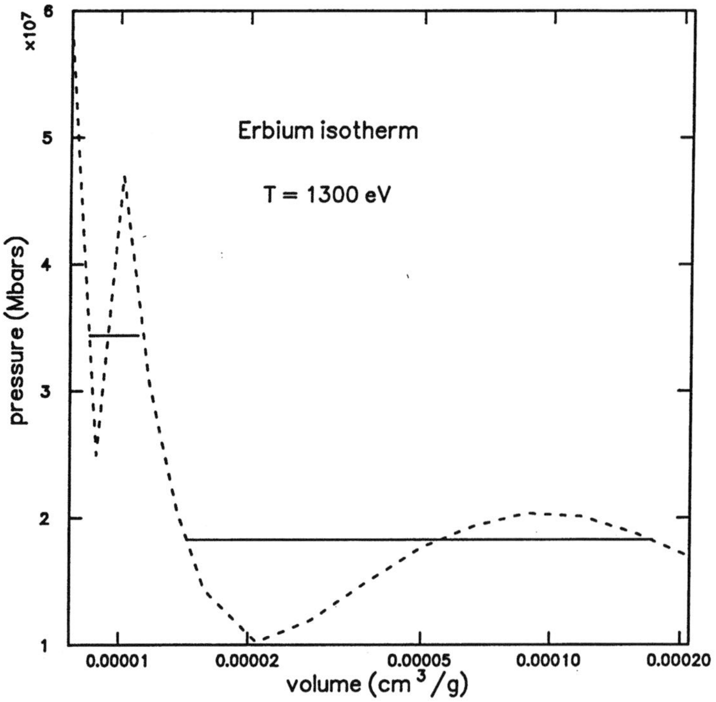

Fig. 7. An isotherm for erbium ($Z = 68$). This case illustrates the possibility of having two, two-phase regions. The $T = 1300$ eV isotherm is illustrated by the dashed curve. The Maxwell construction which maintains monotonicity of the pressure as a function of the volume for a fixed temperature is shown by the solid horizontal lines. The reason that the equal areas feature of the Maxwell construction is not visually apparent is that the volume is plotted on a log scale so that the low volume two-phase region would be clearly seen. The discontinuities in slope result from the joining of the computed values by straight lines.

where $m^*/m = 1$ for the anti-parallel case. The generalized expression for $\epsilon_{l,\lambda}(\vec{k})$ is

$$\epsilon_{l,\lambda}(\vec{k}) = \frac{1}{2}\left(1 + \frac{m^*}{m}\right)\mathcal{E}_{l,\lambda}(\vec{k}) + \frac{3Ze^2}{10r_b}g(y^2) + \frac{3Z^2e^2}{5r_b}F(y^2Z)$$
$$- \frac{1}{2}\left(1 - \frac{m*}{m}\right)\left\langle \phi_{l,\lambda}\left|\sum_{j=1}^{Z}\frac{Ze^2}{r_j} - \frac{1}{2}\sum_{j\neq l}\frac{e^2}{|\vec{r}_j - \vec{r}_l|}\right|\phi_{l,\lambda}\right\rangle$$
$$+ \frac{e^2}{r_b}F\left(\frac{y^2}{Z}\right)\left[\frac{3}{4}Z + \frac{m^*}{4m}\sum_{j=1}^{Z}\left\langle \phi_{l,\lambda}\left|\frac{r_j^2}{r_b^2}\right|\phi_{l,\lambda}\right\rangle - Z\left(\frac{3Z}{\pi\zeta}\right)^{\frac{1}{3}} f_{\frac{1}{2}}(z(\zeta))\right]. \tag{15}$$

For the anti-parallel case, $m^*/m = 1$ and the $f_{\frac{1}{2}}$ term is dropped. Unfortunately, this model is currently intractable.

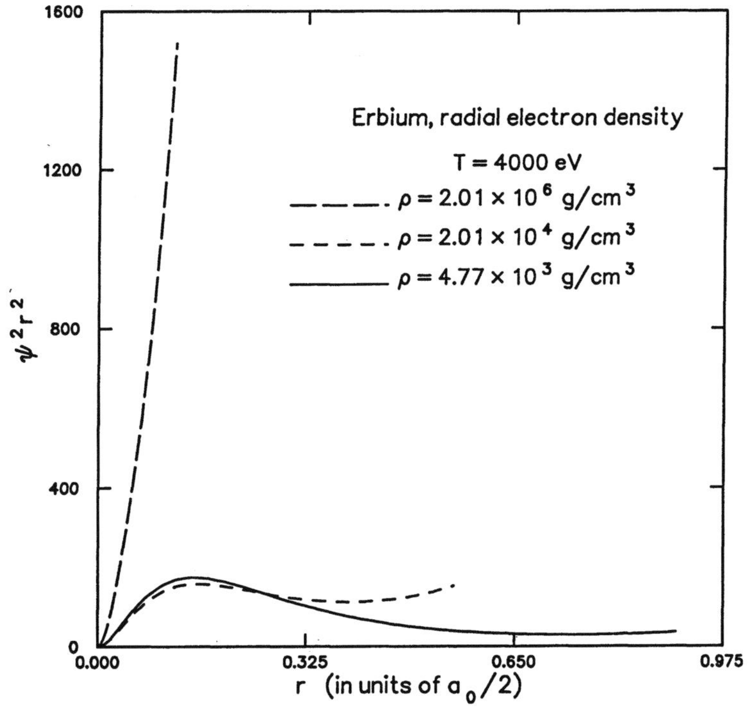

Fig. 8. The radial, electron density times r^2 computed for the spherical model for erbium, $Z = 68$, at a temperature of 4000 eV. For high compression, the weighted sum of ψ^2 is nearly constant, whereas for lower densities, a concentration is seen. a_0 is the Bohr radius.

4. THE INDEPENDENT ELECTRON APPROXIMATION

Since the Z electron model is currently intractable, I consider the simplification of using "independent electrons." The first step, as was done by Hartree,[10] is to use the form of the wave function, $\phi_\lambda(\vec{r}_1, \ldots, \vec{r}_Z) = \prod_{i=1}^{Z} \phi_i(\vec{r}_i)$. In eq. (14) all the terms except the electron-electron interaction can be neatly divided so as to depend on the single vector variable $\vec{r}_i$ alone. The reduction to dependence on a single $\vec{r}_i$ leads to a very complex self-consistency problem for each i. Instead, I impose the condition of a single, temperature and density dependent, self-consistent charge density. With these conditions I propose, instead of (14), the equation,

$$\left\{\frac{\hbar^2}{2m^*}\left[k^2 - 2i\vec{k}\cdot\vec{\nabla} - \nabla^2\right] - \frac{e^2 v(r_b, T, r/r_b)}{r} - \frac{e^2}{2r_b}\left(\frac{r}{r_b}\right)^2 F\left(\frac{y^2}{Z}\right)\right\}\phi_{l,\lambda}(\vec{r}) \tag{16}$$
$$= \tilde{\mathcal{E}}_{l,\lambda}(\vec{k})\phi_{l,\lambda}(\vec{r}).$$

The potential $e^2 v(r_b, T, r/r_b)/r$ is composed of two parts. The first is the electron-ion interaction which is just Ze^2/r as seen in (14). The second part is a representation of the electron-electron interaction. Since I want to have the full ion potential at the origin, I select $v(r_b, T, 0) = Z$. Since an electron does not screen itself, I want to see the potential of only a single ionic charge at the cellular surface, so I select, $v(r_b, T, 1) = 1$. It is important to note however that, when I add up all the energies,

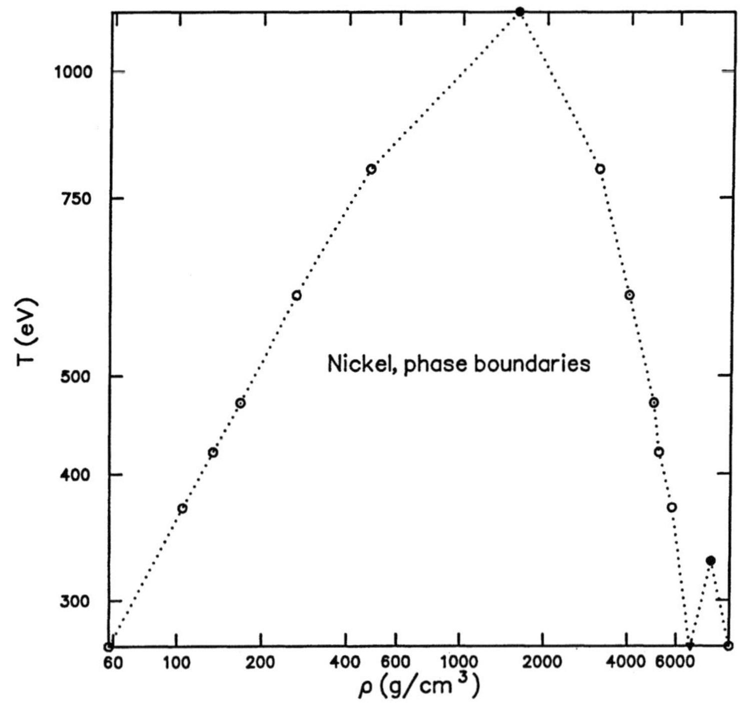

Fig. 9. The phase boundary of the spherical cellular model of nickel ($Z = 28$) in the $T - \rho$ plane. The solid dots are the two critical points and the open circles are the data points on the phase boundary. The discontinuities in slope result from the joining of the computed values by straight lines, except of course, at the triple point, marked by $\bigtriangledown$, where the two, two-phase regions join.

I will have counted $Z(Z-1)$ terms, when, as we saw in (14), I should have only $\frac{1}{2}Z(Z-1)$ such terms. In the computation of the ϵ's I must therefore subtract the extra terms off. The electron-electron repulsion is given by

$$\frac{Ze^2}{r} - \frac{e^2 v(r_b, T, r/r_b)}{r} \tag{17}$$

Thus for the corresponding ϵ,

$$\begin{aligned}\epsilon_{l,\lambda}(\vec{k}) =& \frac{1}{2}\left(1+\frac{m^*}{m}\right)\left[\tilde{\mathcal{E}}_{l,\lambda}(\vec{k}) - \frac{1}{2}\left\langle \phi_{l,\lambda}(\vec{r})\left|\left(\frac{Ze^2}{r} - \frac{e^2 v(r_b, T, r/r_b)}{r}\right)\right|\phi_{l,\lambda}(\vec{r})\right\rangle\right] \\ & - \frac{1}{2}\left(1-\frac{m*}{m}\right)\left\langle \phi_{l,\lambda}(\vec{r})\left|\frac{v(r_b, T, r/r_b)e^2}{r}\right|\phi_{l,\lambda}(\vec{r})\right\rangle \\ & + \frac{m^* e^2}{4 m r_b} F\left(\frac{y^2}{Z}\right)\left\langle \phi_{l,\lambda}(\vec{r})\left|\frac{r^2}{r_b^2}\right|\phi_{l,\lambda}(\vec{r})\right\rangle + \Delta\epsilon.\end{aligned} \tag{18}$$

where the state independent part is

$$\begin{aligned}\Delta\epsilon_{||} =& \frac{3e^2}{10 r_b} g(y^2) + \frac{3Ze^2}{5 r_b} F(y^2 Z) + \frac{e^2}{r_b} F\left(\frac{y^2}{Z}\right)\left[\frac{3}{4} - \left(\frac{3Z}{\pi\zeta}\right)^{\frac{1}{3}} f_{\frac{1}{2}}(z(\zeta))\right] \\ \Delta\epsilon_{\text{anti}-||} =& \frac{3e^2}{10 r_b} g(y^2) + \frac{3Ze^2}{5 r_b} F(y^2 Z) + \frac{3e^2}{4 r_b} F\left(\frac{y^2}{Z}\right)\end{aligned} \tag{19}$$

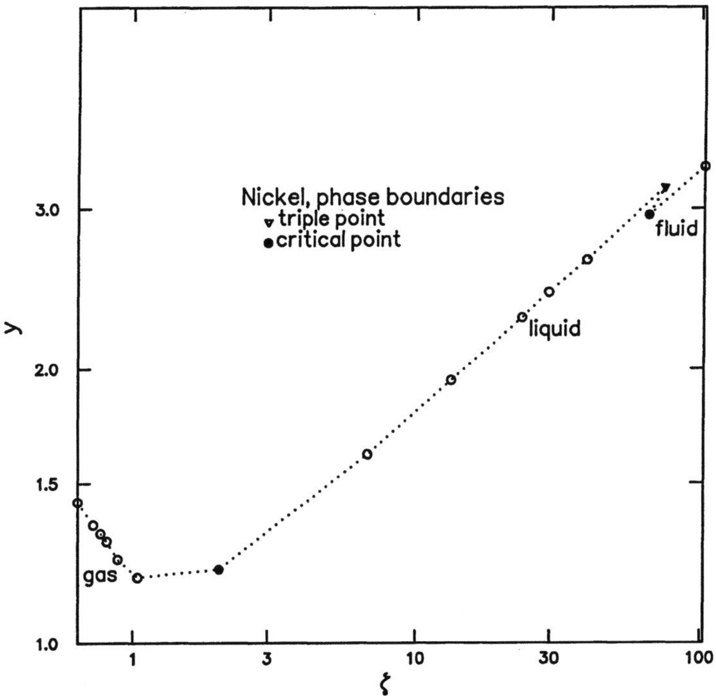

Fig. 10. The phase boundary of the spherical cellular model of nickel ($Z = 28$) in the $\zeta - y$ plane. The solid dots are the two critical points, the open circles are the data points on the phase boundary, and the ∇ is a triple point.

Again, for the anti-parallel case $m^*/m = 1$ and I drop the $f_{\frac{1}{2}}$ term. The modifications to take account of the exchange and many-body effects are included.

The numerical implementation involves a large number of computational and technical details[4] which I will not describe here. The determination of the self-consistent potential uses Poisson's equation,

$$\nabla^2 V(\vec{r}) = e^2 \rho. \tag{20}$$

The solution for a heterogeneous sphere of radius r_b with spherical symmetry and a central ionic charge Z is[11]

$$rV(r)/e^2 = \int_r^{r_b} \left(1 - \frac{r}{\alpha}\right) \rho(\alpha) \alpha^2 \, d\alpha \tag{21}$$

Done properly, to obtain the self-consistent potential $-e^2 v(r_r, T, r/r_b)/r$, the electron density which corresponds to the state being computed in the solution of (16), should be subtracted from the total charge density. However I will instead simplify the process by subtracting the $1/Z$ fraction of the density. There will of course then be an uncompensated unit ionic charge contribution to the potential. Thus I obtain

$$v(r_b, T, r/r_b) = 1 + \left(\frac{Z-1}{Z}\right) r_b \int_{(r/r_b)}^{1} \left(1 - \frac{r}{\beta r_b}\right) \mathcal{D}(r_b, T, \beta) \, d\beta \tag{22}$$

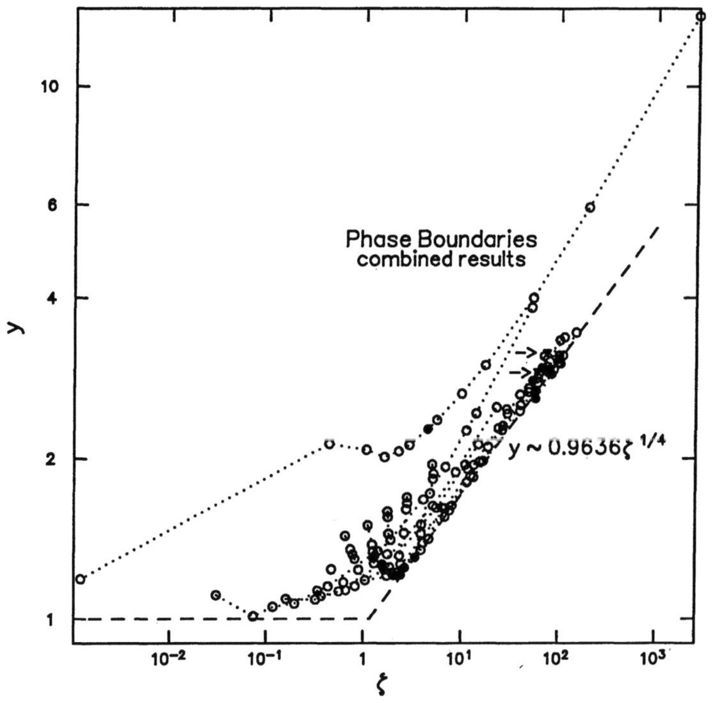

Fig. 11. The spherical-cellular-model, phase boundaries for 10 different elements. The critical points are solid circles and the data points are open circles. The triple points are upside down triangles. Since these triangles are a bit hard to locate, I have placed small arrows pointing towards them. The points corresponding to each element are joined by dotted lines. The dashed line has two parts, the first for smaller values of ζ is just $y = 1$ and the second part is $y \sim 0.9636\zeta^{1/4}$ which appears to be a limit for the phase boundaries. The elements reported are $Z = 1, 3, 7, 11, 19, 28, 37, 46, 55, 68$.

in terms of the electron charge density,

$$\begin{aligned} \text{charge density} &= \mathcal{D}(r_b, T, r/r_b) \\ &= \sum_{l,\lambda} \frac{(2l+1)\phi^*_{l,\lambda}(r)\phi_{l,\lambda}(r)r^2}{\exp[(\epsilon_{l,\lambda} - \mu)/kT] + 1} \end{aligned} \tag{23}$$

5. LIMITING CASES

The most obvious case is when $y \to 0$. Here the structure of the many-body terms, as discussed in the previous section, is such that, the ideal gas limit, and the leading order terms [$O(y^2)$] are correctly given. The next limiting case of interest is the behavior of a very dense system. It is well known that in this limit the kinetic energy per electron is proportional to $\rho^{2/3}$, while potential energy is only proportional to $\rho^{1/3}$. Thus I expect the kinetic energy to dominate and the system to tend to ideal-gas behavior in this limit. This behavior is illustrated in Fig. 1. The system will be approximately independent of temperature for the temperature below

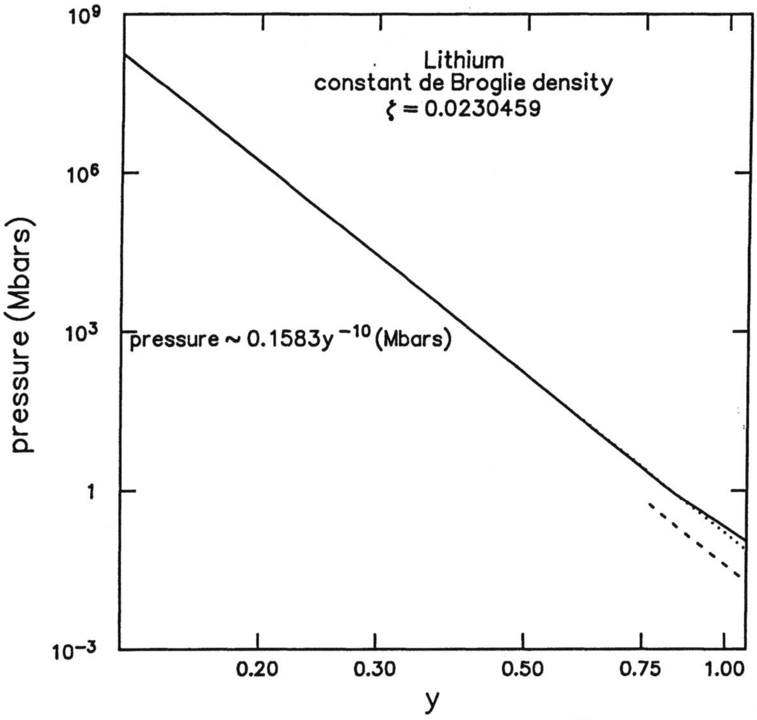

Fig. 12. The pressure for the spherical cellular model of lithium ($Z = 3$) at a constant de Broglie density $\zeta = 0.0230459$. The solid line is the spherical model result and the dotted line (mostly obscured by the solid line) is the formula shown. The short-dashed line is a continuation of the expected large y limiting behavior, as the factor of (1+Z) in the pressure is replaced by unity.

the Fermi temperature, as seen in Fig. 2. Fig. 3 shows the T=0 behavior at high density and makes a comparison with the Thomas-Fermi theory. Fig. 4 shows the behavior of the deviation from the $T = 0$ limit.

In the low density limit, Baker and Johnson[12] have derived the limiting behavior

$$\frac{p_{\text{electron}}(\Omega, T)}{p_{\text{ideal}}(\Omega, T)} \asymp 1 - \frac{1}{\sqrt{3}} \frac{(Z+1)^{3/2}}{2Z} y^3 + \dots \tag{24}$$

which agrees with the standard Debye-Hückel result. Comparison of the spherical cellular model with this result is shown in Fig. 5.

6. NUMERICAL RESULTS

I now turn to the intermediate density regime. Typical isotherms for the spherical cellular model are illustrated in Fig. 6. In Fig. 7 I show an isotherm for a case where there are two critical points. The critical points are computed using the critera,

$$\left.\frac{\partial p}{\partial \Omega}\right|_T = \left.\frac{\partial^2 p}{\partial \Omega^2}\right|_T = 0, \tag{25}$$

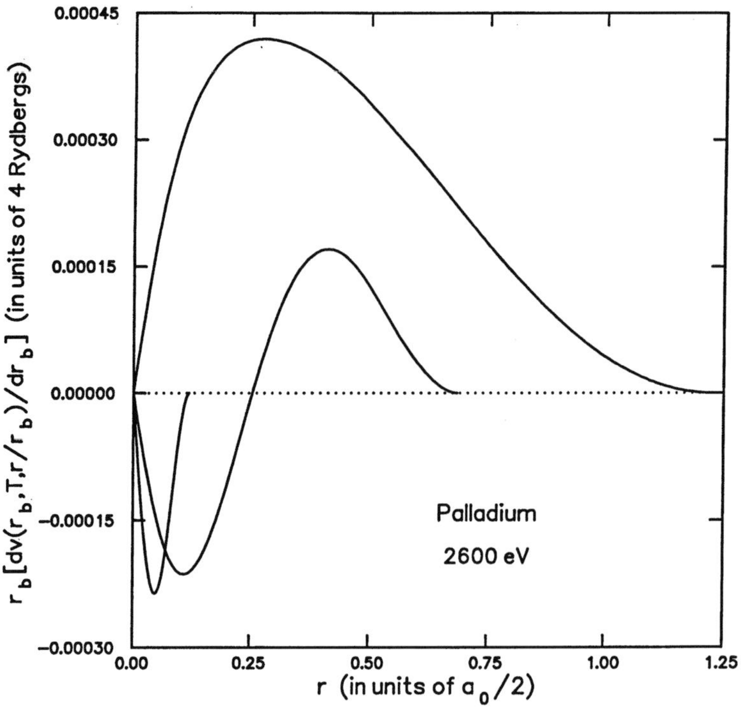

Fig. 13. Three $r_b \partial v(r_b, T, r/r_b)/\partial r_b$ versus r curves for different densities for the spherical cellular model of palladium ($Z = 46$) at a temperature of 2600 eV. a_0 is the Bohr radius. The abscissa is in units of $a_0/2$ and the ordinate is in units of 4 Rydbergs.

In Fig. 8 I show some density profiles for different densities. For low to medium density a similar behavior is shown as the temperature changes. There is an atomic density profile for low temperature and a uniform density (It would look like a parabola in this type of plot.) for high temperature.

In Fig. 9 I show in a temperature-density plot the phase boundaries for nickel. In Fig. 10 I show the same as in Fig. 9, except it is plotted in the ζ-y plane. In Fig. 11 I show the combined results for 10 elements. Fig. 11 leads to the question as to whether any value of y is in the one phase region, if ζ is small enough. A partial study of this question is shown in Fig. 12.

Fig. 13 represents the behavior of $r_b \partial v/\partial r_b|_T$. For large densities the electrons move away from the ion to take advantage of the extra room, which leads to a larger v. For high densities the electrons relax from the relatively uniform density caused by the Pauli principal, which leads to a smaller v.

7. THE ENERGY

The difference between the thermodynamically consistent internal energy and the "physically reasonable" energy is the $T\partial\epsilon/\partial T|_\Omega$ term in Eq. (4). In Fig. 14 I illustrate an example where $T > T_c$, and in Fig. 15 an example where $T < T_c$.

As we have seen, this approximation to the spherical cellular model has many

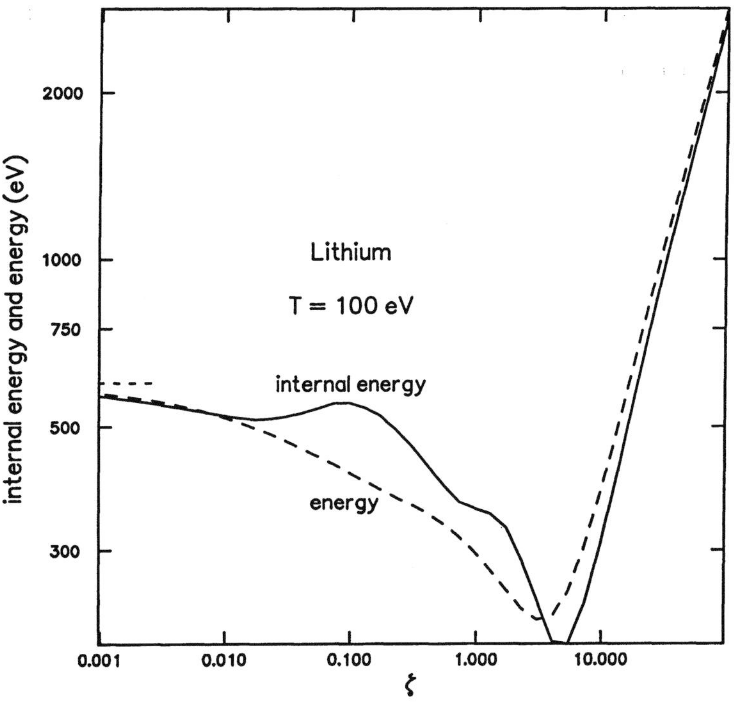

Fig. 14. The "physically reasonable" energy (labeled energy) and the internal energy versus the de Broglie density for the spherical cellular model of lithium ($Z = 3$) at a temperature of 100 eV. The short-dashed line is the low-density, total ionization limit. $T > T_c$

good features and behaves more or less appropriately in the various limits. However, the difference between the "physically reasonable" energy and the thermodynamically consistent internal energy is an issue that requires futher study.

The author wishes to thank J. D. Johnson for helpful discussions. He also wishes to thank the U. S. Army Research Office for partial support of his attendance at the 27th International Workshop on Condensed Matter Theories in Touloue, France.

REFERENCES

1. G. A. Baker, Jr., to be published, *Condensed Matter Theories* **18** (2003).
2. G. A. Baker, Jr., E.V. Ludena, P. Vashishta and R.F. Bishop, eds., *Condensed Matter Theories* 11:187 (Nova Scientific Pubs., Commack, NY, 1996).
3. G. A. Baker, Jr., *Phys. Rev. E* 56:5216 (1997).
4. G. A. Baker, Jr., to be published, *Phys. Rev. E* (2003).
5. L. H. Thomas, *Proc. Cambridge Philos. Soc.* 23:542 (1927).
6. E. Fermi, *Rend. Accad. Naz. Lincei* 6:602 (1927).
7. S. Eliezer, A. Ghatak, and H. Hora *Fundamentals of Equations of State* (World Scientific, Singapore, 2002).
8. See, for example, K. Huang, *Statistical Mechanics* (Wiley, New York, 1963).

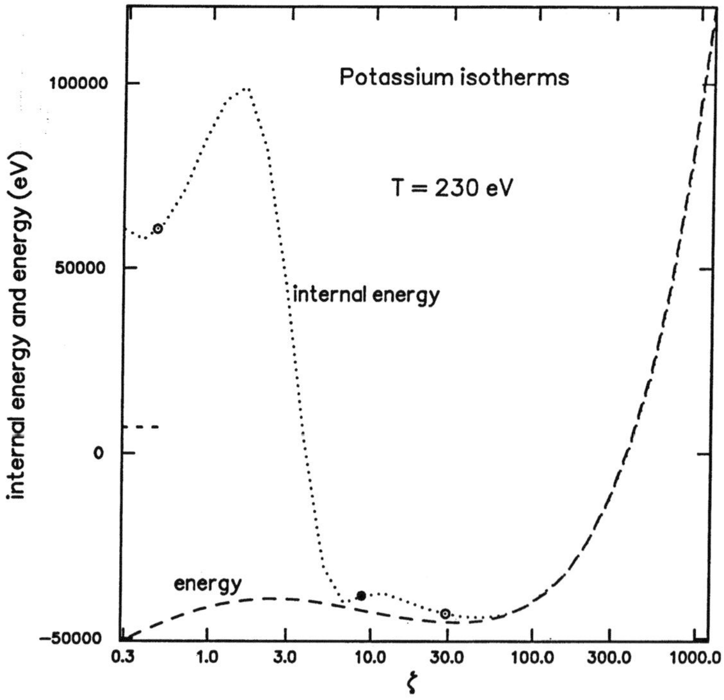

Fig. 15. The "physically reasonable" energy (labeled energy) and the internal energy versus the de Broglie density for the spherical cellular model of potassium ($Z = 19$) at a temperature of 230 eV. The open circles represent the phase boundaries for this temperature. The solid circle represents the critical point value of ζ. The short-dashed line is the low-density, total ionization limit. $T < T_c$

9. G. A. Baker, Jr. and J. D. Johnson, *Phys. Rev. A* 44:2271, (1991).
10. N. W. Ashcroft and N. D. Mermin, *Solid State Physics* (Holt, Rinehart and Winston, New York, 1976).
11. H. Jeffreys and B. S. Jeffreys, *Methods of Mathematical Physics, second edition* (Cambridge Univ. Press, London, 1950).
12. G. A. Baker, Jr. and J. D. Johnson, *Physica A* 265:129 (1999).

THE SPECTRAL FUNCTION OF ATOMIC AND MOLECULAR HYDROGEN

H. Reinholz, G. Röpke, and C. Neißner
Fachbereich Physik, Universität Rostock, D-18051 Rostock, Germany
and School of Physics, University of Western Australia, Crawley, Australia

1. INTRODUCTION

The electron spectral function gives the most detailed information about the electronic properties of a dense plasma. A Green's function approach can be formulated which goes beyond a single-particle approach by taking into account many-particle effects in a systematic way. In particular, it should be able to bridge between different concepts used in low-density plasma physics and, on the other hand, in condensed matter physics. The present work focuses on the situation where neutral atoms are formed in the plasma. At high densities, the atoms are correlated as described by the pair distribution function and the formation of molecules. It is not a simple task to follow the modification of the electron spectral function in such high-density systems, in particular near the Mott transition where the electrons which are bound within atoms become itinerant. An attempt to include hopping processes in a systematic Green's function approach to dense plasmas has already been discussed in [1], and [2]. In this paper, we will present a consistent treatment of the spectral function and the density of states, initially considering atoms as the "elementary" constituents. In a further step, the electron spectral function is derived decomposing the atom into its substructure.

At low densities, an appropriate concept to describe a charged particle system at high temperatures is the model of a partially ionized plasma (PIP model), see [3] and references therein. The system is imagined to consist of distinguishable components of (quasi)particles such as free electrons, ions and atoms. The different components are considered to be in chemical equilibrium which is described by a mass action law, in the simplest approximation via the Saha equation. Such an approach can be extended to higher densities if medium modifications are taken into account. A systematic expansion with respect to the density is possible using the method of thermodynamic Green's functions, see [4-6]. In particular, the energy shifts of free particles and bound states due to screening effects will lead to the Mott effect where the bound states merge with the continuum of scattering states. As a consequence, the transition from dielectric to metallic behavior (MIT) happens when the lowest bound state disappears. However, important aspects like the broadening of the bound state energy levels due to hopping processes cannot be described adequately within this picture.

At high densities, models known from liquid metals or disordered solids have been used to describe the electron structure in dense plasmas. As an example, the average atom model shall be mentioned [7]. Here, the formation of bands from atomic bound states is obtained when the atoms are approaching each other. Technically, a Wigner-Seitz cell with different boundary conditions for the wave function is constructed. Aspects of a description of disordered systems are relevant since dense plasmas can be considerd as a system with a liquid like disorder. In particular, the density functional formalism can be used to describe the electron subsystem at a given ionic configuration. Considering the closure of the gap between different bands, the averaged atom model is also able to describe the MIT. While the quasi-particle states with respect to the potential of ions are optimally treated, the systematic inclusion of electron-electron correlations and the formation of molecules remains an open problem within this approach.

The disordered Anderson-Hubbard model (DAH model) is another condensed matter concept to treat charged particle systems at high densities. The electrons are considered as bound to randomly distributed fixed ionic sites. Hopping of electrons between ions can be described within a tight binding model. Thus, the electronic properties are determined by the electrons moving in a potential formed by the disordered system of ions (topological disorder), similar to amorphous solids or liquids, which can be described by a dynamical structure factor. Within the Anderson model, mobility edges may occur separating localized from delocalized states in the density of states. The MIT occurs if a mobility gap opens near the Fermi energy. Within the Hubbard model, electron correlations are accounted for by the single-site electron-electron repulsion. A correlation gap may arise which closes at intermediate densities so that a MIT is expected to occur [8]. For more details of the DAH in the context of dense plasmas, see [9].

Different concepts to describe the MIT such as screening of the binding force, band closure, correlation gap closure and localization by disorder have been outlined above. Up to now it is an open question which mechanism is most important to explain the metal-insulator transition in strongly coupled Coulomb systems, in particular dense hydrogen plasmas. As a systematic many-particle approach, the method of thermodynamic Green's function should contain these different mechanisms and give a unified description of dense plasmas including the PIP model as well as the DAH model.

The concepts of quasi-particles, free-particle density, bound-state density, ionization degree etc. as used in the PIP model are not well defined in dense plasmas, in particular near the MIT. Instead, the spectral function is considered. As shown in [1], in the perturbation expansion of the self-energy a singularity arises which is related to hopping processes between bound states. To avoid this singularity, the tight-binding solution can be used where the binding energy level splits off and broadens into a band structure. Thus we have to go beyond the solution of the two-particle problem which only describes the interaction between electrons and protons to form a hydrogen atom. The next step will be the use of the solution of the three-particle problem describing the motion of electrons in the potential of two protons, which is known from the literature [10], and includes hopping processes between neighboring bound states [11]. This means the inclusion not only of the formation of hydrogen molecules in the ground state but also of the excited states.

In this paper, we elaborate the formation of bands within a Green's function approach. In particular, we address such questions as the positivity of the density of states and the sum rules. For transparency, we discuss firstly a picture where atoms are considered as "elementary" particles, interacting via a potential which depends on the distance between the atoms and the symmetry character of the overlapping ground-state ($1s$) electronic wave functions. After presenting and comparing the classical and the quantum mechanical treatment, the atoms are decomposed into electrons and protons, and the corresponding electronic spectral function is constructed. As a numerical example, hydrogen at T = 5000K and particle densities of a few $10^{26}\mathrm{m}^{-3}$ to $10^{27}\mathrm{m}^{-3}$ is considered.

2. CLASSICAL TREATMENT

As a prerequisite for the quantum description, we consider the classical virial expansion of interacting hydrogen atoms in the canonical ensemble, where the free energy $F(T,\Omega,N_c) = -k_BT\ln Z_{\mathrm{can}}(T,\Omega,N_c)$ as a function of the temperature T, the volume Ω and the particle numbers N_c is the thermodynamic potential. We introduce different species c in order to take into account the spin of the particles (combinations of electron spin $\uparrow,\downarrow$, and proton spin $\uparrow,\downarrow$). Note that the interaction potential of atoms is assumed to not depend on the spin of the protons leading only to a degeneration factor. In the following, we want to derive virial expansions for state variables such as the pressure or the chemical potentials μ_c. In particular, we aim to find an expression $N_d/\Omega = n_d(T,\mu_c)$ for the density of the atoms n_d in dependence of the chemical potentials and the temperature. The canonical partition function is given as

$$Z_{\mathrm{can}}(T,\Omega,N_c) = \int \mathrm{d}\Gamma \mathrm{e}^{-\beta E} = \prod_c \frac{1}{N_c!\Lambda_c^{3N_c}} \int \mathrm{d}^{3N_c}\mathbf{r}_c \prod_{d,N_d>c,N_c} \mathrm{e}^{-\beta V_{cd}(\mathbf{r}_c-\mathbf{r}_d)} \quad (1)$$

with the interactions $V_{cd}(\mathbf{r}_c-\mathbf{r}_d)$. After expanding up to the first order with respect to the Mayer cluster function, the free energy is found as

$$F(T,\Omega,N_c) = -k_BT\sum_c N_c\left[\ln\frac{\mathrm{e}\Omega}{N_c\Lambda_c^3} + \frac{1}{2}\sum_d \frac{N_d}{\Omega}\int \mathrm{d}^3\mathbf{r}\ (\mathrm{e}^{-\beta V_{cd}(r)}-1)\right]. \quad (2)$$

The inversion of the chemical potentials $\mu_d(T,\Omega,N_c) = (\partial F/\partial N_d)_{T,\Omega,N_c\neq N_d}$, again taken up to the first iteration only, leads to the final expression for the particle densities in the grand canonical ensemble,

$$n_c = \frac{1}{\Lambda_c^3}\mathrm{e}^{\beta\mu_c} + \sum_d \frac{1}{\Lambda_c^3\Lambda_d^3}\mathrm{e}^{\beta(\mu_c+\mu_d)}\int \mathrm{d}^3\mathbf{r}\ (\mathrm{e}^{-\beta V_{cd}(r)}-1)\ .$$

The total atomic density is $n_a = \sum_c n_c$. After taking into account the nuclear spin by a degeneration factor 2, the internal states c refer only to the electron spin which is of relevance for the interaction. The interaction is $V^t(r)$ or $V^s(r)$ depending on whether the electron spins are parallel (triplet) or antiparallel (singlet), respectively. The weighting has to be taken from a quantum mechanical consideration. Since $\mu_c = \mu_a$ and $\Lambda_c = \Lambda_a$ are independent on c, we find the expected result,

$$n_a = \frac{4}{\Lambda^3} e^{\beta\mu_a} + \frac{4}{\Lambda_a^6} e^{2\beta\mu_a} \int d^3\mathbf{r} \left(e^{-\beta V^s(r)} + 3e^{-\beta V^t(r)} - 4 \right) . \tag{3}$$

Assuming the atoms to be in the ground state 1s, the potentials can be given as $V^{s/t}(r) = E^{s/t}(r) - 2E_{1s}$ where the energies can be taken from the calculation of the diatomic molecule of hydrogen [10] with the well-known expressions for the overlap S, the Coulomb C and the exchange term A,

$$E^s(r) = 2E_{1s} + 2\frac{C(r) + S(r)A(r)}{1 + S^2(r)} ,$$
$$E^t(r) = 2E_{1s} + 2\frac{C(r) - S(r)A(r)}{1 - S^2(r)} . \tag{4}$$

Eq. (3) is a virial expansion and has to be applied with caution. Obviously, the density cannot become negative. We estimated the range of validity of the virial expansion for hydrogen. In Fig. 1, the parameter values are given where the correction due to the second virial coefficient amounts to 20%. It should be noted that in the quantum description the range of validity of the virial expansion can be extended if the molecules and further bound states are considered as new constituents of the system.

3. QUANTUM MECHANICAL FORMULATION

Within a quantum statistical approach, the spectral function $A_c(\mathbf{P}, \omega)$ and the density of states $D_c(\omega) = \Omega^{-1} \sum_{\mathbf{P}} A_c(\mathbf{P}, \omega)$ are derived as functions of the energy ω, and the argument $\mathbf{P}$ represents the vector of the c.o.m. linear momentum of the atom and c refers to the internal quantum numbers including spin. The dependence on the thermodynamic parameters temperature and chemical potentials is not explicitly stated. The particle number density $n_c(\beta, \mu_d)$ follows from the particle number operator as

$$n_c(\beta, \mu_d) = \sum_{\mathbf{P}} \langle a^\dagger_{\mathbf{P},c} a_{\mathbf{P},c} \rangle = \int_{-\infty}^{\infty} \frac{d\omega}{2\pi} f_c(\omega) D_c(\omega) \tag{5}$$

where $f_c(\omega) = [\exp(\beta(\omega - \mu_c)) \pm 1]^{-1}$ denotes the Bose or Fermi distribution function, respectively, as given by the spin of the elementary particle. The spectral function $A_c(\mathbf{P}, \omega)$ can be related to the atomic Green's function $G_c(\mathbf{P}; z_\nu)$ which is defined at the bosonic Matsubara frequencies $z_\nu = i\pi\nu/\beta$, $\nu = 0, \pm 2, \pm 4, \ldots$. After analytical continuation into the complex z-plane, one has

$$A_c(\mathbf{P}, \omega) = i \lim_{\epsilon \to 0} [G_c(\mathbf{P}; \omega + i\epsilon) - G_c(\mathbf{P}; \omega - i\epsilon)] . \tag{6}$$

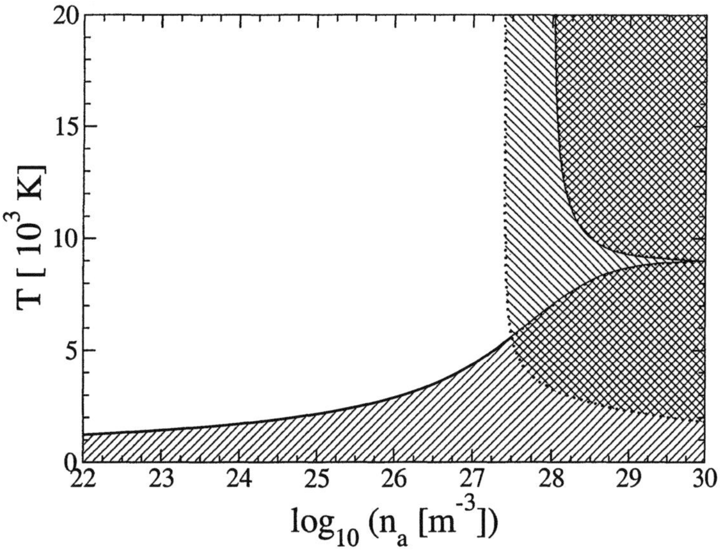

Figure 1. Correction in the virial expansion due to the molecules is larger then 20% right of the solid line. The approximation (19) for $D(\omega)$, becomes unphysical to the right of the dotted line. Area of validity: left of solid and dotted line.

The spectral function obeys the sum rule $\int A_c(\mathbf{P},\omega)\, \mathrm{d}\omega/2\pi = 1$. For the calculation of the Green's function $G_c(\mathbf{P}; z_\nu)$, perturbation theory can be applied. Considering the zeroth order, the propagation of free particles is described. All interaction effects can be taken into account via a self-energy $\Sigma_c(\mathbf{P}; z_\nu)$ which is introduced through a Dyson equation. In momentum representation, the Green's function is diagonal, and the Dyson equation is immediately solved leading to the relationship $G_c(\mathbf{P}; z_\nu) = [z_\nu - E_c(\mathbf{P}) - \Sigma_c(\mathbf{P}; z_\nu)]^{-1}$ with $E_c(\mathbf{P}) = P^2/2m_c$. Then, the spectral function (6) is directly related to the self-energy according to

$$A_c(\mathbf{P},\omega) = \frac{2\ \mathrm{Im}\ \Sigma_c(\mathbf{P},\omega)}{[\omega - E_c(\mathbf{P}) - \mathrm{Re}\ \Sigma_c(\mathbf{P},\omega)]^2 + [\mathrm{Im}\ \Sigma_c(\mathbf{P},\omega)]^2}\ . \tag{7}$$

Now, different expressions for the spectral function are obtained from approximations to the self-energy, which can be obtained within perturbation theory. While Eq. (7) is still exact as such, we will also consider the following approximation for the Green's function,

$$G_c(\mathbf{P}; z_\nu) = \frac{1}{z_\nu - E_c^{(\mathrm{qu})}(\mathbf{P})} \left[1 + \frac{\Sigma_c(\mathbf{P}; z_\nu) - \mathrm{Re}\ \Sigma_c(\mathbf{P}; E_c(\mathbf{P}))}{z_\nu - E_c^{(\mathrm{qu})}(\mathbf{P})} \right] \tag{8}$$

with the quasi-particle energy $E_c^{(\mathrm{qu})}(\mathbf{P}) = E_c(\mathbf{P}) + \mathrm{Re}\ \Sigma_c(\mathbf{P}; E_c(\mathbf{P}))$. The Green's function (8) is obtained from an expansion with respect to the self-energy up to first order. The corresponding spectral function reads

$$A_c(\mathbf{P},\omega) = 2\pi\ \delta\left(\omega - E_c^{(\mathrm{qu})}(\mathbf{P})\right) + 2\ \mathrm{Im}\ \Sigma_c(\mathbf{P},\omega)\ \frac{\mathrm{d}}{\mathrm{d}\omega}\ \mathcal{P}\!\int \mathrm{d}\omega\ \frac{1}{\omega - E_c^{(\mathrm{qu})}(\mathbf{P})} \tag{9}$$

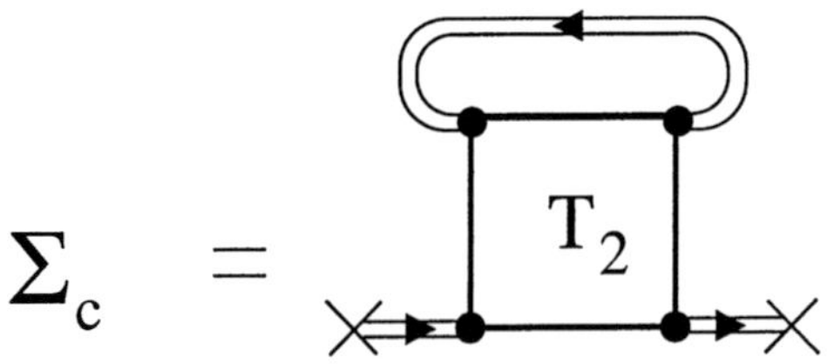

Figure 2. Self-energy of an atom in T-Matrix approximation including interatomic interaction to form correlated states of two atoms. The ⇒ indicate free atomic propagation and T_2 generates an infinite ladder summation of the interatomic interaction. Inverse Green's functions × are used to amputate the corresponding free propagators.

where $\mathcal{P}$ denotes the principal value.

4. DENSITY OF STATES ON ATOMIC LEVEL

The atomic system shall now be treated starting from the self energy due to the interaction with another atom. Applying the bilinear expansion for the diagram in Fig. 2, the self energy is given as

$$\Sigma_c^L(\mathbf{P}, z_\nu) = \sum_{P', z_{\nu'}} \frac{1}{z_{\nu'} - E_{P'}} \sum_m (E_c(\mathbf{P}) + E_{c'}(\mathbf{P}') - E_m) \times \frac{\psi_m(P, P')\psi_m^*(P, P')}{z_\nu + z_{\nu'} - E_m} (E_c(\mathbf{P}) + E_{c'}(\mathbf{P}') - z_\nu - z_{\nu'}) , \quad (10)$$

where $\psi_m(P, P')$ denotes the eigenstate of a hydrogen molecule with internal quantum number m and energy E_m, given in the representation P, P' which includes the atomic linear momenta $\mathbf{P}, \mathbf{P}'$ and spins σ, σ'. The $z_{\nu'}$ summation can be executed. Taking only the term in the lowest density order, we find

$$\Sigma_c^L(\mathbf{P}, z_\nu) = \sum_{P', m} f_{c'}(E_{c'}(\mathbf{P}')) \left|\psi_m(P, P')\right|^2 (E_c(\mathbf{P}) + E_{c'}(\mathbf{P}') - E_m) \times \left[\frac{E_c(\mathbf{P}) + E_{c'}(\mathbf{P}') - E_m}{z_\nu + E_{c'}(\mathbf{P}') - E_m} - 1 \right] . \quad (11)$$

From the approximation (9) the spectral function follows as

$$A_c(\mathbf{P}, \omega) = 2\pi\delta(\omega - E_c^{(\mathrm{qu})}(\mathbf{P})) + 2\pi \sum_{P', m} f_{c'}(E_{c'}(\mathbf{P}')) \left|\psi_m(P, P')\right|^2 \times \left[\delta(\omega + E_{c'}(\mathbf{P}') - E_m) - \delta(\omega - E_c^{(\mathrm{qu})}(\mathbf{P})) \right] , \quad (12)$$

in which the sum rule is fulfilled and the density of states reads

$$D(\omega) = \frac{1}{\Omega} \sum_P A_c(\mathbf{P}, \omega) = 2\pi \sum_P \delta(\omega - E_c^{(\mathrm{qu})}(\mathbf{P})) + 2\pi \sum_{P, P', m} f_{c'}(E_{c'}(\mathbf{P}')) \left|\psi_m(P, P')\right|^2 \left[\delta(\omega + E_{c'}(\mathbf{P}') - E_m) - \delta(\omega - E_c^{(\mathrm{qu})}(\mathbf{P})) \right] . \quad (13)$$

For the further treatment of the molecular wave functions

$$\psi_m(P,P') = \psi^{s/t}_{\mathbf{k},\mathbf{k}',\mathbf{x},\mathbf{x}'}(P,P') = \chi^{s/t}(\sigma,\sigma')\,\phi_{\mathbf{k},\mathbf{k}',\mathbf{x},\mathbf{x}'}(\mathbf{P},\mathbf{P}')\ , \tag{14}$$

where we have singlet (s) and triplet (t) states

$$\chi^s(\sigma,\sigma') = \frac{1}{\sqrt{2}}(\delta_{\sigma\uparrow}\delta_{\sigma'\downarrow} - \delta_{\sigma\downarrow}\delta_{\sigma'\uparrow}) \quad \chi^t(\sigma,\sigma') = \begin{cases} \delta_{\sigma\uparrow}\delta_{\sigma'\uparrow} \\ \frac{1}{\sqrt{2}}(\delta_{\sigma\uparrow}\delta_{\sigma'\downarrow} + \delta_{\sigma\downarrow}\delta_{\sigma'\uparrow}) \\ \delta_{\sigma\downarrow}\delta_{\sigma'\downarrow} \end{cases}$$

with respect to the electron spins σ, σ'. The interaction potential in the energies

$$E_m = E_{\mathbf{k}} + E_{\mathbf{k}'} + V^{s/t}(\mathbf{x}-\mathbf{x}') \tag{15}$$

depends on the electron spin state. Via Fourier transformation we have for the momentum representation of the spatial component of the wave function

$$\phi_{\mathbf{k},\mathbf{k}',\mathbf{x},\mathbf{x}'}(\mathbf{P},\mathbf{P}') = \frac{1}{\Omega}\int \mathrm{d}^3\mathbf{r} \int \mathrm{d}^3\mathbf{r}'\ \mathrm{e}^{-\frac{i}{\hbar}(\mathbf{P}\cdot\mathbf{r}+\mathbf{P}'\cdot\mathbf{r}')}\phi_{\mathbf{k},\mathbf{k}',\mathbf{x},\mathbf{x}'}(\mathbf{r},\mathbf{r}')\ . \tag{16}$$

Within the quasi-classical approximation, we assume a normalized product of Gauss' wave packets for each atom,

$$\phi_{\mathbf{k},\mathbf{k}',\mathbf{x},\mathbf{x}'}(\mathbf{r},\mathbf{r}') = \mathrm{e}^{\frac{i}{\hbar}(\mathbf{k}\cdot\mathbf{r}+\mathbf{k}'\cdot\mathbf{r}')}\frac{1}{(\pi\varrho^2)^{3/2}}\mathrm{e}^{-\frac{(\mathbf{r}-\mathbf{x})^2}{2\varrho^2}}\ \mathrm{e}^{-\frac{(\mathbf{r}'-\mathbf{x}')^2}{2\varrho^2}}\ . \tag{17}$$

Note that in the this approximation for the wave function the spatial component is not symmetrized, since only the center-of-mass motion of the atoms is relevant. It follows for the wave function in momentum space (16)

$$|\phi_{\mathbf{k},\mathbf{k}',\mathbf{x},\mathbf{x}'}(\mathbf{P},\mathbf{P}')|^2 = \frac{(4\pi\varrho^2)^3}{\Omega^2}\mathrm{e}^{-\frac{\varrho^2}{\hbar^2}(\mathbf{k}-\mathbf{P})^2}\mathrm{e}^{-\frac{\varrho^2}{\hbar^2}(\mathbf{k}'-\mathbf{P}')^2}\ . \tag{18}$$

The summation over m is to be taken with respect to the set of quantum numbers $\{s/t, \mathbf{k}, \mathbf{k}', \mathbf{x}, \mathbf{x}'\}$ in the way that

$$\sum_m \longrightarrow \sum_{s/t} \frac{1}{(2\pi\hbar)^3}\int\int \mathrm{d}^3\mathbf{k}\ \mathrm{d}^3\mathbf{x}\ \frac{1}{(2\pi\hbar)^3}\int\int \mathrm{d}^3\mathbf{k}'\ \mathrm{d}^3\mathbf{x}'\ .$$

In addition, a factor 2 for each nuclear spin has to be taken into account. In the quasi-classical approximation, the Gaussian wave packets give a $\delta^3(\mathbf{k}-\mathbf{P})$ if the parameter ϱ is taken in the limit of infinity. Then, due to the compensation $\omega + E_{c'}(\mathbf{P}') - E_m = \omega - V^{s/t}(x-x') - E_c(\mathbf{P})$ of the kinetic energy terms occurring in the δ function, we find finally

$$D(\omega) = \tag{19}$$

$$\frac{\sqrt{32\ m_a^3}}{\pi\hbar^3}\left[\sqrt{\omega} + \frac{\mathrm{e}^{\beta\mu_a}}{\Lambda_a^3}4\pi\int_0^\infty \mathrm{d}x\ x^2\left(\sqrt{\omega - V^s(x)} + 3\sqrt{\omega - V^t(x)} - 4\sqrt{\omega}\right)\right]\ .$$

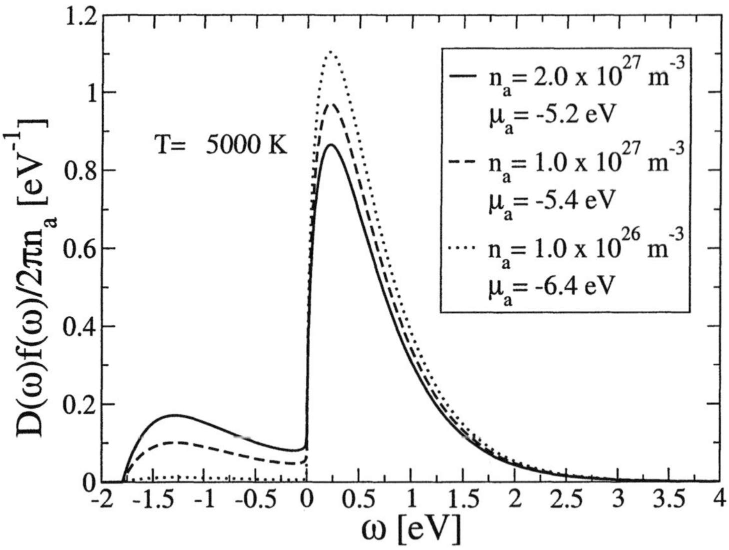

Figure 3. Normalized distribution of occupied states $D(\omega)f(\omega)/2\pi n_a$ including free and correlated atoms for three densities at 5000K. Boltzmann distribution is used for $f(\omega)$ and n_a is the particle density of bound and free atoms.

The results for this density of states is shown in Fig. 3. The chosen parameters are within the validity range of the virial expansion as shown in the previous section and Fig. 1. It turns out that another restriction can be found following the analysis of the density of states (19). For densities higher than indicated by the dotted line in Fig. 1, the density of states shows an unphysical oscillation and becomes also negative around $\omega = E_{1s}$. In Fig. 3, the distribution for positive energies is related to the atomic quasi-particle. For increasing densities, the formation of bound states becomes more relevant which can be seen from the spectral weight for negative energies. The calculations corroborate an increasing importance of the molecular contribution for higher densities. This leads to a broad energy distribution for free and correlated atoms.

Following on from the density of states (19), the number of particles (5) is calculated in the non-degenerate limit of the distribution function to be the same result as found in the classical limit, see Eq. (3). This shows the consistency of our approach on the level of the second virial coefficient. The unphysical behavior leading to negative values of the density of states is caused by the expansion of the spectral function with respect to the self-energy. This can be circumvented by calculating the spectral function in a more rigorous way. We insert expression (11) for the self energy into the exact relationship for the spectral function (7). From inspection of the expression for the self energy (11) it is clear that the imaginary part

$$\begin{aligned} &\mathrm{Im}\, \Sigma_c^L(\mathbf{P},\omega) \qquad (20)\\ &= \pi \sum_{P',m} f_{c'}(E_{c'}(\mathbf{P}'))\, |\psi_m(\mathbf{PP}')|^2\, (E_c(\mathbf{P}) + E_{c'}(\mathbf{P}') - E_m)^2\, \delta(\omega + E_{c'}(\mathbf{P}') - E_m) \end{aligned}$$

is positive and therefore the spectral function as well as the density of states should be positive at all frequencies. This avoids the problem which occurs with Eq. (19).

We calculate the imaginary part of the spectral function explicitly, and apply the Kramers-Kronig relation to determine the real part,

$$\text{Re}\ \Sigma_c^L(\mathbf{P},\omega) = \frac{1}{\pi}\ \mathcal{P}\int_{-\infty}^{\infty} \mathrm{d}\omega'\ \frac{\text{Im}\ \Sigma_c^L(\mathbf{P},\omega')}{\omega'-\omega}$$
$$- \sum_{c'\mathbf{P}',m} f_{c'}(E_{\mathbf{P}})\left|\psi_m(\mathbf{P}\mathbf{P}')\right|^2 (E_c(\mathbf{P}) + E_{c'}(\mathbf{P}') - E_m)\ . \quad (21)$$

Inserting the wavefunction (14), we can execute the $\mathbf{k}, \mathbf{k}'$, and $\mathbf{x}'$ integrations. In the quasi-classical approximation, as discussed after Eq. (18), the compensation $\omega + E_{c'}(\mathbf{P}') - E_m = \omega - V^{s/t}(x-x') - E_c(\mathbf{P})$ can be applied in the δ-function and in the square of the energy term. It leads to

$$\text{Im}\ \Sigma_\sigma^L(\mathbf{P},\omega) = \frac{2\mathrm{e}^{\beta\mu_a}}{\Lambda_a^3}\int \mathrm{d}^3\mathbf{x}\ \Big\{ \left[V^s(x)\right]^2\ \delta(\omega - V^s(x) - E_c(\mathbf{P})) \quad (22)$$
$$+3\left[V^t(x)\right]^2\ \delta(\omega - V^t(x) - E_c(\mathbf{P}))\Big\}\ .$$

This expression is inserted into the first contribution of Eq. (21) for the real part and the second part is treated in the same way as the imaginary part, leading to

$$\text{Re}\ \Sigma_\sigma^L(\mathbf{P},\omega) = \frac{2\mathrm{e}^{\beta\mu_a}}{\Lambda_a^3}\ \mathcal{P}\int \mathrm{d}^3\mathbf{x}\ \Bigg\{ \left[\frac{\left[V^s(x)\right]^2}{V^s(x) + E_c(\mathbf{P}) - \omega} - V^s(x)\right] \quad (23)$$
$$+3\left[\frac{\left[V^t(x)\right]^2}{V^t(x) + E_c(\mathbf{P}) - \omega} - V^t(x)\right]\Bigg\}\ .$$

If expressions (22) and (23) are used to calculate the spectral function via (7) and further on the density of states, it can be shown that the positivity of $D(\omega)$ is warranted for all densities. As has been discussed above for the expansion of the spectral function in the low-density limit, in addition to the contribution of free atoms, spectral weight occurs at negative frequencies indicating the contribution of bound (molecular) states. A detailed analysis of this approach will be given in an upcoming publication.

5. TRANSITION TO ELECTRONIC DENSITY OF STATES

Up to now we considered the atoms as elementary particles, interacting via an effective potential. They are able to form bound states (molecules), and the interaction was treated in the quasi-classical approximation. In the following, we want to give a description of our system on the level of the underlying substructure, considering electrons and protons as elementary particles interacting via the Coulomb potential to form atoms or molecules. This transition is also denoted as the transition from a chemical picture to a physical picture. Within the physical picture, the diagrams which we are considering to evaluate the self energy of the electrons are

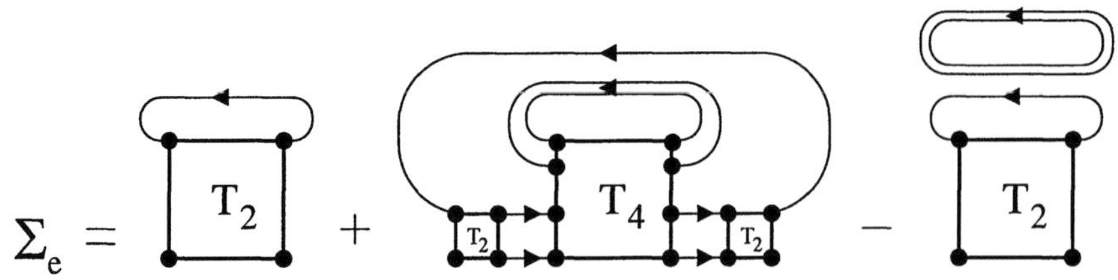

Figure 4. Electronic self-energy including the formation of atoms, molecules and related scattering states. Here the atomic and molecular bound states are realized by infinite ladder summations in T_2 and T_4, respectively. Once more the ⇒ indicate propagations of free atoms, while → represent free fermionic propagators.

shown in Fig. 4. Besides the formation of the atomic bound state, they describe also the interaction of atoms to form molecules. In particular, as discussed in [1,2], the summation of such diagrams is necessary in order to avoid divergent terms when hopping processes are considered. The latter leads to a broadening of the atomic bound states into a band structure as well as the formation of molecular states. Disconnected diagrams included in T_4 are subtracted as given by the last diagram in Fig. 4. It should be mentioned that further diagrams might be included if we are interested in the formation of additional clusters such as the H^- ion or the H_2^+ molecule ion.

Introducing a different notation on the new elementary level, $1 = \{\mathbf{p}, \sigma, c\}$ denotes the momentum, spin and species (electron or proton). The Matsubara frequencies z_1 are now fermionic. The analysis of the first diagram describing the formation of atomic bound states with total momentum $\mathbf{P}$ and internal quantum number n is in analogy to expression (11) of the previous section, except that the energies are now related to electrons, ions and atoms, respectively. It gives the result

$$\Sigma_2^L(1, z_1) = \sum_{2,n\mathbf{P}} f_2(E_2)|\psi_{n\mathbf{P}}(12)|^2(E_1 + E_2 - E_{n\mathbf{P}}) \left[\frac{E_1 + E_2 - E_{n\mathbf{P}}}{z_1 + E_2 - E_{n\mathbf{P}}} - 1\right] . \quad (24)$$

The second and third diagrams lead to the following contribution,

$$\begin{aligned}
\Sigma_4^L(1, z_1) = & \sum_{2,z_\nu,n\mathbf{P}} \frac{\psi_{n\mathbf{P}}(12)}{z_\nu - E_{n\mathbf{P}}} \frac{E_1 + E_2 - z_\nu}{z_\nu - z_1 - E_2} \qquad (25) \\
& \times \sum_{z'_\nu,n'\mathbf{P}'} \frac{T_4(n\mathbf{P}n'\mathbf{P}', n\mathbf{P}n'\mathbf{P}', z_\nu + z'_\nu)}{z'_\nu - E_{n'\mathbf{P}'}} \frac{\psi^*_{n\mathbf{P}}(12)}{z_\nu - E_{n\mathbf{P}}}(E_1 + E_2 - z_\nu) \\
= & \sum_{2,z_\nu,n\mathbf{P}} \frac{|\psi_{n\mathbf{P}}(12)|^2}{(z_\nu - E_{n\mathbf{P}})^2} \frac{(E_1 + E_2 - z_\nu)^2}{z_\nu - z_1 - E_2} \sum_{z_{\nu'},n'\mathbf{P}',m} \frac{1}{z_{\nu'} - E_{n'\mathbf{P}'}} \\
& \times (E_{n\mathbf{P}} + E_{n'\mathbf{P}'} - E_m) \frac{|\psi_m(n\mathbf{P}, n'\mathbf{P}')|^2}{z_\nu + z_{\nu'} - E_m}(E_{n\mathbf{P}} + E_{n'\mathbf{P}'} - z_\nu - z_{\nu'}) .
\end{aligned}$$

Disconnected diagrams included in Fig. 4 are considered only for the decaying processes of molecule dissociation and ionisation of atoms. Other disconnected diagrams

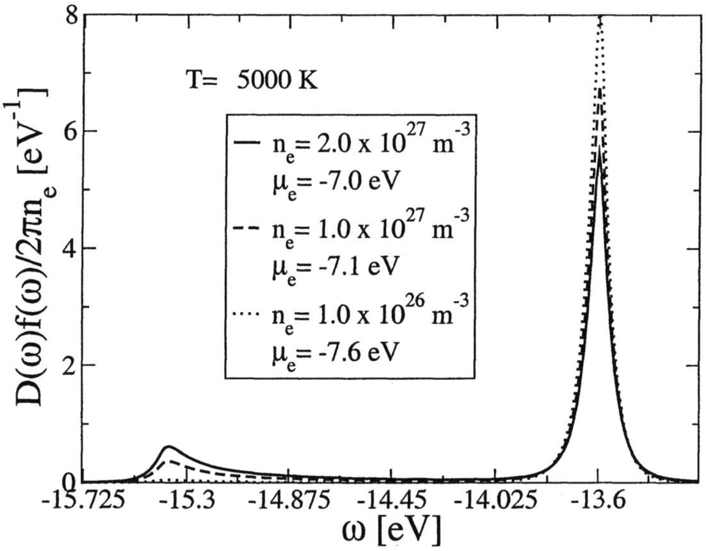

Figure 5. Normalized distribution of occupied electronic states $D(\omega)f(\omega)/2\pi n_e$ including atomar and molecular bound electrons for three densities at 5000K. Here, Boltzmann distribution is applied for $f(\omega)$ and n_e is the whole electron density of the system.

of T_4 are neglected. The summations over $z_{\nu'}$ and z_ν can be executed and lead in lowest density order to

$$\Sigma_4^L(1,z_1) = \sum_{2,n\mathbf{P},n'\mathbf{P}',m} f_2(E_2) f_{n'}(E_{n'\mathbf{P}'}) |\psi_{n\mathbf{P}}(12)|^2 \, |\psi_m(n\mathbf{P},n'\mathbf{P}')|^2 \times \left[\frac{(E_1+E_2+E_{n'\mathbf{P}'}-E_m)^2}{z_1+E_2+E_{n'\mathbf{P}'}-E_m} - \frac{(E_1+E_2-E_{n\mathbf{P}})^2}{z_1+E_2-E_{n\mathbf{P}}} + (E_{n\mathbf{P}}+E_{n'\mathbf{P}'}-E_m) \right] . \tag{26}$$

From the approximation (9) for the spectral function, one can derive

$$\begin{aligned} A_e(1,\omega) =& 2\pi\delta(\omega - E_1^{(\mathrm{qu})}) \\ &+ 2\pi \sum_{2,n\mathbf{P}} f_2(E_2) \, |\psi_{n\mathbf{P}}(12)|^2 \left[\delta(\omega + E_2 - E_{n\mathbf{P}}) - \delta(\omega - E_1^{(\mathrm{qu})}) \right] \\ &+ 2\pi \sum_{2,n\mathbf{P},n'\mathbf{P}',m} f_2(E_2) f_{n'}(E_{c'}(\mathbf{P}')) |\psi_{n\mathbf{P}}(12)|^2 \, |\psi_m(n\mathbf{P},n'\mathbf{P}')|^2 \\ &\times [\delta(\omega + E_2 + E_{n'\mathbf{P}'} - E_m) - \delta(\omega + E_2 - E_{n\mathbf{P}})] \end{aligned} \tag{27}$$

where the first term is related to the quasi-particle, the second term is due to the atomic contribution, see the first diagram in Fig. 4. The last term is the expression for the last two diagrams which contain contributions of the formation of molecules. Following the analysis of the self-energy, the occuring divergency for infinite separation is eliminated. Obviously, this expression fulfills the sum rule for the spectral function. In the following, we will restrict ourselves to the ground state $n = \{1s\}$

with the corresponding energy $E_{1s,\mathbf{P}} = -13.6 \text{ eV} + P^2/2(m_e + m_i)$ and the wave function

$$\psi_{1s,\mathbf{P}}(\mathbf{p}_1, \mathbf{p}_2) = \delta_{\mathbf{P},\mathbf{p}_1+\mathbf{p}_2}\phi_{1s}(\mathbf{p}) = \delta_{\mathbf{P},\mathbf{p}_1+\mathbf{p}_2}\frac{8\sqrt{a_0^3\,\pi}}{\sqrt{\Omega}\left(1+\frac{a_0^2\,p^2}{\hbar^2}\right)^2}\,.$$

where $\mathbf{p} = (m_i\,\mathbf{p}_1 - m_e\,\mathbf{p}_2)/(m_i + m_e)$ is the relative momentum. In addition, applying the adiabatic approximation $(m_e/m_i \to 0)$ to the wave function, $\phi_{1s}(\mathbf{p}) = \phi_{1s}(\mathbf{p}_1)$, the evaluation of the corresponding electronic density of states gives $(p_1 \to p)$

$$D_e(\omega) = \frac{\sqrt{8\,m_e^3\,\omega}}{\pi\hbar^3}\left\{1 - \frac{2\mathrm{e}^{\beta\mu_i}}{\Lambda_i^3}\,\Omega\,|\phi_{1s}(\sqrt{2m_e\omega}/\hbar)|^2\right\} \tag{28}$$

$$+\sqrt{\frac{8\,m_i\,\beta}{\pi^3\hbar^6}}\frac{\mathrm{e}^{\beta\mu_i}}{\Lambda_i^3}\Omega\int_0^\infty \mathrm{d}p\,p\,|\phi_{1s}(p)|^2\left\{\mathrm{e}^{-\frac{\beta m_i}{2p^2}\left(\frac{p^2}{2m_i}+E_{1s}-\omega\right)^2} + \frac{\mathrm{e}^{\beta(\mu_i+\mu_e-E_{1s})}}{\Lambda_i^3}\right.$$

$$\times 4\pi\int_0^\infty \mathrm{d}R\,R^2\left[3\mathrm{e}^{-\frac{\beta m_i}{2p^2}\left(\frac{p^2}{2m_i}+E_{1s}+V^t(R)-\omega\right)^2} + \mathrm{e}^{-\frac{\beta m_i}{2p^2}\left(\frac{p^2}{2m_i}+E_{1s}+V^s(R)-\omega\right)^2}\right.$$

$$\left.\left. -4\mathrm{e}^{-\frac{\beta m_i}{2p^2}\left(\frac{p}{2m_i}+E_{1s}-\omega\right)^2}\right]\right\}$$

Again, as has been seen in the virial expansion for the atomic system, the positivity of the density of states is violated at high densities. Alternatively, the spectral function can be derived from the Kramers-Kronig relation for the self energy as shown in the atomic case.

In Fig. 5, the density of states weighted by the distribution function is shown for different densities at $T = 5000$K. To be comparible with the calculations shown in Fig. 3, the contribution of free electrons, as which the first term in (28) can be interpreted, is not shown. The densities are chosen in the same range. For the lowest density a dominating resonance at the electronic ground state of an hydrogen atom is observed. Thermal motion causes a finite bandwith. For higher densities a second resonance occurs at the molecular binding energy which is shifted 1.75 eV lower from the atomic peak as was also seen in the atomic case, compare Fig. 3.

4. CONCLUSIONS

It was shown in detail how the description of band formation in a dense plasma can be achieved within a Green's function approach. In particular, we have focussed on the inclusion of the formation of hydrogen molecules within a quasi-classical treatment. The spectral function, the density of states and the corresponding virial expansion for the equation of state were considered on the level of atoms as elementary constituents as well as on the level of electrons. The validity of the sum rule for the spectral function was checked. By considering whether the density of states is positively defined, we could specify the region of validity of our approximations. For a range of paramter values, calculations for hydrogen have been performed and the formation of bands has been seen. In an upcoming paper, we will extend this approach by considering correlations between the electrons as well as the quantum description of the formation of molecules and other clusters.

ACKNOWLEDGMENTS

G.R. and C.N. are grateful for the hospitality and the financial support during the 27th Workshop on CMT in Toulouse/ France. H.R. was supported by a Fellowship of the German DFG.

REFERENCES

[1] G. Röpke and H. Reinholz, *phys. stat. sol.* (b) **234**, 254 (2002).

[2] G. Röpke, H. Reinholz, and C. Neißner, *J. Phys. A* **36**, 5931 (2003)

[3] R. Redmer, *Phys. Rep.* **282**, 36 (1997).

[4] W. D. Kraeft, D. Kremp, W. Ebeling, and G. Röpke, *Quantum Statistics of Charge Particle Systems* (Plenum, New York, 1986).

[5] L. P. Kadanoff, and G. Baym, *Quantum Statistical Mechanics: Green's Function Methods in Equilibrium and Nonequilibrium Problems* (Addison-Wesley, Redwood City, Calif., 1989).

[6] A. L. Fetter, and J. D. Walecka, *Quantum Theory of Many-Particle Systems* (McGraw-Hill,New York, 1971).

[7] B. F. Rozsnyai, *Phys. Rev.* A **5**, 1137 (1972).

[8] M. A. Tusch, and D. E. Logan, *Phys. Rev.* B **48**, 14843 (1993).

[9] Th. Koslowski, D. G. Rowan, and D. E. Logan, *Ber. Bunsenges. Phys. Chem.* **100**, 101 (1996).

[10] A. S. Davydov, *Quantum Mechanics* (Pergamon, Oxford, 1976), original in Russian: *Kvantovaia Mekhanika* (Nauka, Moscow, 1973).

[11] R. Redmer, G. Röpke, S. Kuhlbrodt, and H. Reinholz, *Phys. Rev* B **63**, 233104 (2001).

Nanoparticles, Clusters and Large Molecules

MIXED TRANSITION METAL NANOPARTICLES STRUCTURAL AND MAGNETIC PROPERTIES

J. Morillo, S. Dennler, M. C. Fromen, M. J. Casanove and P. Lecante
CEMES/CNRS, 29 rue Jeanne Marvig, 31055 Toulouse Cedex 4, France

G. M. Pastor
LPQ-IRSAMC/CNRS, 31062 Toulouse Cedex 4, France

1. INTRODUCTION

In the last twenty years due to large improvements in synthesis techniques objects with nanometer scale dimensions have become a very common material for both experimental and theoretical investigators. The size reduction gives them new and unexpected properties with very promising applications in various fields. From the experimental point of view most of the usual observation techniques reach their limits. From the theoretical point of view, they represent a challenge since none of the usual approaches of neither the molecular or the solid state physics can be applied directly. Understanding the "why and how" of the properties of these materials is then a very important goal. In the present paper, we will show how a joint experimental and theoretical approach could be efficient in the study of a particular nanosized material: nanoparticles of transition metal alloys.

Indeed, small transition-metal nanoparticles are today the subject of considerable interest due to their possible applications in magnetic recording technologies. In this respect, alloying 3d and 4d elements could be an effective way to combine a large magnetic moment with a high anisotropy, which is the goal for this kind of applications, due to the 4d strong spin-orbit coupling and the 3d high magnetic moments.

We will briefly review part of the experimental and theoretical work, that has been done in our laboratories in collaboration with [1,2] on 3d/4d transition metal binary nanoparticles and more precisely those concerning

Co_xRh_{1-x} nanoparticles [3-9], 1 nm ($\approx$ 100-200 atoms), to 3 nm ($\approx$ 400-500 atoms) large synthesized by a soft chemical route [1,10]. In their atomic state Co and Rh are both magnetic with a 3 μ_B magnetic moment. In their crystalline

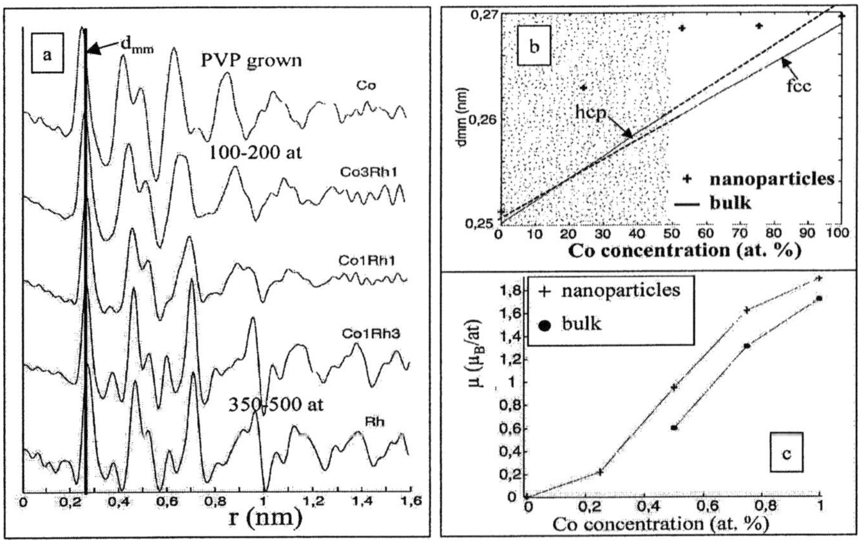

Figure 1. Structural and magnetic experimental results: (a) Radial distribution function of the nanoparticles as deduced from the WAXS measurements [3] ; (b) First neighbour distance d_{mm} vs composition x in bulk fcc and hcp alloys [14] and nanoparticles (from Fig. 1-a) ; (c) Measured bulk alloys [15,16] and nanoparticles [4,5] magnetic moments.

state, Rh looses completly its magnetic character whereas Co retains half of it, $\mu(\text{Co}) = 1.58\ \mu_B$. From the structural point of view, both have a compact but different structure: the fcc one for Rh and the hcp one for Co. However their first neighbour distances d_{mm} are rather different: 2.493 Å for Co and 2.690 Å for Rh. So one can expect a large variety of structural and magnetic properties of their mixed nanoparticles that could be very sensitive to their size, mean composition and local chemical order.

Their structural properties have been investigated using high-resolution transmission electron microscopy (HRTEM) and wide angle x-ray scattering (WAXS) techniques. Their magnetic properties were studied with a SQUID magnetometer between 1.5 and 300K and magnetic fields up to 30 T.

From the theoretical point of view, ab initio Density Functional Theory (DFT) calculations have been performed on small clusters (up to 13 atoms), free surfaces and the corresponding bulk alloys. They have been performed by means of the Vienna ab initio DFT simulation program VASP developed at the Institut für Materialphysik of the Universität Wien [11,12].

A detailed description of the computational parameters that have been monitored in order to control the accuracy of the results can be found elsewhere [7-9].

Concerning the small clusters calculations one must emphasize that the presence of numerous close-lying electronic configurations with different spin multiplicities or geometries necessitates to carry out geometry optimizations for several fixed relevant values of the total spin magnetic moment S_z, and for various initial geometries.

The reported local magnetizations $\mu(i)$ have been obtained by integration of the magnetization density in spheres centered on each atom with radii $r_{sph}(\mathrm{Co}) = 1.30$ Å and $r_{sph}(\mathrm{Rh}) = 1.40$ Å.

From these ab initio calculations an N-body semiempirical interaction model has been designed and applied to the study of the structure and chemical order of nanoparticles comparable to the experimental ones [3,6]. This interaction model has been derived within the second moment approximation of the tight binding scheme. The monoatomic interaction parameters are those of [13]. The heteroatomic ones are those that have given the best fit between the interaction model and the previously calculated ab initio values of the cohesive energy differences and lattice parameters of the ordered alloy phases. The absolute energy scale has been fixed by the introduction of the absolute value of the equiatomic disordered phase, as experimentally determined, in the fitting constraints. Surface energies were then calculated to test the validity of the model to reproduce open structures. Molecular and quenched Molecular Dynamics as well as simulated annealing within the relaxation and exchange Monte Carlo Metropolis scheme have been performed on nanoparticles of different compositions and sizes, starting from various initial temperatures, structures and chemical species distributions.

Within the limited available space we will focus on a couple of points for which the combination of these three approaches has been particularly efficient and we invite the interested readers to look at the quoted references for a detailed description of our work. In the second section the material and the concerned experimental results will be presented. Section 3 will be devoted to the description of the ab initio DFT results whereas the semiempirical ones will be presented in section 4.

2. EXPERIMENTAL RESULTS

Experimentally, the Co-Rh bulk alloys are known to form a continuous series of disordered solid solutions [14]. At room temperature their structure is fcc for a Co concentration $x \leq 49.5\%$ and hcp for higher concentrations.

Vegard's law applies rather well to the lattice parameter or first neighbour distance d_{mm} versus x in both phases (Fig. 1-b).

As can be seen on Fig. 1-b, the corresponding d_{mm} of the studied nanoparticles (embedded in a polymer, the polyvinylpyrrolidone, or PVP polymer) as measured on the radial distribution functions (RDF)(Fig. 1-a), deduced from the WAXS experiments [3], are significantly higher than those of the bulk alloys. Similarly, there is a large increase of the magnetic moment per atom of the nanoparticles [4,5] compared to the bulk material [15,16] (Fig. 1-c). The question is then: did these properties, the local dilation and the magnetic enhancement, result from the reduced size of the particles, from specific structures different from the bulk ones, from some chemical order effect or any combination of these three effects?

Indeed the HRTEM observations give us a partial answer to this question [3-6]. They reveal that the Co_1Rh_3 and Rh nanoparticles have the fcc structure of the corresponding alloy, although with slight disorder. Consequently their RDF could be accurately reproduced with fcc nanoparticles models. On the contrary for the Co rich particles the structure is neither hcp or fcc as confirmed by the impossiblity to fit the Co-rich RDF results with hcp or fcc models. This is related to the observed progressive desappearance of the second peak of the RDF (Fig. 1-a) when increasing Co concentration: a peak corresponding to the second neighbour distance characteristic of compact fcc or hcp structures. One must then conclude that the nanoparticles with high Co concentration have a non optimal compact structure without any long range periodic order.

3. AB INITIO DFT RESULTS

These nanoparticles are far too large to allow a theoretical determination of their strutural and chemical order by any ab initio approach, even with the density functional theory (DFT), the less demanding one in terms of computational time and memory. Their magnetic properties could possibly be studied within the DFT (spin magnetic moment only) for the smallest ones for various fixed geometries and chemical order and certainly for all of them with the less accurate tight binding approach which moreover allows the treatment of both spin and orbital magnetism [17-20]. However here also these calculations can only been performed at fixed geometry and chemical order which are unknown.

Their properties can then be approached from an ab initio point of view only through those of their limiting cases, bulk crystals, surfaces and smaller nanoparticles. The obtained structural and chemical order results can then be used to design a semiempirical interaction model in order to explore the structure and chemical order of the larger ones of interest here.

Let us start with what happens on the smallest limit: the dimers. Tab. 1 reports their main properties. We would like to emphasize the following points: there is a slight stabilisation of the mixed dimer compared to the pure ones and a magnetic moment transfer from Rh to Co in the mixed dimer. This can be easily explained by the energy difference between the highest occupied Kohn-Sham eigenvalues of the isolated atoms ($E_{\mathrm{HOMO}}(\mathrm{Co}) - E_{\mathrm{HOMO}}(\mathrm{Rh}) = 0.88$ eV) or by their empirical Pauling electronegativities ($\chi_{\mathrm{P}}(\mathrm{Co}) = 1.88$ and $\chi_{\mathrm{P}}(\mathrm{Rh}) = 2.28$), both effects being favorable to a Co to Rh electron transfer. For the 3 dimers the bond length d is much smaller than the first neighbour distance d_{mm} of the corresponding bulk material (Fig.1-b).

Let us now look at what happens in the opposite limit: the bulk materials. Fig. 2-a reports the calculated mean magnetic moment per atom vs Co concentration for pure metals and alloys with different local coordination and/or chemical environment.

For both pure metals the most stable phase is the experimental one: fcc for Rh and hcp for Co, with lattice parameter and magnetic moment values in good agreement with the experimental ones [14-16]. The disordered almost ideal solid solution behaviour of the alloy is well reproduced: the different fcc based alloys have cohesive energies almost independent of the local chemical order with an almost linear variation with Co concentration. The same holds for the lattice parameter or first neighbour distance. A sensible difference both in cohesive energy and magnetic

Table 1

Cohesive energy E_c (eV/atom),
total magnetic moment S_z (μ_B), integrated local magnetic moments μ(M) (μ_B), and equilibrium bond length d (Å) of the dimers.

	Rh–Rh	Co–Rh	Co–Co
E_c	1.71	1.83	1.53
S_z	4	4	4
μ(Co)		2.29	1.93
μ(Rh)	1.82	1.43	
d	2.21	2.08	1.96

moment was observed only for the bcc based phase (B2) which has a lower local coordination and a larger first neighbour distance.

The comparison of magnetic and non-magnetic calculations reveals a significant contribution of magnetism to cohesion for Co rich alloys. This contribution is absent for pure Rh, is about 5% for pure Co and turns out to be at the origin of the stabilization of the hcp phase in agreement with previous local spin density calculations [21]. Magnetism also induces a lattice parameter expansion that amounts to ≈ 2 % for pure Co.

The observed non-linear behavior on Fig. 2-a is the result of an increasing induced magnetic moment on the Rh atoms with increasing x_{Co}, marginally compensated by a very slight decrease of the Co one (Fig. 2-b). Despite the fact that our calculations refer to ordered fcc-based structures, the obtained local magnetic moments are in better agreement with the experimental ones [15,16] than previous TB-LMTO-ASA calculations [22] in the case of Co_3Rh.

It appears then that in these two limits the behaviours are somehow opposite: -i- slight stabilisation of the mixed dimer vs almost ideal disordered solid solution for the alloy, -ii- magnetic moment transfer from Rh to Co in the dimer and reverse transfer for the alloy. One can say that heteroatomic bonds are prefered in the dimer whereas the local coordination and the magnetic energy are much more important than the local chemical order in the bulk phase.

Before turning out to the results concerning the small clusters, We would like to emphasize the importance of magnetic energy contribution to the structural properties in that case. The rather low 5% magnetic contribution to the cohesive energy of bulk Co concomitent with a small lattice parameter expansion can be misleading. This is illustrated on Fig. 3, where the magnetic contribution to the cohesive energy and bond length of a square cluster are shown to be very large (up to 30% for the cohesive energy).

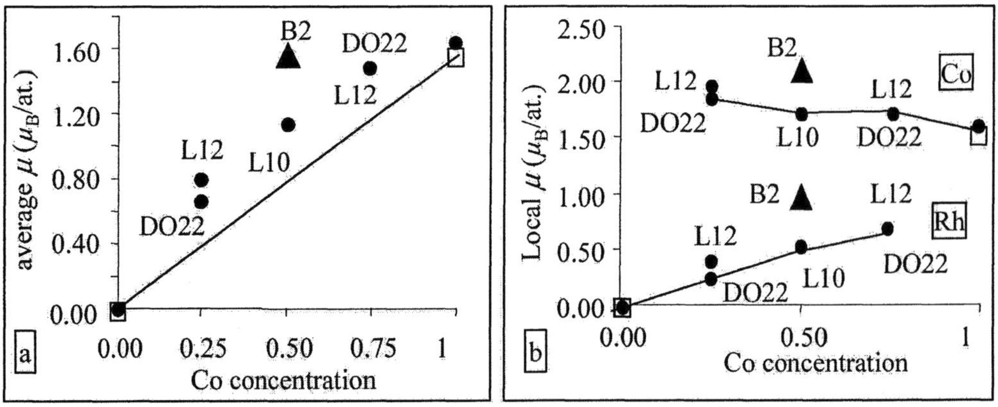

Figure 2. Calculated magnetic moments of various alloys [7]: (a) Mean magnetic moment per atom vs Co concentration, "circles" fcc based, "triangle" bcc based structures and "square" hcp structure ; (b) Local magnetic moment on Co and Rh atoms vs concentration.

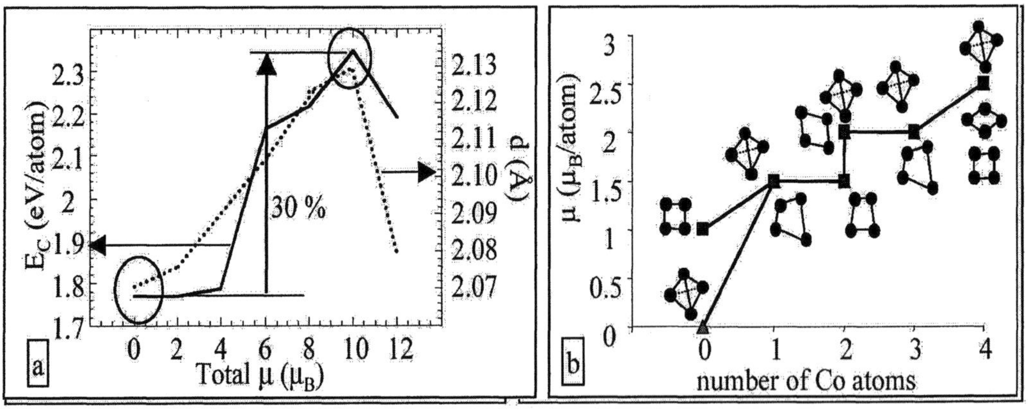

Figure 3. (a) Cohesive energy E_c and square side dimension d for a square Co_4 cluster vs the total magnetic moment. The circles correspond to the magnetic ($\mu = 0\ \mu_B$) and non magnetic ($\mu = 10\ \mu_B$) fundamental states.

(b) Magnetic moment vs number of Co atoms for various planar and tridimensional 4 atom clusters.

Let us turn now to the results concerning the clusters (from 2 to 13 atoms) [7-9]. All the mixed ones are found to be magnetic with an average magnetic moment per atom $\overline{\mu}$ that is smaller than for the isolated atoms but remarkably enhanced with respect to the macroscopic bulk alloys. For a given cluster size, $\overline{\mu}$ increases with increasing x_{Co} as illustrated on Fig. 3-b. The most stable isomers are usually not the most magnetic ones. However, the energy differences always remain small, which

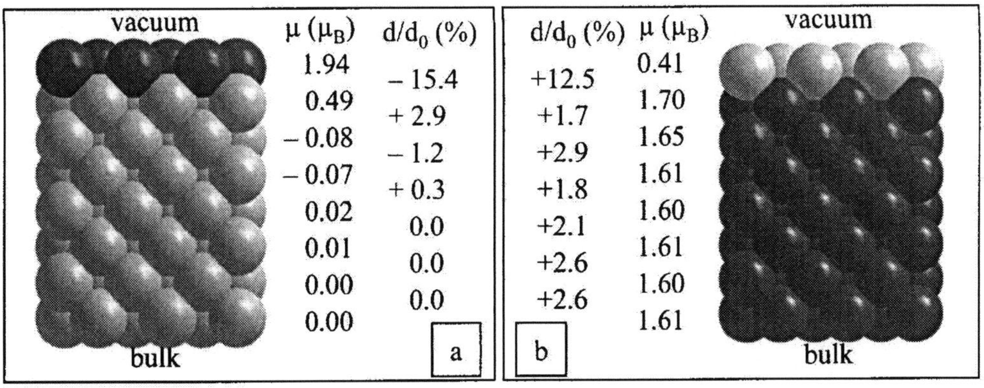

Figure 4. Surface magnetism, d/d_0 relative interplanar distance (d_0 bulk one), μ magnetic moment per atom in each layer: (a) Co monolayer on fcc Rh(001) ; (b) Rh monolayer on fcc Co(001).

implies the possible coexistence of several isomers.

Even if the average magnetic moment globally increases with increasing x_{Co}, there is no simple correlation between Co substitution and magnetic enhancement. In the considered size range, Rh_N clusters are in general magnetic. For low-symmetric open structures (linear Rh_3, some Rh_7 isomers) the Co substitution has an efficient spin-polarization effect, even at low Co concentrationand results in a remarkable increase of the local magnetic moments at the Rh neighbours. In this case, the magnetic enhancement can reach more than 1 μ_B per Rh atom.

On the other hand, the effect of Co doping can be masked in geometries of higher symmetry in which pure Rh clusters already show a high magnetic moment (7-atom decahedral isomer). From the Co point of view, one observes that the Co atoms retain their magnetic moments even in a Rh-rich environment. In some cases, a small enhancement of the Co local moments is found like in the CoRh dimer.

Surface induced magnetism is a very well known phenomenon. In order to quantify what could be its contribution to the magnetic moments of these nanoparticles we have started a series of calculations on Rh or Co atoms on low index surfaces of pure and alloyed crystals. Two kinds of calculations were performed: -i- single Co or Rh atoms up to full monolayer coverage, -ii- single atoms burried at different distances from the surface. As illustrated on Fig. 4, there is a strong surface magnetic effect. The Co atoms of a monolayer over a pure Rh(001) crystal (Fig. 4-a) exhibit a large 1.94 μ_B/at magnetic moment, 20% higher than that of the pure Co crystal. They also induce an appreciable .49 μ_B/at magnetic moment onto the adjacent Rh layer. The magnetic surface enhancement is less pronounced for the reverse situation (Fig. 4-b). Nevertheless a .41 μ_B/at induced magnetic moment is observed on the Rh atoms, larger than that induced in the bulk alloys. It is accompanied by a small enhancement of the magnetic moment of the 2 adjacent Co layers. The resulting total enhancements are then of the order of 2.5 μ_B per surface Co atom and .5 μ_B per Rh atom.

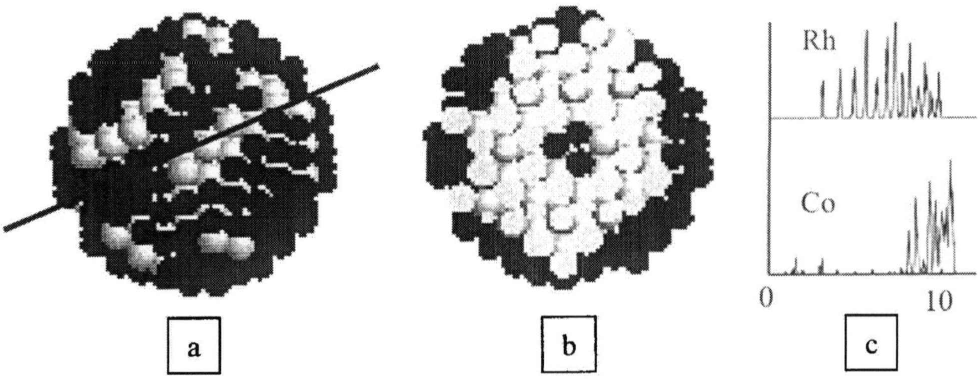

Figure 5. Chemical species distributions of a Co_1Rh_1 hcp nanoparticle of 420 atoms after a Monte Carlo Metropolis run at 300K, "white balls" Rh, "black balls" Co : (a) 3 dimensional vue ; (b) cross section along the plane shown on Fig. a ; mean final (10000 MC steps mean values) distribution of atomic distances to the center of the nanoparticle in Å.

Similar slightly higher magnetic enhancements are found for both Co or Rh terminated $Co_1Rh_1(001)$ fcc L10 ordered alloy surfaces. Preliminary results indicate that in Co/Rh(001) surfaces the Co atoms lead to an effective magnetic moment larger than 2 μ_B per Co atom. This enhancement results from an almost coverage independent Co magnetic moment of about 2 μ_B and from the Rh neighbours magnetic induced moments.

So, it seems that, whatever the bulk alloy, one must expect a strong magnetic enhancement at the surface if Co surface segretation occurs, with values of the order of 2-3 μ_B per Co surface atom, and a less strong one for Rh segregation, .5-1 μ_B per Rh surface atom.

4. SEMIEMPIRICAL RESULTS

First of all one must emphasize that for a given nanoparticle, whatever the initial species distribution and structure, the Monte Carlo Metropolis runs at 300K lead to final chemical orders that were all statistically equivalent [3]. The main characteristic of these final structures is that they present a marked segregation of Co atoms at the surface and a very small Co core for the Co rich ones as illustrated on Fig. 5 for a Co_1Rh_1 nanoparticle of 420 atoms with an hcp structure. This tendency is preserved, although less marked, even after simulated annealing from 1600K [3].

From the structural point of view they tend to preserve their initial structure (hcp, fcc, polytetrahedral, ...) after the 300K runs. It must be quoted that even if the final hcp and fcc structures have energy differences which are very small, less than 10 meV per atom, we have not observed any spontaneous transition from one structure to the other. However, after the simulated annealing from 1600K they all

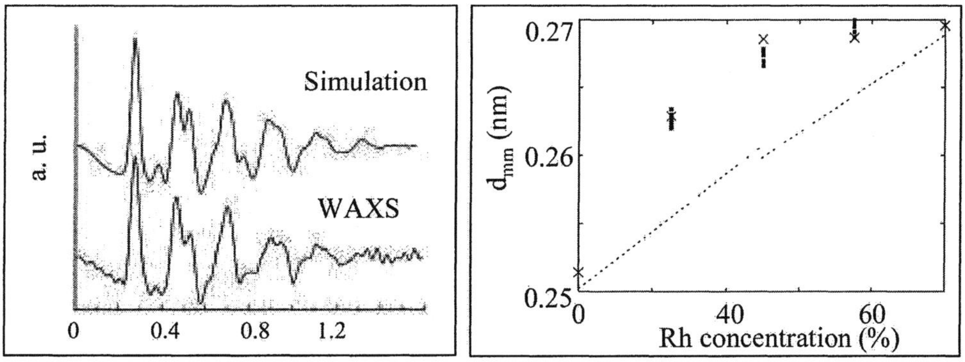

Figure 6. (a) Co_1Rh_1 nanoparticle: comparison between the experimental RDF of the nanoparticle of Fig. 1 and that of a 137 atoms simulated one (1600K simulated annealing) . (b) First neighbour distances : "dots" bulk, "crosses" experience, "squares" simulation.

tend to converge towards identical poorly crystallized structures.

A typical example of such a final structure is given on Fig. 6-a, where the RDF deduced from the final simulated positions is compared to the experimental one for a Co_1Rh_1 nanoparticle of 137 atoms showing an almost perfect agreement. Moreover these poorly crystallized structures have first neighbour distances that are close to the experimental ones as can be seen on Fig. 6-b.

So these semiempirical simulations clearly speak in favor of a strong Co surface segregation in all cases, with a small Co core segregation for the Co rich nanoparticles, and poorly ordered structures as a result of the growth process.

5. CONCLUSIONS

Even if there is no simple correlation between Co substitution and the existence of an induced Rh magnetic enhancement, as the contradictory behaviour of the dimer and bulk materials evidences, one can draw some general conclusions.

The ab initio calculations have shown that small CoRh clusters are magnetic with average magnetic moments that are significantly larger than those of the corresponding bulk materials and increase with the Co concentration.

In most cases, like in the bulk alloys, there is an induced magnetic moment onto the Rh neighbours and Co seems to retain its magnetic properties even in a highly mixed environment.

This results, in general, in a strong magnetic enhancement, as far as the corresponding Rh pure clusters are not themselves highly magnetic, which is precisely the case for the 1-3 nm large nanoparticles studied here.

From the structural point of view, the most important point is that energy differences between the various isomers remain relatively small, which implies the possible coexistence of several isomers in the experimental preparations and non fully relaxed structures. The observed agreement between the structural experimental data and those of the simulations with the semiempirical model tells us that this is certainly what happens with the studied nanoparticles which are embedded in a polymer as a result of a low temperature synthesis by a soft chemical route.

On the other hand, the simulations have clearly shown a preferred tendency to Co surface seggregation for these nanoparticles. A tendency more pronounced for Rh rich particles but still present in the Co rich ones but then associated to a small Co core. At the same time, the ab initio surface calculations clearly demonstrate that Co surface seggregation is more favorable than Rh to obtain high magnetic moments whatever the composition.

It seems then that one can conclude with some confidence that there is a cobalt surface segregation in these 1-3 nm nanoparticles resulting in a large magnetic moment enhancement.

Obviously, the use of the present multiple approach, has allowed us to gain a good understanding of both the structural and magnetic properties of these nanoparticles. Finally, starting from these optimized structures it would be worthwhile to perform tight binding calculations including spin-orbit coupling to test the accuracy of our results and to quantify to what extent the presence of the rhodium atoms induces a significant magnetic anisotropy in these nanoparticles.

ACKNOWLEDGMENTS

Helpful discussions with M. Respaud, D. Zitoun, C. Amiens and B. Chaudret are gratefully acknowledged. This work has been financed in part by the EU GROWTH project AMMARE (G5RD-CT-2001-00478). Computer resources were provided by CALMIP and IDRIS (France). The calculations have been performed using the VASP ab initio total-energy and molecular-dynamics program (Vienna ab initio simulation program) developed at the Institut für Materialphysik of the Universität Wien.

REFERENCES

[1] Laboratoire de Chimie de Coordination, LCC/CNRS, Toulouse, France.

[2] Service National des Champs Magnétiques Pulsés, SNCMP - LPMC/INSA Toulouse, France.

[3] M. C. Fromen, "Etude Experimentale et modélisation de la structure de nanoparticules magnétiques: des particules isolées aux assemblages" PhD Thesis, 8 Oct. 2003, INSA Toulouse, France.

[4] M.C. Fromen *et al*, *J. Magn. Mag. Mat.* **242-246**, 610 (2002).

[5] D. Zitoun *et al*, *Phys. Rev. Lett.* **89**, 37203 (2002).
[6] M.C. Fromen *et al*, *MRS proceedings*, accepted for publication (2004).
[7] S. Dennler *et al*, *Surf. Sci.* **532-535**, 334-340 (2003).
[8] S. Dennler *et al*, *Eur. Phys. J. D* **24**, 237-240 (2003).
[9] S. Dennler *et al*, *J. Phys C*, accepted for publication (2004).
[10] See in this same conference B. Chaudret's talk.
[11] G. Kresse and J. Hafner, *Phys. Rev. B* **47**, RC558 (1993).
[12] G. Kresse, and J. Furthmüller, *Phys. Rev. B* **54**, 11169 (1996).
[13] F. Cleri and V. Rosato, *Phys. Rev. B* **48**, 22 (1993).
[14] W. Koster and E. Horn, *Z. Metallkunde* **43**, 444 (1952).
[15] G.R. Harp *et al*, *J. Appl. Phys.* **76**, 6471 (1994).
[16] G.R. Harp *et al*, *Phys. Rev. B* **51**, 12037 (1995).
[17] G.M. Pastor *et al*, *Phys. Rev. Lett.* **75**, 326 (1995).
[18] R. Guirado-López *et al*, *Phys. Rev. Lett.* **90**, 226402 (2003).
[19] R. Guirado-López *et al*, *Eur. Phys. J. D* **24**, 73 (2003).
[20] See in this same conference G. M. Pastor's talk.
[21] B. I. Min *et al*, *Phys. Rev. B* **33**, 7852 (1986).
[22] G. Moraitis *et al*, *Phys. Rev. B* **54**, 7140 (1996).

APPLICATION OF SELF CONSISTENT TIGHT BINDING METHOD TO THE STUDY OF ANATASE NANOCRYSTALS

J. W. Halley, S. Erdin and Y.Lin

School of Physics and Astronomy
University of Minnesota
Minneapolis, MN 55455 USA

Peter Zapol

Argonne National Laboratory
Argonne, IL 60439 USA

1. INTRODUCTION

The theoretical modeling of nanoparticles is a computational challenge because the systems of interest are neither small enough, either in unit cell size, as for periodically continued bulk solids, or in cluster size, as in molecules and very small clusters, to lend themselves to numerical first principles techniques. Typically, one is concerned with systems of around 10^4 atoms. Mean field electronic structure techniques, such as density functional theory[1], are feasible for study of atomic dynamics for up to 10^3 atoms at most and more typically are used for systems of around 10^2 atoms. Many body methods going beyond the mean field level[2] are even more restricted, usually to 10^2 atoms at most and more typically to a few 10's of atoms. As a result, workers are using various schemes to try to carry out atomic relaxation and dynamic studies which take some account of the electronic structure as it changes during atomic motion, without keeping the full description of the electronic structure which is present in these first principles methods. Here we describe application of one of these approaches, which we have called self consistent tight binding[3], (SCTB) to a problem of nanoparticle modeling.

Self consistent tight binding has been quite fully described elsewhere [3-6]. We base the formal description on the Kohn-Sham variational principle[7] which we formulate in a tight binding context. We select a small, physically reasonable tight binding basis for each element. By minimization of an energy functional, we obtain effective one-electron equations which are solved self consistently in the Mulliken charges at each atomic site. Correlations are implicitly included in onsite energies which are functions of the local charges and, in some cases, of the ionic spins. These onsite functions, which describe the model in the limit of infinite separation of the atoms, are fit as a function of ionic charge and spin to the known ionic energy levels. The remaining parameters of the tight binding model fix intersite matrix elements of the kinetic energy, contributions to electrostatic multipoles at each site (subject to constraints of the Wigner Eckhart theorem) and onsite 'environmental' terms associated with each atomic site. The latter take account of the effects of atomic neighbors on the onsite matrix elements associated with orbitals assigned to each site. These remaining parameters are fit by requiring that the self consistent tight binding model reproduce the cohesive energies and band structures of a selected set of distorted periodic bulk solid structures as calculated from a first principles method (usually density functional theory (DFT) implemented in local density approximation (LDA) in a plane wave basis) . (Alternatively, in some case we have fitted to first principles cluster data.) Typically, the number of parameters for an oxide is of the order of 50. We are beginning to develop a library of parametrizations and often fix parameters associated, for example, with oxygen, when extending the model to new elements of the periodic table.

This approach has many features in common with those of others, but differs in its details from any of which we are aware. In particular our approach is similar to that of the Frauenheim[8] group but differs in at least the following respects: We use no explicit wave functions but parametrize the matrix elements, within the well known Slater two center scheme. We include multipole moments, which have proved vital in several applications. We fit directly to DFT calculations on bulk solids. We can include spins and have demonstrated[9] an ability to postdict noncollinear spin structures. There are no classical forces on the atoms (though the environmental terms in the Hamiltonian play a similar physical role to such classical forces in other approaches.)

Applications have been made of this approach to oxides of titanium, ruthenium, vanadium and manganese and to liquid water, particularly to vacuum-solid and water-solid surfaces . We have also been able to describe titanium metal surfaces successfully in this way.

In the present contribution we report applications of this approach to the study of nanocrystals of the anatase form of titanium dioxide. It is well known experimentally [10] that the rutile form of titania is the stable one in bulk. In nanocrystals, however, the anatase form is more commonly seen, and it has been suggested that there may be a surface driven transition from rutile to anatase as the crystallite size shrinks. The existence of such a transition can occur if the cohesive energy decreases more rapidly with surface-to-volume ratio in anatase than in rutile. Here we report a calculation of the cohesive energy of bulk and two nanocrystals of anatase in SCTB to obtain an estimate this rate of decrease which is in quite reasonable agreement with experimental estimates. This lends some support to the idea of a surface driven transition from rutile to anatase.

In the next section we describe calculations of the properties of bulk anatase and of low index surfaces on anatase crystals. These calculations, which were made with a parametrization determined only from first principles calculations on rutile titania, are in quite reasonable agreement with most bulk and surface anatase parameters as determined from first principles and experiment and encouraged us to carry out the calculations on nanocrystals described in section 3.

2. CALCULATIONS ON BULK ANATASE AND ITS SURFACES

We used a parametrization of the SCTB method for titania described in [3] except that s and p orbitals on the Ti sites were added to the basis. Parameters were determined using a fit to water dimers, rutile titania and hcp titanium metal. The DFT data for rutile and titanium metal were obtained using plane wave LDA codes provided by Jim Chelikowsky's group [11] and the first principles energies for the water dimer were provided at MP2 level by Larry Curtiss and coworkers [12]. With the resulting parametrization we then determined properties bulk anatase with results shown in Table 1 where they are compared with independent calculations by Lazzeri et al [13]. The table does not show an experimental cohesive energy for anatase. Rutile is reported [14,15] to be more stable than anatase by 1.2 - 1.5 kJ/mol (0.012-0.015 eV) The accuracy of all the first principles methods is worse than 0.01eV so one cannot expect to get the relative cohesive energies of anatase and rutile right in the first principles calculations and indeed they are reversed in the results shown in the table. We do find with SCTB that anatase is less stable than rutile by somewhat more than the amount reported experimentally but this should be attributed to chance and not to the virtues of the method.

Table 1.

Structure, Method	E_{coh}(eV)	a(A)	c(A)
Anatase SCTB	22.34	3.782	11.50
Rutile SCTB	22.40	4.64	3.04
Anatase FP	21.54[a]	3.786	9.737
Rutile FP	21.44[a]	4.634	2.963
Anatase EXP		3.782[b]	9.502[b]
Rutile EXP	19.9[c]	4.587[b]	2.954[b]

a- M.L.Lazzeri, Andrea Vittadini, and Annabella Selloni, PHYS REV B 63 , 155409 (2001)

b - Data from: J.K. Burdett, T. Hughbanks, G.J. Miller, J.W. Richerdson, Jr., and J.V. Smith, J. Am. Chem. Soc. 109, 3639 (1987)

c - Data from: CRC Handbook of Chemistry and Physics 64th ed. (CRC, Boca Raton, FL, 1983)

Comparison of SCTB results on bulk rutile and anatase with an independent first principles calculation and with experiment.

The SCTB results for anatase in Table 1 are in good agreement with the experimental and first principles results with respect to cohesive energies and the lattice constant a but the calculated c/a ratio is wrong by about 20 % . It would be within the rules of our approach to try to correct this deficiency by refitting the model to DFT results on both bulk rutile and anatase simultaneously but we have not done that in the work reported here.

We next studied bulk anatase low index surfaces using our SCTB parametrization with results compared with the first principles results of reference [13] in Table 2.

Table 2.

surface	method	energy(J/m^2) (unrelaxed)	energy (J/m^2) (relaxed)
101	SCTB	2.51	0.34
101	DFT-LDA	1.56	0.84
101	DFT-PBE	1.28	0.44
001	SCTB	1.60	1.49
001	DFT-LDA	1.46	1.38
001	DFT-PBE	1.12	0.90
100	SCTB	2.08	0.28
100	DFT-LDA	1.90	0.96
100	DFT-PBE	1.59	0.53

Comparison of SCTB and first principles results for low index surfaces of anatase. The first principles results are from reference [13]. DFT-PBE means density functional theory with the Perdew-Burke-Ernzerhof exchange and correlation function and DFT-LDA means density functional theory with the local density approximation.

From the table one sees that the SCTB surface energies are within a few tenths of a joule/m^2 of the first principles ones. The SCTB calculation gave a reversed energy order for the 101 and 100 surfaces relative to the two first principles calculations (100 $<$ 101 $<$ 001 for SCTB versus 101 $<$ 100 $<$ 001 for the first principles calculations). The 101-100 differences are in all cases less than 0.15 joules/m^2.

3. CALCULATIONS ON ANATASE NANOPARTICLES

A preliminary shape for thermodynamically stable clusters was determined by a Wulff construction [16]. Knowing the surface energy $E_{surf}(\hat{\mathbf{n}})$ in particular direction $\hat{\mathbf{n}}$, in the Wulff construction, one draws a plane perpendicular to $\hat{\mathbf{n}}$. The distance between the plane and the center of the mass of the structure is proportional to the corresponding surface energy. Repeating this method to all other directions, the shape can be determined . Using the first principles data in Table 2 in the Wulff construction gave a crystal shape shown in Figure 1. Using the SCTB surface energies in Table 2 in the Wulff construction gave topologically identical crystal shapes, but the aspect ratios were significantly different.

Taking care to preserve approximate local charge neutrality on the surfaces and guided by these crystal shapes inferred from the Wulff construction, we constructed two atomically specific clusters, one with 33 TiO_2 units (99 atoms)and the other with 163 TiO_2 units (489 atoms) . These are shown, in their preliminary, unrelaxed form on the left side of Figures 2 and 3. Then, using the SCTB model, the structures were relaxed until the maximum force on any atom was 0.1 eV/A^2. The relaxed structures are shown on the right hand side of Figures 2 and 3.

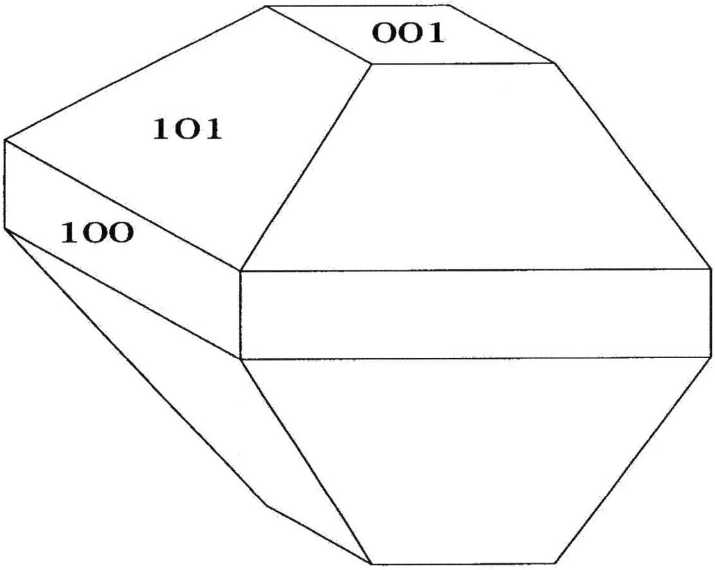

Figure 1. Wulff construction for an anatase crystal.

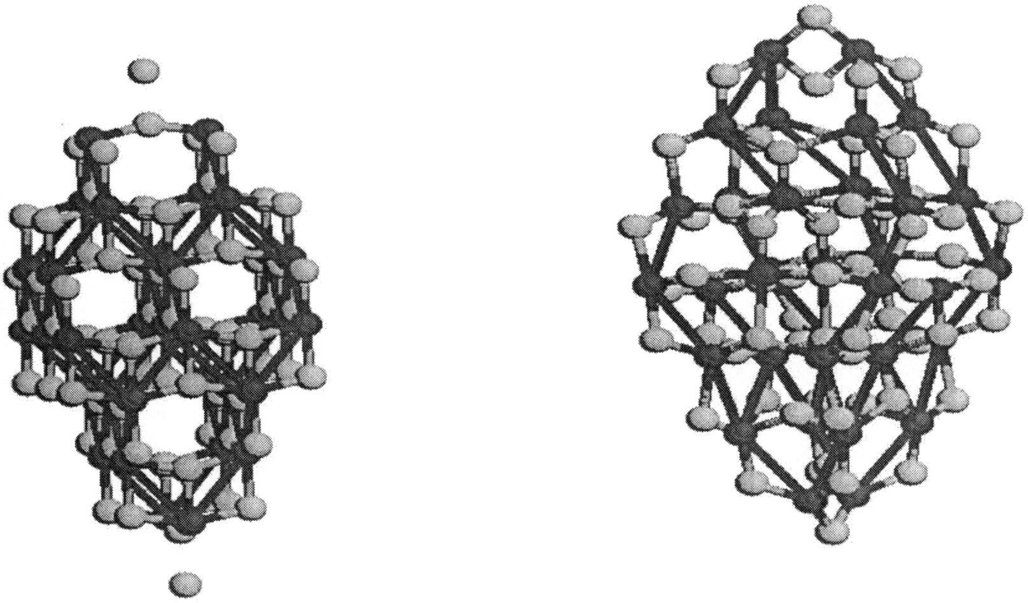

Figure 2. First anatase cluster before relaxation, left and after relaxation, right.

After relaxation, the cohesive energy per mole and the surface area per mole were evaluated for each cluster. The nanocrystal surface areas were evaluated from the

Wulff construction and from triangulation of the surfaces of the relaxed nanocrystals with results consistent to within about 5% (For the small crystal we obtained 370 $\AA^2$ from the Wulff construction and 385 $\AA^2$ from the relaxed nanocrystal. For the larger crystal we obtained: 2264 $\AA^2$ from the Wulff construction and 2212 $\AA^2$ from the relaxed nanocrystal.) We can compare our results with experimental ones from reference [10]. We show the cohesive energy versus surface energy for our two clusters and for bulk anatase as calculated from the SCTB model in Figure 4. The data do not lie on a straight line (as it has sometimes been suggested that they should). However, if we fit a straight line to the three points which we have we find a slope of 6.2 10^-4 kJ/m^2 compared to the experimental value 5.85 10^-4 kJ/m^2 inferred from the experimental data in reference [10]. (The line marked 'fit to experiment' in Figure 4 has this slope.)

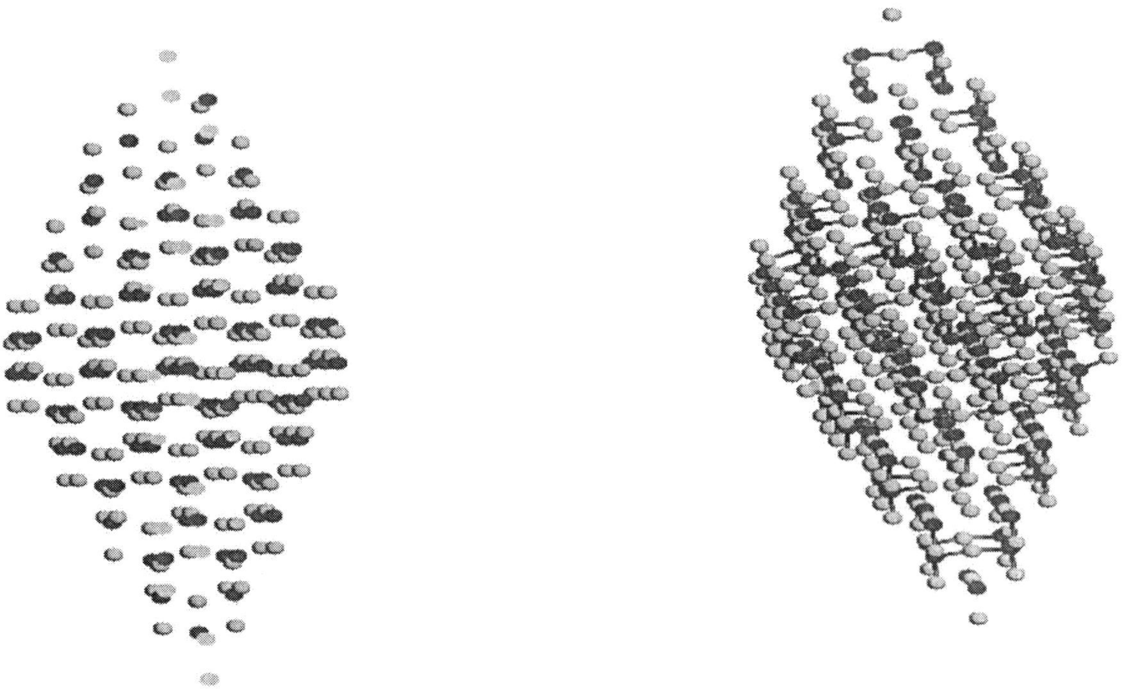

Figure 3. Second anatase cluster before relaxation, left and after relaxation, right.

4. CONCLUSIONS

We have reported a calculation on anatase nanoclusters using the SCTB. The results are consistent with proposed mechanisms of surface induced stabilization of anatase in small clusters. To complete the story, it will be necessary to improve the SCTB parametrization by including bulk anatase in the fitting data set, though the current parametrization, based only on a rutile, titanium metal and water data set, worked quite well for anatase. To establish that our model really predicts anatase stabilization by surfaces, we will carry out similar calculations for rutile nanocrystals.

In further work, we plan to study clusters such as these in water and to model electron transfer and other processes occuring at the cluster water interface. Such processes are of interest in a variety of technologies, including photovoltaic devices and the use of optically active nanoparticles as probes of biological systems.

Though these calculations did not reach the goal of 10^4 atoms mentioned in the introduction, it should be emphasized that they were not very expensive and larger calculations are possible. We believe that SCTB therefore has a useful role to play in nanoscience.

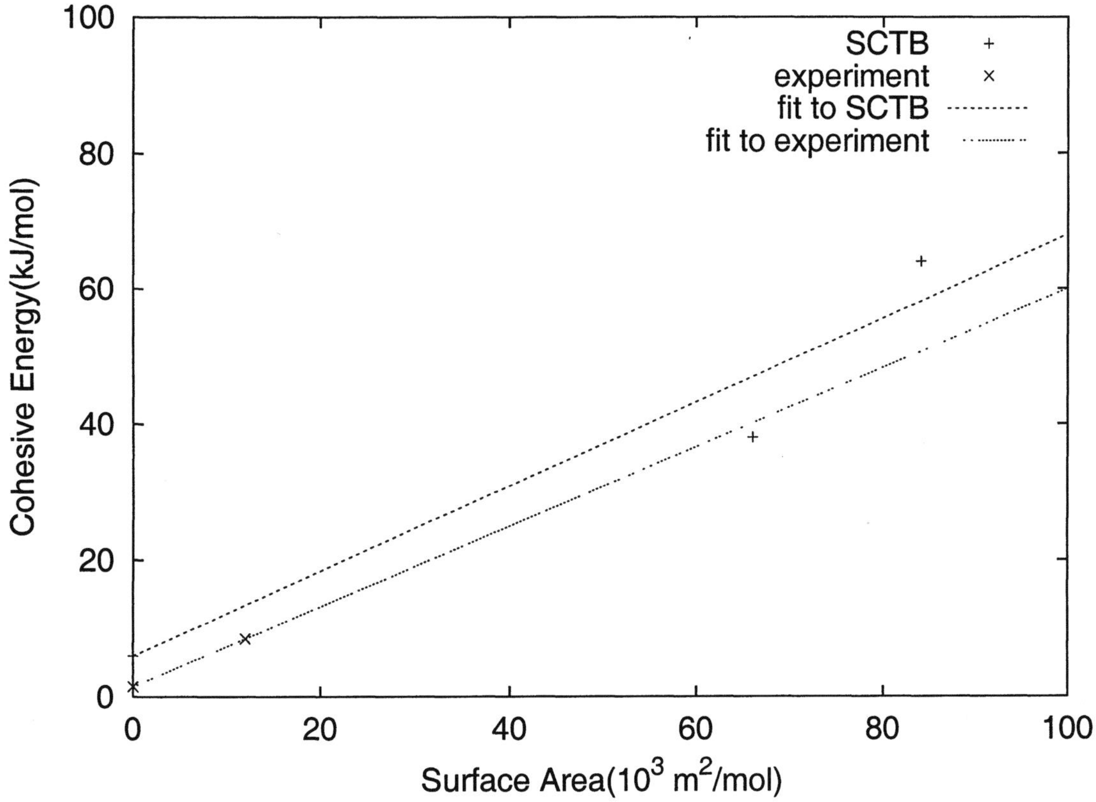

Figure 4. Cluster cohesive energy versus cluster surface area.

ACKNOWLEDGMENTS

The research described here was supported by the Office of Science of the US Department of Energy, Chemical Sciences Division , grant DE-FG02-93ER14376 by the US Army Research Office and by the University of Minnesota Supercomputing Institute. P. Z. acknowledges support by the U. S. Department of Energy's Office of Basic Energy Sciences, Division of Chemical Sciences, under contract no. W-31-109-ENG-38.

REFERENCES

[1] W. Kohn and P. Vashista, in Theory of the Inhomogeneous Electron Gas, edited by N. H. March and S. Lundqvist (Plenum, New York, 1983)

[2] Microscopic Quantum Many-Body Theories and their Applications. Proceedings of a European Summer School Navarro, J.; Polls, A. eds. Source: Springer-Verlag, 1998

[3] P. K. Schelling, N. Yu and J. W. Halley, Phys. Rev. B 58, 1279 (1998)

[4] P. K. Schelling and J. W. Halley, Phys. Rev. B62, 3241 (2000)

[5] J. W. Halley, Y. Lin and M. Zhuang, Faraday Discuss. 121, 85 (2002)

[6] J. W. Halley, Y. Duan, K. Lidke, A. Wynveen and M. Zhuang, Condensed Matter Theories 17, M.P. Das and F. Green, eds. Nova Science Publishers, NY (2003), p. 257

[7] P. Hohenberg and W. Kohn, Phys. Rev. 136, B864 (1964)

[8] D. Orezag, Th. Frauenheim, Th. Kohler, G. Seifert and R. Kaschener, Phys. Rev. B51, 12947 (1995)

[9] M. Zhuang and J. W. Halley, Phys. Rev. B64, 24413 (2001)

[10] M.R. Ranade, S.H.Elder, and A. Navrotsky, Chem. Mater. 14(3),1107 (2002).

[11] K. M . Glassford and J. R. Chelikowsky, Phys. Rev. B46, 1284 (1992)

[12] J.W. Halley, Y.Lin, D. Nguyen, L. Curtiss and P. Redfern, to be published

[13] M.L.Lazzeri, Andrea Vittadini, and Annabella Selloni, PHYS REV B 63 , 155409 (2001)

[14] Handbook of Chemistry and Physics, edited by R.C. West(CRC, Cleveland, 1986)

[15] JANAF Thermodynamical Tables, 3rd ed. J. Phys. Chem. Ref. Data 14, 1680 (1985)

[16] G. Wulff, Z. Kristallogr. Mineral. **34**,449 (1901).

PSEUDOPOTENTIAL INVESTIGATIONS OF SPECTROSCOPY IN INERT CLUSTERS AND MATRICES

Fernand Spiegelman, Gérard Durand and Marie-Catherine Heitz
Laboratoire de Physique Quantique (UMR 5626, CNRS)
IRSAMC, Université Paul Sabatier
118 Route de Narbonne, F31062 Toulouse Cedex, France

1. INTRODUCTION

Beyond their intrinsic interest, spectral properties have always been of great help to get insight into the structural and dynamical behaviour of systems at the microscopic scale, ranging from atoms to bulk matter. For the past decades, high resolution spectroscopy was able to detect extremely detailed features of the electronic structure. More recently, the development of ultra-fast spectroscopy [1-2] has given acces to time-resolved investigations of "simple" systems (isolated atoms and molecules). More complex systems (clusters, nanoparticles, biomolecules, or bulk matter), and even systems with increased complexity due to the interaction with an environment (solvant, surface or matrix) are also now currently investigated. In molecular physics and quantum chemistry dealing with small enough systems, excited states can be determined via explicit Configuration Interaction (CI). For larger systems and in condensed matter theory, significant progresses for *ab initio* determination of the optical response of materials, are now being achieved in the framework of Density Functional Theory (DFT), either in time-dependent theories, or even combining the DFT theory with explicit quantum many body aspects. Whatever the method used for correlation and the determination of excited states, benefit can be gained by using pseudopotential techniques (for recent reviews, see [3]), which have been introduced to reduce the number of electrons or excitations involved in the solution of the Schödinger equation. Developments along this line are often linked with technical constraints, such as the use of Gaussian Type Function (GTO) basis sets in Quantum Chemistry, or Plane Waves in Solid State Physics. The definition and importance of the electronic core/valence partition is not always straightforward. In alkali earth atoms, noble metals, transition metals, or heavier elements with opened f and d shells, inter-shell polarization, correlation or mixing must be taken into account. Cases of strong inter-shell effects have motivated the definition of so-called "small-core" pseudopotentials in which the outermost inner shell electrons remain active, in contrast to "large-core" pseudopotentials. Despite the need to achieve further progress in the field, pseudopotential techniques are now extremely powerful tools in electronic structure computational science and are widely used in the ab initio molecular dynamics either in Born-Oppenheimer versions or non adiabatic time-dependant formulations. Even when using standard pseudopotentials, the number of electrons remains a limiting factor, especially if one wishes to incorporate such electronic structure calculations in extensive dynamical simulations.

We will consider here specifically systems involving inert atoms which do not participate in chemical processes, nor in the low energy excitations. This implies mainly rare gas atoms and also possibly negative ions which have valence closed shell. The interest for systems involving rare gas atoms is multiple. In gas phase, they can form weakly bound molecules, complexes and clusters. Some of the diatomic molecules yielded applications as excimer lasers. Van der Waals complexes with rare gas atoms have often been used as prototype systems to understand interactions with inert solvants. Helium clusters are also very appealing as quantum clusters[4]. They also offer efficient cooling media for very high resolution spectroscopy experiments. Another original application of rare gas clusters is their use as finite size supporting media to elementary chemical processes like in the so-called Cluster Isolated Chemical Reaction scheme[5]. Finally, spectroscopy of chromophores on inert surfaces or in inert matrices [1,2,6,7] has been used for a long time to characterize atoms, molecules and complexes. However, though the environment is inert, it may induce non negligeable effects on the electronic excited states, their nature and even on their existence within the matrix, in particular for the most diffuse states, e.g. Rydberg states. Recent time-resolved experiments have been investigating both trapped molecule and matrix relaxation effects, evidencing specific features with respect to gas phase, such as for instance inhibition of photo-induced fragmentation ("cage effect") or the so-called electronic "bubble effect" when exciting an electron of the chromophore[7].

Negative halogen ions commonly found in salt crystals can also be considered as inert atoms. In those crystals, structural defects are known to induce specific optical properties such as F-centers. Some of these properties have analogous aspects in finite systems. For instance, non-stoichiometric salt clusters have been observed in gas phase. Size and stoichometry dependance provides a variety of localisation patterns for the excess electrons(s) correlated with optical properties ranging from pure salts to fully metallic systems.

From a theoretical point of view, it is appealing to get rid of the internal electronic structure of the rare gas atoms. This has been frequently achieved by considering them as point atoms, possibly polarizable, interacting via classical potentials with the chromophore states. However, such description may turn to be irrelevant for highly diffuse states such as Rydberg states where the difficulty lies in finding force-fields able to represent non-local effects, not straightforwardly reducible to simple additive potentials. In extended systems such as inert matrices or liquids, a continuous medium description can be used through effective dielectric constants. Then however, the microscopic description of the solvant is lost.

In the present paper, we non exhaustively review the possibilities of extended pseudopotential schemes, specific to inert atoms, in which all the rare gas electrons are considered in the core. In such a scheme, only the chromophore electrons are considered explicitly while the inert atoms are described via zero-electron pseudopotentials (ZEP's). This leads to the introduction of an hybrid quantum-classical scheme description for the total system in which the number of electrons treated quantum-mechanically is the same as that of the isolated active or chromophore part. The paper summarizes the methodology and reports applications involving rare gas atoms, clusters and matrices, and alkali-halide clusters which can also receive an hybrid description.

2. HYBRID HAMILTONIAN AND ZERO-ELECTRON PSEUDOPOTENTIALS

The scheme relies on a dissymmetrical partition of the electrons of the total system into an active part and a passive part. In most applications, this active part includes the valence electrons of the atoms of the chromophores (a single atom, a molecule, or a cluster). These active electrons receive an explicit treatment. The passive system includes all the other electrons. It can be divided into an "internal passive system", namely the core electrons of the chromophore atoms, and an "external passive system" including all the rare gas atoms of the environment (cluster, solvant, matrix), replaced by electron-rare gas (e-Rg) pseudopotentials.

Early versions of ZEP, namely model potentials, were developed for alkali- or alkali-earth- rare gas diatomics[8]. The general application to more complex systems presented here relies on the combination of averaged and core-polarization e-Rg pseudopotentials. The average pseudopotential substitutes the presumably frozen electrons of the passive system. It simulates the orthogonalization of the active electrons to the frozen ones and fulfils the exclusion principle. The implementation is often technique-dependant. In the present calculations, semi-local, norm-conserving, shape-consistent pseudopotentials are used:

$$\hat{W_\lambda} = \sum_l W_l(r) P_l$$

Beyond this frozen-core approximation, Müller and Meyer[9] have introduced so-called core polarization pseudopotentials (CPP's) which describe the response of the passive systems λ to changes and fluctuations of the active one. They therefore describe the static polarization and the dynamical polarization (correlation between the active electrons and the passive ones, neglected in the frozen core approximation). The expression of the core-polarization operator takes a phenomenological form and reads on each polarizable center λ,

$$W_\lambda^{pol} = -\frac{1}{2}\sum_\lambda \alpha_\lambda \mathbf{f}_\lambda \cdot \mathbf{f}_\lambda$$

α_λ is the dipole polarizability of site λ refering either to a polarizable core or to a rare gas atom. $\mathbf{f}_\lambda$ is the total electric field at center λ resulting from the electrons and the net effective charges, i.e. the chromophore cores since Rg atoms carry no charge.

$$\mathbf{f}_\lambda = \mathbf{E}_\lambda + \mathbf{e}_\lambda = \sum_i \frac{\mathbf{r}_{i\lambda}}{r_{i\lambda}^3}\Theta_\lambda(r_{i\lambda}) - \sum_{\lambda' \neq \lambda} \frac{Z_{\lambda'}^* \mathbf{R}_{\lambda\lambda'}}{R_{\lambda\lambda'}^3}$$

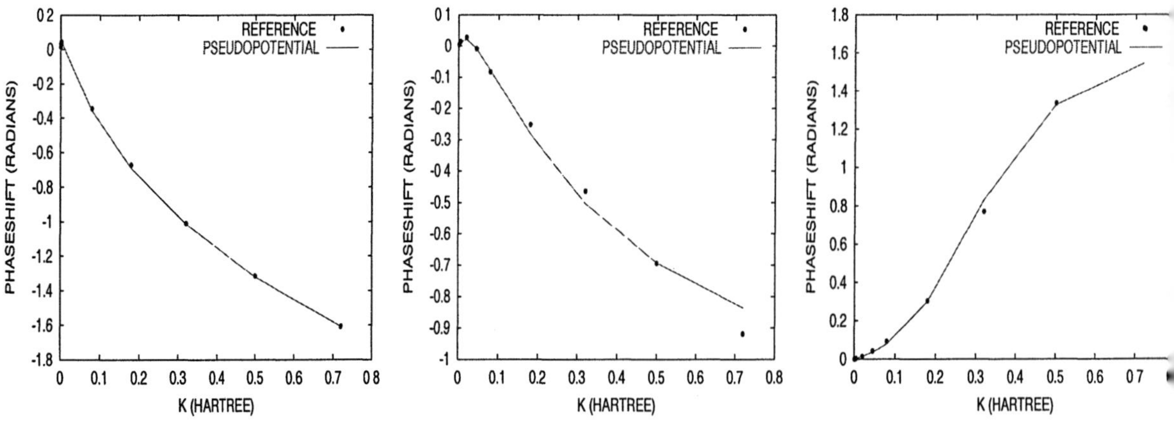

Figure 1. Differential electron-Argon elastic scattering phaseshifts for s (left), p (center) and d (right). Solid line: pseudopotential fit. Dots: reference data from experiments or all-electron calculations, see Chebanier de Guerra in ref[8].

$\Theta_\lambda(r)$ is a cut-off fonction to avoid integral divergence. For a chromophore in interaction with a system of rare gas atoms, one can then define the following hybrid quantum-classical hamiltonien. The quantum part for the chromophore valence electrons reads (A labels the chromophore nuclei, Z_A^* their effective ionic charge)

$$H = \sum_i^{val} \left\{ -\frac{\Delta_i}{2} + \sum_A \left(-\frac{Z_A^*}{|\mathbf{r}_i - \mathbf{R}_A|} + \hat{W}_A(i) + \hat{W}_A^{pol}(i) \right) \right\} + \sum_{i<j}^{val} \frac{1}{|\mathbf{r}_i - \mathbf{r}_j|}$$

to which must be added the interaction of the valence electrons with Rg atoms represented via zero-electron pseudopotentials

$$+ \sum_i^{val} \sum_\lambda^{Rg} \left\{ \hat{W}_\lambda(i) + \hat{W}_\lambda^{pol}(i) \right\}$$

The classical part describes the passive subsystems

$$+ \sum_{A<B} \frac{Z_A^* Z_B^*}{|\mathbf{R}_A - \mathbf{R}_B|} + \sum_A \sum_\lambda^{Rg} V_{ARg}(\mathbf{R}_A, \mathbf{R}_\lambda) + \sum_{\lambda<\mu}^{Rg} V_{RgRg}(|\mathbf{R}_\lambda - \mathbf{R}_\mu|)$$

and includes respectively the core-core, core-Rg and Rg-Rg interactions.

The extraction of e-Rg pseudopotential must be carried out specifically since the electron-rare gas system does not practically exhibit any bound state. However, the e-Rg pseudopotential can be determined from the continuum states corresponding to electron-rare gas elastic scattering differential phase shifts [8], namely inverting the single electron Schrödinger equation for each l manifold

$$[-\frac{\Delta}{2} + \frac{l(l+1)}{2r^2} + W_l(r) - \frac{1}{2}\frac{\alpha}{r^4}\Theta(r)]\phi_k(r) = \frac{K^2}{2}\phi_K(r)$$

Fig. 1 illustrates the fits of the phase shifts via ZEP in the e-Ar case.

For negative halogen ions, the extraction process is less straighforward due to the lack of data evidencing uniquely elastic electronic e-X^- cross sections and alternative attempts have been achieved, like artificially stabilizing the system with the help of an external positive shell or positive point counter-ions[10]. However, in the case of negative ions, the penetration of the active electrons into the core is hindered by the Coulomb repulsion and the W_l operator is of smaller importance than for positive ions or neutrals and can be omitted.

The present technique relies on concepts similar to those developed in the AIMP scheme of Barandiaran and coworkers[11] to deal with the spectroscopy of metal impurities in matrices involving positive ions.

3. ATOMIC CHROMOPHORES IN VAN DER WAALS CLUSTERS

Simple diatomics involving a single argon atom are good test cases because accurate high resolution spectroscopy data or standard valence calculations do exist. Like the alkali-erath calcium atom treated with large core pseudopotentials (namely two external electrons complemented with CPP), alkali-earth argon diatomics become in the present scheme two-electron systems. They can receive exact resolution via quantum-chemical full CI (consisting here of all single and double excitation) in a given single particle basis (the calculation are achieved with GTO basis sets). The electronic spectrum of the CaAr molecule for instance is reported in Fig. 2. Such pseudopotential scheme allows for the calculation of high excited states in the optical range with an averaged accuracy of 100-300 cm^{-1} on the transitions[12], since, due to the simplification of the CI, extensive effort can be made to augment the diffuse functions in the basis set.

Whereas the ground state of the CaAr molecule is weakly bound due to Van der Waals forces (calculated data D_e=82 cm^{-1} and R_e=9.18 a_0), some excited states may roughly be described at least at short internuclear distance in terms of single excitations, qualitatively corresponding to a [$CaAr^+$] core with a single electron excited in an outer orbital. However doubly excited molecular states disssociating into Ca($4p^2$) or Ca(4p3d) are also obtained in good correspondance with experimental spectroscopic data[12]. Several authors have investigated single active electron alkali-argon clusters[13]. We present here results for Ca interacting with a rare gas cluster. $CaAr_4$ (Fig. 3) is bound by D_e=249 cm^{-1} with respect to Ca+Ar_4. The equilibrium distance, between Ca and the closest Ar_3 facet, is R_e=8.50 a_0 . This stability is about three times the dissociation energy of CaAr ($D_e \approx$ 80 cm^{-1}). Table 1 shows the spectral shifts for transitions from ground to excited states of $CaAr_4$ with respect to those in free Ca. At equilibrium geometry, the three electronic transitions towards $^3P(4p_z)$, $3D(3d_{3s^2-r^2})$ and $^1P(4p_z)$ are blue-shifted. This corresponds to upper states where the excited electron orbital $(4p_z, 3d_{3z^2-r^2})$ points towards the argon cluster, screening the Ca^+ ion and also yielding larger repulsion than in the ground state due to orthogonalization to the argon atoms via the repulsive pseudopotentials. State $^3D(3d_{3z^2-r^2})$ is an exception and has very small red shift. All other states are red-shifted, and correspond to excited orbitals perpendicular to the C_3 cluster

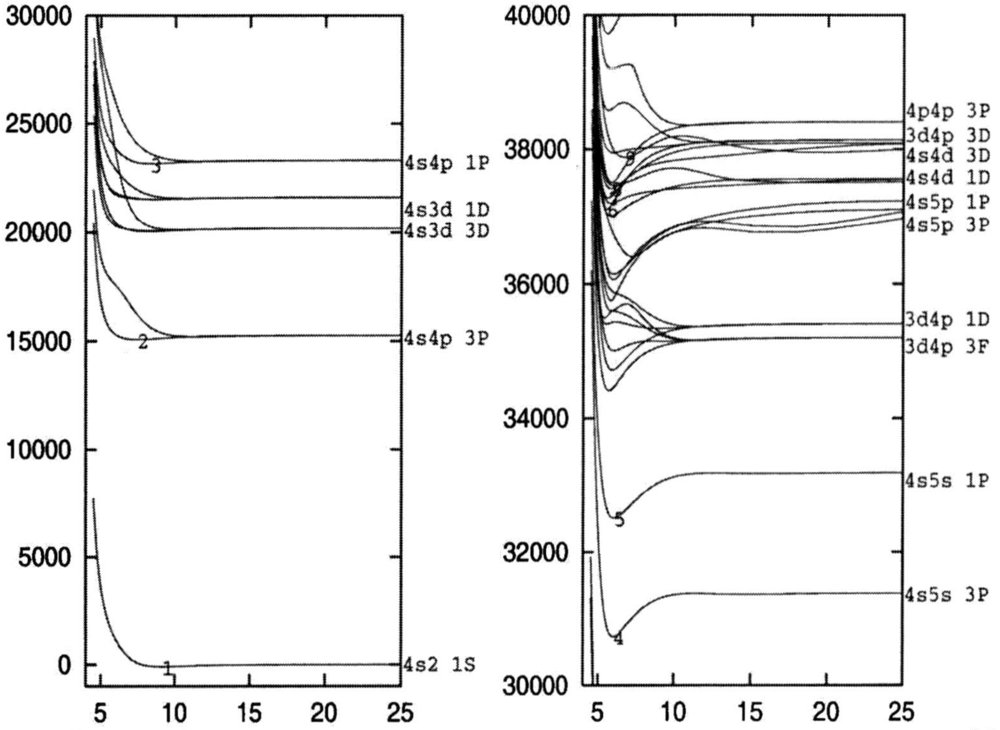

Figure 2. Potential energy curves of the CaAr molecule in the range [0-30000 cm^{-1}] and [30000 - 38000 cm^{-1}]. Energies in cm^{-1} ; distances in a_0 . Numbered potentials have been experimentally characterized.

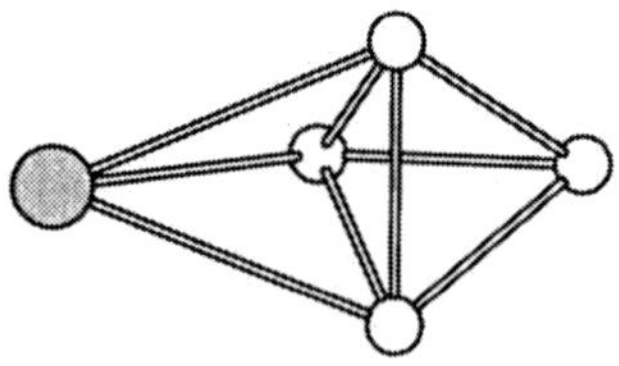

Figure 3. C_{3v} equilibrium geometry of CaAr4.

Table 1

Spectral shifts ΔE (cm^{-1}) in cluster $CaAr_4$ with respect to free Ca atom for transition from the ground state. The C_3 axis is along z.

State	^3P	^3P	^3D	^3D	^3D	^1D	^1D	^1D	^1P	^1P
Excitation	$4p_{x,y}$	$4p_z$	$3d_{x^2-y^2,xy}$	$3d_{xz,yz}$	$3d_{3z^2-r^2}$	$3d_{x^2-y^2,xy}$	$3d_{xz,yz}$	$3d_{3z^2-r^2}$	$4p_{x,y}$	$4p_z$
ΔE	-53	320	-267	-239	-13	-218	-195	16	-98	185

axis. This orbital orientation reduces both the repulsion and the axial screening and yields more attractive upper states. The dependance of spectral shifts on cluster size and excitation level can be thus investigated theoretically. To our knowledge, no measurements are yet available on $CaAr_n$ neutral size selected clusters.

4. CHROMOPHORES IN RARE GAS MATRICES

We present here results for a NO molecule trapped in an argon matrix, which is described as a cluster piece of the *fcc* lattice. Obviously, in this cluster approach of matrix embedded excited states, the cluster size must be large enough to ensure that the states under investigation are safely contained within the cluster and do not spill out outside the surface. Despite the fact that argon atoms do not bring any electrons in the system, argon-centered basis sets, although small, are necessary in order to ensure enough flexibility of the wavefunction locally to adapt to the pseudopotentials.

NO has been widely studied in gas phase and present numerous Rydberg states, namely states which result from the interaction of a $[NO^+]$ core with an external electron in a diffuse orbital. NO has also been used as an experimental benchmark system for optical spectroscopy in matrices, in particular by Chergui *et al.*[7]. One interesting issue is the cut-off of the number of Rydberg states and its correlation with matrix relaxation. In its ground state, NO (X $^2\Pi^+$) is a small molecule (R_e=2.17 a_0) and substitutes easily a single argon atom of the hardly distorted *fcc* lattice (the NO-Ar equilibrium distance is slightly smaller than the nearest neigbour Ar-Ar distance in the lattice and the interaction weaker). Single photon absorption at this initial geometry experimentally shows that, whereas numerous states of NO are observed in gas phase, only a few of them are experimentally observed in the matrix[7]. This reduction was theoretically understood using the present model[14] with a single orbital picture for NO obtained from a mean-field (Hartree-Fock) treatment of NO^+, the argon matrix being described via ZEP's. The valence electronic configuration of the NO^+ molecular ion is $2s\sigma^2 2s\sigma'^2 2p\sigma^2 2p\pi^4$. Taking into account the Rydberg nature of the excited states adressed, the problem was further reduced to a single electron description by projection of the the Fock operator

$$h = -\frac{1}{2}\Delta + \sum_{A}^{N,O}\left\{-\frac{Z_A^*}{r_A} + \hat{W}_A\right\} + W_{NO^+}^{pol} + \sum_{j\in NO^+}\left\{2\hat{J}_j - \hat{K}_j\right\} + \sum_{Ar}(W_{Ar} + W_{Ar}^{pol})$$

onto the virtual Fock space, thus describing only the external electron. $\hat{J}_j$ and $\hat{K}_j$ are the Coulomb and exchange terms. This is even consistent for the ground state of NO described as $[NO^+]2p\pi^*$. Incorporating the classical part which adds to the single electron energy ϵ_m, the total energy reads

$$E_m(R) = \epsilon_m + E_{NO^+}(R) + \sum_{\lambda}^{Ar} V_{Ar-NO^+}^{\lambda} + \sum_{\lambda,\lambda'}^{Ar} V_{ArAr}(R_{\lambda\lambda'})$$

Investigation of non-Rydberg states would require a full valence calculation. The left plot of Fig. 4 shows the lowest part of calculated Rydberg spectrum of the free

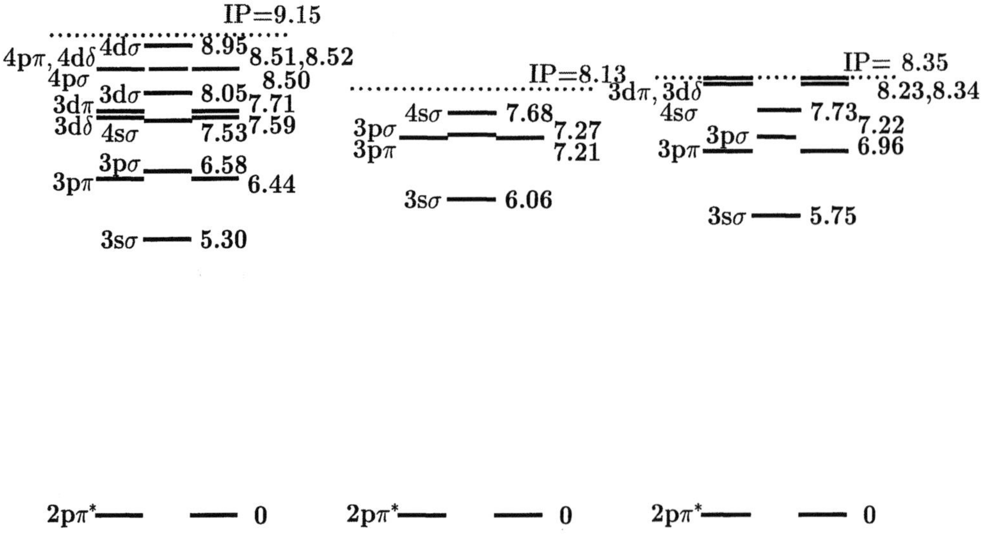

Figure 4. Excited states and IP of NO molecule (in eV). Free NO (left); NO in unrelaxed matrix (center); matrix relaxed with NO in $3s_\sigma$ excited state (right). The energy zero is that of the ground state.

NO molecule, whereas the central plot shows the levels calculated for NO in the unrelaxed matrix. Two factors do contribute to the matrix cut-off. Firstly, since the excited electron orbitals (namely $3s_\sigma$, $3p_\pi$, $3p\sigma$..) are more diffuse than the initial $2p\pi^*$ orbital singly occupied in NO ground state, the repulsion with the matrix is enhanced, blue shifting the lowest transitions from the ground state by about 0.6-0.8 eV. Secondly, the ionization potential of the system is lowered, due to the polarization of the matrix $E^{pol}_{mat} = -\sum_\lambda^{Ar} \frac{1}{2}\alpha_\lambda \mathbf{E}^2_\lambda$. Both effects narrow the spectral window and reduce the number of bound excited states.

If we now examine post-absorption matrix relaxation with NO excited in the $3s_\sigma$ state, recalculating the levels at the relaxed geometry, it turns out that lattice polarization is smaller and the ionization potential larger than in the unrelaxed geometry . The volume avalaible for the electronic "bubble" is correlatively increased and some of the excited states are less confined in the new geometry. This relaxation effect on the electronic levels is shown in Fig. 4(right). The increase of the number of accessible bound states in NO was experimentally demonstrated by Chergui *et al.*[7] in two-photon femtosecond scale spectroscopy experiments, the first photon exciting the system into $3s_\sigma$, a second photon exciting the system into higher states, after matrix relaxation has occured.

5. NON-STOIECHIOMETRIC ALKALI HALIDE CLUSTERS

Non stoiechiometric alkali halide clusters M_nX_{n-p} (M=Alkali, X=halogen) can also be considered with an hybrid scheme, assuming that all halogen atoms have captured an electron from alkali atoms, and that the clusters can be safely described

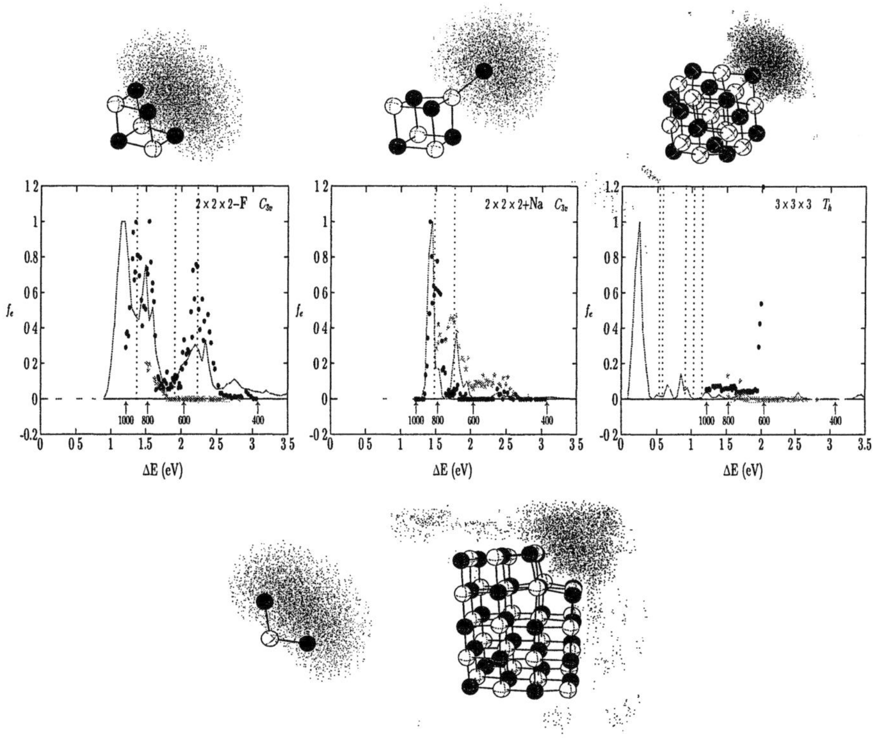

Figure 5. Top and middle: structure, electronic localization and absorption spectra of typical Na_nF_{n-1} clusters (n=4, 5 and 13). Bottom: structure and electronic localization for n=2 and 29. Spectra from [15]: theoretical MC simulation (full lines); experimental (symbols); the vertical dashed lines indicate the transition positions at cluster equilibrium geometry. The absorption range of n=13 was not probed experimentally.

as n positive ions M^+, $n-p$ negative ions X^- and p excess electrons. The alkali atoms are here single-electron atoms and one can define a hybrid hamiltonian with a quantum part describing explicitely the p excess electrons interacting with the ions

$$H = \sum_i^p \left\{ -\frac{\Delta_i}{2} + \sum_{I=M,X} \left(-\frac{q_I}{r_{iI}} + \hat{W}_I(i) + \hat{W}_I^{pol}(i) \right) \right\} + \sum_{i<j}^p \frac{1}{r_{ij}}$$

with $q_I = \pm 1$, and a classical description of the repulsive and Coulomb interactions between the ions

$$\sum_{M,X} \rho(R_{MX}) + \sum_{M<M'} \frac{1}{R_{MM'}} + \sum_{X<X'} \frac{1}{R_{XX'}} - \sum_{M,X} \frac{1}{R_{MX}}$$

Exhaustive work has been achieved within this hybrid framework on single electron Na_nF_{n-1} clusters, investigating structural properties in the ground state, localization of the excess electron, and excitation spectra up to rather large sizes ($n = 29$

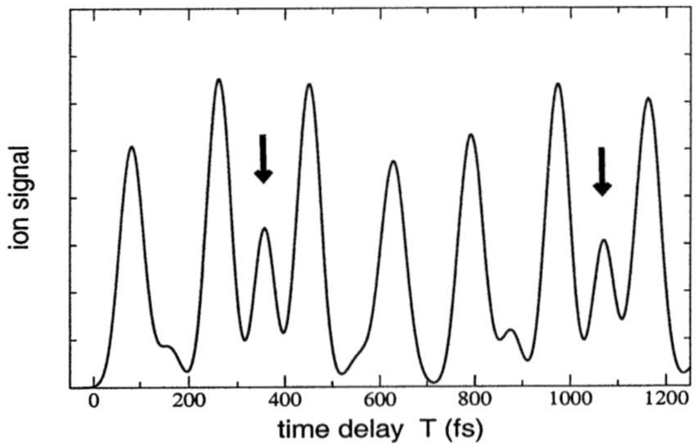

Figure 6. Wavepacket simulation iof the pump-probe ion signal in Na_2F as a function of pump-probe time delay. The main periodicity is 180 fs. The arrows indicate secondary maxima resulting from mode coupling.

in [15]) . For the smallest species ($n < 6$), the calculated properties compare numerically very well with standard valence CI calculations whenever available[16]. Fig. 5 shows typical electron localization patterns in the ground state and their spectral signatures in absorption spectroscopy. Spectra widths were obtained from Monte-Carlo simulations on the ground state potential energy surface and the Franck-Condon hypothesis for absorption[15]. In Na_4F_3, electron localization is analogous to that of a crystal F-center in the sense that the excess electron substitutes the missing fluorine atom and ensures electrostatic stability. $Na_{14}F_{13}$ has a 3x3x3 cuboidal structure. Its weakly bound surface electron tends to localize on one apex of the cluster, coupled with an indirect Jahn-Teller deformation of the ionic array. In $Na_{29}F_{28}$, the electron localizes at a missing edge.

Another issue is the insight in real-time motion [17]. Fig. 6 for instance shows a simulation of the pump-probe ion signal for the small Na_2F cluster. In such an experiment, the excited state dynamics is initiated by a femtosecond laser pulse (pump pulse). A second laser pulse (probe pulse) is supposed to ionize the system. The photo-electron and/or ion signal can be recorded as a function of time delay between the pump and probe pulses and their time dependance provides information on the excited states dynamics. Photoelectron spectroscopy was adressed in a previous publication[16]. We show here the theoretical Na_2F signal, calculated with quantum wawepacket propropagation as in [17]. The highest maxima of the signal (see Fig. 6) are separated by a periodicity of τ=180 fs. The secondary maxima (indicated by arrows) are due to excitation of the symmetric stretch vibration induced by coupling to the bending mode. Work is in progress to address clusters with two active electrons such as Na_3F within the same hybrid model.

6. EXTENSION TO RESONANT SYSTEMS

The chromophore- inert environment model relies on the definition of an active-passive partition. Nevertheless, there is a possible extension to homogenous systems, by taking into account the resonance[18].

For a system of identical rare gas atoms, one starts by developping the excited multiconfigurational wavefunction Ψ_m in a hole-particle basis set of valence $\longrightarrow$ Rydberg single excitations from the ground state Φ_0

$$\Phi^{i\sigma}_{A\mu\zeta} = a^\dagger_{i\sigma}\, a_{A\mu\zeta}\, \Phi_0$$

$a_{A\mu\zeta}$ is a hole creation operator in a np valence spinorbital localized on site A with orientation $\mu = x, y, z$, spin $\zeta = \alpha, \beta$ (n=2, 3, 4, 5 for Ne, Ar, Kr or Xe respectively). $a^\dagger_{i\sigma}$ is a particle creation operator in a Rydberg one-electron state $\phi_{i\sigma}$. All the single electron states are assumed orthonormal. Each basis determinant correponds to a Rg_n^+ ion core with a localized hole associated with an external electron ϕ_i

$$\Psi_m = \sum_{A,\mu,\zeta,i,\sigma} c^{i\sigma m}_{A\mu\zeta} \Phi^{i\sigma}_{A\mu\zeta}$$

One may then define the hamiltonian matrix elements in the hole -particle basis. The diagonal terms read

$$H^{i\sigma,i\sigma}_{A\mu\zeta,A\mu\zeta} = H^{Rg_n^+}_{A\mu\zeta,A\mu\zeta} + < \phi_{i\sigma}|h^*_{A\mu}|\phi_{i\sigma} >$$

They involve a classical contribution

$$H^{Rg_n^+}_{A\mu\zeta,A\mu\zeta} = E(Rg^+) + (n-1)E(Rg) + \sum_{B\neq A} V^{\mu}_{RgRg^+}(R_{AB}) + \frac{1}{2} \sum_{B,C\neq A} V_{RgRg}(R_{BC})$$

which is obtained via additive potentials for the Rg^+Rg and RgRg pairs respectively, and a quantum electronic contribution based on pseudopotential for the external electron.

$$h^*_A = -\frac{1}{2}\Delta + (W_{A^+} + W^{pol}_{A^+}) - \frac{1}{r_A} + \sum_{B\neq A} (W_B + W^{pol}_B)$$

This hamiltonian describes the field exerted over the excited electron by a given hole on atom A. It is therefore analogous to the above dissymmetrical chromophore-environment case, with an e-Rg^+ pseudopotential on a single active site and e-Rg on the other argon sites.

The main off-diagonal terms involve either hole transfer terms $a_{A\mu\zeta} \longleftrightarrow a_{B\nu\xi}$

$$H^{i\sigma,i\sigma}_{A\mu\zeta,B\nu\xi} = H^{core}_{A\mu\zeta,B\nu\xi}\, \delta_{\zeta\xi} = F^{\mu\nu}_{RgRg^+}(R_{AB})\delta_{\zeta\xi}$$

which can be obtained as in the well known Diatomics in Molecules model widely used for rare gas cluster ions[17], or excitation transfer terms $\phi_{i\sigma} \longleftrightarrow \phi_{j\gamma}$

$$H^{i\sigma,j\gamma}_{A\mu\zeta,A\mu\zeta} =< \phi_{i\sigma}|h^*_A|\phi_{j\gamma} > \delta_{\sigma\gamma}$$

and the main two electron contributions can be added with some approximations. Whenever spin-orbit coupling is added, like for instance in xenon, one then has to diagonalize a $H + H^{SO}$ complex hamiltonian of dimension $12nm^2$ where n is the number of Rg atoms and m the dimension of the ϕ_i basis set. This extension has been applied to excitations in homogenous diatomics and small rare gas clusters[19].

7. CONCLUSION

Drastically reducing the number of electrons, ZEP's allow to investigate systems for which a dissymmetrical partition is relevant and which are difficult to compute otherwise. Another interest is that the method provides wavefunctions and thus dipole moments and oscillator strengths, unlike methods using additive potentials or force fields which can only deal with energies. Clearly, the method is restricted to a class of systems involving closed shell inert atoms. The large scale study of excitons in extended systems or investigation of chromophore or high electronic excited states spectroscopy in quantum solvants remains to be explored. Development could be achieved in several directions. The first one would be to combine energy calculations of the excited states with so-called "on-the-fly" schemes avoiding the tedious parametrization of potential energy surfaces. This could in particular provide a convenient framework to investigate dynamical processeslike relaxation or fragmentation in excited states for chromophore-rare gas complexes and matrices. Another direction is the study of mixed Rydberg-valence excitation for molecular chromophores in rare gas matrices. Finally, similar pseudopotentials description could be used for inert molecular solvants.

ACKNOWLEDGMENTS

The authors thank F. Calvo and C. Meier for help and fruitful discussions.

REFERENCES

[1] A.H. Zewail, *Femtochemistry, Ultrafast Dynamics of the Chemical bond, vols I and II* (World Scientific, Singapore, 1994).

[2] M. Chergui, *Femtochemistry, Ultrafast Chemical and Physical Processes in Molecular systems* (World Scientific, Singapore, 1996).

[3] C. Teichteil, L. Maron and V. Vallet, in *Relativistic Electronic Structure Theory*, P. Schwerdtfeger Ed., Part 2, Applications. Elsevier, Amsterdam (2004); F. Finocchi, J. Goniakowski, X. Gonze and C. Pisani, in Handbook of Numerical Analysis, Vol. X, C. Le Bris Ed., North Holland,(2003), page 377.

[4] M. Hartman, R.E. Miller, J.P. Toennis and A.F. Vilesov, *Science* **272**, 1631 (1996); C. Callegari, J. Higgins, F. Stienkemeier and G. Scoles, *J. Phys. Chem. A* **102**, 95 (1998) .

[5] C. Gée, M. A. Gaveau, J. M. Mestdagh, M. Osborne, O. Sublemontier, and J. P. Visticot, J. Phys. Chem. **100**, 13421 (1996); C. Gée, M. A. Gaveau, O. Sublemontier, J. M. Mestdagh, and J. P. Visticot, J. Chem. Phys. **107**, 4194 (1997); M. A. Gaveau, C. Gée, J. M. Mestdagh, and J. P. Visticot, Comments

in At. Mol. Phys. **34**, 241 (1999).

[6] N. Schwentner, E.E. Koch and J. Jortner, *Electronic Excitations in Condensed Rare Gases Solids* (Springer, Berlin, 1985).

[7] M. Chergui, N. Schwentner and W. Böhmer, J. Chem. Phys. **85**, 2472 (1986); F. Vigliotti, G. Zerza, M. Chergui, and J. Rubayo-Soneira, J. Chem. Phys **109**, 3508 (1998); C. Jeannin, M. T. Portella-Oberli, S. Jimenez, F. Vigliotti, B. Lang and M. Chergui , Chem. Phys. Lett. **316**, 51 (2000); S. Jimenez, A. Pasquarello, R. Car and M. Chergui , Chem. Phys. **233**, 343 (1998).

[8] J. Pascale and J. Vandeplanque, J. Chem. Phys. **60**, 2278 (1974); M. Philippe, F. Masnou-Seeuws and P. Valiron, J. Phys. B **12**, 2493 (1979); P. Valiron, R. Gayet, R. Mc Carrol, F. Masnou-Seeuws and M. Philippe, J. Phys B **12**, 53 (1979); A. Chebanier de Guerra, PhD. thesis, Orsay, France (1982); J. Pascale, Phys. Rev. A **28,** 632 (1983).

[9] W. Müller, J. Flesch and W. Meyer J. Chem. Phys. **80**, 3297 (1984); W. Müller, and W. Meyer J. Chem. Phys. **80**, 3311 (1984); M. Foucrault, Ph. Millié and J.P. Daudey, J. Chem. Phys. **96**, 1257 (1992).

[10] V. Robert, F. Spiegelman and M. B. Lepetit, Chem. Phys. **287**, 217 (2003)

[11] L. Seijo, Z. Barandiaran and L. G. M. Pettersson, J. Chem. Phys. **98**, 4041 (1993);

[12] C. Tsoo, D. A. Estrin and S. J. Singer J. Chem. Phys. **93**, 7187 (1990); C. Tsoo, D. A. Estrin and S. J. Singer, J. Chem. Phys. **96**, 7977 (1992). G. Martyna, C. Cheng and M. L. Klein J. Chem. Phys. **95**, 1318 (1991); A. V. Nehmukin, B .L. Grigorenko and G. B. Sergeev Can. J. Phys. **72,** 909(1994); M. Gross and F. Spiegelmann J. Chem. Phys. **108**, 4148 (1998).

[13] F. Spiegelman, L. Maron, W. Breckenridge, J.M. Mestdagh, and J. P. Visticot J. Chem. Phys. **117**, 7534 (2002).

[14] M. Gross and F. Spiegelmann, Eur. Phys. J. D. **4**, 219 (1998).

[15] G. Durand, J. Giraud-Girard, D. Maynau, F. Spiegelmann, and F. Calvo J. Chem. Phys. **110**, 7871 (1999) G. Durand, F. Spiegelmann, Ph. Poncharal, P. Labastie, J.M. L'Hermite, and M. Sence, J. Chem. Phys. **110**, 7884 (1999)

[16] V. Bonačić-Koutecký and J. Pittner, Chem. Phys., **225**, 173 (1997).

[17] M.-C. Heitz, G. Durand, F. Spiegelman and C. Meier J. Chem. Phys. **118**, 1282 (2003)

[18] P. Duplàa and F. Spiegelmann, J. Chem. Phys. **105**, 1492 (1996); P. Duplàa and F. Spiegelmann, J. Chem. Phys. **105**, 1500 (1996); C. Jonin, P. Laporte and F. Spiegelmann, J. Chem. Phys. **117**, 3049 (2002); C. Jonin and F. Spiegelmann, J. Chem. Phys. **117**, 3059 (2002); G. Durand, P. Duplàa and F. Spiegelman , Z. Physik D**40**,177 (1997).

[19] M. Grigorov and F. Spiegelman, Surf. Rev. and Lett. **3**, 211 (1996).

DESIGN OF NOVEL SILICON NANOSTRUCTURES

P. Jena, S.N. Khanna, B.K. Rao, Q. Sun, and Q. Wang
Physics Department,
Virginia Commonwealth University Richmond,
VA 23284-2000

Calculations based on density functional theory show that it is possible to alter the chemistry of silicon atoms at the nano-meter length scale by doping metal atoms. This ability can be exploited in the design of novel silicon-based nanostructures with unique electronic, optical, and magnetic properties. It is hoped that these calculations will motivate experimentalists in the synthesis of new silicon based nano-materials.

1. INTRODUCTION

A considerable amount of research in the last two decades has shown that the properties of materials can be fundamentally altered by reducing their length scale to a few nano-meters. At this length scale, the nano-particles have more atoms on the surface than in the bulk. As a result, they have low dimensionality and fewer number of nearest neighbor atoms. The reduced coordination number and dimensionality of the particles influence both the atomic and electronic structure of the particle. For example, the inter-atomic distances, the geometry as well as the electronic, optical, and magnetic properties are no longer same as those in their crystalline form.

It is this aspect of nano-particles that the researchers have been recently trying to exploit in the design and synthesize materials with novel properties. A good example in this regard is carbon. As is well known, carbon forms two stable phases: diamond and graphite. In the former, the C-atom behaves as a sp^3 system that prefers tetrahedral bonding while in the latter it exhibits sp^2 character that gives rise to planar structures. In the nano-meter scale, on the other hand, carbon forms fullerene structures with very different bonding character. Although silicon belongs to the same group in the periodic table as carbon, it only exhibits sp^3 bonding characteristics and clusters of Si do not exhibit fullerene structures.

Recently there is considerable interest [1] in exploring if the chemistry of Si atoms at the nano-meter length scale can be altered by doping metal atoms so that Si atoms can form planar structures like graphite, and if Si clusters can be stabilized in the fullerene form [2]. In this paper we review the current status of this filed and show that this, indeed, can be achieved by doping Si clusters with suitable transition metal elements. We also explore the possibilities that the metal stabilized Si cage structures can be assembled to form cluster assembled materials with unique properties [3]. In the following we discuss our theoretical procedure and present illustrative examples.

2. THEORETICAL PROCEDURES

The calculations for free clusters are carried out using molecular orbital theory [4] where the wave function is expressed as a linear combination of atomic orbitals. We have used Gaussian basis sets to represent the atomic orbitals, and the reader is referred to our earlier work [2,3] for details. The total energy of the cluster was calculated using the density functional theory and generalized gradient approximation for exchange and correlation [5]. The geometry of the cluster was optimized without symmetry constraints by starting from different initial configurations and varying the spin multiplicities, $M = 2S+1$ (S being the total spin of the cluster). Stability of these clusters is studied as a function of size and composition. The most stable clusters are then embedded in a carbon nano-tube [3] to examine if they continue to be stable and if they exhibit novel properties not seen either in the nano-tubes or in the clusters. This phase of the work is carried out using the band structure algorithm within the super-cell concept. The Vienna ab initio simulation package (VASP) was used for these calculations [6]. Again, details of these calculations can be found from our earlier publications [3].

3. RESULTS

We discuss three different examples. The first one deals with the stabilization of the Si_{12} cluster in a cage structure by using Cr and W atoms as dopants [1, 7]. The second example deals with the stabilization of Si_{20} in the fullerene structure by using Ba, Sr, Ca, and Pb atoms as endohedral units [8]. In the third example [3], we demonstrate that a Si_{60} cluster can also be stabilized in a cage structure by using magic clusters such as $Al_{12}Si$ as endohedral complexes. Finally, we illustrate that $Si_{12}W$ clusters which tend to coalesce in the gas phase [9], can be stabilized by encapsulating them inside a carbon nano-tube.

3.1. Transition Metal Encapsulated Si_n ($11 \leq n \leq 14$) Clusters

In Fig. 1 we show [2] the equilibrium structure of Si_n clusters for n = 11, 12, 13, and 14. We note that these structures are not symmetric and Si atoms prefer to form three dimensional structures rather than planar structures. The energy gained in adding a Si atom to a Si_{n-1} cluster is 4.05, 3.59, and 4.36 eV for n = 12, 13, and 14 respectively. As a Cr atom is added to these Si clusters, the geometry as well as the relative stability of the Cr-doped Si clusters change markedly.

In Fig. 1 we show how these structures are modified when a metal atom such

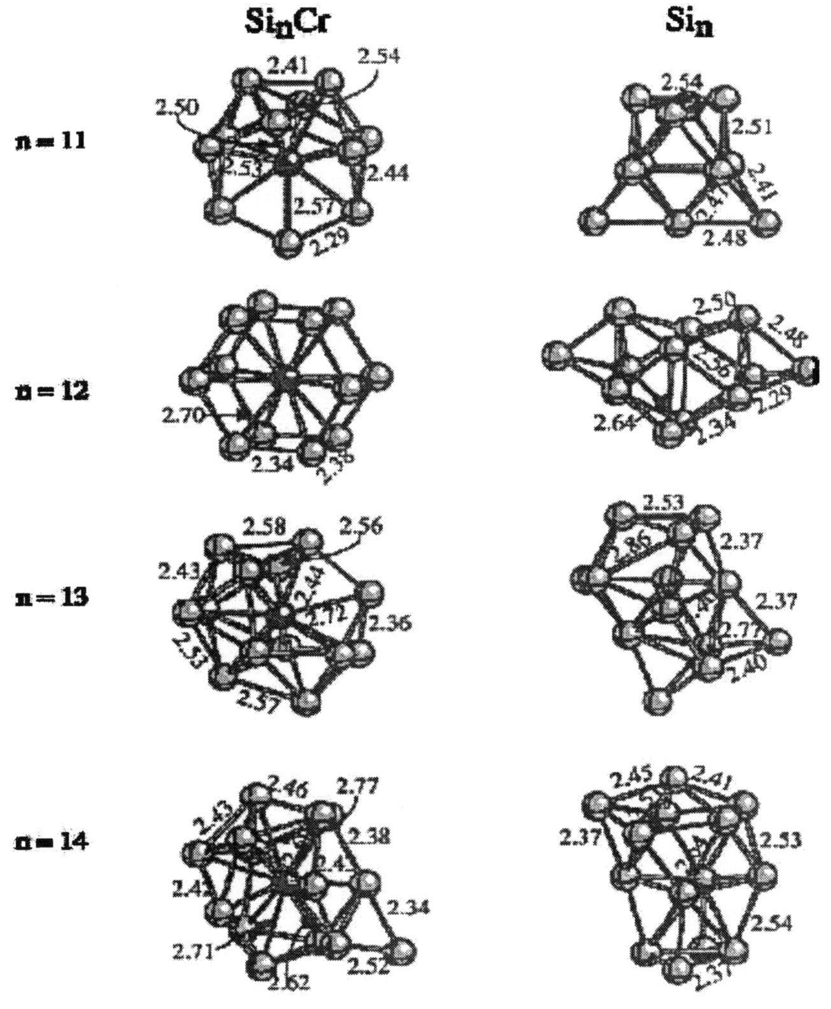

Figure 1. The ground state geometries of neutral Si_nCr and Si_n clusters. All bond lengths are in Å [7]

as Cr is incorporated. Note that Si atoms now form cage-like structures with the Cr atom buried inside the Si cage. In particular, the structure of $Si_{12}Cr$ is the most symmetric one with six Si atoms forming hexagonal structures much the same way carbon forms in graphite. The Cr atom is encapsulated inside the two Si hexagons. The energy gained in adding a Si atom to a preexisting $Si_{n-1}Cr$ cluster is 4.65 eV, 3.60 eV, and 4.08 eV respectively for n =12, 13, and 14. This shows that a $Si_{12}Cr$ cluster gains more energy by adding a Si atom to $Si_{11}Cr$ than a Si_{12} cluster does by adding a Si atom to a Si11 cluster. The enhanced stability of the $Si_{12}Cr$ cluster as well as its unique structural symmetry suggest that it can be regarded as a magic cluster analogous to those observed in alkali metal clusters two decades ago [10]. The enhanced stability of the $Si_{12}Cr$ cluster can be understood by noting that Cr atom

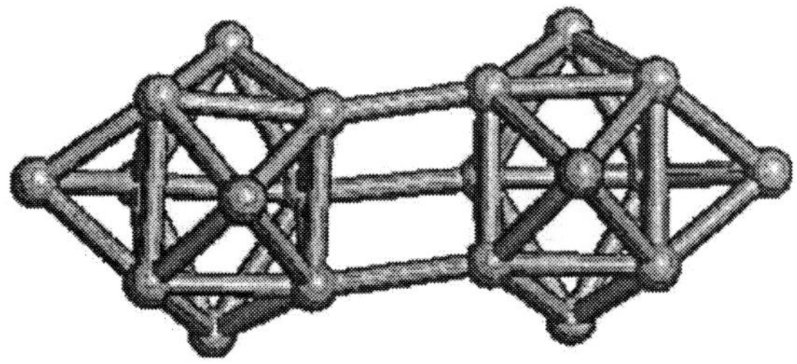

Figure 2. Equilibrium structure of Si_{20} cluster.

with an atomic configuration of $3d^5 4s^1$ can be regarded as contributing 6 electrons to the valence electron pool. If the Si atom can be assumed to have sp^2 configuration like C has in graphite, the Si atom can contribute one valence electron per atom to the valence electron pool. Thus, the number of valence electrons of $Si_{12}Cr$ cluster is 18 which forms close electronic shells and hence can account for its enhanced stability. This is consistent with the recent experiment [1] where $Si_{12}W$ cluster was found to be unusually stable. Note that Cr is isoelectronic with W.

Unfortunately, the geometry of a cluster cannot be determined independently from experiment at present. Thus, one must rely on other calculated electronic properties that can be compared with experiment to validate the reliability of the computed cluster structure. We have, therefore, calculated [2] the electron affinity of $Si_{12}Cr$ which measures the energy gained by adding an electron to a neutral $Si_{12}Cr$ cluster. This was obtained by first optimizing the geometry and spin multiplicity of the $Si_{12}Cr$ anion. The calculated value of 3.11 eV was found to agree with the experimental value [11] of 3.10 eV. It is important to point out that the experimental investigation followed the theoretical prediction.

It is also interesting to note that the ground state spin multiplicity of $Si_{12}Cr$ cluster was found to be a singlet, i.e. the magnetic moment at the Cr site was found to be zero. This is important since Cr has the highest magnetic moment (6 Bohr magneton) of any atom in the 3d-transition metal series. The fact that the magnetic moment of a transition metal atom can be changed by encapsulating it in a Si cage may be exploited in the design of electronic devices.

3.2. Stabilization of Si_{20} in a Cage Structure

We recall that the smallest fullerene structure of carbon clusters is C_{20} which has a dodecahedral structure. However, the structure of Si_{20} is that of two weakly coupled Si_{10} clusters (see Fig. 2). To see if Si_{20} can be stabilized in a cage structure much the same way as $Si_{12}Cr$, we have examined the possibility [7] of using metal atoms as endohedral complexes. We calculated the structure of M@Si_{20} (M = Ba, Sr, Ca, and Pb). The stable structures, including their vibrational frequency analysis, are given in Fig. 3. Note that once again an endohedral metal atom is able to stabilize the Si_{20} in a cage structure.

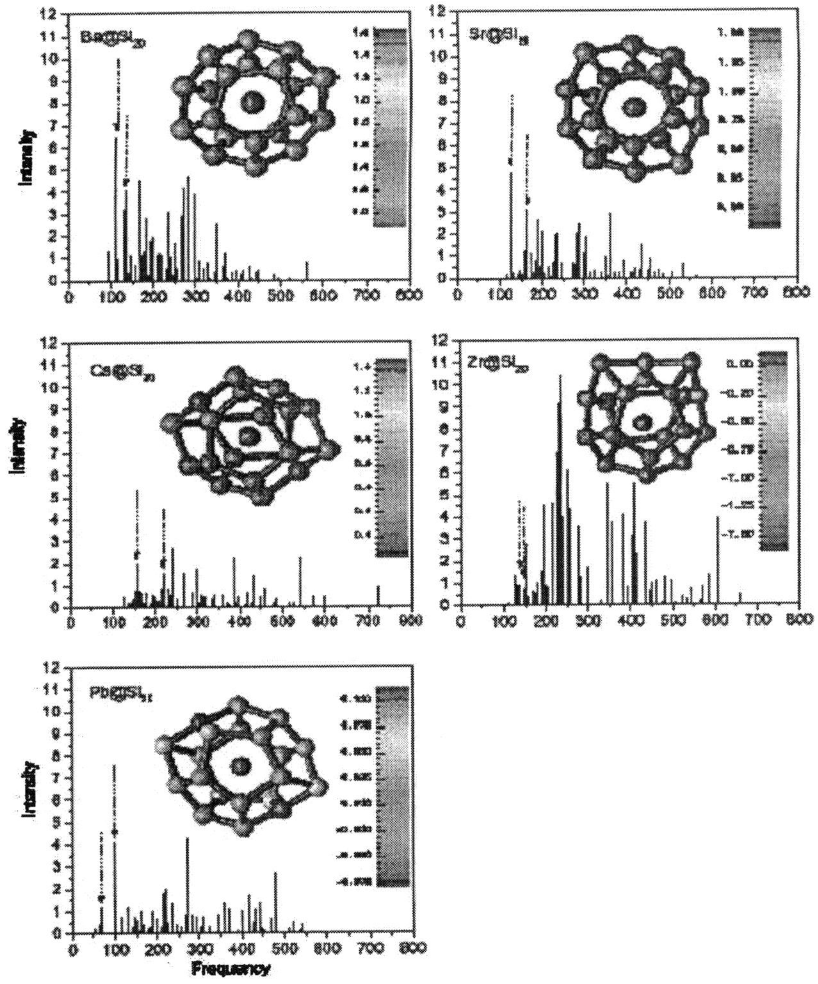

Figure 3. Vibrational spectra and charge distributions for M@Si_{20}, M=Ba, Sr, Ca, Zr, and Pb. The frequency is in cm^{-1}, and the IR intensity in km/mol. The arrows indicate the frequencies arising from the metal atoms [8].

3.3. Stabilization of the Si_{60} cage

Unlike C_{60}, Si_{60} cluster also does not form the fullerene structure. Although numerous attempts have been made to determine the equilibrium structure of Si_{60}, it is not certain that the most stable structure has yet been identified. This is because of the complex bonding characteristic of Si atoms and the numerous local minima that exist in the potential energy hyper-surface. Often, the equilibrium structure obtained from geometry optimization depends upon the initial starting configuration. However, what is clear is that Si_{60} in the fullerene structure is not stable, and that

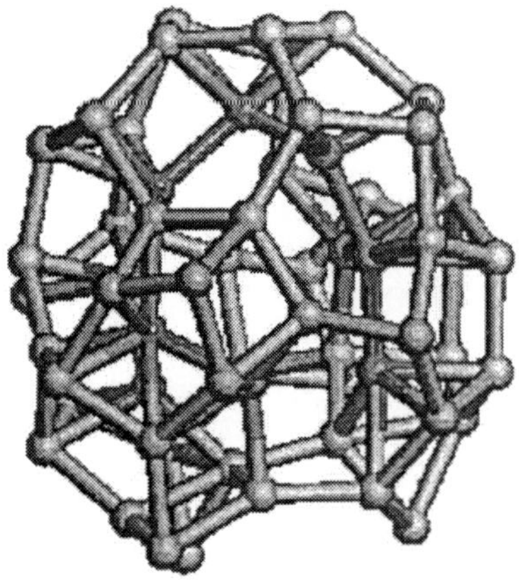

Figure 4. Equilibrium geometry of Si_{60} cluster [2].

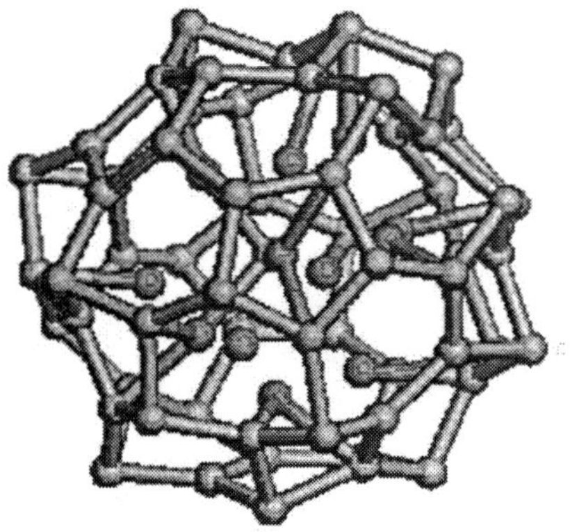

Figure 5. The optimized geometry of $Al_{12}Si@Si_{60}$ cluster [Ref. 2].

the most stable structure which has been obtained for Si_{60} thus far is that of a stuffed fullerene [3] shown in Fig. 4.

Ways of stabilizing Si_{60} in the fullerene structure have been explored by using endohedral complexes onto which Si_{60} can be grown. The initial idea [12] that Si_{60} grown on a C_{60} endohedral complex can be stable has not materialized. This is because of the large size of the C_{60} fullerene and the resulting strain it causes on the bonds between Si atoms that encapsulate the C_{60} cluster. Indeed, the total energy of $C_{60}@Si_{60}$ is higher than two separated C_{60} and Si_{60} clusters by about 23 eV.

Recently Sun *et al.* [3] studied the structure of a Si_{60} cluster by having it encapsulate smaller clusters such as $Al_{12}X$ (X = Si, Sn) as well as $Ba@Si_{20}$ clusters. Note that $Al_{12}X$ clusters are very stable [13] due to electronic shell closure brought about by its 40 valence electrons. In addition, the structure of $Al_{12}Si$ is an icosahedron that has 12 atoms on the surface. These atoms can be aligned along the center of the

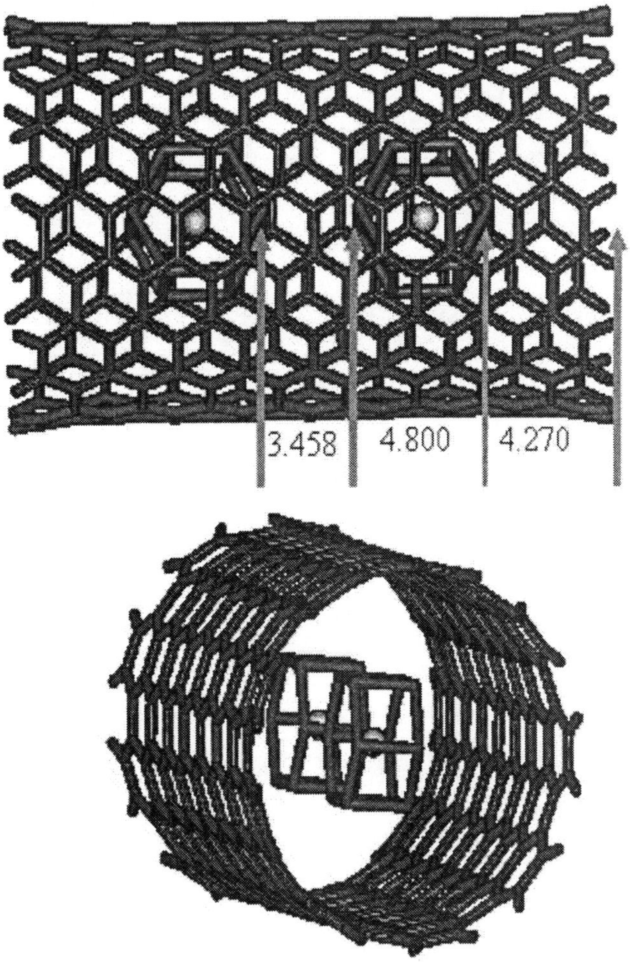

Figure 6. Preferred orientation of two $Si_{12}W$ clusters embedded inside a (9,9) carbon nano-tube [3].

12 pentagons that characterize a C_{60}/Si_{60} fullerene structure. Similarly, $Ba@Si_{20}$, discussed earlier, has twenty surface atoms which can be aligned along the center of the 20 hexagons of the fullerene cage. Thus, it is possible that these clusters as endohedral complexes can be used to stabilize Si_{60} in the fullerene structure. Optimizations of the structure of $Al_{12}Si@Si_{60}$ and $Si_{20}Ba@Si_{60}$ show [3] that these structures are indeed stable. Furthermore, the sixty Si atoms form a fullerene-like cage (see Fig. 5). These structures are stable against the separated clusters by 9.53 eV in $Al_{12}Si@Si_{60}$ to 14.15 eV in $BaSi_{20}@Si_{60}$ clusters. Thus, it is possible to stabilize Si_{60} in a cage structure similar to that of Si_{20} provided one judiciously chooses the appropriate endohedral complex.

3.4. Assembling $Si_{12}W$ Clusters inside a C-nano-tube

One of the promising aspects of magic (very stable) clusters is that they could

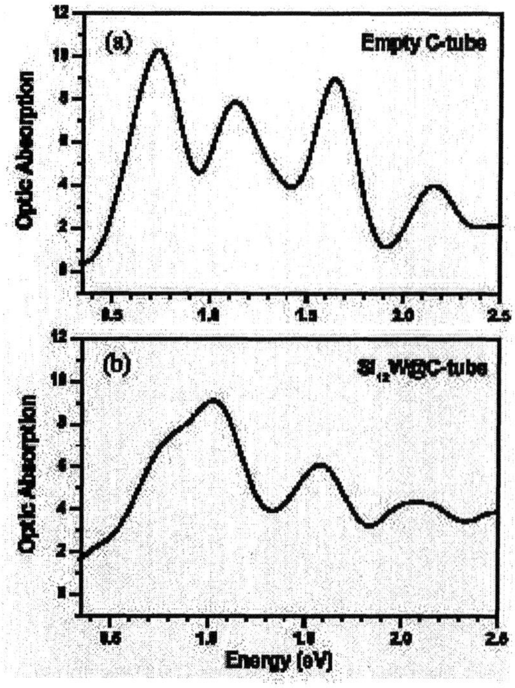

Figure 7. Optical absorption spectra of carbon (9,9) tube and Si12W clusters embedded inside the carbon (9,9) tube [Ref. 3].

be suitable building blocks for a new class of cluster assembled materials [13]. We consider the possibility that $Si_{12}W$ cluster may be one such candidate. However, calculations showed that when two $Si_{12}W$ clusters are allowed to interact with each other, they coalesced to form a larger cluster, and the $Si_{12}W$ cage structure was significantly altered [8]. We explored the possibility that these clusters can be assembled inside a carbon nano-tube [3]. We have, therefore, studied the interaction between $Si_{12}W$ clusters embedded inside a carbon nano-tube. We have determined the minimum diameter of the nano-tube as well as the preferred orientation of the $Si_{12}W$ clusters inside the tube by carrying out geometry optimization without symmetry constraint. The resulting structure is shown in Fig. 6. We have found that a (9,9) carbon nano-tube can accommodate the $Si_{12}W$ cluster, and, unlike in the gas phase interaction, the two $Si_{12}W$ clusters embedded inside the nano-tube do not coalesce and maintain their structural identity. This is due to the interaction of Si atoms with the C-atoms in the nano-tube that prevent the Si atoms from interacting strongly with Si atoms on the neighboring $Si_{12}W$ cluster. Thus, it is possible to synthesize magic clusters by choosing an appropriate substrate.

In Fig. 7 we show the optical absorption spectrum of an empty C-nano-tube and compare it with the one that contains $Si_{12}W$ clusters. Note that they are different. It is interesting to note that the optical absorption of empty C-tubes is similar to those with C_{60} clusters embedded inside it. These are referred to as "pea pods". The fact that "hetero-pea pods" that have clusters of dissimilar atoms embedded inside

C-nano-tube exhibit characteristic optical absorption spectra can be exploited in the design of novel Si-based nano-structures.

4. CONCLUSIONS

In summary, we have shown through first principles calculations that it is possible to design and synthesize Si-based nano-clusters with unusual cage-like geometries and properties by using metal atoms or clusters as endohedral units. These stable (or so-called magic clusters) clusters can then be assembled on a suitable substrate, and such a cluster assembled material can have unusual properties. This suggests that a new class of nano-structured materials with tailored properties can be designed and eventually synthesized by choosing the size, composition, and the embedding medium.

ACKNOWLEDGMENTS

This work was supported in part by a grant from the Department of Energy (DEFG02-96ER45579). One of the authors (PJ) also acknowledges partial support from the Army Research Office.

REFERENCES

[1] H. Hiura, T. Miyazaki, and T. Kanayama, Phys. Rev. Lett. **86**, 1733 (2001).

[2] Q. Sun, Q. Wang, P. Jena, B. K. Rao, and Y. Kawazoe, Phys. Rev. Lett. **90**, 135503 (2003).

[3] Q. Sun, Q. Wang, Y. Kawazoe, and P. Jena, Phys. Rev. B **66**, 245425 (2002).

[4] W. J. Hehre, L. Radom, P. V. Schleyer, and J. A. Pople, *Ab Initio Molecular Orbital Theory* (Wiley, New York, 1986).

[5] J. P. Perdew, K. Burke, and M. Ernzerhof, Phys. Rev. Lett. **77**, 3865 (1996).

[6] G. Kresse and J. Heffner, Phys. Rev. B **54**, 11169 (1996).

[7] S. N. Khanna, B. K. Rao, and P. Jena, Phys. Rev. Lett. **89**, 016803(2002).

[8] Q. Sun, Q. Wang, T. M. Briere, V. Kumar, Y. Kawazoe, and P. Jena, Phys. Rev. B **65**, 235417 (2002).

[9] Q. Sun, Q. Wang, T. M. Briere, and Y. Kawazoe, J. Phys. C **14**, 4503 (2202).

[10] W. D. Knight *et al.*, Phys. Rev. Lett. **52**, 2141 (1984).

[11] K. Bowen, private communication.

[12] M. Harada *et al.*, Chem. Lett. **1**, 1037 (1994).

[13] S. N. Khanna and P. Jena, Phys. Rev. Lett. **69**, 1664 (1992).

EXCITED ELECTRONIC STATE PROCESSES IN LARGE BIO-MOLECULES
Modus Operandi

Henrik Bohr

Quantum Protein (QuP) Centre
Department of Physics, Technical University of Denmark
DK-2800 Kgs. Lyngby, Denmark

Holger Bech Nielsen

Niels Bohr Institute
Department of Physics, High Energy Theory, University of Copehagen
DK-2100 Blegdamsvej 17, Copenhagen, Denmark

ABSTRACT

In the present contribution we shall discuss molecular reaction kinetics from a quantum mechanical viewpoint. A special case of the DNA-repair protein, the reactivating Photolyase, is being discussed with respect to electronic processes. In the general discussion of reaction kinetics we are especially interested in that which involves electronical excited state dynamics and here we have tried to prove that the barrier for the repair process in the ground state is larger than the corresponding barrier in the excited state.

1. INTRODUCTION

The research in the quantum nature of proteins has become a new exciting field of bio-physics. The importance of quantum effects is very clearly evidenced by excited electronic states processes and occurrence of particular reaction pathways [1]. The photolyase repair protein is a beautiful example of that. Photolyase repairs UV-damage on DNA by utilizing an intricate set of electronic processes that cannot be understood by classical molecular mechanics. An excited state mechanism explains why UV damage can be repaired by less energetic blue light [2]. The UV damage

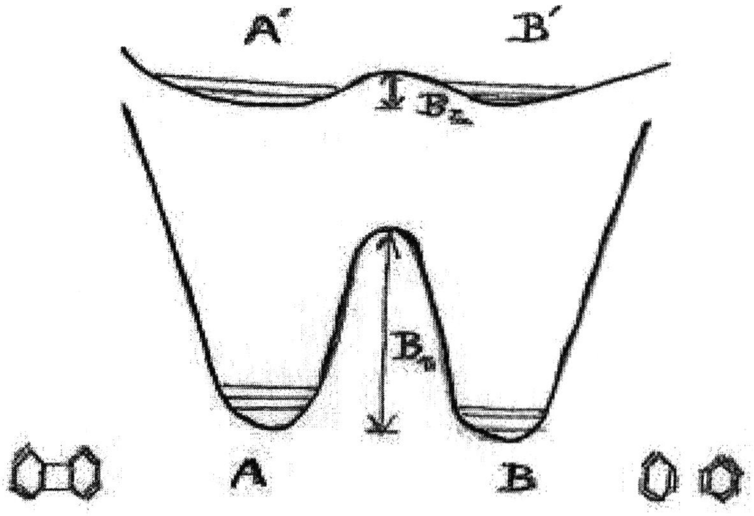

Figure 1. Potential energy barriers for reaction going from A to B through excited electron states A^1 and B^1 such that the process now reads $A \to A^1 \to B^1 \to B$ with the last decay from B^1 to B. We have included vibrational states in the potential wells as lines parallel to the x-axis. q along the x-axis is a conformational coordinate measured as a difference in nuclear positions.

is in this case causing two thymine nucleotides to form a dimer due to bonding between the pyrin rings that are then brought back or repaired to the original state of two separate nucleotides [3]. We shall in the following explain why excited state electronics more generally is important for a big class of enzymatic processes [4].

In general, the use of excited state electronic processes open up for other channels in reaction kinetics [2]. These channels facilitate possibilities that otherwise were prohibited in chemical reactions due to energy conservation or reasons of symmetry rules. It can be shown that potential barriers in enzymatic reactions get diminished when going to excited electronic states as shown schematically in the Figure below. In fact, the usual picture of enzymes stabilizing and using intermediate transition states as means for overcoming potential barriers in chemical reactions can be explained instead by utilization of excited state mechanisms. Such pictures, of considering electronic processes in excited states, are especially relevant for enzymes containing transition metals connected to their reaction centres. The fact that the presence of enzymes will cause a diminishing of the barrier for a reaction leads to an exponential increase of the rate constant for that reaction as explained by the Ahrenius law: The rate constant $k \approx const \cdot e^{\frac{-\Delta B}{k_B T}}$, where ΔB is the barrier height. A decrease of the barrier ΔB, when lifting the process to the excited state level for crucial electrons, will clearly speed up the process by increasing the rate constant and make the repair possible [5].

2. POTENTIAL ENERGY SURFACES

We shall in the following be using a popular graphical representation of the energy landscape where the potential energy is pictured in 1-dimension with a few minima and an important reaction coordinate that constitute the crucial abscissa in the picture (Figure 1). Such a choice is in this case quite obvious since the 2 minima, in Figure 1 at the ground state level, clearly are for the reactant and product or, in other words, the UV damaged state of DNA, the dithymine state A, and the repaired state of two separate thymines B. Therefore the choice of the reaction coordinate can be a nuclear distance, i.e. a difference in the coordinates of the center of mass of the pyrine rings in the two thymine nucleotides.

In the specific case of the repair protein photolyase a cofactor, Riboflavin, works as an electron donor that delivers electrons to dithymine via photolyase [6]. A quantum physical electron can only move from Riboflavin to DNA when it is in an excited state (in flavin) that is closer to an excited state in thymine of DNA, closer than in the ground state, energetically, and with off-diagonal elements (growing up when the orbitals in the atoms in question get closer. We use Born Oppenheimer approximation and look at the nuclear position and can at each instance calculate electron coordinates.

3. EXCITED STATE DYNAMICS

We will now focus our attention on electronic excited state dynamics [7]. Coming back to the proof of the diminished potential barriers at the electronic excited states: An electron will get excited out of an orbital and either end up in another orbital further from the nucleus or it will get free by photo dissociation. In many other cases of enzymatic processes a lone pair electron is being excited and will be easy for treatment.

3.1 The tight binding approximation for diatomic systems

Let us first consider a diatomic system with the Hamiltonian H, the unperturbed energy state $E_{1,2}$ for the 2 orbitals and the interaction potential $V(R_{ij})$, where (R_{ij} is the nuclear distance between the atoms i and j corresponding to the 2 electronic orbits) beside an electrostatic potential:

$$H = E_1 + E_2 + V(R_{ij}) + \frac{Z_i Z_j e^2}{R_{ij}} \tag{1}$$

and

$$H_1^i \phi_i^1 = \epsilon_i \phi_i^1, H_2^j \phi_j^2 = \epsilon_j \phi_j^2 \tag{2}$$

and where ϵ_i, ϵ_j are single energies. In the tight binding approximation we have

$$V(R_{ij}) = E - \epsilon_i - \epsilon_j \tag{3}$$

where

$$E = < \phi_i^1 \phi_j^2 | H | \phi_i^1 \phi_j^2 > \tag{4}$$

The electrons drive the nuclei. In the specific case of the photo repair process 2 electronic orbitals ϕ^1, ϕ^2 are, as mentioned, crucial. One in the cofactor ribo-flavin acting as a donor and an electron orbital in di-thymine being excited by a photon.

One can expect superposition of the states: $a_1\phi^1 + a_2\phi^2$. In the case of the photolyase (not a diatomic but rather a di-molecular system) the ground electronic state configuration is:$\phi_i = (1S)^2(2S)^2(2P)^2, \phi_j = (1S)^2$ and the excited electron state configuration is:$\phi_i = (1S)^2(2S)^2(2P)(3S)$ and ionisation energy ϵ^{io} is (for the ground state) $\epsilon^{io} = 10 - 12eV$ while for the excited state $\epsilon^{io'} = 2 - 5eV$.

In Figure 1 above we have depicted the barriers B_1 and B_2 for, respectively, the ground state and the excited state. We want later to argue that $B_1 > B_2$. A small barrier means greater over-lap and involves often bonding/localization or anti-bonding/delocalization. Delocalization is standing for states spread out in space in a superposition far away from the position of the eigenstates. In Figure 2 we have depicted these bonding and anti-bonding possibilities as energy potential surfaces, and in Figure 3 the electron orbitals are schematically illustrated as more or less elongated ellipsis.

3.2. Level repulsion

We shall now argue for a level repulsion between the ground state and excited state in a simple system in 2-dimensions, again with 2 orbitals ϕ_1, ϕ_2. We will first construct the potential in 2-dimensions as Pauli matrices $\sigma_\mathbf{i}$ which always can be done since the Hilbert space was reduced to 2-dimension. Any 2-dimensional matrix can be expanded on (and proportional to) a Pauli matrix and the unity matrix. We have $Det(n\vec{\sigma} - \lambda) = 0 \Rightarrow \lambda = \pm 1$. The split-up of eigenvalues is given by $| a |$, which means that $\vec{a}(q)\vec{\sigma} + a_0\mathbf{1} = | \vec{\mathbf{a}} | \vec{\mathbf{n}}_\mathbf{a} \cdot \vec{\sigma}$, where the second term $a_0\mathbf{1}$ in this example vanishes. The gap is given by $| a |$. The proof for $\lambda = \pm 1$ is given by the following, having in mind that:

$$\sigma_z = \begin{pmatrix} 1 & 0 \\ 0 & -1 \end{pmatrix} \tag{5}$$

The main assumption is that $a_0 = 0$. In details:

$$\begin{aligned} det(\vec{n} \cdot \vec{\sigma} - \lambda) =& det \begin{pmatrix} n_3 - \lambda & -in_2 + n_1 \\ in_2 + n_1 & -n_3 - \lambda \end{pmatrix} \\ =& - n_3^2 + \lambda^2 - n_2^2 - n_1^2 \\ =& \lambda^2 - \vec{n}^2 \end{aligned} \tag{6}$$

$$\xrightarrow[since\ \vec{n}^2 = 1]{} \lambda^2 = 1 \Rightarrow \lambda = \pm 1$$

which tells us that the levels can not easily cross each other or the upper levels stays the upper one as a single (or dual) continuous parameter is varied. Therefore,

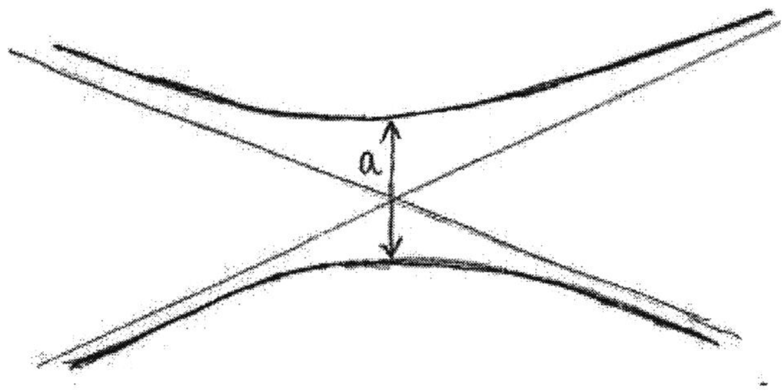

Figure 2. Bonding and anti-bonding potentials with a gap in between.

there will generically be a finite gab all along. (In a less simplified case one can immagine a crossing of the gab.)

Since the nuclear motion is relatively slow compared to the electron system, with time parameter $\frac{1}{\Delta E_{el}}$, the electron system stays in n'th state (level) if it starts in the n'th level.

Emission processes with photons are slower than the chemical processes where the coordinates of the nuclei matter. Hence it is clear that the states will not cross over (Figure 2), i.e., the excited state will not decay back to the ground level immediately but proceeds at the excited level.

Concerning the electron landscape at the excited level we can express electronic state behaviour by the following sentence:

The electron goes to less localized (nx) states $\Rightarrow$ *more overlap of electron orbitals* $\Rightarrow$ *smaller barrier* $\Rightarrow$ *more superposition* $\Rightarrow$ *jumping from one orbital in one molecule to another orbital in a different molecule.*

These arguments require that the electron is in energy-eigenstates. The electronic process can go into superposition of two orbitals in different molecules being thus less localized.

Crossing is possible with a certain conserved quantity and Δ=0. One could schematically illustrate the excitation of electron orbitals in terms of overlap by the following Figure 3.

The level repulsion caused by the Δ can be written as:

$$\begin{pmatrix} E_1 & \Delta \\ \Delta & E_2 \end{pmatrix} \textit{ which gives the levels } \left.\begin{matrix} \overline{} & \\ \uparrow & E_1 \\ \overline{} & \\ \overline{} & E_2 \\ \downarrow & \\ \overline{} & \end{matrix}\right\} \textit{level repulsion}$$

Let us use as a basis approximate electron position eigenstate with average energies E_1 and E_2 being the diagonal elements in the 2-dimension energy matrix. The actual basis for such split-up of eigenstates is consisting of the two obitals ϕ_1, ϕ_2 which could be (2p) and (3s). If actually, against expectations, the potentials

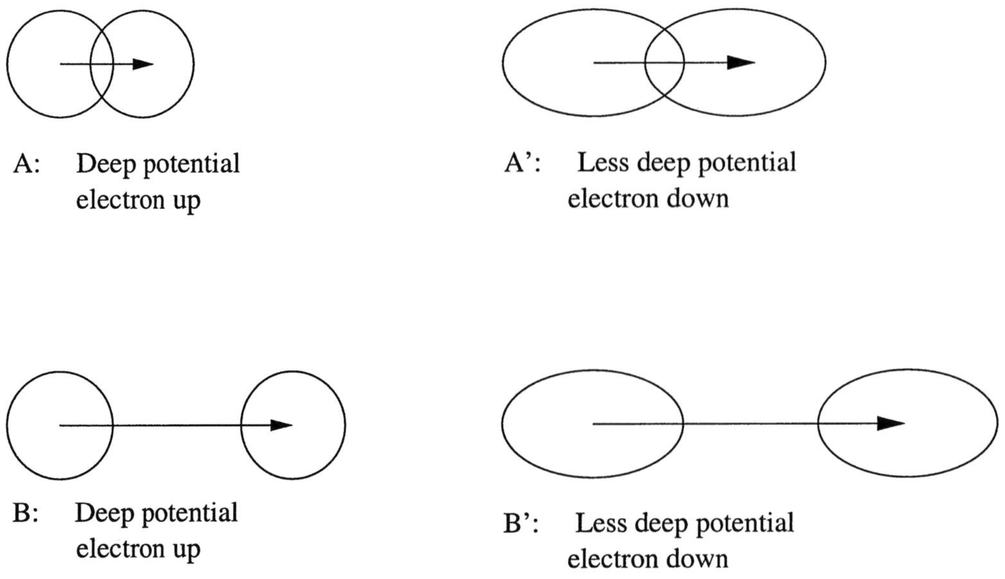

Figure 3. The diagram shows the pull apart of 2 electronic systems. It depictures the level repulsion in energy space, and in a sense, being the predecessor for Figure 2.

(eigenvalues) V_1 and V_2 could cross as function of dist, then Δ will typically be: $\Delta \approx 0$.

It is in the following crucial that we develop a metric on the potential surface. This is often a hard problem when talking about processes involving proteins with complex potential surfaces since there are no obvious way of choosing 1 distance from thousands others in the many dimensional space of interaction. Without a special choice of coordinate the energy surface is unimaginable. However, in this case of 2 crucial electron orbitals an obvious distance, which we here call dist is the one between the position of the 2 nuclei corresponding to the 2 orbitals from different atoms.

3.3 Barriers on the potential surface

We now turn to the barrier discussion. It is, as mentioned, essential for reaction kinetics that the excited state barrier are smaller than that of the ground states, since otherwise the reaction will not proceed because blue light photons, for initiating the repair, are much less enegitically than UV photons that caused the damage and possibly made the crossing of the barrier between di-thymine/thymine in the ground state. Hence we expect the second derivatives of the potential surface $V_{upper/lower}$ (eigenvalues) to satisfy the following in-equality which we shall try to argue for.

We should expect that crossing of E_1 and E_2 in the basis discussed then render second order derivatives at "middle point in dist", denoted as $(\text{dist})_{cr}$ to satisfy:

$$\frac{d^2}{d\ dist^2}V_{upper}(dist)_{cr} > \frac{d^2}{d\ dist^2}V_{lower}(dist)_{cr} \tag{7}$$

and this cross-over point is where we should compare the barrier heights.

Even after adding an overall $a_0(dist)\mathbf{1}$ term you would keep this inequality because

$$V_{upper} = V_{upper} + a_0$$

$$V_{lower} = V_{lower} + a_0$$

so if E_1 and E_2 crossed then indeed a peak for the upper level would be less sharp than the one for the lower level suggesting $B_2 < B_1$. (see Figures 1 and 2)

With

$$\vec{a}\cdot\vec{\sigma} + a_0 1, one\ \ gets\ \ \lambda = \left\{ \begin{matrix} +|\vec{a}| \\ -|\vec{a}| \end{matrix} \right\} + a_0, so \quad \Delta\lambda = 2|\vec{a}| \tag{8}$$

so $\vec{a}$ will generally be $\vec{a} \neq \vec{0}$ even along a one-dimensional path. $\vec{a}$ has 3 components and so it is on a one-dimensional curve extremely unlikely to satisfy $\vec{a} = \vec{0}$. Actually, in 3-dim we can always find a situation where 3 parameters describe the reaction passage with $\vec{a} = \vec{0}$ being met generically.

We are now going back to the arguments for lower barriers at the excited states. Such proof will make use again of Pauli matrices. The following gives a proof for the inequality (7). Near the point where $E_1 = E_2$, E_i being function of dist, we Taylor expand H:

$$H = \vec{a}\cdot\vec{\sigma} + a_0\mathbf{1} \tag{9}$$

$$H|_{diagonal} = \frac{1}{2}(E_1^{a_0} + E_2^{a_0}) + \frac{1}{2}(E_1 - E_2)\sigma_z \tag{10}$$

and the second order derivative I, of the difference of the potentials, is calculated in order to check the barrier height of $V_{upper/lower}$:

$$I \equiv \frac{d^2}{d\ (dist)^2}(V_{upper} - V_{lower}) \tag{11}$$

$$= \frac{d^2}{d\ (dist)^2}\sqrt{\vec{a}_\perp^2 + \frac{1}{2}(E_1 - E_2)\sigma_z} \approx \frac{d^2}{d\ (dist)^2}\sqrt{\Delta^2 + (dist - dist_{cr})^2)\alpha^2}$$

where ($dist_{cr}$ is the dist at a cross over).

We make a Taylor expansion, where $(dist - dist_{cr})\alpha << \Delta$.

$$I \approx \frac{d^2}{d\ (dist)^2}(\Delta + \frac{(dist - dist_{cr})\alpha^2}{2\Delta})\ \xrightarrow{For\Delta = const}\ = \frac{2\alpha^2}{2\Delta} > 0 \tag{12}$$

So we have shown the inequality (7) above. We have used the following definitions:

$$\vec{a} = (a_1, a_2, E_2 - E_1)$$

$$\vec{a}_\perp = (a_1, a_2, 0)$$

$$a_\perp^2 = \Delta^2$$

$$E_2 - E_1 = \alpha \cdot (dist - dist_{cr}), \qquad for \quad (dist - dist_{cr})\alpha << \Delta$$

Concerning the upper level potential, V_{upper}, we imagine that the pressumed minimum on Figure 2 got converted by a (**1**-proportional term) to the mild maximum of Figure 1. Of course, the two figures, Figure 1 and Figure 2, are describing potential surfaces of different species, the former representing molecules and the later orbits.

If dist $\approx$ $dist_{cr}$ then (dist - $dist_{cr}$) $\alpha \approx 0$ and if $\Delta \neq 0$, then in a small region where dist $\sim$ $dist_{cr}$, one may consider Δ roughly constant, i.e, it has to be non-singular.

A strong assumption is that there are diagonal "*a priori* eigenvalues" elements E_1, E_2 that cross each other for a certain parameter value ($dist_{cr}$) and where (being quite obvious) the lower level of the potential V_{lower} at least has a maximum.

Let us finally try to discuss the other assumptions in this proof: Δ has to behave nicely around $dist_{cr}$ (see page 5). For Δ varying, with no negative second order derivative, it is still true that $I > 0$. Δ being linear is also OK. This completes a simplified proof for not strongly varying Δ and with no negative second order derivatives.

One could be sceptical about such a proof, since it did not involve detailed chemical knowledge about the potential surface, but actually such details are implied in the choice of a suitable crucial distance for which the diagonal energy values are close to each other and involving level repulsion and that is in general the case for such electronic enzyme processes and therefore the proof provides surprising generality.

We will now like to give some general comments about this proof. The assumption about E_1 and E_2 crossing each other has to be considered as a case for a certain dist=$dist_1$. Thus in general we have curves of the ground state and the excited state potentials $V_{1,2}$ as shown in Figure 4 as function of dist and where the crossing line energies are special cases.

In the cases of the diagonal energies E being linear we have the following cases:

Case 1: In the case of the diagonal energies $E_{1,2}$ crossing, where one holds the off-diagonal element Δ fixed and vary E, then $I > 0$ in the neighbourhood of the crossing.

Case 2: In the case right at the minimum, where $E_{1,2}$-lines are parallel, Δ is fixed and E is constant which makes $I = 0$.

In order to get a more general view of the real potential surface we might appeal to some new development of random matrices. The crucial question to pose in this 2-dimensional Hilbert space is how the eigenvalues depend on the matrix as a function of the dist-parameter. The answer to this question can probably be found in the theory of these random matrices. It is actually known that in such random matrix dynamics the fluctuations in the outer states, e.g., the ground state, are larger than the fluctuations in the middle states (the excited states). These fluctuations make

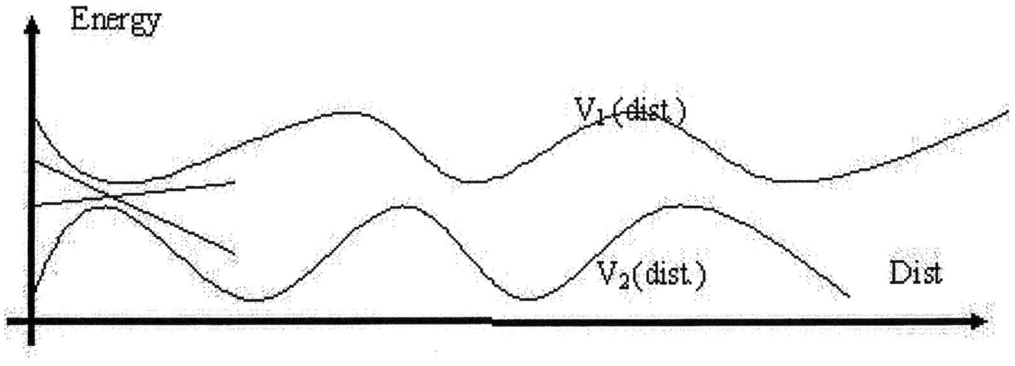

Figure 4. Here we show two arbitrary energy potentials of $V_{1,2}$ for varying dist.

the curvature or the Hessian behave the same way, i.e., larger in the ground state than in the excited state.

3.4 Barrier heights in reactions kinetics

If we go back to the arguments around equation (4), we can actually give another proof of barriers being lower at the excited state level. As we found out, in the general form of a 2-dimensional Hamiltonian, $H = \vec{a} \cdot \vec{\sigma} + a_0 \cdot \mathbf{1}$ we have the following eigenvalues $\lambda = \mathrm{V}_1, \mathrm{V}_2$, where V_1 and V_2 are respectively the ground state and excited state potentials. We shall now try to find the lowest order polynomials that can satisfy the behaviour in Figure 1, and make arguments, based on pictures of potential surfaces, sound more real. The polynomials arise from a Taylor expansion of the potentials as a function of dist. It is possible to satisfy the behaviour of the potentials in Figure 1 by having $\mathrm{V}_1 = \mathrm{a}_0$ - $|\vec{a}|$ $\mathrm{V}_2 = \mathrm{a}_0$, + $|\vec{a}|$ where $|\vec{a}|$ is linear in dist, i.e., $|\vec{a}| = |\vec{k}_1 + dist\vec{k}_2|$ (k's are constants) and $a_0 = k_3(dist)^2 + k_4$. With this form of potentials $\mathrm{V}_{1,2}$ we have precisely the behaviour of Figure 1 with a large barrier on the V_1 potential and a smaller barrier at the potential V_2. This argument requires $|\vec{a}|$ to be small. The crucial step in this argument is the inclusion of the numerical value $|\vec{a}|$ which brings in a square-root function.

4. Conclusions

In all, it seems plausible that the barrier B_2 of excited state energy potentials will be lower (and often considerably lower) than that of the barrier B_1 (see Figure 1) between ground states. The argument of the diagonal elements having to cross each other, which was prohibitet in the case of $a_0 \cdot \mathbf{1} = 0$, but otherwise needed in the case of $a_0 \cdot \mathbf{1} \neq 0$, is a crucial point in the arguments for $B_2 < B_1$. This outcome is essential in reaction kinetics of enzymes since it (i.e., the excited state dynamics) gives means for lowering the barriers and speed up the reaction, and holds especially (considering the assumptions) for proteins containing transition metals with non-paired electrons as well as for photon induced reactions, such as the photo-reactivation process. Such mechanism provides in turn important means for the life processes and explains why enzyme processes work so effectively, often raising the reaction rate constants 10^{16} times higher than without employing such mechanisms. The role of the proteins in the reaction process, which was not discussed here explicitly, seems to be to fix and hold the reactants together thus facilitating the process discussed.

ACKNOWLEDGMENTS

The research described herein was supported by the Danish National Research Foundation and the Quantum Protein (QuP) Centre at the Technical University of Denmark and K.J. Jalkanen (QuP) for scientific discussions.

REFERENCES

[1] D.B. Truhlar, Potential Energy Surfaces and Dynamic Calculations, Plenum Press, London, 1980.

[2] H. G Bohr and F. B. Malik, *Phys. Rev. E.*, submitted for publication, (2003).

[3] M. P. Cheung, I. Daizadeh, A. A .Stuchebrukhov, and P. F. Hellis, *Biophys. J.* **76**, 1241-1249 (1999).

[4] P. F. Hellis, R. F. Hartman and S. D. Rose, *Chem. Soc. Rev.* **24**, 289-297 (1995).

[5] J. T. Hynes, T.-H. Tran-Thi, and G. Granucci, *J. Photochem. and Photobiol. A: Chem.* **154**, 3-11 (2002).

[6] A. Sancar, *Biochemistry* **33**, 2-9 1994).

[7] J. Pitarch-Ruiz, S. Evangelisti and D. Maynau, *Chemical Physics Letters* **372** , 22-27 (2003).

Density Functional Theory

CALCULATION OF THE GROUND-STATE PROPERTIES OF THE DIMERIZED ONE-DIMENSIONAL HUBBARD MODEL

R. López-Sandoval

Instituto Potosino de Investigación Científica y Tecnológica
Camino a la presa San José 2055, 78216 SLP Mexico

G. M. Pastor

Laboratoire de Physique Quantique, Centre National de la Recherche Scientifique, Université Paul Sabatier, 31062 Toulouse France

1. INTRODUCTION

Density functional theory (DFT) provides a rigorous framework for studying the physics of the many-body problem [1-3]. The fundamental concept behind DFT is to replace the conventional dynamical variables that completely define a many-particle state by considering the particle-density distribution $\rho(\vec{r})$ as the basic variable. For this purpose the energy E of the system is expressed as a functional of $\rho(\vec{r})$ separating the various energy terms in two main groups. The first one contains the contributions that depend explicitly on the problem under study, which result from the coupling between $\rho(\vec{r})$ and the external fields $V_{ext}(\vec{r})$. The second one concerns the intrinsic energy of the many-particle system, namely, the kinetic energy T and the interaction energy W of the particles. These terms are universal functionals of $\rho(\vec{r})$ in the sense that they are independent of the problem under study. While the general functional dependence of $T[\rho]$ and $W[\rho]$ is not known explicitly, they can be formally expressed as the result of integrating out the microscopic degrees of freedom. In the case of ground-state electronic properties, this is achieved by imposing that $T[\rho]$ and $W[\rho]$ correspond to the minimum possible value of $T + W$ for a given $\rho(\vec{r})$ [3-4]. These basic concepts have general validity and are therefore relevant to a wide variety of situations which may have very different physical origins.

In past years a number of investigations have been performed by applying the concepts of DFT to lattice models. Among the studied problems one should mention the determination of band-gaps in semiconductors [5], the role of off-diagonal elements of the density matrix and the non-interacting v representability in strongly correlated systems [6], etc. In previous works we have considered a lattice density functional theory (LDFT) of many-body models and applied it to the Hubbard Hamiltonian on different dimensions [7-9]. The interaction energy W of the Hubbard model has been calculated exactly as a function of the density matrix γ_{ij} for various periodic lattices having $\gamma_{ij} = \gamma_{12}$ for nearest neighbors (NNs) i and j. An analysis of the functional dependence of $W(\gamma_{12})$ for different band fillings and lattice structures revealed a remarkable pseudo-universal behavior of W as a function of the degree of electron delocalization [7]. On this basis, a simple general approximation to $W(\gamma_{12})$ has been proposed which derives from exact dimer results, the scaling properties of W, and known limits. In this way several ground-state electronic properties of one-dimensional (1D) systems have been obtained in good agreement with available exact solutions. At the same time, the ground-state energy and charge-excitation gap of the 2D Hubbard model have been successfully predicted in the complete range of interaction strength [8].

The purpose of this paper is to review recent calculations of the ground-state properties of dimerized Hubbard chains performed in the framework of lattice-density functional theory [9]. The basic formalism is recalled in Sec. II. The properties of the interaction-energy functional W of the dimerized Hubbard model are discussed in Sec. III. The domain of the representability of γ_{ij} and the scaling behavior of W are investigated. A simple explicit approximation to W is derived, which is appropriate for direct calculations. In Sec. IV several ground-state properties are determined as a function of Coulomb repulsion U/t and hopping-integral alternation δt. Finally, Sec. V summarizes the main conclusions.

2. LATTICE-DENSITY FUNCTIONAL THEORY

We consider the many-body Hamiltonian

$$H = \sum_{ij\sigma} t_{ij}\, \hat{c}^{\dagger}_{i\sigma} \hat{c}_{j\sigma} + \frac{1}{2} \sum_{\substack{klmn \\ \sigma\sigma'}} V_{klmn}\, \hat{c}^{\dagger}_{k\sigma} \hat{c}^{\dagger}_{m\sigma'} \hat{c}_{n\sigma'} \hat{c}_{l\sigma} \;, \tag{1}$$

where $\hat{c}^{\dagger}_{i\sigma}$ ($\hat{c}_{i\sigma}$) is the usual creation (annihilation) operator for an electron with spin σ at site or orbital i. The hopping integrals t_{ij} define the lattice (e.g., 1D chains, square or triangular 2D lattices) and the range of single-particle interactions (e.g., up to first or second neighbors). From the *ab initio* perspective t_{ij} is given by the external potential $V_{\text{ext}}(\vec{r})$ and by the choice of the basis. V_{klnm} defines the type of many-body interactions. Eq. (1) is mainly used in this section to present the general formulation which can then be applied to various specific lattice models.

The hopping matrix t_{ij} plays the role given in conventional DFT to the external potential $V_{ext}(\vec{r})$. Consequently, the single-particle density matrix γ_{ij} between lattice sites replaces the continuum density $\rho(\vec{r})$ as basic variable. The situation is similar to the density-matrix functional theory proposed by Gilbert for the study of non-local pseudo-potentials $V_{\text{ext}}(\vec{r}, \vec{r}')$ [10-12]. The ground-state energy E_{gs} and density matrix γ^{gs}_{ij} are determined by minimizing the energy functional $E[\gamma_{ij}] = E_K[\gamma_{ij}] + W[\gamma_{ij}]$ with respect to γ_{ij}. $E[\gamma_{ij}]$ is defined for all density matrices that can be written as $\gamma_{ij} = \sum_\sigma \gamma_{ij\sigma} = \sum_\sigma \langle\Psi|\hat{c}^{\dagger}_{i\sigma}\hat{c}_{j\sigma}|\Psi\rangle$ for all i and j, where $|\Psi\rangle$ is an N-particle state.

The first term in E is given by $E_K = \sum_{ij} t_{ij}\gamma_{ij}$. It represents the kinetic energy associated with the electronic motion in the lattice and includes all single-particle contributions. Notice that in LDFT the exact (correlated) kinetic energy is taken into account and that no corrections on E_K have to be included in other parts of the energy functional as in the KS approach. The second term in E is the interaction-energy functional given by [4]

$$W[\gamma_{ij}] = \min \left[\frac{1}{2} \sum_{\substack{klmn \\ \sigma\sigma'}} V_{klmn} \, \langle \Psi[\gamma_{ij}] | \, \hat{c}^{\dagger}_{k\sigma} \hat{c}^{\dagger}_{m\sigma'} \hat{c}_{n\sigma'} \hat{c}_{l\sigma} \, | \Psi[\gamma_{ij}] \rangle \right] , \tag{2}$$

where the minimization implies a search over all N-particles states $|\Psi[\gamma_{ij}]\rangle$ that satisfy $\langle \Psi[\gamma_{ij}] | \sum_\sigma \hat{c}^{\dagger}_{i\sigma}\hat{c}_{j\sigma} \, |\Psi[\gamma_{ij}]\rangle = \gamma_{ij}$ for all i and j. $W[\gamma_{ij}]$ represents the minimum value of the interaction energy compatible with a given density matrix γ_{ij}. It is expressed in terms of the Hartree-Fock energy $E_{\mathrm{HF}}[\gamma_{ij}] = \frac{1}{2}\sum_{\substack{ijkl \\ \sigma\sigma'}} V_{ijkl} \, (\gamma_{ij\sigma}\gamma_{kl\sigma'} - \delta_{\sigma\sigma'}\gamma_{il\sigma}\gamma_{kj\sigma})$ and the correlation energy $E_{\mathrm{C}}[\gamma_{ij}]$ as $W[\gamma_{ij}] = E_{\mathrm{HF}}[\gamma_{ij}] + E_{\mathrm{C}}[\gamma_{ij}]$. W and E_{C} are universal functionals of γ_{ij} in the sense that they are independent of t_{ij}, i.e., of the system under study. They depend on the considered interactions or model, as defined by V_{klmn}, on the number of electrons N_e, and on the structure of the many-body Hilbert space, as given by N_e and the number of orbitals or sites N_a.

$E[\gamma]$ is minimized by expressing $\gamma_{ij} = \gamma_{ij\uparrow} + \gamma_{ij\downarrow}$ in terms of the eigenvalues $\eta_{k\sigma}$ (occupation numbers) and eigenvectors $u_{ik\sigma}$ (natural orbitals) as $\gamma_{ij\sigma} = \sum_k u_{ik\sigma} \, \eta_{k\sigma} \, u^*_{jk\sigma}$. Lagrange multipliers μ and $\lambda_{k\sigma}$ ($\varepsilon_{k\sigma} = \lambda_{k\sigma}/\eta_{k\sigma}$) are introduced in order to impose the usual constraints $\sum_{k\sigma} \eta_{k\sigma} = N_e$ and $\sum_i |u_{ik\sigma}|^2 = 1$. Derivation with respect to $u^*_{jk\sigma}$ and $\eta_{k\sigma}$ ($0 \le \eta_{k\sigma} \le 1$) yields the eigenvalue equations [8,10]

$$\eta_{k\sigma} \sum_i \left(t_{ij} + \frac{\partial W}{\partial \gamma_{ij}} \right) u_{ik\sigma} = \varepsilon_{k\sigma} u_{jk\sigma} \tag{3}$$

with the subsidiary conditions $\varepsilon_{k\sigma} < \mu$ if $\eta_{k\sigma} = 1$, and $\varepsilon_{k\sigma} = \mu$ if $0 < \eta_{k\sigma} < 1$, and $\varepsilon_{k\sigma} > \mu$ if $\eta_{k\sigma} = 0$. Self-consistency is implied by the dependence of $\partial W/\partial \gamma_{ij}$ on $\eta_{k\sigma}$ and $u_{ik\sigma}$. Eq. (3) holds exactly in all interaction regimes. It is analogous to well-known results of density-matrix functional theory in the continuum [10]. However, notice the difference with the KS-like approach considered in Ref.6 , which assumes non-interacting v-representability, and where only integer occupations are allowed.

The importance of fractional occupations of natural orbitals has already been stressed in previous density-matrix functional studies in the continuum. In fact, in the case of models one observes that $0 < \eta_{k\sigma} < 1$ for all $k\sigma$ except in very special situations like the uncorrelated limit ($V_{klmn} = 0$) or the fully-polarized ferromagnetic state in the Hubbard model. This can be understood from perturbation-theory arguments —none of the $\eta_{k\sigma}$ should be a good quantum number for $V_{klmn} \neq 0$— and has been explicitly demonstrated in exact solutions for finite systems or for the 1D Hubbard chain. Therefore, the case with $0 < \eta_{k\sigma} < 1$ is the only relevant one in general. All $\varepsilon_{k\sigma}$ must be degenerate or equivalently

$$t_{ij} + \partial W/\partial \gamma_{ij\sigma} = \delta_{ij} \, \mu \, . \tag{4}$$

Clearly, approximations of W in terms of the diagonal γ_{ii} alone can never yield such a behavior. Given a self-consistent scheme that implements the variational principle, the challenge remains to find good approximations to $W[\gamma_{ij}]$ that are simple enough to be applied in practical calculations.

3. INTERACTION ENERGY FUNCTIONAL

In order to determine $W[\gamma_{ij}]$ from Eq. (2) we look for the extremes of

$$F = \sum_{\substack{klmn \\ \sigma\sigma'}} \left[V_{klmn} \langle \Psi | \hat{c}^\dagger_{k\sigma} \hat{c}^\dagger_{m\sigma'} \hat{c}_{n\sigma} \hat{c}_{l\sigma} | \Psi \rangle \right] + \varepsilon \left(1 - \langle \Psi | \Psi \rangle \right) + \sum_{i,j} \lambda_{ij} \left(\langle \Psi | \sum_{\sigma} \hat{c}^\dagger_{i\sigma} \hat{c}_{j\sigma} | \Psi \rangle - \gamma_{ij} \right) \tag{5}$$

with respect to $|\Psi\rangle$. Lagrange multipliers ε and λ_{ij} have been introduced to enforce the normalization of $|\Psi\rangle$ and the representability of γ_{ij}. Derivation with respect to $\langle\Psi|$, ε and λ_{ij} yields the eigenvalue equations [7]

$$\sum_{ij\sigma} \lambda_{ij} \; \hat{c}^\dagger_{i\sigma} \hat{c}_{j\sigma} \; |\Psi\rangle + \sum_{\substack{klmn \\ \sigma\sigma'}} V_{klmn} \; \hat{c}^\dagger_{k\sigma} \hat{c}^\dagger_{m\sigma'} \hat{c}_{n\sigma} \hat{c}_{l\sigma} \; |\Psi\rangle = \varepsilon \; |\Psi\rangle \; , \tag{6}$$

and the auxiliary conditions $\langle\Psi|\Psi\rangle = 1$ and $\gamma_{ij} = \langle\Psi| \sum_\sigma \hat{c}^\dagger_{i\sigma} \hat{c}_{j\sigma} |\Psi\rangle$. The Lagrange multipliers λ_{ij} play the role of hopping integrals to be chosen in order that $|\Psi\rangle$ yields the given γ_{ij}. The pure-state representability of γ_{ij} ensures that there is always a solution. The subset of γ_{ij} that can be represented by a ground-state of Eq. (6) for some λ_{ij} is the physically relevant one, since it necessarily includes the absolute minimum γ^{gs}_{ij} of $E[\gamma_{ij}]$. Nevertheless, it should be noted that pure-state representable γ_{ij} may be considered that can only be described by excited states or by linear combinations of eigenstates of Eq. (6) [7].

The general functional $W[\gamma_{ij}]$, valid for all lattice structures and for all types of hybridizations, can be simplified at the expense of universality if the hopping integrals are short ranged. For example, if only NN hoppings are considered, the kinetic energy E_K is independent of the density-matrix elements between sites that are not NN's. Therefore, the constrained search in Eq. (2) may be restricted to the $|\Psi[\gamma_{ij}]\rangle$ that satisfy $\langle\Psi[\gamma_{ij}]| \sum_\sigma \hat{c}^\dagger_{i\sigma} \hat{c}_{j\sigma} |\Psi[\gamma_{ij}]\rangle = \gamma_{ij}$ for $i = j$ and for NN ij. This reduces significantly the number of variables in $W[\gamma_{ij}]$ and renders the determination and interpretation of the functional dependence far simpler.

A. Exact calculated $W[\gamma_{ij}]$ of the dimerized Hubbard model

In the following we consider the dimerized 1D Hubbard model which in the usual notation is given by [13]

$$H = \sum_{\langle ij \rangle \sigma} t_{ij} \hat{c}^\dagger_{i\sigma} \hat{c}_{j\sigma} + U \sum_i \hat{n}_{i\downarrow} \hat{n}_{i\uparrow} \; . \tag{7}$$

The NN hopping integrals t_{ij} take two alternating values: $t_{i,i+1} = t_{12} = t + \delta t$ for i odd and $t_{i,i+1} = t_{23} = t - \delta t$ for i even. The corresponding interaction-energy

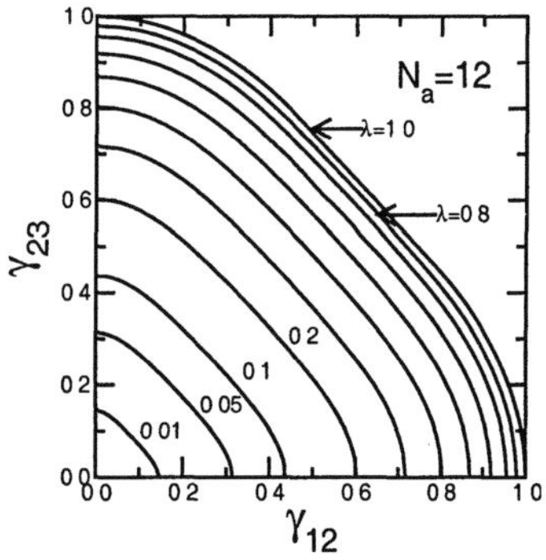

Figure 1. Constant interaction-energy curves of the $N_a = 12$ site Hubbard ring as given by $W(\gamma_{12}, \gamma_{23}) = \lambda E_{HF}$, where $E_{HF} = U/4$ is the Hartree-Fock energy and λ is a constant $(0 \leq \lambda \leq 1)$. The NN density-matrix elements are $\gamma_{i,i+1} = \gamma_{12}$ for odd i and $\gamma_{i,i+1} = \gamma_{23}$ for even i. $\lambda = 1$ corresponds to uncorrelated states. Unless indicated, the differences in λ between contiguous curves is $\Delta\lambda = 0.1$.

functional reads

$$W[\gamma_{ij}] = \min \left[U \sum_{l} \langle \Psi[\gamma_{ij}] | \, \hat{n}_{l\uparrow} \hat{n}_{l\downarrow} \, | \Psi[\gamma_{ij}] \rangle \right] , \tag{8}$$

where $\langle \Psi[\gamma_{ij}] | \sum_\sigma \hat{c}^\dagger_{i\sigma} \hat{c}_{j\sigma} | \Psi[\gamma_{ij}] \rangle = \gamma_{ij}$ for NN ij. For repulsive interactions $W[\gamma_{ij}]$ represents the minimum average number of double occupations corresponding to a given degree of electron delocalization, i.e., to a given γ_{ij}. Eq. (6) reduces to

$$\sum_{\substack{\langle ij \rangle \\ \sigma}} \lambda_{ij} \, \hat{c}^\dagger_{i\sigma} \hat{c}_{j\sigma} \, | \Psi \rangle \; + \; U \sum_i \hat{n}_{i\uparrow} \hat{n}_{i\downarrow} \, | \Psi \rangle = \varepsilon \, | \Psi \rangle . \tag{9}$$

This eigenvalue problem can be solved numerically for finite systems.

In Fig. 1 the interaction energy W of dimerized Hubbard chains is shown in the form of constant-energy curves given by $W(\gamma_{12}, \gamma_{23}) = \lambda E_{\mathrm{HF}}$, where $\gamma_{12} = \gamma_{i,i+1}$ for i odd and $\gamma_{23} = \gamma_{i,i+1}$ for i even are the density-matrix elements or bond orders between NN's. $E_{\mathrm{HF}} = U/4$ stands for the Hartree-Fock energy, and λ is a constant $(0 \leq \lambda \leq 1)$. Results are presented for the $N_a = 12$ site ring which were obtained from Eq. (9) by using Lanczos-diagonalization [14]. Only positive γ_{12} and γ_{23} are considered since this is the relevant domain when all the hopping integrals have the same sign. In bipartite lattices, like open chains or rings with even N_a, the sign of the NN bond orders can be changed without altering W by changing the sign of the local orbitals at one of the sublattices. Thus, $W(\gamma_{12}, \gamma_{23}) = W(-\gamma_{12}, -\gamma_{23})$. Moreover, $W(\gamma_{12}, \gamma_{23}) = W(\gamma_{23}, \gamma_{12})$ as even an odd sites can be interchanged by a simple translation (N_a even for rings).

The domain of definition of W is restricted by the pure-state representability of γ_{ij}. The axes $\gamma_{12} = 0$ and $\gamma_{23} = 0$ in Fig. 1 represent a collection of disconnected dimers (fully dimerized states) while $\gamma_{12} = \gamma_{23}$ corresponds to non-dimerized states. In between, the degree of dimerization can be measured by the angle $\phi = \arctan(\gamma_{12}/\gamma_{23})$. The degree of electron delocalization for each ϕ is characterized by $\gamma = \sqrt{\gamma_{12}^2 + \gamma_{23}^2}$, which is bounded by $\gamma^\infty(\phi) \leq \gamma \leq \gamma^0(\phi)$ in order that γ_{ij} remains pure-state representable. The density-matrix elements along the curve $\gamma = \gamma^0(\phi)$ are the largest bond orders that can be achieved on a given lattice and for given N_a and N_e $[(\gamma_{12}^0, \gamma_{23}^0) = \gamma^0(\phi)(\cos\phi, \sin\phi)]$. They represent the maximum electron delocalization for each ϕ and yield the extremes of the kinetic energy $E_K = \sum t_{ij}\gamma_{ij}$, with different ϕ corresponding to different t_{12}/t_{23}. Thus, for $\gamma = \gamma^0(\phi)$ the density matrix can be represented by the ground state of the uncorrelated Hubbard model for some t_{12}/t_{23} ($U = 0$). In the absence of degeneracy the underlying electronic state $|\Psi_0\rangle$ is a single Slater determinant and $W(\gamma_{12}^0, \gamma_{23}^0) = E_{\text{HF}}$. Consequently, the upper bound for γ coincides with the $\lambda = 1$ curve in Fig. 1. The correlation energy $E_C = W - E_{\text{HF}}$ vanishes as expected in the fully delocalized limit. For $U = 0$ the minimization of the energy $E = E_K$ as a function of γ_{ij} can be stated in terms of the representability of γ_{ij} alone. In this case the equilibrium condition yielding γ_{ij}^{gs} is achieved at the borders of the domain of representability, more precisely, when the normal to the curve $\gamma = \gamma^0(\phi)$ is parallel to $\vec{\nabla} E_K = (t_{12}, t_{23})$.

Concerning the lower bound $\gamma^\infty(\phi)$, one should first note that as γ decreases, $\gamma < \gamma^0(\phi)$, it is possible to construct correlated states $|\Psi[\gamma_{ij}]\rangle$ having increasingly localized electrons. Charge fluctuations can then be reduced more efficiently for smaller γ, and therefore the Coulomb interaction energy decreases with decreasing γ [see Eq. (8) and Fig. 1]. W reaches its minimum value $W_\infty = U max\{0, N_e - N_a\}$ in the strongly correlated limit where $\gamma = \gamma^\infty(\phi)$. For half-band filling this corresponds to a fully localized state having $\gamma^\infty(\phi) = 0$ and $W_\infty = 0$. However, note that for $N_e \neq N_a$, W reaches W_∞ already for $\gamma^\infty(\phi) > 0$ since partially delocalized states can be found having minimal Coulomb repulsion. This is the case for example in a fully-polarized ferromagnetic state.

Fig. 1 also provides a qualitative picture of the functional dependence of W for dimerized chains. On the one side, for strongly dimerized states ($\phi \simeq 0$ or $\phi \simeq \pi/2$) the constant-W curves resemble circumference arcs, the gradient $\vec{\nabla} W$ being approximately radial. This type of behavior is most clearly seen for weak or moderate correlations ($\lambda \geq 0.3$), while in the localized regime ($\lambda \leq 0.1$) it holds only for a very limited range of ϕ around $\phi = 0$ or $\phi = \pi/2$. On the other side, for weakly to moderately dimerized states ($\phi \simeq \pi/8$–$\pi/4$) the level curves can be regarded in first approximation as straight lines parallel to $\gamma_{12} = -\gamma_{23}$. The very weak dependence of $\vec{\nabla} W$ on ϕ implies that for $\phi \simeq \pi/4$ the ground-state values of γ_{12}^{gs} and γ_{23}^{gs}, which result from the minimization of $E = E_K + W$, are very sensitive to the hopping alternation δt. In fact, significant variations of ϕ are necessary until $\vec{\nabla} W = -\vec{\nabla} E_K \propto (1 + \delta t/t, 1 - \delta t/t)$ even for $\delta t/t \ll 1$. This is particularly notable for weak correlations since the $W = E_{\text{HF}}$ curve is strictly linear for $|\phi - \pi/4| < 0.05$. Therefore, a discontinuous change from $\gamma_{12}^{gs}/\gamma_{23}^{gs} = 1$ to $\gamma_{12}^{gs}/\gamma_{23}^{gs} = 0.91$ is found at $U = 0$ and arbitrary small δt. For $U > 0$, γ_{12}^{gs} and γ_{23}^{gs} are continuous functions of δt, although the dependence on δt remains very strong for small δt, as can be inferred from the level curves in the figure.

In Fig. 2(a) the interaction energy W is shown as a function of γ for representative values of ϕ, including in particular the fully-dimerized ($\phi = 0$) and non-dimerized ($\phi = \pi/4$) cases. Despite the quantitative differences among the various ϕ, several qualitative properties are shared by all the curves: (i) As already discussed, the domain of representability of γ is bound for each ϕ by the bond order $\gamma^0(\phi)$ in the

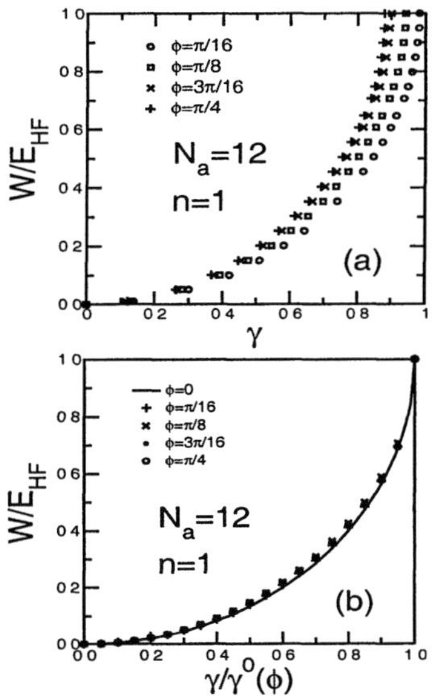

Figure 2. (a) Interaction energy W of the 1D Hubbard model at half-band filling ($N_e = N_a$) as a function of $\gamma = \sqrt{\gamma_{12}^2 + \gamma_{23}^2}$ for different values of $\phi = \arctan(\gamma_{12}/\gamma_{23})$. (b) Interaction energy W of the 1D Hubbard model as a function of γ/γ^0 for different $\phi = \arctan(\gamma_{12}/\gamma_{23})$. $\gamma_{12}^0(\phi)$ is the largest representable values of γ for a given ϕ, which corresponds to the uncorrelated limit.

uncorrelated limit. γ^0 decreases monotonously with increasing ϕ for $0 \leq \phi \leq \pi/4$ showing that a compromise between γ_{12} and γ_{23} is made when the two bonds are active. This is an important contribution to the ϕ-dependence of W. (ii) In the delocalized limit, $W(\gamma^0, \phi) = E_{\rm HF} = U/4$ for all ϕ, since the electronic states yielding the largest γ are single Slater determinants. Moreover, one observes that $\partial W/\partial\gamma$ diverges at $\gamma = \gamma^0$ for all ϕ. This is a necessary condition in order that the ground-state density matrix satisfies $\gamma^{gs} < \gamma^0$ for arbitrary small $U > 0$, as expected from perturbation theory. (iii) Starting from $\gamma = \gamma^0$, W decreases with decreasing γ reaching its lowest possible value $W = 0$ for $\gamma = 0$ ($N_e = N_a$). The decrease of W with decreasing γ means that the reduction of the Coulomb energy due to correlations is done at the expense of kinetic energy or electron delocalization. (iv) In the limit of small γ one observes that $W \propto \gamma^2$. Therefore, for $U/t \gg 1$, $\gamma^{gs} \propto t/U$ and $E_{gs} \propto t^2/U$, a well known result in the Heisenberg limit of the half-filled Hubbard model.

B. Scaling approximation to $W[\gamma_{ij}]$

In order to compare the γ-dependence of W for different ϕ and to analyze its scaling behavior it is useful to bring the domains of representability for different ϕ to a common range by considering $W(\gamma, \phi)$ as a function of $\gamma/\gamma^0(\phi)$, as displayed in Fig. 2(b). In this form the results for different ϕ appear as remarkably similar, showing that the largest part of the dependence of W on the ratio γ_{12}/γ_{23} comes from the domain of representability of γ_{ij} given by its upper bound $\gamma^0(\phi)$ [$\gamma^\infty(\phi) = 0$ for half-band filling]. An analogous scaling behavior has been found in previous numerical studies of $W(\gamma_{12})$ of non-dimerized Hubbard models, where γ_{12} refers to the NN density-matrix element [7]. In this case one observes that $W(\gamma_{12})$ depends weakly on system size N_a, band-filling $n = N_e/N_a$, and lattice structure, if W is measured in units of the Hartree-Fock energy E_{HF} and if γ_{12} is scaled within the relevant domain of representability $[\gamma_{12}^{\infty}, \gamma_{12}^{0}]$. In the present context, Fig. 2(b) implies that the change in W associated to a given change in the degree of delocalization $\gamma/\gamma^0(\phi)$ can be regarded as nearly independent of ϕ and system size. A good general approximation to $W(\gamma, \phi)$ can then be obtained by applying such a scaling to the functional dependence extracted from a simple reference system. An appropriate choice is provided by the fully-dimerized chain corresponding to $\phi = 0$, which can be worked out analytically. In this case the system consists of a collection of dimers and the exact interaction energy reads

$$W(\gamma, \phi{=}0) = \frac{UN_a}{4}\left(1 - \sqrt{1-\gamma^2}\right). \tag{10}$$

Scaling the functional dependence of the dimer interaction energy to the ϕ-dependent domain of representability one obtains

$$W_0(\gamma, \phi) = \frac{UN_a}{4}\left(1 - \sqrt{1 - \left[\frac{\gamma}{\gamma^0(\phi)}\right]^2}\right), \tag{11}$$

which we propose as approximation to W for dimerized systems. Notice that $W_0(\gamma, \phi)$ preserves the previous general properties (i)–(iv) and that it is of course exact for $\phi = 0$ $[\gamma^0(\phi{=}0) = 1]$. In practice, the system specific function $\gamma^0(\phi)$ can be easily obtained by integration of the single-particle spectrum.

It is interesting to observe that the density matrices γ_{ij} involved in the approximate functional W_0 are pure-state N-representable. Eq. (11) applies to the γ_{ij} obtained by scaling the off-diagonal elements of the density matrices γ_{ij}^0 that derive from uncorrelated states $|\Psi_0\rangle$ having N_e electrons on N_a sites, and a uniform density distribution $\langle\Psi_0|\sum_\sigma \hat{n}_{i\sigma}|\Psi_0\rangle = N_e/N_a = 1$. In other terms, γ_{ij} has the form $\gamma_{ij} = \lambda\gamma_{ij}^0$ with $0 \le \lambda \le 1$ for all $i \ne j$, and $\gamma_{ii} = \gamma_{ii}^0 = 1$ for all i. In order to show the pure-state representability of γ_{ij}, we consider two normalized N-particles states $|\Psi_a\rangle$ and $|\Psi_b\rangle$ satisfying $\langle\Psi_a|\sum_\sigma \hat{c}_{i\sigma}^\dagger \hat{c}_{j\sigma}|\Psi_b\rangle = 0$ for all ij. This condition is fulfilled, for example, by states a and b having different defined total spins S or S_z, or by superpositions of pure-S or pure-S_z states sharing no common eigenvalues. The density-matrix represented by $|\Psi\rangle = \alpha|\Psi_a\rangle + \beta|\Psi_b\rangle$ with $\alpha^2 + \beta^2 = 1$ is then given by $\gamma_{ij} = \langle\Psi|\sum_\sigma \hat{c}_{i\sigma}^\dagger \hat{c}_{j\sigma}|\Psi\rangle = \alpha^2\gamma_{ij}^a + \beta^2\gamma_{ij}^b$, where γ_{ij}^a and γ_{ij}^b are the density matrices corresponding to $|\Psi_a\rangle$ and $|\Psi_b\rangle$. Therefore, all the density matrices in the segment defined by γ_{ij}^a and γ_{ij}^b are pure-state N-representable. The representability of a scaled uncorrelated γ_{ij}^0 at half-band filling follows from the previous lemma by taking $|\Psi_a\rangle = |\Psi_0\rangle$, which has $S = 0$ or $1/2$, and $|\Psi_b\rangle$ equal to the fully localized state with one electron per site and maximal $S = N_e/2$, for which $\gamma_{ij}^b = 0$ for all $i \ne j$, and $\gamma_{ii}^b = 1$ for all i. Consequently, the γ_{ij} in the domain of definition of W_0 and the ground-state density matrices γ_{ij}^{gs} derived from it are all pure-state N-representable.

In the following, Eq. (11) is applied in the framework of LDFT to determine several properties of the dimerized 1D Hubbard model. Comparison is made with exact results whenever possible in order to assess the performance of the method.

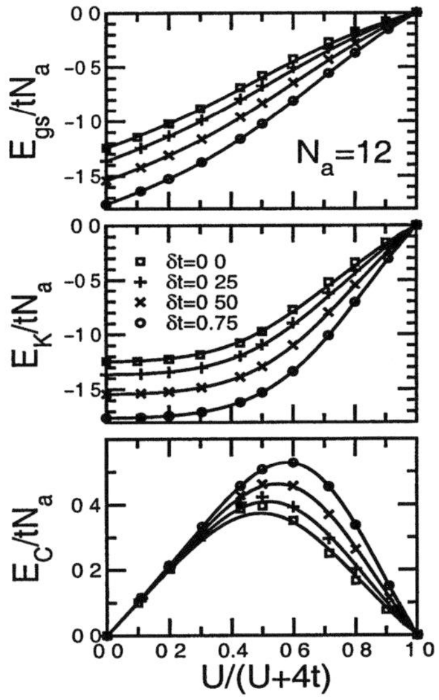

Figure 3. Ground-state energy $E_{gs} = E_K + E_C$, kinetic energy E_K, and Coulomb energy E_C of dimerized Hubbard rings with hopping integrals $t_{ij} = t(1 \pm \delta t)$, Coulomb repulsion U, and $N_e = N_a$ electrons. The symbols are obtained from exact Lanczos diagonalizations and solid curves correspond to LDFT results.

4. DIMERIZED HUBBARD CHAINS

In Fig. 3 and the ground-state energy E_{gs}, kinetic energy E_K, and Coulomb energy E_C of the 1D Hubbard model are given as a function of the Coulomb repulsion strength U/t for different hopping alternations δt. Accurate numerical results are also shown which were obtained using the Lanczos diagonalization method [14] for $N_a = 12$. E_{gs} increases monotonically with U/t since $\partial E_{gs}/\partial U = \langle \hat{n}_{i\uparrow}\hat{n}_{i\downarrow}\rangle > 0$, vanishing in the limit of $U/t = \infty$. For $U/t < 4$ this is essentially a consequence of the increase of $E_C \propto U$, as E_K and γ_{ij} remain very much like in the uncorrelated $U = 0$ state. In contrast, for $U/t > 4$ the electrons become increasingly localized, and the increase of E_{gs} results form the increase of E_K which approaches zero as $|\gamma_{ij}|$ decreases. At the same time E_C tends to zero as charge fluctuations are suppressed (see Fig. 3).

Comparison between LDFT and the exact results shows a very good agreement. This concerns not only E_{gs} but also the separate kinetic and Coulomb contributions indicating that electron localization and intra-atomic correlations are correctly described for all U/t. Moreover, this also shows that the results obtained for the ground-state energy are not the consequence of strong compensations of errors. Concerning the accuracy of E_K and E_C one generally observes that a somewhat higher precision is achieved for E_K, which functional dependence is known exactly, as compared to E_C, which derives from an approximation to W. It is important to recall that no artificial symmetry breaking is required to describe correlation-induced localization correctly, as it often occurs in other approaches (e.g., mean-field spin-density-wave state). Moreover, the present calculations remain simple and numerically not demanding, since the minimization of $E[\gamma_{ij}]$ is performed using analytical expressions for E_K and W. One concludes that LDFT, combined with Eq. (11) as approximation to the interaction energy functional, provides an efficient and correct description of the ground-state properties of the 1D Hubbard model in the complete range of interaction strengths and of the degree of dimerization.

5. CONCLUSION

A density functional approach to lattice fermion models has been applied to the dimerized 1D Hubbard Hamiltonian. We have first investigated the functional dependence of W on the density-matrix elements γ_{12} and γ_{23} between nearest neighbors in dimerized chains. Rigorous results for $W(\gamma_{12}, \gamma_{23})$ were derived from finite-rings Lanczos diagonalizations. An analysis of these exact results shows that W can be appropriately scaled as a function of $\gamma/\gamma(\phi)$. A simple approximation to W was the proposed which takes advantage of this scaling behavior. Finally, using this approximation, several ground-state properties of dimerized chains have been determined successfully.

ACKNOWLEDGMENTS

This work has been supported by CONACYT Mexico through Grant No. J-41452 and Millenium Iniative W-8001. Computer resources were provided by IDRIS (CNRS, France).

REFERENCES

[1] P. Hohenberg and W. Kohn, *Phys. Rev.* **136**, B864 (1964).

[2] W. Kohn and L. J. Sham, *Phys. Rev.* **140**, A1133 (1965).

[3] R. M. Dreizler and E. K. U. Gross, *Density Functional Theory* (Springer, Berlin, 1990) and references therein.

[4] M. Levy, *Proc. Natl. Acad. Sci. U.S.A.*, **76**, 6062 (1979).

[5] O. Gunnarsson and K. Schönhammer, *Phys. Rev. Lett.* **56**, 1968 (1986); A. Svane and O. Gunnarsson, *Phys. Rev. B* **37**, 9919 (1998); K. Schönhammer, O. Gunnarsson and R. M. Noack

[6] A. Schindlmayr and R. W. Godby, *Phys. Rev. B* **51**, 10427 (1995).

[7] R. López-Sandoval and G. M. Pastor, *Phys. Rev. B* **61**, 1764 (2000).

[8] R. López-Sandoval and G. M. Pastor, *Phys. Rev. B* **66**, 155118 (2002).

[9] R. López-Sandoval and G. M. Pastor, *Phys. Rev. B* **67**, 035115 (2003).

[10] T. L. Gilbert, *Phys. Rev. B* **12**, 2111 (1975).

[11] R. A. Donnelly and R. G. Parr, *J. Chem. Phys.* **69**,4431 (1978).

[12] S. M. Valone, *J. Chem. Phys.* **73**,1344 (1980).

[13] J. Hubbard, *Proc. R.Soc. London, Ser. A* **276**, 238 (1963)

[14] C. Lanczos, *J. Res. Natl. Bur. Stand.* **45**, 255 (1950); B. N. Parlett, *The Symmetric Eigenvalue Problem* (Prentice-Hall, Engelwood Cliffs, NJ, 1980)

MAGNETO-OPTICS IN PARABOLIC THREE-DIMENSIONAL QUANTUM DOTS IN MAGNETIC FIELDS OF ARBITRARY DIRECTION

Martí Pi

Departament d'Estructura i Constituents de la Matèria
Facultat de Física
Universitat de Barcelona, E-08028, Spain.

Francesco Ancilotto

INFM (Udr Padova and DEMOCRITOS National Simulation Center, Trieste, Italy) and Dipartimento di Fisica, Università di Padova, I-35131 Padova, Italy

Enrico Lipparini

Dipartimento di Fisica, Università di Trento, and INFM sezione di Trento, I-38050 Povo, Italy.

ABSTRACT

We generalize the Kohn's theorem to the case of parabolic three-dimensional quantum dots in magnetic fields of arbitrary direction. We show numerically that the exact resonance frequencies in the magneto-optical absorption of these dots are reproduced by the adiabatic time-dependent local spin density approximation theory (TDLSDA). We use TDLSDA to predict spin density excitations in the dots.

1. INTRODUCTION

Longitudinal dipole excitations in quantum dots (QD's) under applied magnetic fields have been observed in photo-absorption experiments in the far infra-red region[1,2], and more recently in Raman scattering experiments[3,4]. These modes are excited by the dipole operator $\vec{D} = \sum_j \vec{r}_j$, and the resonance frequencies in the magneto-optical absorption spectrum of a QD with asymmetric parabolic confinement potential are found to be independent of the electron-electron interaction and of the number of electrons in the dot, and they coincide with the single-electron transition frequencies. This statement, known as the generalized Kohn theorem, was demonstrated some years ago by Peeters[5] for a two-dimensional QD under an external magnetic field (B) perpendicular to the plane of motion of the electrons. Peeters gave the following explicit formula for the resonance frequencies:

$$\omega_{1,2}^2 = \frac{1}{2}\left\{(\omega_x^2+\omega_y^2+\omega_c^2) \pm \sqrt{(\omega_x^2+\omega_y^2+\omega_c^2)^2 - 4\omega_x^2\omega_y^2}\right\} , \tag{1}$$

where $\omega_c = eB/mc$ is the cyclotron frequency, and ω_x, ω_y are the confinement frequencies in the x and y directions. Time-dependent theories as time-dependent Hartree-Fock, and adiabatic time-dependent local spin density approximation (TDLSDA) fulfill the generalized Kohn theorem[6-8], and thus any numerical implementation of these methods should reproduce the exact result of Eq. (1). Vice versa, static mean field theories like Hartree, Hartree-Fock and Kohn-Sham theories violate the theorem[9].

In this paper we generalize the result given in Eq. (1) to the case of a parabolic three-dimensional QD in a magnetic field of arbitrary direction, and present and discuss adiabatic TDLSDA results for the dipole excitations of the same system. For density modes, the numerical calculation reproduces the exact result, and must be considered as a stringent test of our three-dimensional (3D) TDLSDA code in view of its application to study other excitation modes, like the spin dipole modes considered here, or to address the far-infrared response of more complex systems such as vertical diatomic artificial molecules[10].

2. GENERALIZED KOHN'S THEOREM FOR 3D QUANTUM DOTS IN MAGNETIC FIELDS OF ARBITRARY DIRECTION

In the effective mass approximation, the Hamiltonian for N noninteracting electrons confined in a QD by harmonic potentials of frequencies ω_x, ω_y and ω_z in the x, y and z directions, in a constant magnetic field $\vec{B}$, is written as

$$H_0 = \sum_{j=1}^{N} h_0(j) = \sum_{j=1}^{N} \left\{ \frac{1}{2m}\left[\vec{p}_j - \frac{e}{c}\vec{A}_j\right]^2 \right.$$
$$\left. + \frac{1}{2}m\left(\omega_x^2 x_j^2 + \omega_y^2 y_j^2 + \omega_z^2 z_j^2\right) + g_s^* \mu_B \vec{B}\cdot\vec{s}_j \right\} , \tag{2}$$

where $m = m^* m_e$ is the electron effective mass, $\vec{A}$ is the vector potential which we write in the symmetric gauge as $\vec{A} = (\vec{B}\wedge\vec{r})/2$, and g_s^* is the effective gyromagnetic factor. In the numerical calculations we have used the values of m^*, dielectric constant ϵ and g^* of GaAs, namely, $m^* = 0.067, \epsilon = 12.4$, and $g^* = -0.44$. Without loss of generality, we write $\vec{B} = B(\sin\theta, 0, \cos\theta)$, where θ is the angle between the magnetic field and the z axis. Using hereafter effective atomic (dot) units (d.u.) $\hbar = e^2/\epsilon = m = 1$, it can be easily checked that

$$h_0 = \frac{1}{2}\vec{p}^{\,2} + \frac{1}{2}\left(\omega_x^2 x^2 + \omega_y^2 y^2 + \omega_z^2 z^2\right) + h_m \,, \tag{3}$$

where

$$h_m = \frac{1}{8}\omega_c^2\left[x^2\cos^2\theta + y^2 + z^2\sin^2\theta - 2xz\cos\theta\sin\theta\right] + \frac{1}{2}g_s^*\mu_B\eta_\sigma$$
$$-\frac{i}{2}\omega_c\left[\sin\theta\left(y\frac{\partial}{\partial z} - z\frac{\partial}{\partial y}\right) + \cos\theta\left(x\frac{\partial}{\partial y} - y\frac{\partial}{\partial x}\right)\right],$$

and $\eta_\sigma = +1(-1)$ for $\sigma =\uparrow (\downarrow)$ with respect of the direction of $\vec{B}$. The interacting system is described by the Hamiltonian $H = H_0 + V$, where V is the electron-electron interaction

$$V = \sum_{i<j=1}^{N} \frac{1}{|\vec{r}_i - \vec{r}_j|} \,. \tag{4}$$

The single particle Hamiltonian h_0 can be exactly diagonalized:

$$h_0 = \sum_{\alpha=1}^{3} \omega_\alpha \left(c_\alpha^+ c_\alpha^- + \frac{1}{2}\right), \tag{5}$$

with the creation operator c_α^+ given by

$$c_\alpha^+ = a_\alpha x + b_\alpha y + c_\alpha z + i[d_\alpha p_x + e_\alpha p_y + f_\alpha p_z] \,. \tag{6}$$

The operator c_α^- is the Hermitian conjugate of c_α^+, and the coefficients $a_\alpha, ..., f_\alpha$ in Eq. (6), and the energies ω_α are determined by solving the equation

$$[h_0, c_\alpha^+] = \omega_\alpha c_\alpha^+ \,, \tag{7}$$

together with the normalization condition $[c_\alpha^-, c_\alpha^+] = 1$.

Defining $C_\alpha^+ = \sum_{j=1}^{N} c_{j,\alpha}^+$, it is easy to prove from Eqs. (4) and (6) that

$$[V, C_\alpha^\pm] = 0 \,, \tag{8}$$

which is valid not only for the Coulomb interaction but also for any V that depends only on the relative distance between any two electrons. From Eqs. (7) and (8) it follows immediately that the Hamiltonian $H = \sum_j h_0(j) + V$ satisfies the equation of motion

$$[H, C_\alpha^\pm] = \pm\omega_\alpha C_\alpha^\pm \,, \tag{9}$$

which implies that if $|n\rangle$ is an eigenstate of H with energy E_n so are $C_\alpha^\pm|n\rangle$ with energies $E_n \pm \omega_\alpha$. Since in the long-wavelength limit light photoabsorption is induced by the dipole transitions, and the dipole operator can be written as a sum of C_α^+ and

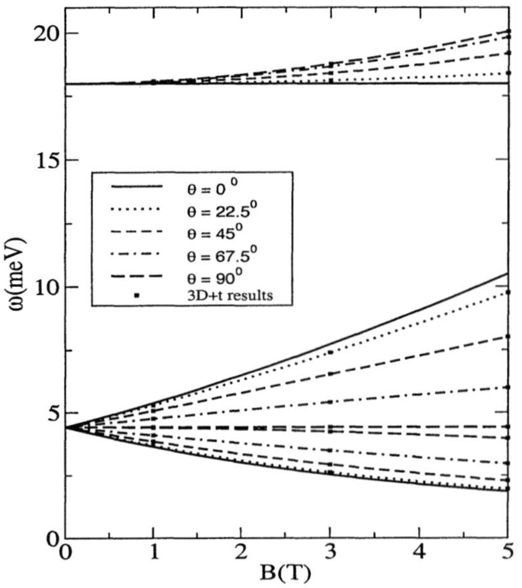

Figure 1. Exact dispersion relation for dipole density modes. Filled squares are from TDLSDA calculations.

C_α^- operators, one recovers that dipole transitions can only occur from an eigenstate $|n\rangle$ to the eigenstates $C_\alpha^\pm|n\rangle$, and the absorption spectrum consists of three peaks of frequencies ω_1, ω_2, and ω_3.

As an example, we have solved Eqs. (7) in the case of an axially symmetric parabolic QD with $\omega_x = \omega_y = \omega_0$ by taking ω_0 =4.42 meV and ω_z=18 meV, for some values of the θ angle. The results for the three ω_α energies are reported in Fig. 1. Due to our choice of axial symmetry, at $B = 0$ the energies $\omega_{1,2}$ are degenerate and equal to ω_0, and ω_3 coincides with ω_z. At $\theta = 0$, when $\vec{B}$ is parallel to the symmetry axis of the dot, the solution for $\omega_{1,2}$ coincides with Peeters' expression Eq. (1), and ω_3 is B independent and equal to ω_z. At $\theta = 90^o$, when $\vec{B}$ is perpendicular to the symmetry axis of the QD, it is possible to write down an analytical expression for $\omega_{2,3}$:

$$\omega_{2,3}^2 = \frac{1}{2}\left\{(\omega_0^2 + \omega_z^2 + \omega_c^2) \pm \sqrt{(\omega_z^2 + \omega_0^2 + \omega_c^2)^2 - 4\omega_z^2\omega_0^2}\right\} , \tag{10}$$

whereas ω_1 is B independent and equal to ω_0.

The dipole strength

$$S_{\hat{\mathbf{e}}}(\omega) = \sum_n |\langle n| \sum_j \hat{\mathbf{e}} \cdot \vec{r}_j |0\rangle|^2 \delta(\omega - (E_n - E_0)) , \tag{11}$$

where $\hat{\mathbf{e}}$ is the polarization direction and $D_{\hat{\mathbf{e}}} = \sum_j \hat{\mathbf{e}} \cdot \vec{r}_j$ the dipole operator, can be also analytically calculated, and is different from zero only when the excitation energy $(E_n - E_0)$ is equal to the frequencies ω_α. One can show that the energy-weighted sum rule m_1

$$m_1 = \int S(\omega)\,\omega\,d\omega = \sum_n (E_n - E_0)\,|\langle n\,|D_{\hat{\mathbf{e}}}|\,0\rangle|^2\,\delta(\omega - (E_n - E_0)) = \frac{N}{2}\,, \tag{12}$$

is exhausted by the three excited states at the energies $\omega_{1,2,3}$. The m_{-1} sum rule, related with the static polarizability, can also be worked out yielding a result that is also $\vec{B}$ independent:

$$m_{-1} = \int S(\omega)\frac{d\omega}{\omega} = \frac{N}{2}\sum_q \frac{e_q^2}{\omega_q^2},\; q = x, y, z \tag{13}$$

(see also Ref. [11]). By changing the values of θ and B, some strength moves from one state to another, always preserving the values of m_{-1} and m_1.

3. TDLSDA CALCULATIONS

We now turn to our main goal which is to numerically study within TDLSDA the dipole modes both in the density and spin-density channels. As we have indicated in the Sec. I, in this approach the generalized Kohn theorem discussed previously still holds and the TDLSDA numerical results provide only a test of the 3D+time TDLSDA code. In the spin density channel the theorem does not hold, and the calculations provide an alternative prediction for this mode to that provided by the explicit evaluation of the spin-density correlation function[6]. We recall that spin dipole modes have been experimentally detected in Raman scattering experiments[3,4].

To obtain the dipole strength in the two channels, we study the time evolution, following an initial perturbation, of the dipole signal

$$\mathcal{D}(t) = \hat{\mathbf{e}} \cdot \langle \vec{D} \rangle\,, \tag{14}$$

where $\vec{D} = \sum_j \vec{r}_j$ for density dipole, and $\vec{D} = \sum_j \vec{r}_j \sigma_j^z$ for spin dipole modes, and $\langle \vec{D} \rangle$ means average over the time dependent state. This method has been used in Refs. [17-20] to study charge and current modes of two-dimensional QD and quantum molecules; what follows is a generalization to the 3D case.

To calculate $\mathcal{D}(t)$, we firstly solve the static Kohn-Sham (KS) equations

$$\left[-\frac{1}{2}\left(\frac{\partial^2}{\partial x^2} + \frac{\partial^2}{\partial y^2} + \frac{\partial^2}{\partial z^2}\right) + \frac{1}{2}(\omega_x x^2 + \omega_y y^2 + \omega_z z^2)\right.$$
$$\left. + V^H + V^{xc} + W^{xc}\eta_\sigma + h_m\right]\Psi_\sigma(x,y,z) = \epsilon_\sigma \Psi_\sigma(x,y,z)\,,$$

where the expression in the square brackets is the KS Hamiltonian $\mathcal{H}_{KS}$. More precisely, $V^H(x,y,z)$ is the direct Coulomb potential, $V^{xc} = \delta\mathcal{E}_{xc}(n,m)/\delta n|_{gs}$, and

$W^{xc} = \delta\mathcal{E}_{xc}(n,m)/\delta m|_{gs}$ are the variation of the exchange-correlation energy density $\mathcal{E}_{xc}(n,m)$ written in terms of the electron ground state (gs) density $n(x,y,z)$, and of the local spin magnetization $m(x,y,z) \equiv n^{\uparrow}(x,y,z) - n^{\downarrow}(x,y,z)$. The exchange-correlation energy has been taken from Perdew and Zunger,[12] and $\mathcal{E}_{xc}(n,m)$ has been constructed as indicated in Ref. [13]. It is worth noticing that if $B \neq 0$ the single particle wave functions $\Psi_\sigma(x,y,z)$ are complex and their real and imaginary parts are coupled by h_m.

The KS equations are solved in a 3D mesh with $\Delta_x = \Delta_y = 0.51$ d.u., and $\Delta_z = 0.135$ d.u., by using 11 points formulas for the differential operators and a fast-Fourier transform to solve the Coulomb potential (for more details see Ref. [14].

Appropriate static solutions of the KS equations are then used as initial conditions for solving the time-dependent KS equations

$$i\frac{\partial}{\partial t}\psi_\sigma(\mathbf{r},t) = \mathcal{H}_{KS}\,\psi_\sigma(\mathbf{r},t)\,, \tag{15}$$

Specifically, to describe the interaction of the system with an external dipole field the gs orbitals are slightly perturbed according to

$$\psi'_\sigma(\mathbf{r}) = U\psi_\sigma(\mathbf{r}) \tag{16}$$

with

$$U = \exp[i\lambda\hat{\mathbf{e}}\cdot\vec{r}]\;, \tag{17}$$

for the density dipole modes, and

$$U = \exp[i\lambda\eta_\sigma\hat{\mathbf{e}}\cdot\vec{r}] \tag{18}$$

for the spin dipole modes. Eqs. (16) and (17) give rise to an initial state in which all the electrons of the dot have a rigid velocity in an arbitrary direction $\hat{\mathbf{e}}$. In the spin dipole case, Eqs. (16) and (18) give initially to spin up and spin down electrons a rigid velocity field in opposite directions. The parameter λ is taken small enough to keep the response of the system in the linear regime.

We have solved Eqs. (15) following the method of Ref. [15]. One writes

$$\psi_\sigma(\mathbf{r},t+\delta t) - \psi_\sigma(\mathbf{r},t-\delta t) = \left[e^{-i\mathcal{H}_{KS}\,\delta t} - e^{i\mathcal{H}_{KS}\,\delta t}\right]\psi_\sigma(\mathbf{r},t) \tag{19}$$

and then expands the square bracket in a Taylor series:

$$\psi_\sigma(\mathbf{r},t+\delta t) = \psi_\sigma(\mathbf{r},t-\delta t) + 2\sum_{j=0}^{j_{max}}(-1)^{j+1}\frac{i}{(2j+1)!}\left(\delta t\,\mathcal{H}_{KS}\right)^{(2j+1)}\psi_\sigma(\mathbf{r},t)\,. \tag{20}$$

At $t = 0$ we follow the iteration procedure of Ref. [16] up to seventh order. After the first δt step, we use Eq. (20), taking in the expansion $j_{max} = 3$. Typical δt are $\sim 2\times10^{-2}$ d.u. (1 d.u. is $\sim 5.55\times10^{-14}s$). After 15000 iterations the total energy

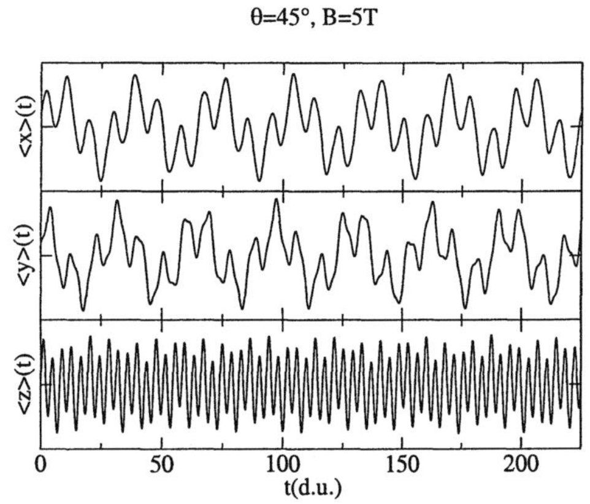

Figure 2. Real time evolution of the dipole density signal. Shown are the x, y and z-components of the dipole signal for $\theta = 45^o$ and B=5T.

is conserved with a relative error smaller than 10^{-11}. The dipole signal Eq. (14) is calculated every time-step.

In the linear regime the Fourier transform of the dipole signal

$$\mathcal{D}(\omega) = \int dt e^{i\omega t} \mathcal{D}(t) \tag{21}$$

is directly related to the dipole strength $S_{\hat{\mathbf{e}}}(\omega)$ Eq. (11) by

$$S_{\hat{\mathbf{e}}}(\omega) = |\mathcal{D}(\omega)| \,. \tag{22}$$

Hence, a frequency analysis of $\mathcal{D}(t)$ provides the absorption energies and their associate intensities[17].

A real time simulation of the dipole evolution is shown in Fig. 2 for a $N = 6$ quantum dot for $\theta = 45^o$ and $B = 5$ T. The analysis is made for the three components of the dipole operator in the density channel, and the frequency analysis of the numerical signals providing the density dipole strength is plotted in Fig. 3 for different values of θ and B. In this figure, the energies $\omega_{1,2,3}$ yielded by the exact calculation of Sect. 2 are indicated with arrows. The peak energies of the TDLSDA strength are also reported with squares in Fig. 1. From these figures one may conclude that our 3D TDLSDA calculations reproduces very accurately the exact results of the previous section. From Fig. 3 one may also see how, by changing the values of θ and B, some strength moves from one mode to another.

Performing the same simulation in the spin channel we obtain the results shown in Figs. 4 and 5. Differently from the density channel, in the spin channel all the strength is mainly concentrated in one collective low energy mode. The peak energy is lower in the spin than in the density channel. This is due to the character of the TDLSDA particle-hole residual interaction, which is attractive but weak in the spin channel, and repulsive and rather strong in the density channel, shifting the TDLSDA response from the single-particle one in opposite directions[6].

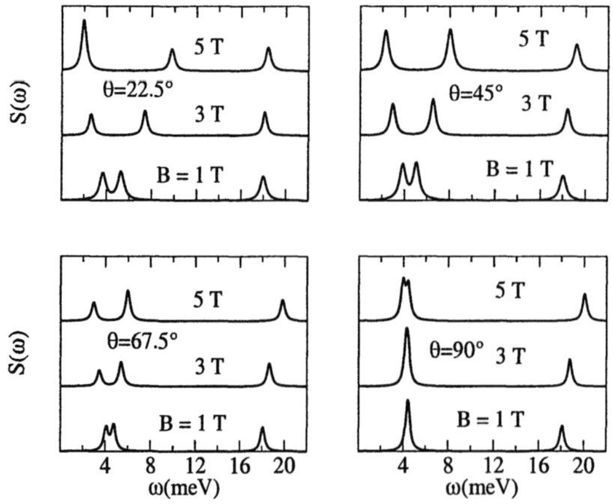

Figure 3. Strenght function (arbitrary units) for the dipole density response corre-ponding to different angles and magnetic fields.

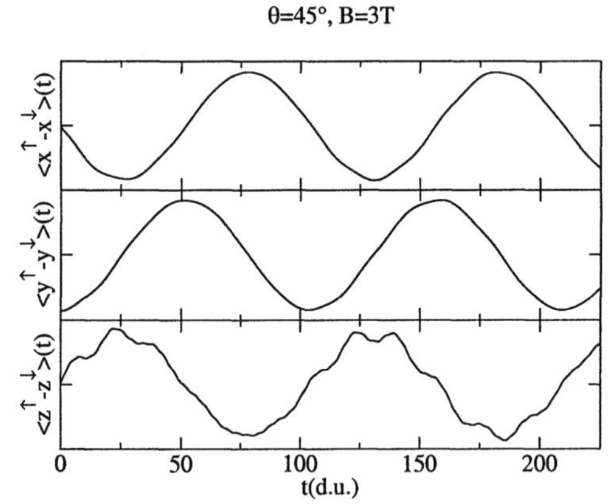

Figure 4. Real time evolution of the dipole spin signal. Shown are the x, y and z-components of the dipole spin signal for $\theta = 45^o$ and B=3T.

Increasing the value of B, the spin density excitation (SDE) becomes progressively softer. A spin mode with these features has been observed by Raman spectroscopy in GaAs quantum dots[4] submitted to a perpendicular magnetic field. The calculations of Ref. [6] also yield a very soft SDE at B values corresponding to filling factors between $\nu = 1$ and 2, that are above the largest B for which the intensity of SDE's allows for an experimental detection[4]. It is worth to note that the softening of the SDE has been experimentally observed in quantum wells[23], but at electron densities much lower than the ones of the QD's we have discussed.

Fig. 5 shows that the SDE also becomes softer as B increases. In addition, at fixed B the SDE's moves towards lower energies as θ decreases. This is not surprising as in this case the projection of B on the z axis increases.

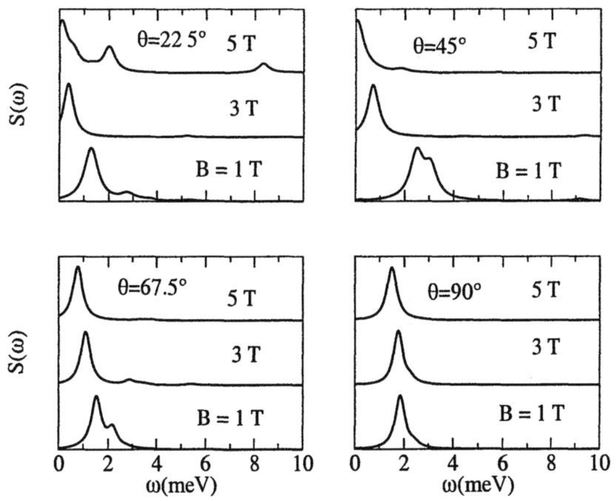

Figure 5. Strenght function (arbitrary units) for the dipole spin response corresponding to different angles and magnetic fields.

4. SUMMARY

The dipole and spin dipole responses of a 3D quantum dot in a magnetic field of arbitrary direction have been analyzed by means of real time simulations within TDLSDA. The fragmentation of the strength due to the non circular shape of the QD and to the θ angle between the magnetic field $\vec{B}$ and the axis perpendicular to the plane of motion of the electrons has been studied. The density dipole strengths splits in three collective states which are exactly found at the energies predicted by the generalized Kohn theorem. By changing the values of θ and of B, some strength moves from one state to another in a way which could be easily detected.

A key result from our study is the evidence that it is possible to develop a 3D code implementing TDLSDA with a magnetic field in an arbitrary direction with very high accuracy. This opens the possibility of addressing the far-infrared response of more complicated systems, such as double QD's[10] or quantum rings vertically coupled, whose description using the density-density or spin-density correlation functions[6] is prohibitive. Work along this line is now in progress.

ACKNOWLEDGMENTS

This work has been performed under grants BFM2002-01868 from MCyT and 2001SGR-00064 from Generalitat of Catalunya, and has been partially supported by INFM and COFIN 2001. Useful and fruitful discussions with Prof. Manuel Barranco are gratefully acknowledged.

REFERENCES

[1] Ch. Sikorski, and U. Merkt, Phys. Rev. Lett. **62**, 2164 (1989).

[2] T. Demel, D. Heitmann, P. Grambow, and K. Ploog, Phys. Rev. Lett. **64**, 788 (1990).

[3] R. Strenz, U. Bockelmann, F. Hirler, G. Abstreiter, G. Böhm, and G. Weimann, Phys. Rev. Lett. **73**, 3022 (1994).

[4] C. Schüller, K. Keller, G. Biese, E. Ulrichs, L. Rolf, C. Steinebach, and D. Heitmann, Phys. Rev. Lett. **80**, 2673 (1998).

[5] F.M. Peeters, Phys. Rev. B **42**, 1486 (1990).

[6] Ll. Serra, M. Barranco, A. Emperador, M. Pi, and E. Lipparini, Phys. Rev. B **59**, 15290 (1999).

[7] E. Lipparini, M. Barranco, A. Emperador, M. Pi, and Ll. Serra, Phys. Rev. B **60**, 8734 (1999).

[8] O. Steffens and M. Suhrke, Phys. Rev. Lett. **82**, 3891 (1999).

[9] E. Lipparini. *Modern Many Particle Physics-Atomic Gases, Quantum Dots and Quantum Fluids*, (World Scientific, Singapore 2003).

[10] J.H. Oh, K.J. Chang, G. Ihm, and S.L. Lee, Phys. Rev. B **53**, R13264 (1996); J. Hu, E. Dagotto, and A.H. MacDonald, Phys. Rev. B **54**, 8616 (1996); O. Mayrock, S.A. Mikhailov, T. Darnhofer, adn U. Rössler, Phys. Rev. B **56**, 15760 (1997); B. Partoens, A. Matulis, and F.M. Peeters, Phys. Rev. B **57**, 13039 (1998).

[11] E. Lipparini, N. Barberán, M. Barranco, M. Pi, and Ll. Serra, Phys. Rev. B **56**, 12375 (1997).

[12] J. P. Perdew, and A. Zunger, Phys. Rev. B **23**, 5048 (1981).

[13] M. Pi, A. Emperador, M. Barranco, F. Garcías , Phys. Rev. B **63**, 115316 (2001).

[14] F. Ancilotto, D.G. Austing, M. Barranco, R. Mayol, K. Muraki, M. Pi, S. Sasaki, and S. Tarucha, Phys. Rev. B **67**, 205311 (2003).

[15] R. Kosloff, J. Phys. Chem. **92** 2087 (1988).

[16] H. Flocard, S.E. Koonin, and M.S. Weiss, Phys. Rev. **C17** 1682 (1978).

[17] A. Puente and Ll. Serra, Phys. Rev. Lett. **83**, 3266 (1999).

[18] Ll. Serra, A. Puente and E. Lipparini, Phys. Rev. B **60**, R13966 (1999).

[19] M. Valín-Rodríguez, A. Puente and Ll. Serra, Eur. Phys. J. D **16**, 387 (2001).

[20] E. Lipparini, Ll. Serra and A. Puente, Eur. Phys. J. B **27**, 409 (2002).

[21] C.A. Ullrich and G. Vignale, Phys. Rev. B **61**, 2729 (2000).

[22] M. Ciorga, A. Wensauer, M. Pioro-Ladriere, M. Korkusinski, J. Kyriakidis, A.S. Schrajda, and P. Hawrylak, Phys. Rev. Lett. **88**,256804 (2002)

[23] M. A. Eriksson, A. Pinczuk, B. S. Dennis, S. H. Simon, L. N. Pfeiffer, and K. W. West, Phys. Rev. Lett. **82**, 2163 (1999).

DENSITY FUNCTIONAL THEORY FROM FIRST PRINCIPLES

Jaime Keller

Department of Physics and Theoretical Chemistry,
Facultad de Química & Facultad de Estudios Superiores-Cuautitlán,
Universidad Nacional Autónoma de México
Apartado Postal 70-528, 04510 México, D. F.
MÉXICO

1. DENSITY FUNCTIONAL THEORY FROM START

We present a systematic derivation of a formal theory, denoted here by KKW-DFT, of a class of extended objects that we will call energy carriers. The objects are defined in such a way that they can describe an object through the use of a density. Each point of that density is additionally attributed a property called the energy of the carrier. The integral of the product of these two quantities is called the energy of the system and the formal properties of this system are explicitly studied. Once the theory is developed it is shown to include the well known density functional theory (DFT) as used for the study of the electronic structure of atoms, molecules and condensed matter. First the theory is formally presented, second some computational remarks are made, in particular about and exact exchange-correlation energy functional and the general formal validity of DFT.

The aim of the present paper is to show that a simple set of postulates about the description of objects in Nature allows the derivation of the principles of DFT, transforming this theory into a deductive approach to Physics. In our approach the main postulate is: Objects are described as energy distributions in Space-Time. The theory is in fact a systematic mathematical analysis of this postulate and of other general considerations about action, energy–momentum and the role of the theory as a useful description of Nature. The paper also shows the fundamental and basic status of Density Functional Theory. The presentation is strongly guided by the knowledge of the usual computational approach to study atoms, molecules and condensed matter electronic structure.

1.1 The Quadratic Form in Physics

Formally our approach, a Space–Time–Action Relativity Theory: START [6], represents the physical world as a 5-D continuum with a quadratic form. In this geometrical setup we use a 5-D Relativity Principle "**For physical systems all trajectories are null for all observers**". Within this geometry, to obtain a comprehensive theory, the development of the theory has been:

	The Geometrical Structures of Physics	
	SPACE + TIME + ACTION	
	+	
	Fundamental **Principles** and **Postulates** (Carriers)	
	⇓	
	START Geometry	
↙	↓	↘
General Relativity	**DFT and Quantum Mechanics**	Standard Model

In this program: **Principles** refer to primitive concepts and relations as, for example, the existence of a unified geometry for space, time and action. **Postulates** refer to complementary concepts as the geometrical union of the manifold of those variables through the use of two universal constants c and κ_0, generating the geometry we have called START, a quadratic space. For a given observer the physical objects constituents of a system are the **carriers**, defined as a distribution of energy over space $E_{(c)}(x,t) = \varepsilon_{(c)}\rho_{(c)}(x,t)$ where $\varepsilon_{(c)}$ is the energy per equivalent carrier of type D. Two basic additional principles introduce the **unit of action** h in relation to the amount of action that can be given or taken from a system (usually described as energy and angular momentum being exchanged, this is tautologically the definition of a system) and to a **freedom of description** of matter within START.

1.1.1 Hypothesis and Principles in START

For this we consider that Physics is the science which describes the basic phenomena of Nature within the procedures of the Scientific Method. The mathematization of the anthropocentric, primary, concepts of space, time and the existence of the physical objects (action **carriers**), is a suitable point of departure for creating intellectual structures which describe Nature.

The set of principles we have introduced are [6]: **Relativity**, complex Poincaré group and complex Lorentz transformations. **Existence**, physical objects are represented by energy densities. **Least Action**, (null trajectories in START). **Quantized Exchange of Action**, defines systems or subsystems as those among a quanta of action can be exchanged. **Choice of Descriptions**, allows all useful physical models to be employed.

1.2 Derivation of the Structure of DFT

The formal steps to be followed, schematically presented here, are

Steps	Subject	Formal Relation
1a define	Action Density in Space-Time	$a(X) \to E(x,t)$,
1b or	Energy Density in Space	$E(x,t) = \sum^{(c)} E_{(c)}(x,t)$,
2 using	Definition of (equivalent) Carriers	$E_{(c)}(x,t) = \epsilon_{(c)}\rho_{(c)}(x,t)$,
3 and	Energy-Momentum condition	$p_\mu \doteq \partial_\mu a(X)$,
4a with	Analyticity requirement	$\rho_{(c)}(x,t) = \Psi^\dagger(x,t)\Psi(x,t)$,
5 with	Gauging and Description Choice	$\Psi \to \Psi \exp(i\phi(X))$.

That is matter is considered a (time-dependent) distribution of energy in space as a summation among carriers. Equivalent carriers in a system are attributed by definition the same amount of energy per carrier. If a different amount of energy has to be attributed to two, otherwise considered identical, carriers then they are not equivalent. Energy-momentum is defined as the rate of change of action. The finiteness of the amount of matter and the corresponding energy require that action and then the density obey analytical conditions, to fulfil this condition, as shown below (Keller and Weinberger [7]), the density has to be written as a product of the corresponding pair of square integrable analytical functions. In order to obtain the least action state we follow the Schrödinger procedure (Schrödinger 1926 [8]) to optimize the total action variable functional, which produces the wave equation. Finally because of the analyticity requirement, the auxiliary amplitude functions are only defined up to a general multivector phase factor s: $\phi = \sum^{multivectors\ A} \phi_A\gamma^A$ scalar, vector, bivector, etc.

Classification of Carriers	
Carrier Type	**Description Type**
Elementary (Simple)	$\rho_C(\mathbf{x},t) = \rho_c(\mathbf{x},t)$.
Elementary (Composite)	$\rho_C(\mathbf{x},t) = \sum_c A^c \rho_c^{\{c\in C\}}(\mathbf{x},t)$.
Decomposable	$\rho_C(\mathbf{x},t) = n^D \rho_D(\mathbf{x},t)$.
Pseudo-Carriers	$\{\rho_c(\mathbf{x},t)\} \to \rho_C^{eff}(\mathbf{x},t) \quad [V_{eff.}]$.

The energy(action) carriers can be given specific names according to the mathematical structure of the corresponding densities. The words simple and composite referring to one term or several terms, the word decomposable to the fact that each of the terms is proportional to one given density (as in the case of equivalent electrons in atomic, molecular, and solid state structure). Because we can use for the description an average description, we can either define the average carrier or an average description. In most cases we are in fact using the definition of the carrier in a system through the introduction of some effective potential acting upon it. Then, as this kind of carrier can not be studied in the absence of that potential, we should really call that carrier a pseudo-carrier. This is summarized above.

2. The Density

We come back to the conditions to be obeyed by the analytical function $\rho_c(\mathbf{x}, t)$.

D1.- $\rho_c(\mathbf{x}, t)$ is a real quantity $\rho_c(\mathbf{x}, t) \subset \mathbf{R}$.

D2.- The density $0 \leq \rho_c(\mathbf{x}, t) < \infty$ to represent a finite amount of action.

D3.- The derivatives of the density $-\infty < \partial_\mu \rho_c(\mathbf{x}, t) < +\infty$ in order to represent a finite amount of energy–momentum.

D4 - Integral of the density $\int_{\Omega_C} \rho_c(\mathbf{x}, t) d\Omega = n$ in the n carriers' volume Ω_c.

Theorem 1 *(Keller and Weinberger 2002)*
If $\Psi(x, t)$ is an analytical quadratic integrable complex or multivector function, conditions D1, D2 and D3 are fulfilled identically if $\rho_c(x, t) = |\Psi_c(\mathbf{x}, t)|^2$. Here $|f|^2$ means the real quadratic form of any more general function f, even if f itself is not necessarily a real function and we define: if $|f|^2 = f^+ f$ then $\partial_\mu |f|^2 = (\partial_\mu f^+) f + f^+ (\partial_\mu f)$.

Proof. Reality condition D1 is fulfilled by the definition $\rho_c(\mathbf{x}, t) = |\Psi_c(\mathbf{x}, t)|^2$, **Carrier Finiteness** D2 by the requirement of quadratic integrability, **Energy Finiteness** D3 by the definition $\partial_\mu |f|^2 = (\partial_\mu f^+) f + f^+ (\partial_\mu f)$ and the analytical properties of $\Psi(\mathbf{x}, t)$. □

It can be seen that the conditions D1, D2, D3 and **normalization** correspond to the $\Psi(\mathbf{x}, t)$ being quadratic integrable **Hilbert functions**. In any Lagrangian type formulation this last definition of ρ can be used as a condition introduced via a Lagrange multiplier.

3. KKW-DFT

We proceed now to the specific analysis corresponding to density functional theory. The result is that the theorems of Hohenberg and Kohn [1] and of the present author and collaborators appear now as basic natural conditions in the logical structure of the theory [2][3]. Our initial approach is not related with the replacement of the local study of the properties of the density with those of an equivalent density of a gas of carriers (free electron gas for example).

¿From the considerations above we describe each and any of the n carriers obeying Fermi–Dirac statistics through an auxiliary amplitude function $\psi_i = \phi_s^{\{l,m\}}$ (describing carriers in the system S) where $< \psi_i \psi_j >= \delta_{ij}$, then

$$\psi_i = \sum_\lambda a_i^\lambda \varphi_\lambda, \; \sum_\lambda \left|a_i^\lambda\right|^2 = l \text{ for all } i = 1, ..., n \text{ where } \sum_i \left|a_i^\lambda\right|^2 = w^\lambda, \tag{1}$$

and the weight of every spin–orbital

$$\sum_\lambda w^\lambda = n \text{ number of electrons, such that } \left|a_i^\lambda\right|^2 = \left|a_j^\lambda\right|^2 \; i, j = 1, ..., w, \tag{2}$$

according to the requirement that the density descriptions of all carriers are equivalent. That is

$$\left(a_i^\lambda\right)^* a_j^\lambda + a_i^\lambda \left(a_j^\lambda\right)^* = 2w^\lambda \delta_{ij} \text{ and } \int \frac{1}{2}\left(\varphi_\lambda^* \varphi_\mu + \varphi_\lambda \varphi_\mu^*\right) dv = \delta_{\lambda\mu}, \tag{3}$$

consequently all φ_λ should be solutions of the same differential equation corresponding to different eigenvalues. Also we define

$$\int \rho \, d \text{ vol } = n, \tag{4}$$

$$\rho = \sum_i |\psi_i|^2 = \sum_i \rho_i = n\rho_i = n\rho_{(1)}, \ \rho_i = \rho_j = \rho_{(1)} \text{ all } i, j. \int \rho \, d \text{ vol } = n, \tag{5}$$

With these definitions we can compute the total (equivalent inter-carriers) interaction energy from that of one pair, carrier i–carrier j, interaction energy as the sum $\varepsilon_{\text{c-c}} = \varepsilon_{\text{coul}} + \varepsilon_{\text{xc}}$, where

$$\varepsilon_{\text{coul}} = \frac{(n-1)}{2} \int\int \rho(2)\rho(1)\frac{e^2}{r_{12}} dv_2 dv_1, \tag{6}$$

$$\varepsilon_{xc} = -2\left(\frac{n}{2}-1\right)\int\int \sum\nolimits_{\lambda\lambda'} \rho_{\lambda\lambda'}(2)\rho_{\lambda'\lambda}(1)\frac{e^2}{r_{12}} dv_2 dv_1, \tag{7}$$

$$\rho_{\lambda\mu}^s(x) = \frac{1}{2}\left[\left(a_i^\lambda\right)^* a_i^\mu \varphi_\lambda^*(x)\varphi_\mu(x) + a_i^\lambda \left(a_i^\mu\right)^* \varphi_\lambda(x)\varphi_\mu^*(x)\right]^s, \tag{8}$$

where the super-index s stands for spin.

The negative term we have denoted as ε_{xc} arises from the orthogonality of the descriptions for $i \neq j$. Also from the equal value of any reference description. Consider, to illustrate this point, the product $|\psi_i|^2 |\psi_k|^2$ of the $|\psi_i|^2 = \left(\sum_\lambda a_i^\lambda \varphi_\lambda\right)^\dagger \sum_\mu a_i^\mu \varphi_\mu$ in the following condensed representation where I.- $\psi_i = a(i) + b(i)$ and $\psi_k = a(k) - b(k)$ and also, from the equivalence of the carriers, where II.- $\psi_i = a(i) - b(i)$ and $\psi_k = a(k) + b(k)$; considering real $a(j)$ and $b(j)$ functions to simplify the expressions and show the origin of the negative signs in the exchange terms above:

$$\begin{aligned} &\text{I.} - |\psi_i|^2 |\psi_k|^2 = (a(i) + b(i))^2 (a(k) - b(k))^2, \\ &\text{II.} - |\psi_i|^2 |\psi_k|^2 = (a(i) + b(i))^2 (a(k) - b(k))^2, \\ \frac{1}{2}\,&(\text{I} + \text{II}).- \left(a^2(i) + b^2(i)\right)\left(a^2(k) + b^2(k)\right) - a(i)a(k)b(i)b(k). \end{aligned} \tag{9}$$

where the first term corresponds to what has been denoted as "coulomb" and the second as "exchange". Note that the negative term in (9) arises from the requirement of different descriptions for any pair of carriers (fermions).

3.1 The Pauli Exclusion Principle, Exchange and Correlation

The above formulation of density functional theory includes the crucial concept of carrier statistics in its formulation for a set of carriers, the one corresponding to what, in the standard literature, is called **fermions**. This is, a type of carriers for which, although being indistinguishable, an "exclusion principle" applies stating that "not two identical carriers can be described the same". That is what is usually called the Exclusion Principle after Wolfgang Pauli's formulation in 1923. For these type of carriers even if the density per carrier is the same as far as they are indistinguishable, for each carrier there should be a description, through the auxiliary amplitude function, which must be explicitly different.

• *The description of each carrier of any pair of equivalent carriers should be different.*

In short for fermion carriers the density distribution of each carrier has to be the same but the auxiliary function for each carrier must be different (and is not necessary different for boson carriers).

3.1.1 The START Formulation of the Exchange and Correlation Density Functionals and Local Potentials

The existence of the exchange distribution density allows the direct formulation of the density functional for the exchange–correlation energy and of, through derivation with respect to the density, the local exchange–correlation potentials.

The exchange–correlation energy, as stated above, consists of two parts: the pair-wise interaction terms arising from the exchange distribution density (here $\sum^s$ stands for the two spin values in the different potentials for different spin formulation)

$$\varepsilon_{xc}^{(1,2)} = -\sum\nolimits^s \int \frac{(n^s - 1)}{2\rho^s(1)} \int \sum\nolimits_{\lambda\lambda'} \rho^s_{\lambda\lambda'}(2)\rho^s_{\lambda'\lambda}(1)\frac{e^2}{r_{12}} dv_2 \rho^s(1) dv_1, \tag{10}$$

and the self-coulomb part which is, in view of the equivalence of all electrons, the fraction $-1/n$ of the Coulomb interaction energy arising from the density–density pair-wise interaction (this term is already included above as part of the definition of the correct density–density Coulomb interaction energy)

$$\Delta\varepsilon_{\text{self-coul}} = -\frac{1}{2}\int\int \rho_{(1)}(2)\rho_{(1)}(1)\frac{e^2}{r_{12}} dv_2 dv_1, \tag{11}$$

if a comparison is made with the usual approach the two terms above should be added. From these terms the local exchange–correlation potential $V^s_{xc}(1)$ is directly obtained through a functional derivative: the equations to solve for the auxiliary functions (central charge Ze atomic-like calculation) are

$$-\frac{1}{2m}\nabla^2\psi_i + \left[-\frac{Ze^2}{r_1} + V^s_{xc}(1) + (n-1)\int \rho(2)\frac{e^2}{r_{12}} dv_2\right]\psi_i = \varepsilon_i \psi_i, \tag{12}$$

and the calculation of the total electronic energy

$$E = \sum_i \varepsilon_i - \frac{1}{2}\left[(n-1)\int\int \rho(2)\rho(1)\frac{e^2}{r_{12}} dv_2 dv_1 - \varepsilon_{xc}^{(1,2)}\right]. \tag{13}$$

As the auxiliary functions corresponding to descriptions of equivalent carriers are a unitary linear transformation (a_i^μ) of a basis set $\{\varphi_\mu\}$, the same equation (12) can be used to solve for the basis functions φ_μ. Also the eigenvalues ε_i (the same for the ψ_i) can be given in terms of the eigenvalues ε'_μ of the φ_μ as $\varepsilon_i = \sum_\mu \|a_i^\mu\|^2 \varepsilon$.

For systems with a small number of electrons the dominant factor is $((n-1)/n)$ in the electron-electron Coulomb interaction. It is basic for the calculation of the hydrogen atom, it is dominant in the calculation of the Helium atom where each of the two electrons interacts with the other but not with itself, and progressively less important for larger systems where the exchange density and the, to it related, exchange interaction grows.

In the case of the calculation of the Beryllium atom, for example, $((n-1)/n) = 3/4$ and therefore the exchange density, is now as important as the basis functions densities. The relevant energies for Ne, for example, in this case are:

Energy Contribution (Ne atom)	**energy (Hartree units)**
electron-nuclear	−310.0951
electron-electron coulomb	59.20975(+6.5788)
electron-electron exchange correlation including self-coulomb	−13.2254 −6.5788
kinetic energy	128.766
total energy (exp.−128.94)	−128.766.

The calculation is simple. The same procedure and code to obtain the total density can be used to obtain the exchange density from the same auxiliary functions. The same procedure to obtain the electron–electron coulomb potential and energy is used to obtain the (local) exchange potential and exchange energy. The self-consistent algorithm remains the same.

4. Final Comment

We have shown that within START, by definition, both a local density $\rho(r)$ and an energy ϵ per particle exist. In the formulation using the auxiliary amplitude function the differential equation to be obeyed by $\psi(r)$ is obtained as the rate of change of energy with respect to the density multiplied by the rate of change of the density with respect to the (adjoint-)amplitude function. Several terms are obtained which are given useful accepted names as kinetic energy, external potential energy, coulomb-interaction energy and exchange-correlation potential energy. The sum of all these quantities is a constant and the first three terms are local, then the fourth term must itself be a local term $V_{xc}(r)$. The final expression from our definitions of charges densities and exchange charge densities, after considering the symmetries of the coefficients in (8) for the $m = n$ case, is:

$$\epsilon\psi(r) = H_1\psi(r) + \left[\frac{n-1}{n}\sum_{k=1}^{n}\int \phi_k^*(x_2)\,\phi_k(x_2)\left(e^2/r_{12}\right)dx_2\right]\psi(r) \tag{14}$$

$$-\left[\frac{\frac{1}{2}\int\sum_{(k\neq i)=1}^{n}\sum_{i=1}^{n}\phi_k^*(x_2)\,\phi_i(x_2)\left(e^2/r_{12}\right)dx_2\phi_i^*(x_1)\,\phi_k(x_1)}{\sum_{j=1}^{n}\phi_j^*(x_1)\,\phi_j(x_1)}\right]\psi(r)$$

$$+\left\{\epsilon - \sum_{i=1}^{n}\epsilon_i\frac{\phi_i^*(x_1)\,\phi_i(x_1)}{\sum_{j=1}^{n}\phi_j^*(x_1)\,\phi_j(x_1)}\right\}\psi(r).$$

There are no non-local terms in this differential equation. $H_1 = -(i\hbar/2m) + V_{ext}(r)$ contains the kinetic energy and the external potential energy terms. The last term, in curly brackets, in equation (14) comes from the variational procedure when we require that the wave function $\psi(r)$ should be the one corresponding to the sum of the $\phi_k(r)$, each one of these functions in turn being the solution of the equation above without the term in curly brackets and where the corresponding eigenvalues are ϵ_k. These auxiliary functions obey different boundary condition each and the additional (last, integrating to *zero*) term forces the wave function $\psi(r)$ to be that corresponding to the weighted sum (see Keller, Keller and Flores 1990 [3]. In practice, for the linearity of the solutions of the equation (14) we can solve for each $\phi_k(r)$ and construct $\psi(r)$.

The middle term in (14) corresponds to what was called "averaged exchange potential" by Slater (Slater 1951 [10] in his analysis of the Hartree-Fock scheme. Here it has arisen not from the use of Slater determinants but from the physically equivalent requirement of different descriptions for different carriers and the consideration that no description is to be preferred for each carriers' pair as in (9).

Our, independent from Quantum Mechanics, derivation of Density Functional Theory containing all the features of standard DFT should be considered as giving a wider range of validity and usefulness to this class of methods. Also it shows that the use of a local exchange potential is a formally correct approach and of workable useful approximations to V_{xc} is fully justified.

4.1 Comment on Wave Function Quantum Mechanics

It is universally accepted that Quantum Mechanics is a successful model to describe physical phenomena, in particular of the electronic structure of atoms, molecules and solids. As such it has been reformulated in several different forms (see for example: *Nine formulations of quantum mechanics*, Daniel F. Styer et al. [9]. In our case considering that there is an additional number of conditions that the auxiliary amplitude function will have to fulfil in order to be adequate to describe different physical situations and systems as discussed below. Besides conditions of purely mathematical origin there will be additional conditions from physical considerations about the system to be described. There are two main ones. First the description of **alternate possibilities** $\phi_s^{\{l,m\}} = \sum^i a_i\varphi_i^{(S)}$ which are to be included together in the formulation, alternatives which can be either of fundamental physical origin or arising from the choice of describing a system with several alternatives without the selection of only one or only one set of alternatives. This first choice will be immediately related to concepts of either statistics of probabilities in the measurement.

That is if an actual measurement will be performed, some statistical distributions would be found, probabilistic in the sense that one or one set of states would be found with an attached probability.

ACKNOWLEDGMENTS

I would like to thank Mrs. Irma Vigil de Aragon for her technical assistance.

REFERENCES

[1] Hohenberg, P., and Kohn, W., *Phys. Rev. B.*, **136**, 864–867 (1964). Lundquist, S., and March, N.H., Theory of the Inhomogeneous Electron Gas. (Plenum, New York, 1983); Dreizler, R. and Providencia, J., Density-Functional Methods in Physics. (Plenum, New York, 1985); Pickett, W., Comments Solid State Phys. 1985, V 12, (1); Keller, J. and Gazquez, J.L., Density Functional Theory. Lectures Notes in Physics, **187** (Springer-Verlag, Berlin, 1983); Parr, R.G. and Yang, W., Density-Functional Theory of Atoms and Molecules (Oxford University Press, Oxford, 1989).

[2] Keller, J., *Int. J. Quantum Chem. Symp.*, **20**, 767 (1986). Keller, J., and Ludeña, E., *Int. J. Quantum Chem. Symp.*, **21**, 171 (1987). Keller, J., *J. Mol. Struct.*, **166**, 51 (1988).

[3] Keller, J., Keller, A., and Flores, J.A., *Acta Chimica Theoretica Latina*, **4**, 175–186 (1990). Flores, J.A. and Keller, J., *Phys. Rev. A*, **45** (9), 6259–6262 (1992). Keller J., *Rev. Soc. Quim. Mex.*, **44**, (1), 22–28 (2000).

[4] Keller, J., *Int. J. of Theor. Phys.*, **30**, (2), 137-184 (1991).

[5] Keller J.,*Advances in Applied Clifford Algebras*, **9**, (2), 309–395 (1999).

[6] Keller J., The Theory of the Electron **A Theory of Matter from START**, In the series: Fundamental Theories of Physics, **115** (Kluwer Acad Publ., Dordrecht, 2001). Also e-book, http://www.wkap.nl/prod/b/0-7923-6819-3G . Keller J., General Relativity from START, Clifford Analysis and Related Topics, Editors K. Gürlebeck, X. Ji and W. Sprössig, *Adv. in Applied Clifford Algebras,* **11,** (S2), 183-204 (2001). Keller J., General Relativity as a Symmetry of a Unified Space-Time-Action Geometrical Space, in: "*Symmetry in Nonlinear Mathematical Physics*", **43,** (2), 557 (2002). http://www.imath.kiev.ua/~appmath/cont01.pdf See also: Keller J., Unification of electrodynamics and Gravity form START, *Annales de la Fond. Louis de Broglie*, **27**, (3), 359 (2002). http://www.ensmp.fr/aflb/AFLB-272/aflb272p359.htm. J. Keller, START Theory of the Neutrino, *Electromagnetic Phenomena*, **3**, (1), 115, (2003).

[7] Keller J., and Weinberger P., A Formal Definition of Carriers , *Advances in Applied Clifford Algebras*, **12,** (1), 39-62 (2002).

[8] Schrödinger, E. *Annalen der Physik*, **79**, 361 (1926), 489, 734; **81**,109 (1926).

[9] Styer D., Balkin M., Becker K., Burns M., Dudley C., Forth S., Gaumer J., Kramer M., Oertel D., Park L., Rinkoski M., Smith C., and Wotherspoon T., Nine formulations of quantum mechanics, *American Journal of Physics*, **70**, (3), 288-297 (2002).

[10] Slater, J. C. *Phys. Rev.*, **81** (3), 385–390 (1951).

THE LOCAL EXCHANGE POTENTIAL IN DENSITY FUNCTIONAL THEORY

Valentin V. Karasiev and Eduardo V. Ludeña

Chemistry Center, Venezuelan Institute for Scientific Research, IVIC
Apartado 21827, Caracas 1020-A, Venezuela

1. INTRODUCTION

Exchange appears in quantum mechanics as a result of the antisymmetry condition on Fermion wavefunctions [1-3]. Thus, for example, in the Hartree-Fock approximation this condition is incorporated by expressing the wavefunction as a Slater determinant. In turn, this leads to an exchange energy that is given as a functional of the Hartree-Fock orbitals and which upon application of the variational calculus yields a non-local exchange potential [4]. The presence of non-local exchange potentials also occurs for the case of more complicated wavefunctions, such as for example, those of the Jastrow-Feenberg type [5] (written as the product of a Slater determinant times a correlation function). The one-particle equations ensuing from this ansatz, i.e., the correlated Hartree-Fock equations, contain non-local potentials both for exchange and correlation. Similarly, in the case of many-body perturbation theory, the one-particle equations determining the so-called Brueckner orbitals also contain non-local potentials [6].

In density functional theory, DFT, [7-11] the Kohn-Sham formulation [12,13] assumes the existence of a non-interacting system described by a single Slater determinant that yields the exact density. The N orbitals are obtained by solving the Kohn-Sham equation, namely, a one-particle Schrödinger equation containing only a local effective potential. Clearly, there are many computational and conceptual advantages to having a local exchange (and correlation) potential and, for this reason, much emphasis has been placed in DFT in the development of approximate local exchange functionals, particularly, in the context of the general gradient approximation, GGA [14]. However, the state-of-the-art GGA local exchange potentials in DFT are not sufficiently refined so as to guarantee chemical accuracy. Realizing that the requirement to keep the potential local may be too restrictive, hybrid functionals that incorporate a part of the Hartree-Fock non-local exchange and introduce, therefore, non-local one-particle potentials into the Kohn-Sham equations have been developed. The justification for such hybrid functionals essentially requires that we consider a generalization of the Kohn-Sham scheme and go into what has been called the Hartree-Fock-Kohn-Sham hybrid approach [15]. Nevertheless, as even with hybrid functionals there remain important properties that cannot be correctly described [16], the question of how to design exact local functionals in DFT, has acquired renewed relevance.

The possibility of having a local exchange potential that replaces the non-local one in orbital theories is given by the optimized effective potential method, OEP. It was initially formulated, outside the framework of DFT, by Sharp and Horton [17] and later refined by Talman and Shadwick [18]. However, as in this method, the equations allowing for the calculation of local potentials are difficult to solve, it has had a very limited application either in orbital theories or in DFT. Even when simplifications to this method are adopted, such as those introduced in the Krieger-Li-Iafrate, KLI, approximation [19], these equations still remain difficult to solve. However, due to some recent improvements, very accurate solutions to the OEP equations can now be obtained with less –albeit still substantial– effort. These new developments are known as the exact local exchange method, or EXX [16,20]. Variations on this method [21,22], aiming at reducing the computational toil are themes of current research.

In the present work, we present an alternative to the EXX method, which, while retaining its accuracy, is inscribed in a much simpler approach to the construction of local exchange potentials. It is based on the idea, introduced by Slater [23] several decades ago, of replacing the non-local Hartree-Fock exchange potential by an average local potential. This approximation reduces to the Dirac exchange potential [24] for the case of the homogeneous electron gas. In order to deal with situations that deviate from the homogeneous electron gas, a heuristic improvement on this potential consisting in multiplying this potential times a parameter α was suggested by Slater [25]. This idea was further developed and led to the $X\alpha$ method and its sequels. In the present self-consistent α method [26-29], SCα, we depart, however, from Slater's approach in that we require that α be defined as a functional of the one-particle orbitals, chosen so as to guarantee that the approximate SCα exchange energy coincides with the Hartree-Fock one. In addition, we require that this functional be determined self-consistently.

In Section 2, we discuss some general properties of exchange potentials such as the correct asymptotic behavior and the self-interaction correction and examine, in view of these properties, some of the shortcomings of both GGA and hybrid functionals. In Section 3, we review the optimized effective potential method, OEP, and its approximations. We also discuss the formulation of what has been recently called "exact local exchange", EXX, plus current improvements and modifications. In Section 4, we succinctly present the SCα method including its asymptotically adjusted version and present some of its applications for the local representation of hybrid functionals. Finally, in Section 5, we give some results and conclusions.

2. SOME GENERAL CONSIDERATIONS ON EXCHANGE FUNCTIONALS

2.1 The Hartree-Fock exchange functional, the Hartree-Fock non-local exchange potential and Slater's local approximation

In the independent particle model, i.e., the Hartree-Fock approximation, the electron-electron interaction energy is given by the following functional of the N occupied Hartree-Fock orbitals:

$$E_{ee}[\{\phi_i\}] = E_{Coul}[\{\phi_i\}] + E_x[\{\phi_i\}], \tag{1}$$

where the Coulomb direct interaction functional is

$$\begin{aligned} E_{Coul}[\{\phi_i\}] =& \frac{1}{2}\sum_{i=1}^{N}\sum_{k=1}^{N}\int d^3\mathbf{r}_1 ds_1 \phi_i^*(\mathbf{r}_1, s_1)\phi_i(\mathbf{r}_1, s_1) \\ &\times \int d^3\mathbf{r}_2 ds_2 \phi_k^*(\mathbf{r}_2, s_2)\phi_k(\mathbf{r}_2, s_2)\frac{1}{|\mathbf{r}_1 - \mathbf{r}_2|}, \end{aligned} \tag{2}$$

and the exchange functional, similarly,

$$\begin{aligned} E_x[\{\phi_i\}] =& -\frac{1}{2}\sum_{i=1}^{N}\sum_{k=1}^{N}\int d^3\mathbf{r}_1 ds_1 \phi_i^*(\mathbf{r}_1, s_1)\phi_k(\mathbf{r}_1, s_1) \\ &\times \int d^3\mathbf{r}_2 ds_2 \phi_k^*(\mathbf{r}_2, s_2)\phi_i(\mathbf{r}_2, s_2)\frac{1}{|\mathbf{r}_1 - \mathbf{r}_2|}. \end{aligned} \tag{3}$$

Taking the variational derivatives of these functionals w.r.t. ϕ_i^* (and after integrating over spin) one obtains, respectively, the local Coulomb potential,

$$v_{Coul}([\rho]; \mathbf{r}_1)\phi_i(\mathbf{r}_1) = \left[\sum_{k=1}^{N}\int d^3\mathbf{r}_2 \phi_k^*(\mathbf{r}_2)\phi_k(\mathbf{r}_2)\frac{1}{|\mathbf{r}_1 - \mathbf{r}_2|}\right]\phi_i(\mathbf{r}_1), \tag{4}$$

and the non-local Hartree-Fock potential,

$$\widehat{v}_x^{HF}\phi_i(\mathbf{r}_1) = -\sum_{k=1}^{N}\int d^3\mathbf{r}_2 \delta(\sigma_i, \sigma_k)\phi_k^*(\mathbf{r}_2)\phi_i(\mathbf{r}_2)\frac{1}{|\mathbf{r}_1 - \mathbf{r}_2|}\phi_k(\mathbf{r}_1), \tag{5}$$

where its non-local character is manifested by the fact that components of $\widehat{v}_x$ act on the function $\phi_i(\mathbf{r}_1)$ for all k. The term for $k = i$ in the exchange potential, Eq. (5), cancels the unphysical self-interaction Coulomb term $k = i$ appearing in Eq. (4). In other words, in the Hartree-Fock approximation the self-interaction Coulomb term is automatically taken care of by a corresponding exchange term.

For the purpose of simplifying the Hartree-Fock equations Slater proposed the following *local* representation for the exchange potential by taking a weighted average of the individual orbital non-local potentials [23]:

$$v_S(\mathbf{r}_1) = -\frac{1}{\rho(\mathbf{r}_1)}\sum_{i=1}^{N}\sum_{k=1}^{N}\delta(\sigma_i, \sigma_k)\phi_i^*(\mathbf{r}_1)\phi_k(\mathbf{r}_1)\int d^3\mathbf{r}_2 \phi_k^*(\mathbf{r}_2)\phi_i(\mathbf{r}_2)\frac{1}{|\mathbf{r}_1 - \mathbf{r}_2|}. \tag{6}$$

In terms of the Slater local potential, the Hartree-Fock exchange functional can be written as

$$E_x[\rho;\{\phi_i\}] = \frac{1}{2}\int d^3\mathbf{r}_1 \rho(\mathbf{r}_1) v_S([\rho;\{\phi_i\}];\mathbf{r}_1), \tag{7}$$

where we have emphasized the dependence of these terms both on the density as well as on the orbital set.

Now, if we go one step further and assume that the orbitals defining $v_S(\mathbf{r}_1)$ are themselves functions of the one-particle density, namely, $\phi_i(\mathbf{r}) \equiv \phi_i([\rho];\mathbf{r})$ the exchange functional can be rewritten as an implicit functional of the one-particle density

$$E_x[\{\phi_i(\mathbf{r})\}] \longrightarrow E_x[\{\phi_i([\rho];\mathbf{r})\}] \equiv E_x^{DFT}[\rho]. \tag{8}$$

The corresponding potential can be obtained by taking the variational derivative of E_x^{DFT} with respect to ρ

$$v_x^{DFT}(\mathbf{r}) = \frac{\delta E_x^{DFT}[\rho]}{\delta\rho(\mathbf{r})}. \tag{9}$$

Bearing in mind that the one-particle density is given by

$$\rho(\mathbf{r}) = \sum_{i=1}^{N} \phi_i^*([\rho];\mathbf{r})\phi_i([\rho];\mathbf{r}), \tag{10}$$

and using the chain rule, we obtain

$$\frac{\delta E_x[\{\phi_i([\rho])\}]}{\delta\phi_i^*([\rho])} = \frac{\delta E_x^{DFT}[\rho]}{\delta\rho}\frac{\delta\rho}{\delta\phi_i^*} = \frac{\delta E_x^{DFT}[\rho]}{\delta\rho}\phi_i. \tag{11}$$

¿From Eq. (8), and by comparing Eq. (11) and Eq. (5), we conclude that

$$\frac{\delta E_x^{DFT}[\rho]}{\delta\rho}\phi_i = \widehat{v}_x^{HF}\phi_i. \tag{12}$$

Thus, the non-local character of the potential is not modified by the fact that the orbitals are density-dependent even though, in this case, the potential is an implicit function of the density. This simple result is quite indicative of the fact that the variational derivative of a functional of ρ does not necessarily have to be a local multiplicative function [30]. Let us consider the exchange functional written in the form given by Eq. (7). Taking the variational derivative we obtain

$$\frac{\delta E_x[\rho]}{\delta\rho(\mathbf{r})} = \frac{1}{2}v_S(\mathbf{r}) + \frac{1}{2}v_{resp}(\mathbf{r}), \tag{13}$$

where we have defined the *response* potential by [31]

$$v_{resp}(\mathbf{r}) = \int d^3\mathbf{r}'\rho(\mathbf{r}')\frac{\delta v_S(\mathbf{r}')}{\delta\rho(\mathbf{r})}. \tag{14}$$

Clearly, by carrying out the variational derivative in the response potential, we obtain a first term that cancels $(1/2)v_S$ plus the non local exchange potential. This means that, in general, the response potential is non-local and further implies that although the Slater potential is local by definition, its variational derivative with respect to the density is not. A very convenient property of the Slater potential is that it has the correct asymptotic behavior

$$\text{limit}\, v_S(\mathbf{r}) \longrightarrow -\frac{1}{r} \quad \text{when } r \to \infty. \tag{15}$$

2.2 GGA approximate local exchange potentials

In the Hohenberg-Kohn-Sham version of DFT, in analogy with Eq. (5), the following definition of the exchange functional as a functional of the one-particle density and its derivatives is given

$$E_x[\rho] = \int d^3\mathbf{r}\rho(\mathbf{r})\mathcal{E}_x([\rho, \nabla\rho, \nabla^2\rho, ...]; \mathbf{r}) = \int d^3\mathbf{r}\rho^{4/3}(\mathbf{r})F_x(\mathbf{s}). \tag{16}$$

The right hand side expression comes from the fact that in its simplest approximation, namely, the local density approximation, Slater's average local potential goes into the LDA potential (proportional to $\rho^{1/3}$). The exchange modulating factor $F_x(\mathbf{s})$ corrects the LDA approximations. Here $\mathbf{s} = |\nabla\rho(\mathbf{r})|/\rho^{4/3}(\mathbf{r})$. A great deal of work has been devoted in DFT to the modelling of $F_x(\mathbf{s})$. Some exchange functionals have been devised by fitting their parameters to empirical atomic exchange energies [32-35]. One of the most successful functionals is Becke's 1988 version (B88) given in [35] where the functional (but not the potential) satisfies the correct asymptotic conditions. Some closely related functionals are those of Gill [36] and of Filatov and Thiel [35]. Others have been obtained non-empirically by modelling the exchange hole [38-40].

2.3 Hybrid functionals and partially non-local effective potentials

Hybrid functionals contain a small fraction of the exact Hartree-Fock exchange E_x^{HF}. A fairly general form for these functionals is the three-parameter formula introduced by Becke [41]

$$E_{xc}^{hyb} = a_0 E_x^{HF} + a_x(E_x^{LSD} + \Delta E_x^{GGA}) + E_c^{LSD} + a_c \Delta E_c^{GGA}, \tag{17}$$

where ΔE_x^{GGA} and ΔE_c^{GGA} are the GGA type contributions to exchange and correlation, respectively; E_x^{LSD} and E_c^{LSD} are the LSD-type counterparts and where a_0, a_x and a_c are semi-empirical parameters. Other hybrid functionals are discussed in [42-44]. Hybrid functionals can be justified by resorting to an extension of the Kohn-Sham formalism [15].

2.4 Shortcomings of GGA and hybrid functionals

As commented by Görling [16], current implementations of Kohn-Sham theory are not capable to describe exactly the hydrogen atom for which the exact exchange is known [45]. In addition, they fail to describe correctly most anions. These functionals give rise to non-physical one-particle spectra and in particular, the excitation gap between HOMO and LUMO levels is too small. These functional also fail to describe Rydberg series as only a few excited levels are present for neutral systems. These deficiencies of one-particle spectra also have an effect on time-dependent DFT where these Kohn-Sham orbitals and energies are used as inputs.

One important reason for these shortcomings is the inadequate treatmente of the self-interaction correction. As a consequence, GGA and hybrid functionals give an incomplete cancellation of the non-physical Coulombic self-interaction term. [Certainly DFT methods framed in an orbital context have been developed, but, from both practical and conceptual viewpoints they are far from being satisfactory (see, however, Ref. [46])]. Also, the effective Kohn-Sham potential decays too rapidly and does not match in the asymptotic limit of large r the electrostatic potential due to a positive charge (of the type $\frac{1}{r}$) that the electron must feel away from the system. This effect, in turn is responsible for the absence of Rydberg series and for the inability to bind an extra electron for anion formation.

3. LOCAL EXCHANGE POTENTIALS IN ORBITAL THEORIES

3.1 The optimized effective potential method

The optimized effective potential method, OEP, was developed outside DFT for the purpose of introducing the local exchange potential into one-particle equations. It was initially sketched by Sharp and Horton [17] and further developed by Talman and Shadwick [18]. More recently, Görling and Levy [47] have given an equivalent derivation based on DFT peturbation theory (see also [48,49]). Essentially, the local potential $V^{OEP}(\mathbf{r})$ appearing in the one-particle equation

$$-\frac{1}{2}\nabla^2\phi_i(\mathbf{r}) + V^{OEP}(\mathbf{r})\phi_i(\mathbf{r}) = \epsilon_i\phi_i(\mathbf{r}) \tag{18}$$

is defined in this method by requiring that the energy remains unmodified under variations of this potential

$$\frac{\delta < \Phi|\widehat{H}|\Phi >}{\delta V^{OEP}(\mathbf{r})} = \sum_{i=1}^{N}\int d^3\mathbf{r}'\frac{\delta < \Phi|\widehat{H}|\Phi >}{\delta\phi_i(\mathbf{r}')}\frac{\delta\phi_i(\mathbf{r}')}{\delta V^{OEP}(\mathbf{r})} = 0. \tag{19}$$

By imposing this condition on the orbitals one obtains the inhomogeneous equations

$$-\frac{1}{2}\nabla^2\varphi_i(\mathbf{r}) + A(\mathbf{r})\varphi_i(\mathbf{r}) = \delta A(\mathbf{r})\phi_i(\mathbf{r}), \tag{20}$$

where $A(\mathbf{r}) = V^{OEP}(\mathbf{r}) - \epsilon_i$ and $\varphi_i(\mathbf{r}) = \delta\phi_i(\mathbf{r})$. The solution to the homogeneous equation is

$$\delta\phi_i(\mathbf{r}) = -\int d^3\mathbf{r}' G_i(\mathbf{r},\mathbf{r}')\phi_i(\mathbf{r}')\delta V^{OEP}(\mathbf{r}'), \tag{21}$$

where the Green's function is

$$G_i(\mathbf{r},\mathbf{r}') = \sum_{j\neq i}\frac{1}{(\epsilon_j - \epsilon_i)}\phi_j^*(\mathbf{r})\phi_j(\mathbf{r}'). \tag{22}$$

These equations are usually written in terms of the response function

$$\chi(\mathbf{r},\mathbf{r}') = \sum_i^N \sum_j^{unocc} \frac{\phi_i^*(\mathbf{r})\phi_j(\mathbf{r})\phi_j^*(\mathbf{r}')\phi_i(\mathbf{r}')}{(\epsilon_j - \epsilon_i)} \tag{23}$$

in the following way

$$\int d^3\mathbf{r}'\chi(\mathbf{r},\mathbf{r}')V^{OEP}(\mathbf{r}') = \sum_i^N \sum_j^{unocc} \phi_i^*(\mathbf{r})\phi_j(\mathbf{r})\frac{< \phi_j|\hat{v}_x^{HF}|\phi_i >}{(\epsilon_j - \epsilon_i)}. \tag{24}$$

Note that this is a highly non-linear equation whose solution cannot be easily obtained.

In the Krieger-Li-Iafrate, KLI, approximation [19], the potential is represented by

$$V^{OEP-KLI}(\mathbf{r}) = v_S(\mathbf{r}) + C(\mathbf{r}), \tag{25}$$

where $v_S(\mathbf{r})$ is Slater's local exchange potential and $C(\mathbf{r})$ is an approximate correction function. Another way to regard the KLI method is through the following approximation to the Green's function:

$$G_i(\mathbf{r},\mathbf{r}') \simeq \frac{1}{(\bar{\epsilon}_i - \epsilon_i)}\sum_{j\neq i}\phi_j^*(\mathbf{r})\phi_j(\mathbf{r}') = \frac{1}{(\bar{\epsilon}_i - \epsilon_i)}(\delta(\mathbf{r}-\mathbf{r}') - \phi_i^*(\mathbf{r})\phi_i(\mathbf{r}')). \tag{26}$$

3.2 The exact local exchange method, EXX

Another way do deal with the OEP equations has been advanced by Görling [16] and independently and simultaneously by Ivanov et al. [20]. Essentially, this method introduces an exchange charge density $\rho_x(\mathbf{r})$ satisfying the conditions

$$v_x(\mathbf{r}) = \int d^3\mathbf{r}'\frac{\rho_x(\mathbf{r}')}{|\mathbf{r}-\mathbf{r}'|}, \tag{27}$$

and also

$$-\frac{1}{4\pi}\nabla^2 v_x(\mathbf{r}) = \rho_x(\mathbf{r}). \tag{28}$$

As a result, the OEP equations become

$$\int d^3\mathbf{r}' \int d^3\mathbf{r}''\frac{\chi(\mathbf{r},\mathbf{r}')\rho_x(\mathbf{r}'')}{|\mathbf{r}'-\mathbf{r}''|} = \sum_i^N \sum_j^{unocc} \phi_i^*(\mathbf{r})\phi_j(\mathbf{r})\frac{< \phi_j|\hat{v}_x^{HF}|\phi_i >}{(\epsilon_j - \epsilon_i)}. \tag{29}$$

They can be solved expressing

$$\rho_x(\mathbf{r}) = \sum_k c_k f_k(\mathbf{r}), \tag{30}$$

where the functions $f_k(\mathbf{r})$ are orthogonal with respect to the weight $1/|\mathbf{r}-\mathbf{r}'|$. The finite basis set representation of Görling [16] and Ivanov and coworkers [20] requires the inversion of a singular matrix. This step is avoided in the new approach to OEP advanced by Yang and Wu [21]. For other developments, see [22].

3.3 The "Local Hartree-Fock" approximation

Della Sala y Görling [50] have introduced the following local exchange potential

$$v_x(\mathbf{r}) = v_S(\mathbf{r}) + \frac{n_s}{\rho(\mathbf{r})} \sum_{a\leq b}^{occ.'} j_{ab}\phi_a^{KS}(\mathbf{r})\phi_b^{KS}(\mathbf{r}) < \phi_b^{KS}|v_x - \hat{v}_x^{HF}|\phi_a^{KS} >, \tag{31}$$

where n_s is the spin multiplicity, $j_{ab} = 2$ for $a \neq b$ and $j_{ab} = 1$ for $a = b$. The summation does not run over the orbital $a = b = N$. These authors assume that there exists a Slater determinant Φ that is a simultaneous eigenfunction of the N-particle Hartree-Fock operator and the "exchange-only" Kohn-Sham one:

$$[\hat{T} + \hat{V}_{ext} + \hat{U} + \hat{V}_x^{HF}]\Phi = E_s^{HF}\Phi, \tag{32}$$

$$[\hat{T} + \hat{V}_{ext} + \hat{U} + \hat{V}_x]\Phi = E_s^{EXX}\Phi. \tag{33}$$

4. APPROXIMATION TO LOCAL EXCHANGE POTENTIALS BASED ON THE SCα METHOD

4.1 The α parameter revisited

Several models for the exchange functional $E_x^0[\rho]$ that depend explicitly both on ρ and $\nabla\rho$ have been introduced in DFT (cf. Subsections 2.2 and 2.3, above). The corresponding exchange potentials are given by

$$v_x^0([\rho];\mathbf{r}) = \frac{\delta E_x^0[\rho]}{\delta\rho(\mathbf{r})}. \tag{34}$$

We propose to modify this potential by defining a new exchange functional as:

$$E_x^{SC\alpha}[\{\phi_i\}] = \alpha_x[\{\phi_i\}]E_x^0[\rho], \tag{35}$$

where $\alpha_x[\{\phi_i\}]$ is *a functional* guaranteeing that $E_x^{SC\alpha}$ approaches E_x^{HF}:

$$\alpha_x[\{\phi_i\}] = \frac{E_x^{HF}[\{\phi_i\}]}{E_x^0[\rho]}, \tag{36}$$

where $E_x^{HF}[\{\phi_i\}]$ is given by Eq. (3). The potential corresponding to this functional is

$$\frac{\delta E_x^{SC\alpha}[\{\phi_i\}]}{\delta\phi_i^*} = \frac{\delta\alpha_x[\{\phi_i\}]}{\delta\phi_i^*}E_x^0[\rho] + \alpha_x\frac{\delta E_x^0[\rho]}{\delta\phi_i^*} = \Delta\hat{v}_x^{SC\alpha}\phi_i + v_x^{SC\alpha}\phi_i \qquad (37),$$

where $v_x^{SC\alpha} = \alpha_x v_x^0$ and where from Eqs. (37) and (12) we obtain

$$\Delta\hat{v}_x^{SC\alpha} = \hat{v}_x^{HF} - \alpha_x v_x^0. \tag{38}$$

The Kohn-Sham equation for the SCα model becomes:

$$\Big(-\frac{1}{2}\nabla^2 + v_{es} + \Delta\hat{v}_x^{SC\alpha} + v_x^{SC\alpha} + v_c \Big)\phi_i = \epsilon_i \phi_i. \tag{39}$$

In spite of the fact that both components contribute to the exchange potential in the Kohn-Sham equation (39), the important point is that $\Delta\hat{v}_x^{SC\alpha}$ does not contribute directly to the energy, due to the fact that

$$\Delta E_x = E_x^{HF} - \alpha_x E_x^0 = E_x^{HF} - \frac{E_x^{HF}}{E_x^0} E_x^0 = 0, \tag{40}$$

and, hence, this term may be omitted from Eq. (39).

4.2 An asymptotically adjusted local exchange potential

¿From the definition of the Slater potential, and from the Hartree-Fock expression for exchange, given by Eq. (7), and adding and substracting $\frac{1}{2}v_S$ to the right hand side of Eq. (13), it follows that

$$v_x([\rho];\mathbf{r}) = v_S(\mathbf{r}) + \frac{1}{2}[v_{resp}(\mathbf{r}) - v_S(\mathbf{r})]. \tag{41}$$

Calling $\widetilde{v}_{resp}(\mathbf{r}) = [v_{resp}(\mathbf{r}) - v_S(\mathbf{r})]$, from this expression we define

$$v_x^{AASC\alpha}(\mathbf{r}) = v_S(\mathbf{r}) + \frac{1}{2}\alpha_x[\{\phi_i\}]\widetilde{v}_{resp}(\mathbf{r}), \tag{42}$$

where we take

$$\alpha_x[\{\phi_i\}] = \frac{E_x^{HF}[\{\phi_i\}] - E_{xLP}[v_S]}{E_{xLP}[\widetilde{v}_{resp}^0]}. \tag{43}$$

Here we have used the Levy-Perdew expression for exchange. Different approximations to the AASCα potential can be generated depending on the approximate exchange functional one selects [27]. The simplest approximation leads to the Harbola-Sen modified Slater potential [51].

4.3 Application to hybrid functionals

We have examined replacing the Hartree-Fock exchange functional by the local exchange functionals: SCα, AASCα, KLI, LHF (that is, functionals that may be called "Exact Expression Approximate Exchange", EEAX, functionals) [29]:

$$E_{xc}^{EEAX-hyb} = a_0 E_x^{EEAX} + a_x(E_x^{LSD} + \Delta E_x^{GGA}) + E_c^{LSD} + a_c \Delta E_c^{GGA}, \tag{44}$$

Table 1

Total absolute energies obtained by various x-*only* methods for the Ne and Ar atoms and for selected diatomic molecules at the experimental geometries (in mHartrees).

system	GGA	SCα-LDA	AA-m2	KLI	LHF[a]	OEP	EXX[b]
Ne	128569	128533	128544	128544[a]	128544	128546[c]	128545
Ar	526771	526798	526793	526806[a]	526806	526812[c]	526812
H_2	1126	1133	1134	1134[d]	-	-	1133
LiH	7972	7985	7985	7987[a]	7987	-	-
FH	100110	100056	100067	100068[d]	-	-	100057
F_2	198906	198734	198759	198760[d]	-	-	198744
CO	112846	112762	112782	112782[a]	112782	-	112777

[a] Ref. [50]. [b] Ref. [20]. [c] Ref. [52]. [d] Ref. [53].

for which the energy is calculated using the exact expression. In this case, the potential is a local multiplicative operator

$$v_{xc}^{EEAX-hyb} = a_0 v_x^{EEAX} + a_x(v_x^{LSD} + \Delta v_x^{GGA}) + v_c^{LSD} + a_c \Delta v_c^{GGA}. \qquad (45)$$

The potential v_x^{EEAX} may be generated through the use of SCα, AASCα, KLI or LHF methods. The Kohn-Sham equations for these potentials form a system of *differential equations*, whereas in the case of non-local hybrids they form a system of *integro-differential equations.*

5. RESULTS AND DISCUSSION

Let us start by highlighting an important aspect of the SCα method, namely, the fact that the functionals have the appropriate variational behavior. This means that total x-*only* energies calculated using the approximate orbitals SCα and AASCα are upper bounds to the HF values. This can be seen in Table 1, where all SCα and AA-m2 (also KLI and LHF) energies are upper bounds to the exact exchange. (The fact that the "exact" EXX energies for the FH, F_2 and CO molecules lie above the energies corresponding to the local approximations, is due to the error introduced by the finite basis set employed for the EXX calculations.) The GGA functionals, however, do not satisfy the variational principle $E_{Total-x-only}^{approx} \geq E_{Total-x-only}^{EXX} \geq E_{Total}^{HF}$. We see in the first column of Table 1 that these functionals can either be above or below the EXX total energy. The success of the GGAs, as is well known now, relies essentially on error cancellations between the exchange and correlation contributions. We also see from Table 1 that all the local approximations with an exact treatment of the exchange yield total energies quite similar to those of the EXX method.

Table 2

HOMO absolute energies obtained by various x-*only* methods (in eV).

system	GGA	SCα-LDA	AA-m2	KLI	LHF^a	OEP	EXX^b
Ne	12.46	13.21	24.06	23.11^a	23.12	23.15^c	-
Ar	9.36	9.79	17.00	16.03^a	16.06	16.08^c	-
H_2	9.72	10.23	16.18	16.18^d	-	-	16.2
LiH	3.88	4.11	8.40	8.19^a	8.19	-	-
FH	8.83	9.37	18.19	17.56^d	-	-	17.4
F_2	8.60	9.26	18.67	-	-	-	14.5
CO	8.26	8.69	15.00	15.03^a	14.97	-	14.1 (15.03^e)

^{a} Ref. [50]. ^{b} Ref. [16]. ^{c} Ref. [52]. ^{d} Ref. [54]. ^{e} Ref. [20].

Table 3

Atomization energies (in kcal/mol) of selected diatomic molecules obtained from different x-*only* methods calculated at experimental geometries.

system	GGA^a	SCα-LDA^a	AA-m2^b	KLI^c	EXX^b
H_2	85	84	84	84	84
LiH	37	34	33	34	34
FH	118	98	100	97	98
F_2	32	-44	-35	-37	-42
CO	225	168	181	174	172

^{a} Spin-unrestricted calculations from Ref. [28]. ^{b} Spin-restricted calculations from Ref. [27]. ^{c} Calculations at the self-consistent geometries from Ref. [53]. ^{d} Ref. [16].

In the SCα method, the Coulomb self-interaction term is cancelled exactly because the exact HF expression is used to calculate the energy. Also, in the AASCα version of this method, the correct asymptotic behavior is introduced from the outset. The data presented in Table 2 show the importance of such a behavior for exchange potentials. The local approximations with correct long-range exchange potential behavior, AA-m2, KLI and LHF, reproduce the energy of the highest occupied molecular orbital, HOMO, with a value that is very close to the exact OEP or EXX values. This is not the case for the SCα-LDA and GGA functionals.

Another aspect worth emphasizing is the fact that for the SCα and AASCα methods high precision is attained at low cost. For example, the atomization energies calculated by the present approach for molecules of the G2 set lie very close to the exact EXX values. The data of Table 3 illustrate this fact. Results obtained with the SCα, AASCα and KLI local approximations lie in closer agreement with the exact EXX values than those of the GGA functional. Finally, the extension of the SCα and AASCα methods to hybrid functionals through the replacement of the non-local HF potential by the local potentials devised in the present approach does not affect their accuracy although it only requires the solution of differential equations.

ACKNOWLEDGMENTS

E.V.L. would like to acknowledge Fonacit of Venezuela for support of this work through Group Project G-97000741 and to the Secretaría de Estado de Educación y Universidades, of Spain, for financial support during his stay at the Universidad Autónoma de Madrid. V.V.K. is also grateful to Fonacit for a S2 travel grant.

REFERENCES

[1] W. Heisenberg, *Z. Phys.* **38**, 411 (1926); **39**, 499 (1926); **41**, 239 (1927).

[2] P.A.M. Dirac, *Proc. Roy. Soc.* (London), **A 212**, 661 (1926).

[3] J.C. Slater, *Phys. Rev.* **34**, 1293 (1929).

[4] J.C. Slater, *Quantum Theory of Atomic Structure*, Mcgraw-Hill, New York (1960), Vol. II, Ch. 17 and references therein.

[5] C.E. Campbell, E. Krotscheck and T. Pang, *Phys. Rep.* **213**, 1 (1992).

[6] I. Lindgren and S. Salomonson, *Int. J. Quantum Chem.* **90**, 294 (2002).

[7] P. Hohenberg and W. Kohn, *Phys. Rev.* **136**, B864 (1964).

[8] R.G. Parr and W. Yang, *Density Functional Theory of Atoms and Molecules*, Oxford University Press, New York (1989).

[9] E. S. Kryachko and E. V. Ludeña, *Energy Density Functional Theory of Many Electron Systems*, Kluwer, Dordrecht, 1990.

[10] R.M. Dreizler and E.K.U. Gross, *Density Functional Theory*, Springer-Verlag, Berlin (1990).

[11] N.H. March. *Electron Density Theory of Atoms and Molecules*, Academic Press, New York (1992).

[12] W. Kohn and L.J. Sham, *Phys. Rev.* **140**, A1133 (1965).

[13] P.C. Hohenberg, W. Kohn, and L.J. Sham, *Adv. Quantum Chem.* **21**, 7 (1990).

[14] J.P. Perdew and W. Yue, *Phys. Rev. B* **33**, 8800 (1986).

[15] A. Görling and M. Levy, *J. Chem. Phys.* **106**, 2675 (1997).

[16] A. Görling, *Phys. Rev. Lett.* **83**, 5459 (1999).

[17] R.T. Sharp and G.K. Horton, *Phys. Rev.* **90**, 317 (1953).

[18] J.D. Talman and W.F. Shadwick, *Phys. Rev. A* **14**, 36 (1976).

[19] J.B. Krieger, Y. Li, and G.J. Iafrate, *Phys. Rev. A* **45**, 101 (1992).
[20] S. Ivanov, S. Hirata and R.J. Bartlett, *Phys. Rev. Lett.* **83**, 5455 (1999).
[21] W. Yang and Q. Wu, *Phys. Rev. Lett.* **89**, 143002 (2002).
[22] J.J. Fernández, C. Tablero and P. Wahnon, *Int. J. Quantum Chem.* **91**, 157 (2003).
[23] J.C. Slater, *Phys. Rev.* **81** , 385 (1951).
[24] P.A.M. Dirac, *Proc. Cambridge Phil. Soc.* **26**, 376 (1930).
[25] J.C. Slater, *The Self-Consistent Field for Molecules and Solids: Quantum Theory of Molecules and Solids Vol. 4*, McGraw-Hill, New York (1974).
[26] V.V. Karasiev and E.V. Ludeña, *Phys. Rev. A* **65**, 062510 (2002).
[27] V.V. Karasiev and E.V. Ludeña, *Phys. Rev. A* **65**, 032515 (2002).
[28] I. González, C. González, V.V. Karasiev, E.V. Ludeña, and A.J. Hernández, *J. Chem. Phys.* **118**, 8161 (2003).
[29] V.V. Karasiev, *J. Chem. Phys.* **118**, 8576 (2003).
[30] R.K. Nesbet and R. Colle, *Phys. Rev. A* **61**, 012503 (1999).
[31] O.V. Gritsenko and E.J. Baerends, Phys. Rev. A **64**, 042506 (2001).
[32] A.D. Becke, *J. Chem. Phys.* **84**, 4524 (1986).
[33] A.D. Becke, *J. Chem. Phys.* **85**, 7184 (1986).
[34] A.E. De Pristo and J.D. Kress, *J. Chem. Phys.* **86**, 1425 (1987).
[35] A.D. Becke, *Phys. Rev. A* **38**, 3098 (1988).
[36] P.M.W. Gill, *Mol. Phys.* **89**, 433 (1996).
[37] M. Filatov and W. Thiel, *Mol. Phys.* **91**, 847 (1997).
[38] A.D. Becke, *Int. J. Quantum Chem.* **23**, 1915 (1983).
[39] J.P. Perdew and Y. Wang, *Phys. Rev. B* **33**, 8800 (1986).
[40] V. Tschinke and T. Ziegler, *Can. J. Chem.* **67**, 460 (1989).
[41] A.D. Becke, *J. Chem. Phys.* **98**, 1372 (1993).
[42] A.D. Becke, *J. Chem. Phys.* **98**, 5648 (1993).
[43] A.D. Becke, *J. Chem. Phys.* **104**, 1040 (1996).
[44] J.P. Perdew, M. Ernzerhof, K. Burke, *J. Chem. Phys.* **105**, 9982 (1996).
[45] P.M.W. Gill and J.A. Pople, *Phys. Rev. A* **47**, 2383 (1993).
[46] J. Garza, J. Nichols and D.A. Nixon, *J. Chem. Phys.* **112**, 7880 (2000).
[47] A. Görling and M. Levy, *Phys. Rev. A* 50, 196 (1994).
[48] F.R. Manby and P.J. Knowles, *Chem. Phys. Lett.* **296**, 1 (1998).
[49] L.S. Sham, *Phys. Rev. B* **32**, 3876 (1985).
[50] F. Della Sala and A. Görling, *J. Chem. Phys.* **115**, 5718 (2001).
[51] M.K. Harbola and K.D. Sen, *Int. J. Quantum Chem.* **90**, 327 (2002).
[52] E. Engel, and S. H. Vosko, *Phys. Rev. A* **47**, 2800 (1993).
[53] E. Engel, A. Höck, and R. M. Dreizler, *Phys. Rev. A* **62**, 042502 (2000).
[54] T. Grabo, and E. K. U. Gross, *Int. J. Quantum Chem.* **64**, 95 (1997).

Electronic Structure of Solids

TRANSPORT CURRENTS IN METAL FILMS

H. M. Böhm[†], *E. Krotscheck*[†‡], *and S. Natschläger*[†]

[†]Institut für Theoretische Physik
Johannes Kepler Universität
A 4040 Linz, Austria

[‡]Department of Physics, Texas A&M University
College Station, TX 77845-4242, USA

1. INTRODUCTION

Excitations in electronic systems are conventionally discussed in the framework of linear response theory, specifically the random–phase approximation (RPA). Modifications of the RPA include local screening, or time–dependent density–functional theory (TDDFT). Many–body effects are in these approaches either ignored (in the RPA), introduced in an *ad-hoc* manner that is hard to generalize to a non-uniform geometry, or in long–wavelength approximations as in the time–dependent local density approximation (TDLDA) of density functional theory.

The subject of our paper is the determination of the nature, the dispersion relations and the relative strengths of collective excitations in simple metal films. We are particularly interested in the signatures of many–body correlations that might be detectable in excitations. As a new development, we report the calculation of transport currents within a manifestly microscopic many–body approach.

2. THEORETICAL FRAMEWORK

The ground state of simple inhomogeneous electronic systems can be quite well described within the Jastrow–Feenberg variational theory, using the Fermi hypernetted chain (FHNC) method [1,2] for summing infinite sets of ("parquet") diagrams. The theory starts with the *ansatz* for the wave function

$$\Psi_0(1,\ldots,N) = F(1,\ldots,N)\Phi_0(1,\ldots,N)\,,$$

$$F(1,\ldots,N) = \exp\left\{\frac{1}{2}\sum_i u_1(\mathbf{r}_i) + \frac{1}{2}\sum_{i<j} u_2(\mathbf{r}_i,\mathbf{r}_j)\right\}\,, \tag{1}$$

where $\Phi_0(1,\ldots,N)$ is a $N \times N$ Slater determinant of single–particle wave functions. The spatial single–particle orbitals and the pair correlation functions $u_2(\mathbf{r}_i,\mathbf{r}_j)$ are determined by functional minimization of the variational ground–state energy in the FHNC approximation.

A logical generalization of the above variational *ansatz* to excited states consists in replacing the Slater determinant Φ_0 by a time–dependent superposition of Slater determinants

$$|\Psi_X(t)\rangle = \frac{F\,|\Phi_0(t)\rangle}{\langle\Phi_0(t)\mid F^\dagger F \mid \Phi_0(t)\rangle^{1/2}}\,,$$

$$|\Phi_0(t)\rangle = \exp\frac{1}{2}\left[\sum_{p,h} u_{ph}(t)\, a_p^\dagger a_h\right] |\Phi_0\rangle\ . \tag{2}$$

The set of Slater determinants defined in Eq. (2) form states with an arbitrary number of excited single particle–hole pairs; they form a complete but *non–orthogonal* basis of the Hilbert space, correlated by the Jastrow factor F ("correlated basis functions", CBF). Equations of motion for the particle–hole amplitudes $u_{ph}(t)$ are derived from an action principle $\delta\mathcal{S} = 0$ [3] with

$$\mathcal{S}\left[u_{ph}(t), u_{ph}^*(t)\right] \equiv \int dt \left\langle \Psi_X(t) \middle| H^{\rm tot}(t) - i\hbar\frac{\partial}{\partial t} \middle| \Psi_X(t)\right\rangle\,, \tag{3}$$

where $H^{\rm tot}$ includes the ground state Hamiltonian H and the external perturbation $U^{\rm ext}(t)$. Any physical observable of the system, in particular the density $\rho(\mathbf{r},t)$ and the current density $\mathbf{j}(\mathbf{r},t)$ can then be expressed in terms of the $u_{ph}(t)$ determined this way.

For the execution of the theory, we must introduce and calculate a number of quantities:

(a) Ratios of particle–hole normalization integrals

$$z_{ph}^2 \equiv \frac{I_{ph}}{I_{00}} \equiv \frac{\langle\Phi_0|\, a_h^\dagger a_p F^\dagger F a_p^\dagger a_h\, |\Phi_0\rangle}{\langle\Phi_0|\, F^\dagger F\, |\Phi_0\rangle}\,, \tag{4}$$

and analogously $z_{p'p\,h'h}$ for two–particle–two–hole states etc. For electronic systems these quantities are well approximated by unity [4].

b) Overlap integrals between different states ($p \neq p',\ h \neq h'$)

$$N_{0,ph} = \frac{\langle\Phi_0|\, F^\dagger F a_p^\dagger a_h\, |\Phi_0\rangle}{\left(I_{00} I_{ph}\right)^{1/2}} \tag{5}$$

$$N_{p'h',ph} = \frac{\langle\Phi_0|\, a_{h'}^\dagger a_{p'} F^\dagger F a_p^\dagger a_h\, |\Phi_0\rangle}{\left(I_{p'h'} I_{ph}\right)^{1/2}}\,, \qquad N_{0,php'h'} = \frac{\langle\Phi_0|\, F^\dagger F a_p^\dagger a_h a_{p'}^\dagger a_{h'}\, |\Phi_0\rangle}{\left(I_{00} I_{php'h'}\right)^{1/2}}$$

and corresponding matrix elements of the Hamiltonian.

The $N_{0,ph}$ are zero in the bulk limit due to momentum conservation, but they contribute to the ground state density in an inhomogeneous geometry:

$$\langle \hat{\rho} \rangle^0 = \sum_h \langle h|\hat{\rho}|h\rangle + \sum_{ph} z_{ph} N_{0,ph} \langle p|\hat{\rho}|h\rangle \,. \tag{6}$$

The first term is obviously the Hartree Fock (HF) approximation. Note, however, that a special optimized set of single particle wave functions was used to eliminate infinite sets of reducible diagrams [1]. The second term in Eq. (6) arises from the remaining exchange diagram. We show in Fig. 1 the HF density and the correlation correction of Eq. (6) for one of the metal films under investigation here; the situation is very similar for the other cases. The correlation correction is obviously very small, note that it was multiplied by a factor of ten to make it visible on the scale of the HF density. Considering the smallness of the effect for the ground state density, we feel safe to assume

$$N_{0,ph} \approx 0 \tag{7}$$

for metal films.

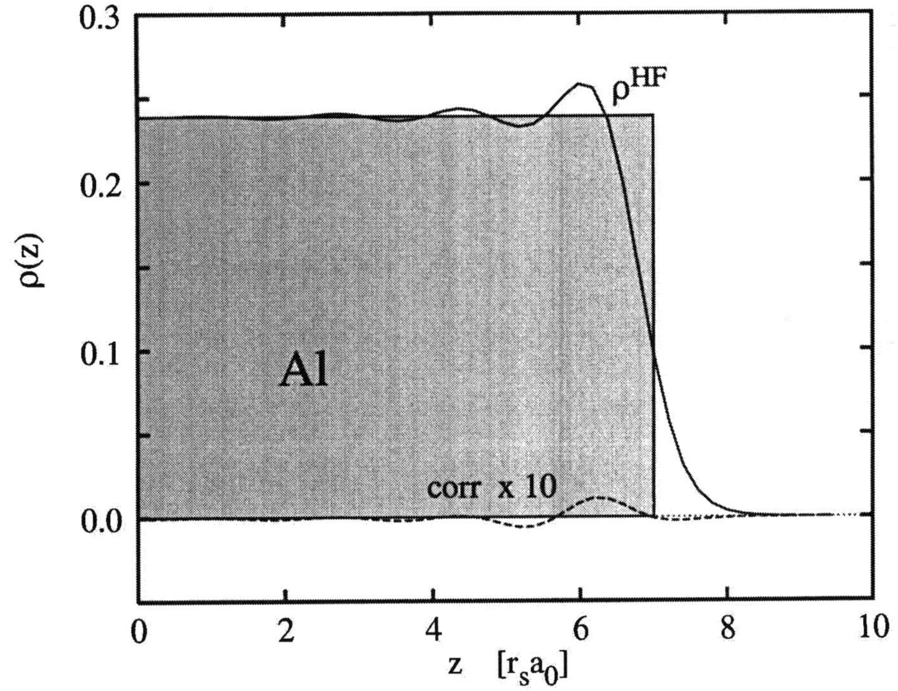

Figure 1. The density correction due to $N_{ph} \neq 0$ for an aluminum slab of width $14 r_s a_0$, where a_0 denotes Bohr's radius and r_s is the usual density parameter. The gray shaded area shows the jellium background, and the solid line is the Hartree–Fock density. The long–dashed line shows the correction, magnified by a factor of 10.

Since we are interested in the response to small, time dependent perturbations, we may expand the equations of motion as well as $\rho(\mathbf{r},t)$ and $\mathbf{j}(\mathbf{r},t)$ in the particle–hole amplitudes $u_{ph}(t)$, $u^*_{ph}(t)$:

$$\rho = \langle\hat{\rho}\rangle^0 + \delta\rho^{(1)}(t) + \delta\rho^{(2)}(t) + \dots\,, \tag{8}$$

$$\mathbf{j} = \langle\hat{\mathbf{j}}\rangle^0 + \delta\mathbf{j}^{(1)}(t) + \delta\mathbf{j}^{(2)}(t) + \dots\,. \tag{9}$$

Similar to the way the $N_{0,ph}$ are needed to calculate the ground state density $\langle\hat{\rho}\rangle^0$, we need the overlap matrix elements involving the excitations of two particles and two holes for calculating the induced density $\delta\rho^{(1)}$. However, through the transformation

$$\begin{pmatrix} v_{ph} \\ v^*_{ph} \end{pmatrix} \equiv \left[\mathbf{1} + \frac{1}{2}\begin{pmatrix} N_{ph,p'h'} & N_{php'h',0} \\ N_{0,php'h'} & N_{p'h',ph} \end{pmatrix}\right]\begin{pmatrix} u_{p'h'} \\ u^*_{p'h'} \end{pmatrix} \tag{10}$$

one can write the leading order density correction $\delta\rho^{(1)}$ in the concise form

$$\delta\rho^{(1)}(\mathbf{r},t) = \frac{1}{2}\sum_{ph}\Big[v_{ph}(t)\ \langle p\,|\,\hat{\rho}(\mathbf{r})\,|\,h\rangle + \ c.c.\Big]\,. \tag{11}$$

We can thus identify the v_{ph} with the particle–hole amplitudes of the *uncorrelated* matrix elements of the density operator.

In order to obtain the induced current density $\delta\mathbf{j}^{(1)}$ we follow exactly the same steps as for ρ. Under the additional assumption that the two–particle–two–hole overlap elements can be described by a *local* pair operator $\mathcal{N}(1,2)$ and by neglecting exchange contributions so that

$$N_{ph,p'h'} = \langle p'h\,|\,\mathcal{N}\,|\,h'p\rangle\ ; \quad N_{ph\,p'h',0} = \langle pp'\,|\,\mathcal{N}\,|\,hh'\rangle\ , \tag{12}$$

the induced current density takes a form analogous to Eq. (11)

$$\delta\mathbf{j}^{(1)}(\mathbf{r},t) = \frac{1}{2}\sum_{ph}\Big[v_{ph}(t)\ \big\langle p\,|\,\hat{\mathbf{j}}(\mathbf{r})\,|\,h\big\rangle + \ c.c.\Big]\,. \tag{13}$$

In order to evaluate $\delta\rho^{(1)}$ and $\delta\mathbf{j}^{(1)}$ we now need to calculate the particle–hole amplitudes v_{ph} for a given perturbing potential $U^{\rm ext}(t)$. Applying the transformation (10) to the equations of motion obtained from the action principle for the u_{ph}, u^*_{ph} allows us to write [5] the equations of motion in exactly the form of time–dependent Hartree–Fock theory [6]

$$-\frac{\hbar}{i}\begin{pmatrix} \dot{v}_{ph} \\ \dot{v}^*_{ph} \end{pmatrix} = \begin{pmatrix} \langle p\,|\,U^{\rm ext}\,|\,h\rangle \\ c.c. \end{pmatrix} + \left[\begin{pmatrix} \varepsilon_p - \varepsilon_h & 0 \\ 0 & \varepsilon_p - \varepsilon_h \end{pmatrix} + \mathbf{V}_{\rm ph}\right]\begin{pmatrix} v_{ph} \\ v^*_{ph} \end{pmatrix}\,, \tag{14}$$

where ε_p denotes the CBF single–particle energies of the system and the so–called particle–hole interaction $\mathbf{V}_{\rm ph}$ is represented by the sum of all non–nodal FHNC diagrams [5]. The theory is known as "correlated RPA". When exchanges and non–local contributions to the particle–hole interaction $\mathbf{V}_{\rm ph}$ are ignored, the equations of motion (14) are identical to the ones of conventional RPA with an effective interaction.

The advantage of the theory is that $\mathbf{V}_{\rm ph}$ is a by–product of the ground state calculations and contains correlations; among others the theory is applicable for hard–core potentials. In Ref. [2] it was found that for metal films this particle–hole interaction is highly anisotropic and cannot be approximated well by any local density approximation.

The use of these CRPA equations in Eq. (11) immediately leads to the density response function

$$\delta\rho^{(1)}(\mathbf{r},\omega) = \int d^3r'\,\chi(\mathbf{r},\mathbf{r}';\omega)\,U^{\rm ext}(\mathbf{r}',\omega) \tag{15}$$

with

$$\chi^{-1} = {\chi_0}^{-1} - \mathbf{V}_{\rm ph}\,, \tag{16}$$

χ_0 denoting the Lindhard function of the inhomogeneous system. Obviously, this is the standard RPA form except that the Coulomb interaction v_C was replaced with the particle–hole interaction $\mathbf{V}_{\rm ph}$ which includes short–ranged correlations.

The CRPA equations imply the continuity equation for $\delta\mathbf{j}^{(1)}(\mathbf{r},t)$. However, the first order current $\delta\mathbf{j}^{(1)}(\mathbf{r},t)$ is *not* the appropriate quantity to describe transport. First, it is periodic in time, hence its time average vanishes. Second, it is asymptotically zero since it is the superposition of matrix elements containing one hole state $|\,h\rangle$, which is bound in the direction perpendicular to the film, *cf*. Eq. (13). In order to calculate a transport current that is asymptotically finite and has a finite time average we must therefore calculate the terms of *second order* in the particle–hole amplitudes. Within the CRPA formalism the result is

$$\delta\mathbf{j}^{(2)}(\mathbf{r},t) \;=\; \frac{1}{4}\left\{\sum_{pp'h} v_{ph}v^*_{p'h}\,\left\langle p\,|\,\hat{\mathbf{j}}(\mathbf{r})\,|\,p'\right\rangle + \sum_{phh'} v_{ph}v^*_{ph'}\,\left\langle h\,|\,\hat{\mathbf{j}}(\mathbf{r})\,|\,h'\right\rangle\right\}\,. \tag{17}$$

Next, the v_{ph} are expressed with help of the CRPA equations of motion in terms of the external perturbing potential. By i) assuming that the external perturbation has a single harmonic time dependence with frequency ω and a single wave vector $\mathbf{q}_{\rm ext}$, ii) performing the time average, and iii) omitting all localized terms this leads to the following final result for the transport current

$$\mathbf{j}_{\rm trp} \;=\; \sum_{h=\mathbf{h}_{\|},h_z} \frac{\theta(k)}{k^2}\,\left|\langle\,k\,|\,\varepsilon^{-1}U^{\rm ext}\,|\,h_z\,\rangle\right|^2 \left(\frac{\mathbf{h}_{\|}+\mathbf{q}_{\rm ext}}{k}\right)\,. \tag{18}$$

Here, k is the wavenumber of the emitted electron

$$\frac{\hbar^2k^2}{2m} \;\equiv\; \hbar\omega + E_{h_z} - \frac{\hbar^2}{2m}\left(2\mathbf{h}_{\|}\!\cdot\!\mathbf{q}_{\rm ext}+\mathbf{q}^2_{\rm ext}\right)\,, \tag{19}$$

(E_{h_z} is the energy level of the binding quantum well); and ε^{-1} is the inverse dielectric function

$$\varepsilon^{-1} = 1 + \mathbf{V}_{\rm ph}\,\chi\,. \tag{20}$$

It contains all the effects due to the many body nature of the system. In particular, the collective excitations correspond to poles in ε^{-1} which in turn, according to

Eq. (18) give rise to peaks in the transport current. We therefore continue with a discussion of these modes.

3. COLLECTIVE EXCITATIONS

For the specific geometry under consideration here, we take the $z-$direction to be perpendicular to the film. The starting point is the quasi–two–dimensional Lindhard function $\chi^0(z, z', \mathbf{q}_{\|}; \omega)$. Its formal definition was given by a number of authors [7]. We evaluate this function with the single particle orbitals numerically obtained from the ground state calculation. We found it most practical to solve the RPA matrix equation, Eq. (16) directly in $z-$coordinate space.

The imaginary part of χ is the dynamic structure factor $S(z, z', \mathbf{q}_{\|}; \omega)$, which we project symmetrically (S_s) and antisymmetrically (S_a) with respect to z and z'. The two quantities S_s and S_a do not accurately yield the absolute magnitude of the peaks measured in electron energy loss experiments. They do contain, however, the correct information about the positions of the peaks and a reasonable estimate of their relative strengths. Certainly, following the positions of the peaks as a function of the parallel momentum $\mathbf{q}_{\|}$ correctly describes the dispersions of the collective modes.

Corresponding to our geometry we are able to identify a number of different types of excitations: By investigating the induced density $\delta\rho$ in the system we can distinguish volume modes (extended throughout the film) and surface modes (located in the surface), and a mode which is of multipole character in $z-$direction. This multipole mode, which is neither a clear surface nor a clear volume mode, was predicted by Bennet [8] and was first observed by Tsuei *et al.* [9]. All these modes can appear in a symmetric and an antisymmetric form. Finally, in the long wavelength regime, further intra– and inter–(sub)band transitions are seen (the latter involve excitations of electrons between different energy levels in the quantum well).

We show in Figs. 2 and 3 the dispersion relations obtained for an aluminum and a cesium film. The width chosen for both films is $14 r_s a_0$, corresponding to 15Å and 41Å, respectively. All energies in these plots are normalized to the value of the corresponding volume plasmon, *i.e.* the experiments are normalized to the experimental value of the volume plasmon. We display the comparison of our theoretical results (using the FHNC particle–hole interaction) with the experiments from Ref. 10 and TDDFT calculations reported therein for an infinite half–space (iHS).

In the small $q_{\|}$ regime both the bulk and the symmetric surface plasmon agree with the limiting behaviors well known from classical electrodynamics

$$
\begin{aligned}
\omega \quad &\to \quad \omega_p \qquad &&\text{for the bulk plasmon} \\
\omega \quad &\to \quad \left\{ \begin{array}{ll} \sqrt{\dfrac{2\pi n e^2}{m}}\sqrt{q_{\|}} & [\text{sy}] \\ \omega_p & [\text{as}] \end{array} \right\} &&\text{for the surface plasmon}
\end{aligned}
\qquad (21)
$$

As discussed in Ref. 11 for potassium, also in Al the multipole mode and the antisymmetric branch of the surface plasmon (bending down from ω_p) hybridize in the

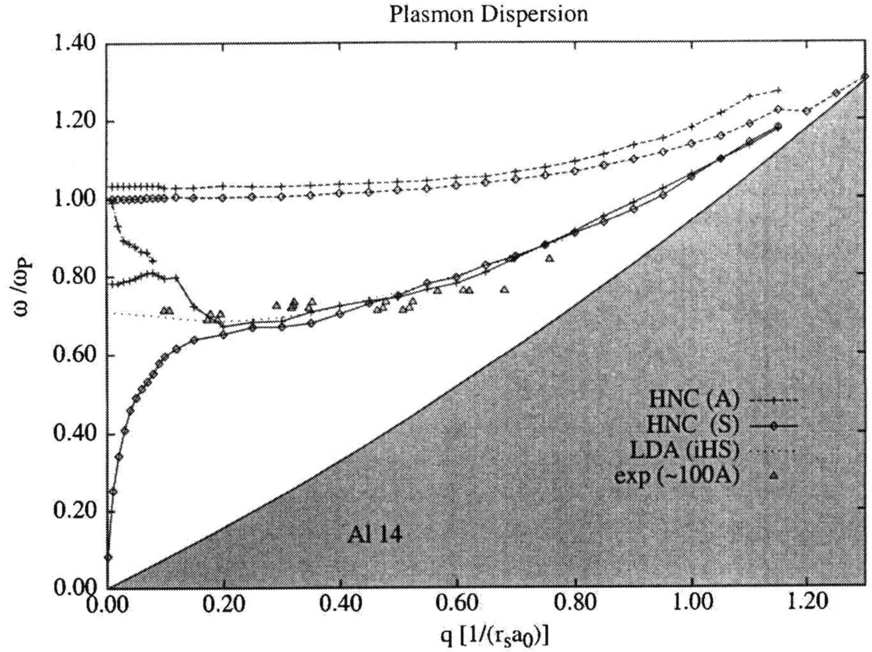

Figure 2. Comparison of plasmon dispersions for an Al slab of $14r_s a_0$ thickness. The lines with diamonds and crosses are the symmetric and the antisymmetric modes, respectively. The triangles denote the experiments [10] on thick films. The dotted line shows calculations for the half–space [10].

"crossing" region. Also, for $q_{\|}$ that are large compared to the inverse width of the film, the two branches of the surface plasmon join at approximately $\omega_p/\sqrt{2}$, the value pertaining to an iHS. In the case of Cs we are not able to identify the induced densities unambiguously with all of the modes. In addition to the antisymmetric multipole mode we also find its symmetric counterpart.

The agreement with the experiment is not very satisfactory. As can be clearly seen from Fig. 3, the experimental values for the surface plasmon in the films of several hundred Ångstrøm width lie much higher than our calculated results. In our films of only a few tens of Ångstrøm, however, the surface plasmon *has to* bend down earlier in order to meet the required $\sqrt{q_{\|}}$–limit. The multipole mode appears to be very sensitive to the correlations in the sample. Calculations on wide films are under progress, but more experimental data on thin samples are also desirable.

4. TRANSPORT CURRENT

In order to evaluate the transport current from Eq. (18) we must specify the perturbing potential. As a starting point we take an electron moving with constant velocity v on a straight trajectory parallel to the surface. Since Eq. (18) does not distinguish between symmetric and antisymmetric modes, we expect to find both types

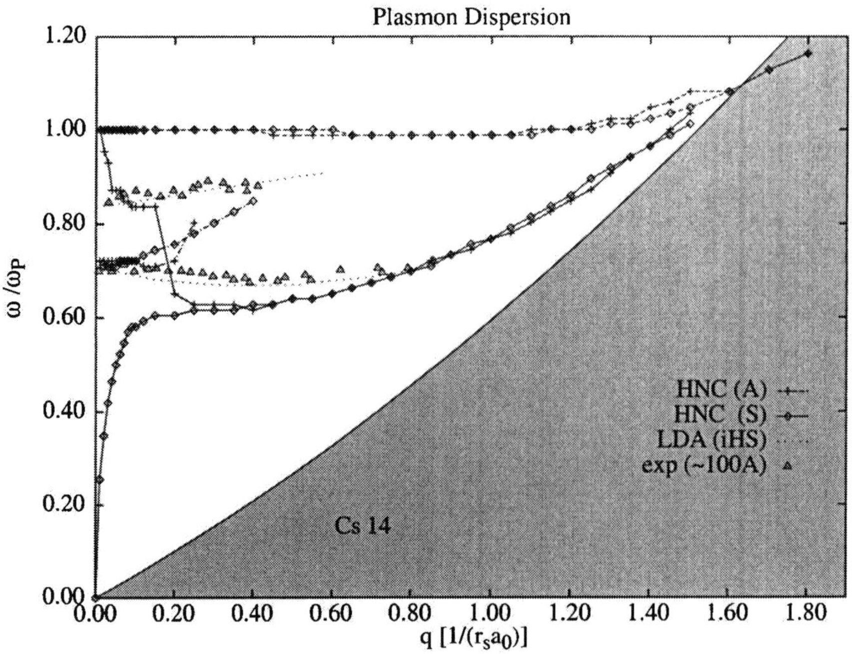

Figure 3. Plasmon dispersions for Cs. Same notation as in Fig. 2.

of modes simultaneously. The condition $k > 0$, corresponding to the requirement that the energy put into the system is enough to lift an electron out of the binding well, leads to a threshold frequency, below which no contributions to $\mathbf{j}_{\rm trp}$ are possible.

In Figs. 4 and 5 we show the $z-$component of the transport current for $v = 0.2c$. In both cases we can clearly identify the symmetric bulk plasmon and the antisymmetric surface plasmon. The symmetric surface plasmon, *i.e.* the $\sqrt{q_{\|}}-$mode, is fully present in Al and partly cut off in Cs due to the threshold condition. The multipole mode could not be found in both cases. There are, however, additional peaks that are well pronounced in both spectra. These can be attributed to interband plasmons. In the dynamic structure factor these modes form only small wiggles. Therefore, except for the $\sqrt{q_{\|}}-$plasmon, which is the dominant long wavelength excitation in any case (unless cut off by the threshold frequency), we can state that the strengths of the various modes are very different for the dynamic structure factor and the transport current.

5. SUMMARY

We have reported here results from the first application of the CRPA method for calculating collective excitations in an inhomogeneous Fermi system. Moreover, we have extended the theory to the calculation of transport currents. For that purpose, one has to expand $\mathbf{j}$ to second order in the particle–hole amplitudes. Modifications of our result may become necessary for geometries where the $N_{0,ph}$ are not small or

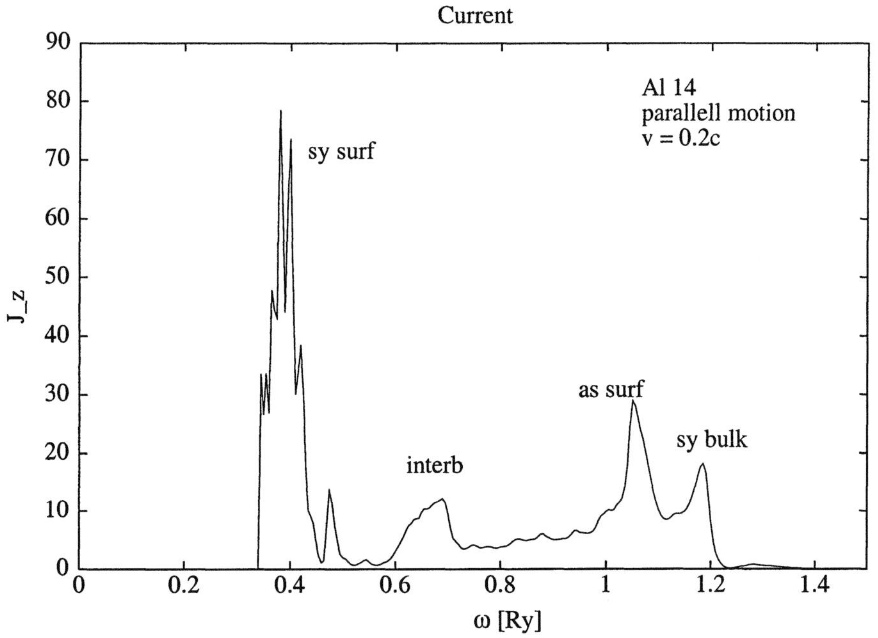

Figure 4. The total asymptotic induced current in $z-$direction predicted for an Al slab of $14r_sa_0$ thickness. The distance of the passing electron is taken to be $10r_sa_0$ and its speed is $0.2c$, c being the speed of light.

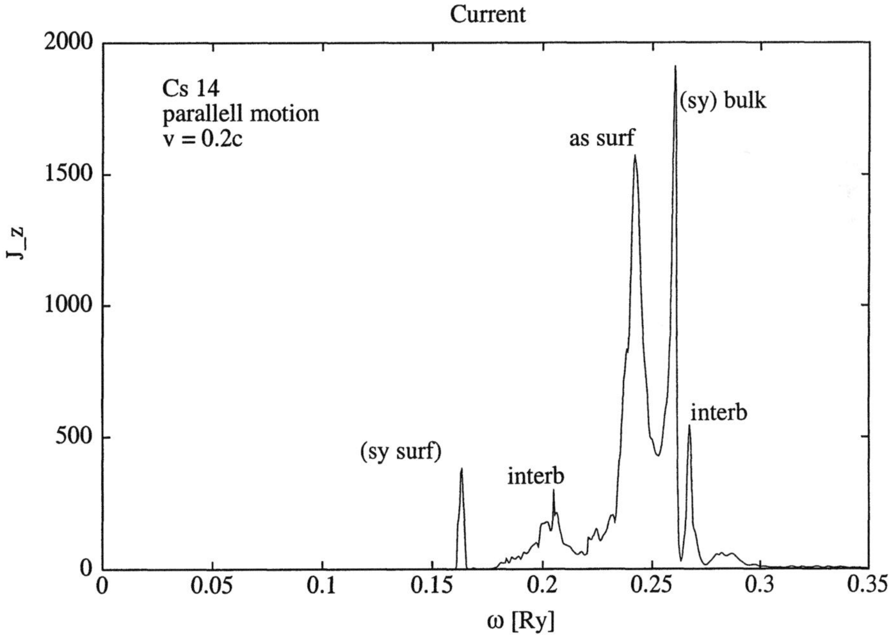

Figure 5. Same as Fig. 4 but for Cs.

when the external perturbation cannot be described by a static external potential U^{ext}, as it is the case in light scattering experiments. Further work in this direction is under way.

We have carried out explicit evaluations of the excitations and the transport current for thin metal films. From the different weights of the miscellaneous modes in the dynamic structure factor and the current it follows that current measurements provide an alternative experimental confirmation for otherwise weakly pronounced modes. An investigation of the transport current resolved with repect to the solid angle will further elucidate this point.

ACKNOWLEDGEMENT

This work was supported, in part, by the Austrian Science fund under project grant No. P12832-TPH. One of us (EK) thanks the Physics Department at Texas A&M University, where a part of this work was done, for hospitality and partial support.

REFERENCES

[1] E. Krotscheck, W. Kohn, and G.-X. Qian, Phys. Rev. B **32**, 5693 (1985).

[2] E. Krotscheck and W. Kohn, Phys. Rev. Lett. **57**, 862 (1986).

[3] A. K. Kerman and S. E. Koonin, Ann. Phys. (NY) **100**, 332 (1976).

[4] E. Krotscheck, Ann. Phys. (NY) **155**, 1 (1984).

[5] E. Krotscheck, Phys. Rev. A **26**, 3536 (1982).

[6] D. J. Thouless, *The quantum mechanics of many-body systems*, 2 ed. (Academic Press, New York, 1972).

[7] *see, e.g.,* A. G. Eguiluz, Phys. Rev. Lett. **51**, 1907 (1983).

[8] A. J. Bennett, Phys. Rev. B **1**, 203 (1970).

[9] K.-D. Tsuei, E. W. Plummer, A. Liebsch, K. Kempa, and P. Bakshi, Phys. Rev. Lett. **64**, 44 (1990).

[10] K. D. Tsuei, E. W. Plummer, A. Liebsch, E. Pehlke, K. Kempa, and P. Bakshi, Surf. Sci. **247**, 302 (1991).

[11] A. Liebsch, B.-O. Kim, and E. W. Plummer, Phys. Rev. B **63**, 125416 (2001).

MESOSCOPIC TRANSPORT: THE ELECTRON-GAS SUM RULES IN A DRIVEN QUANTUM POINT CONTACT

Mukunda P. Das[†], *Jagdish S. Thakur*[‡], and *Frederick Green*[†]

†Department of Theoretical Physics
Research School of Physical Sciences and Engineering
The Australian National University
Canberra ACT 0200, Australia

‡Department of Electrical and Computer Engineering
Wayne State University
Detroit, Michigan 48202, USA

1. INTRODUCTION

The electron gas is characterized, above all, by its response as a correlated many-particle system. In that setting the conserving sum rules have been thoroughly studied and exhaustively applied for many years [1]. The sum rules and their centrality in the electron-gas problem are widely understood throughout the many-body community – if not elsewhere.

At any scale, from the bulk to the near-microscopic, metallic conduction processes are dominated by the physical constraints encoded within the electron-gas sum rules. Thus they apply, with perfect rigor, to mesoscopic devices such as quantum point contacts. They also govern *nonequilibrium* transport and fluctuations, as they do the much more familiar linear-response limit.

In this paper we review the structure of the conserving sum rules in the mesoscopic regime, from the weakest driving fields to the strongest. As compact quantitative expressions of the microscopic conservation laws, the sum rules entail a set of straightforward criteria to be met by proper theoretical descriptions of metallic-electron behavior. As we discuss below, these criteria are quite enough to rule out models of mesoscopic processes that fail to uphold the conservation laws.

We recall the leading sum rules for mesoscopic conduction. In particular we apply one of them, the compressibility sum rule, to strongly driven, open electronic systems. Despite their fundamental importance, very little is known about the role of the sum rules in mesoscopic electronics. Since the latter is so deeply rooted in the electron gas, one expects that those relations, as canonical constraints, carry significant information about the way in which the processes underlying transport and its associated current noise are deployed at short scales.

We first discuss the intimate relationship between the transport response of an open mesoscopic device, connected to macroscopic metallic leads, and the structure of the microscopic excitations, or fluctuations, within the device. This relationship is strongly conditioned by the stabilizing effect of the bounding leads on the internal dynamics of the device. Next, we describe how the microscopic form of the fluctuations in the conductor develops away from equilibrium. This leads, in particular, to the sum rules for perfect screening and compressibility [1]. Then we address the physical implications of the compressibility sum rule, whose conceptual and practical import for mesoscopics is on a par with the familiar fluctuation-dissipation theorem (FDT).

A major, and thus far unexplored, experimental application of the compressibility sum rule is to mesoscopic systems with built-in nonuniformity of their conduction bands. In that context we review some surprising Coulomb effects. These should be clearly manifested through the behavior of the electronic compressibility of inhomogenous quantum wires.

2. BASICS

Sum rules express the microscopic conservation laws at the level of what is measurable in a system. The physical worth of a theory of conduction can be judged, practically and objectively, by the degree to which it satisfies them. Approximate descriptions of an electron system should respect at least the principal ones:

(a) the *fluctuation-dissipation relation*, expressing energy conservation,

(b) the *perfect-screening sum rule* (gauge invariance), and

(c) the *compressibility sum rule* (number conservation).

The importance of (a) in mesoscopic transport is well known. Unfortunately, that of (b) and (c) is not well known at all. All three rules are equally pivotal; all three must be satisfied. *None* of the three is optional; if even one of them is violated by a candidate model of electron transport, that model is manifestly nonviable. Whatever special pleading may be made for it (for example, some fancied phenomenological simplicity), it cannot compensate for basic failures of this order.

Each of the electron-gas sum rules follows a common pattern. Each is an identity in which a measurable function of the one-particle distribution for the system is equated to an integral over a microscopic, *two-particle* correlation function. Let us briefly examine the FDT as a starting point. In the linear-response limit the FDT provides an expression for the average power P in steady state, supplied by the external current generator to the driven system [2,3]:

$$\begin{aligned}
P = VI &= -\lim_{t\to\infty}\left\{\int_0^L E(x)dx\langle j(x,t)/L\rangle_I\right\} \\
&\equiv \lim_{t\to\infty}\left\{\int_0^t dt'\int_0^L dx\int_0^L dx'(-E(x))\frac{\langle[j(x,t)/L, j(x',t')/L]\rangle_0}{k_B T}(-E(x'))\right\} \\
&= \frac{1}{k_B T}\int_0^\infty dt''\int_0^L dx\int_0^L dx'(-E(x))\langle[j(x,t'')/L, j(x',0)/L]\rangle_0(-E(x')) \qquad (1)
\end{aligned}$$

where we specialize to one dimension. (This will be appropriate to a quantum point contact, in which a quasi-one-dimensional wire is attached to macroscopic metallic leads [2].) The thermal energy is $k_{\rm B}T$, the electromotive force across the conductor of length L is $V = -\int_0^L E(x)dx$ and I is the current. The brackets $\langle ... \rangle_I$ represent a trace over the many-body density matrix for the carriers, subject to transport (for $I = 0$ it is the equilibrium trace), and $j(x,t) = -ev(x,t)$ is the particle-flux operator (to be evaluated in the mean over the channel length, following the Ramo-Shockley theorem [4]).

The form of Eq. (1) is paradigmatic. On the left we have the experimentally accessible total power absorbed by the system. On the right, we have the auto-correlation function of the *microscopic* power-loss density $-E(x)j(x,t)/L$, which is not directly accessible. The velocity-velocity correlation $\langle [v(t), v(0)] \rangle / k_{\rm B}T$ is a measure of the excursions of carrier energy taken up by electron-hole pair fluctuations. As the excited pair states propagate, scatter and decay, their excess energy dissipates. Conservation requires that these losses add up to the total electrical power continuously supplied by the generator. Equation (1) expresses this.

In a uniform system, the local electric field $E = -V/L$ is constant. We obtain the standard Kubo conductance formula [5]

$$G = \frac{P}{V^2} = \frac{1}{k_{\rm B}T} \int_0^\infty dt \int_0^L dx \frac{E(x)}{V} \int_0^L dx' \frac{E(x')}{V} \langle [j(x,t), j(x',0)] \rangle / L^2$$
$$\to \frac{1}{L^2 k_{\rm B}T} \int_0^\infty dt \langle [j(t), j(0)] \rangle. \tag{2}$$

For inhomogeneous systems the sum rule for conductance has a more general, but conceptually identical, structure. This is covered more closely in Ref. [3].

The demonstration of the Kubo formula's gauge invariance for an *open* system was given in explicit detail by Sols [6]. Having been established, it furnishes necessary and sufficient criteria for the system's theoretical description to be microscopically *and* globally conserving. This contrasts with the status of gauge invariance within Landauer-Büttiker-Imry approaches; see, for example, the commentary in Ref. [7] following Eq. (51) therein. Eq. (2) leads directly to the quantized Landauer formula as a (very particular) limiting case whose microscopic proof is free of the customary Landauer phenomenology [8]. As Eqs. (9)–(11) below demonstrate, the latter badly compromises both gauge invariance and the compressibility sum rule.

3. CONSERVATION IN OPEN CONDUCTORS

The FDT's far-reaching importance derives from the following. The conductance G, which is directly measurable, can be computed as a one-particle object within a given transport model. If, using the same model, one computes the two-body current auto-correlation (which also determines the measurable Johnson-Nyquist noise), then it must yield precisely the same value of G. That value may, or may not, turn out to be a good fit to experiment. For the model's integrity, however, the essential point is that the consistency of the FDT has to be guaranteed *internally*. Otherwise the physical basis of such a description is flawed, since it fails to conserve energy. It would then be difficult to take such a description seriously.

A similarly fundamental and normative significance attaches to the compressibility sum rule for open conductors, which we now derive. Consider a conductor in electrical contact with a pair of large metallic reservoirs, so that electrons are freely exchangeable. At equilibrium, the whole assembly is strictly neutral. We attach a current generator across the interfaces between the leads and the device, to drive a current I through the structure; from the viewpoint of the nonequilibrium carriers within the conductor, the interfaces appear as an external source and sink for the current.

In this nonequilibrium situation, three boundary conditions apply without qualification:

- *thermodynamic equilibrium of the reservoirs.* Away from the disturbed device and its interface regions, the electron population is equilibrated and stable at any value of I. Thus the local electron density $n(\mu, T)$ in each lead is unchanged as a function of the equilibrium chemical potential μ and bath temperature T.
- *Charge neutrality of the reservoirs.* Within a well-defined finite range beyond the interfaces, strong metallic screening ensures the neutrality of the reservoir carriers with their ionic background, once again independently of I.
- *Charge neutrality of the driven device.* Since global neutrality and that of the individual reservoir leads are each preserved, the neutrality of the intervening, current-bearing conductor is secured for all values of the current. (Note: an independent formal proof of this criterion comes from the global gauge-invariance theorem for open conductors [6].)

Suppose that the bounded region in which the electrons are appreciably disturbed (namely the device with its interfaces) has volume Ω and contains N mobile electrons on average. The electrons are fully compensated at all times. Hence the neutrality conditions are equivalent to the statement that

$$\frac{\delta N}{\delta I} = 0 = \frac{\delta \Omega}{\delta I} \quad \text{for all } I. \tag{3}$$

In a time-dependent situation, the electron distribution function is the trace of the local-number quantum operator $\rho_{\mathbf{k}}(\mathbf{r}, t)$ with the nonequilibrium density matrix in the presence of the current:

$$f_{\mathbf{k}}(\mathbf{r}, t; I) = \langle \rho_{\mathbf{k}}(\mathbf{r}, t) \rangle_I$$

in which $\mathbf{k}$ and $\mathbf{r}$ are, respectively, the wave-vector and real-space labels (spin and valley indices are subsumed in $\mathbf{k}$, and we assign the effective volume normalization $(2\pi)^{-\nu}$ to it). It follows that

$$\int_\Omega d\mathbf{r} \int \frac{d\mathbf{k}}{(2\pi)^\nu} f_{\mathbf{k}}(\mathbf{r}, t; I) = N = \int_\Omega d\mathbf{r} \int \frac{d\mathbf{k}}{(2\pi)^\nu} f_{\mathbf{k}}^{\rm eq}(\mathbf{r}). \tag{4}$$

Since absolute neutrality holds, the number of carriers in the active region cannot change from the equilibrium value determined by the distribution $f^{\rm eq} \equiv \langle \rho \rangle_{I=0}$.

An immediate result of this identity is that *any* fluctuation, δN, in N is determined equally well by the corresponding fluctuation in $f_{\mathbf{k}}(\mathbf{r}, t; I)$ out of equilibrium, as it is by that in $f^{\rm eq}_{\mathbf{k}}(\mathbf{r})$ at equilibrium. Therefore

$$\int_{\Omega} d\mathbf{r} \int \frac{d\mathbf{k}}{(2\pi)^{\nu}} \delta f_{\mathbf{k}}(\mathbf{r}, t; I) = \delta N = \int_{\Omega} d\mathbf{r} \int \frac{d\mathbf{k}}{(2\pi)^{\nu}} \delta f^{\rm eq}_{\mathbf{k}}(\mathbf{r}). \tag{5}$$

This establishes the perfect-screening sum rule in its most general form.

4. NONEQUILIBRIUM COMPRESSIBILITY SUM RULE

We may now vary the population N systematically with respect to the chemical potential, a procedure that takes its shape from the response of the equilibrium state. In the important case of the free electron gas, we know the resulting analytical expressions:

$$\begin{aligned} f^{\rm eq}_{\mathbf{k}}(\mathbf{r}) &= \frac{1}{1 + \exp[(\varepsilon_{\mathbf{k}} + U_0(\mathbf{r}) - \mu)/k_{\rm B}T]}; \\ \frac{\partial f^{\rm eq}_{\mathbf{k}}(\mathbf{r})}{\partial \mu} &= \frac{1}{k_{\rm B}T} f^{\rm eq}_{\mathbf{k}}(\mathbf{r})(1 - f^{\rm eq}_{\mathbf{k}}(\mathbf{r})). \end{aligned} \tag{6}$$

Note that we incorporate the static mean-field potential $U_0(\mathbf{r})$ at equilibrium. This is set up whenever the system has inhomogeneities built into it.

Recalling that $\Delta f^{\rm eq} = k_{\rm B}T\partial f^{\rm eq}/\partial\mu$ defines the *mean-square thermal fluctuation* of the equilibrium occupation number [1], the corresponding nonequilibrium fluctuation $\Delta f(t)$ must satisfy

$$\int_{\Omega} d\mathbf{r} \int \frac{d\mathbf{k}}{(2\pi)^{\nu}} \Delta f_{\mathbf{k}}(\mathbf{r}, t; I) = \Delta N = \int_{\Omega} d\mathbf{r} \int \frac{d\mathbf{k}}{(2\pi)^{\nu}} \Delta f^{\rm eq}_{\mathbf{k}}(\mathbf{r}) \tag{7}$$

where the mean-square total number fluctuation is $\Delta N = k_{\rm B}T\partial N/\partial\mu$. This identity, emerging straight out of the perfect-screening rule, is the heart of the compressibility sum rule.

What does it mean, physically, to subject $f_{\mathbf{k}}(\mathbf{r}, t; I)$ – an inherently nonequilibrium object – to a variation with respect to μ, an equilibrium parameter? The answer is straightforward. Whether at equilibrium or not, the asymptotic density of carriers in the macroscopic leads remains unchanged. They sense nothing of the conditions (possibly extreme) that dominate the driven region. On the other hand, the density in the leads is directly controlled by the chemical potential local to each reservoir. This local value is unique, completely unaffected by the current, and proper to the *local* conduction band. Changing μ is equivalent to replacing the neutral reservoirs at electron density $n(\mu)$, say, with neutral reservoirs at the new density $n(\mu + \delta\mu)$. At equilibrium, that is the variation's physical meaning. Because of perfect screening, the variational procedure remains well defined even when a current is exciting the sample, all the while connected to its large stabilizing leads. Perfect screening confines such a disturbance absolutely to the finite region Ω. Nothing else is touched.

The compressibility sum rule for an open mesoscopic system can now be formulated. At equilibrium, the rule states that the compressibility κ for N mobile particles in volume Ω is given by [1]

$$\kappa = \frac{\Omega}{N^2}\frac{\partial N}{\partial \mu} = \frac{\Omega}{N k_{\rm B} T}\frac{\Delta N}{N}. \tag{8}$$

Note especially that κ is *and must always remain* independent of any transport parameter. This distinguishes Eq. (8) from the fluctuation-dissipation relation and Kubo formula.

The compressibility is the inverse of the stiffness (bulk modulus) of a many-particle system, which determines its sound velocity. Hence, customarily, κ has been investigated through sound-velocity measurements. The pattern typical of the right-hand side of Eq. (2) is repeated here; in analogy with the FDT, it is determined by an integral (equation (7)) of the microscopic electron-hole pair correlation, whose static limit is $-\partial f^{\rm eq}/\partial \mu$. For a careful exposition, see Ref. [1].

It is clear from Eqs. (3), (4) and (7) that, since all the quantities on the right-hand side of the compressibility sum rule are independent of I,

- *the compressibility of an open mesoscopic conductor is strictly invariant under transport.*

This is the principal result that we wish to recall. It articulates the conservation of particle number, just as perfect screening expresses the general gauge invariance of a conducting system.

5. APPLICATIONS

a. Violations of the compressibility sum rule

We are ready to revisit and judge some theoretical assumptions that have gained currency in recent mesoscopic research [9]. Though plausible at first blush, they turn out to vitiate the sum-rule structure of any transport model relying on them. In place of the gauge-invariant and microscopically canonical prescription of current-driven transport presented above, let us instead posit *ad hoc* that the current in a narrow mesoscopic conductor is sustained purely by a difference of chemical potentials between an upstream and a downstream electron reservoir [7],[9],[10].

Assume, for argument, that the density differential $n(\mu_{\rm up}) - n(\mu_{\rm dn})$ induced across the sample by the upstream and downstream chemical potentials, $\mu_{\rm up}$ and $\mu_{\rm dn}$, causes a diffusive-like current. Assume too that the electromotive force measured across the interfaces is $V = -(\mu_{\rm dn} - \mu_{\rm up})/e$ (and note that it makes no difference at all to the generality of the argument, whether V is static or time-dependent; cf Eqs. (4) & (5)).

The density profile along the conductor will be some function $n(\mu_{\rm up} - eV(x))$, taking the boundary values $n(\mu_{\rm up})$ and $n(\mu_{\rm dn})$ at the ends of the sample. According to such an account, in the linear-response limit the total number of carriers in the active structure of length L changes, under transport, by an amount

$$
\begin{aligned}
N(V) - N(0) &= \int_0^L [n(\mu_{\rm up} - eV(x)) - n(\mu_{\rm up})]dx \\
&\to \int_0^L \frac{dn}{d\mu_{\rm up}}(-eV(x))dx \\
&\sim -\Delta N(0)\frac{eV}{2k_{\rm B}T}.
\end{aligned}
\tag{9}
$$

The result is patently counter to Eq. (4), and consequently also breaks the compressibility sum rule.

If the mooted pseudo-diffusive arrangement is not to violate the mandatory invariance of total particle number for any driven, necessarily neutral, mesoscopic structure, the nominal density difference $n(\mu_{\rm up}) - n(\mu_{\rm dn})$ which causes the current (and so the current itself) cannot be accorded a standard physical meaning. This makes any conclusions drawn from such a picture hard – if not impossible – to interpret in a rational way.

The only escape from that unpalatable outcome is to allow effectively arbitrary inflows and outflows of charge between the device and its leads. In the event, the device cannot stay neutral under transport; there is *always* an uncompensated excess (or deficit) of carriers. Such a dilution of the perfect screening sum rule immediately destroys gauge invariance [6]. In any case, one or more of the sum rules is countermanded. Transport arguments based on this scenario are unphysical.

At this stage we have addressed only a single-electron view of the compressibility within pseudo-diffusive transport. However, at the level of the electron-hole pair correlations, the sum-rule violation is far worse (if that is possible). To make the point we take a representative pseudo-diffusive fluctuation analysis, that of Martin and Landauer [10]. In their theory, the current-current correlation function is synthesized from the set of all possible quantum-transmission outcomes that involve a single electron scattering off the core region of a one-dimensional quantum point contact. Its (constant) transmission probability is taken to be $\mathcal{T}$, where $0 \le \mathcal{T} \le 1$. Applying Eqs. (2.6)–(2.15) of Ref. [10], the total one-electron "fluctuation", say dN, can be obtained. This determines every quantity of experimental interest. We apply it now to the compressibility within the model.

Before doing so, it is vital to distinguish dN from the microscopically prescribed number fluctuation

$$
\delta N \sim (-\partial f^{\rm eq}/\partial\mu)\delta\mu
$$

appearing in the perfect-screening sum rule, Eq. (5). δN represents the *intrinsically correlated electron-hole excitations*: the conservation laws that govern electron-hole pair processes means that these are irreducible two-body objects [1]. On the other hand, dN is strictly constructed as a sum of one-body quantities.

The model at hand, and its closely related cousins [7],[9] take the single-carrier dN – not the two-body δN – as the fundamental fluctuation. Therefore the true pair correlations, crucial to the fluctuation structure of the electron gas, are missing.

Here the tacit assumption is, instead, that a fermionic particle-hole pair is always reducible to two kinematically uncorrelated, quite independent, single-particle excitation factors. Such an assumption is entirely contrary to basic Fermi-liquid theory [1],[3].

Following construction of the single-electron $\mathrm{d}N$ after Ref. [10], we arrive at the mean-square expectation ΔN over the quantum point contact:

$$\Delta N \equiv \langle (\mathrm{d}N)^2 - \langle \mathrm{d}N \rangle^2 \rangle = L\frac{n(\mu_{\rm up})}{2\varepsilon_{\rm F}}\left[\mathcal{T}^2 k_{\rm B}T + \mathcal{T}(1-\mathcal{T})\frac{\mu_{\rm up}-\mu_{\rm dn}}{2}\coth\left(\frac{\mu_{\rm up}-\mu_{\rm dn}}{2k_{\rm B}T}\right)\right]$$

$$= N\frac{k_{\rm B}T}{2\varepsilon_{\rm F}}\left[\mathcal{T} + \frac{\mathcal{T}(1-\mathcal{T})}{3}\left(\frac{eV}{2k_{\rm B}T}\right)^2 + \mathcal{O}\Big((eV/2k_{\rm B}T)^4\Big)\right], \qquad (10)$$

where $\varepsilon_{\rm F}$ is the Fermi energy at density $n(\mu_{\rm up})$ in the uniform wire (the Martin-Landauer model works only in the degenerate-electron limit $\varepsilon_{\rm F} \gg k_{\rm B}T$). To leading order in the voltage, the theory duly predicts the *transport-dependent* ratio

$$\frac{\Delta N}{N} = \left[\frac{\Delta N}{N}\right]_{\rm CSR}\left[\mathcal{T} + \frac{\mathcal{T}(1-\mathcal{T})}{3}\left(\frac{eV}{2k_{\rm B}T}\right)^2\right] \qquad (11)$$

in which

$$\left[\frac{\Delta N}{N}\right]_{\rm CSR} = \frac{k_{\rm B}T}{2\varepsilon_{\rm F}}$$

is the equilibrium ratio of the total mean-square number fluctuation to total carrier number as it appears in the transport-invariant compressibility sum rule, Eq. (8).

Equation (11) clearly contradicts the invariance of Eq. (8). *Even at equilibrium*, the total mean-square fluctuation ΔN in pseudo-diffusive theories depends on the transport parameter $\mathcal{T}$. In the strong backscattering limit it will vanish with $\mathcal{T}$.

The electronic compressibility cannot depend on any transport parameter. As we saw in the previous section, κ is an equilibrium property completely insensitive to external sources of elastic scattering (such as potential barriers) which determine the transmission fraction $\mathcal{T}$. Thus Eq. (11) fails to recover the physically required compressibility at equilibrium, much less away from it. Nor can one appeal to Coulomb effects here, since this spurious result is derived for noninteracting one-dimensional conduction electrons.

b. Electronic compressibility in nonuniform quantum channels

We turn our attention to some unexplored mesoscopic implications of the compressibility sum rule. When the conduction band of a quantum point contact, or similar device, differs from that of its bulk leads, there will be contact potentials at the interfaces. In Eq. (6) the mean-field potential $U_0(\mathbf{r})$, which vanishes when there is no band mismatch between device and leads, becomes a nontrivial function of the electron density. The complete variation of $f^{\rm eq}_{\mathbf{k}}(\mathbf{r})$ is

$$\frac{\delta f^{\rm eq}_{\mathbf{k}}(\mathbf{r})}{\delta \mu} = \left(1 - \frac{\delta U_0(\mathbf{r})}{\delta \mu}\right) \frac{\partial f^{\rm eq}_{\mathbf{k}}(\mathbf{r})}{\partial \mu}\bigg|_{U_0}. \tag{12}$$

Since

$$\frac{\delta n(\mathbf{r})}{\delta \mu} = \int \frac{d\mathbf{k}}{(2\pi)^\nu} \frac{\delta f^{\rm eq}_{\mathbf{k}}(\mathbf{r})}{\delta \mu},$$

the implicit Eq. (12) can be solved by integrating over $\mathbf{k}$ on both sides, and feeding back into it the leading right-hand factor in closed form. The result is

$$\frac{\delta f^{\rm eq}_{\mathbf{k}}(\mathbf{r})}{\delta \mu} = \frac{1}{1 + \dfrac{dU_0}{dn}\dfrac{\partial n(\mathbf{r})}{\partial \mu}} \frac{\partial f^{\rm eq}_{\mathbf{k}}(\mathbf{r})}{\partial \mu}. \tag{13}$$

An easy case to analyze is a uniform wire. Then U_0 is constant over most of the wire's length, except in the neighborhood of the interfaces where the band mismatch forces U_0 to vary. The leading factor on the right-hand side of Eq. (13) is nearly constant everywhere. Denote it by γ. It appears as an additional factor in the total compressibility for our inhomogeneous system:

$$\kappa \equiv \frac{\Omega}{N^2}\frac{\delta N}{\delta \mu} = \frac{\Omega}{N k_{\rm B} T}\frac{\gamma \Delta N}{N}. \tag{14}$$

The self-screening response of the contact potential substantially modifies the compressibility that would otherwise be observed in the absence of band inhomogeneity. Such effects are particularly strong in III-V heterojunction quantum-well structures [3].

We state the corollary of the perfect-screening Eq. (5) in this situation. It is the nonequilibrium compressibility sum rule for inhomogeneous mesoscopic systems (see Ref. [3] for its mathematical grounding).

- *The compressibility of a nonuniform mesoscopic conductor, driven at any current, is invariant and its form is given by Eq. (14).*

This is a surprising result, for it asserts that, even with the large changes in the carrier distribution of a device subjected to high current, there is *no* change at all in its electronic compressibility. That quantity is fixed, once and for all, by the electrostatic response of the contact potential at equilibrium.

The Coulomb-induced suppression of compressibility correlates closely with the analogous suppression theoretically anticipated for high-field current noise in heterojunction based, quasi-two-dimensional wires [3]. The nonequilibrium excess noise of such a structure is accessible [11]. It could be systematically measured, and direct comparison made with studies of the static compressibility in the same sample.

5. SUMMARY

The main result in this work is the "rigidity" of the electronic compressibility in a mesoscopic wire, in the sense that it cannot respond *in any way* to the internal

Coulomb effects that alter the nonequilibrium arrangements inside the conductor. That rigidity, coming from the utter dominance of the boundary conditions in mesoscopic transport, is striking evidence of the power and reach of the conservation laws. Novel experiments in this context, especially the comparative examination of static and fluctuation responses, would therefore be of interest.

We recapitulate our findings. The conserving sum rules are universal constraints that apply to any system of mobile electrons. They express the basic conservation laws through a set of relations between, on the one hand, one-body properties that are measurable (conductance, particle number, compressibility) and, on the other hand, expectation values of microscopically calculable, two-body correlation functions.

Sum rules embody the unified origin of single- and many-particle behavior in the electron gas. We have shown that the principal sum rules for *energy dissipation*, *charge neutrality* and *number conservation* are core properties of a mesoscopic conductor. Their consequences are directly observable in the laboratory. A key quantity for experimental investigation is the compressibility.

The implications of the compressibility sum rule have not previously been studied in the mesoscopic setting. In sharp contrast with its crucial and long-established role in electron-gas physics [1], this property has not had any attention paid to it by more popularly accepted phenomenologies of mesoscopic transport and noise [7],[9],[10]. It is not so astonishing, then, to find that the compressibility sum rule is violated by such approaches.

Through the gauge invariance of the boundary conditions and their overriding influence on internal carrier dynamics, it may indeed be said that the conservation laws and their leading sum rules instill the very meaning of "mesoscopic" conduction. Therefore a microscopically credible description of mesoscopics must satisfy *all* these rules, not just a subset, else the description is faulty. Its reliability is void of any guarantee – notwithstanding any perceived empirical or cosmetic merits.

We appear to be enjoying a phase of development in mesoscopics wherein heuristically dominated theory-making is much to be preferred over labor-intensive, assiduously orthodox and microscopically correct analyses of electron transport. In such a climate, Sir Francis Bacon's old warning against subjective confections of knowledge remains apt today:

God forbid that we should give out a dream of our imagination for a pattern of the world.

REFERENCES

[1] D. Pines and P. Nozières, *The Theory of Quantum Liquids* (Benjamin, New York, 1966).

[2] W. Magnus and W. Schoenmaker, *Quantum Transport in Sub-micron Devices: A Theoretical Introduction* (Springer, Berlin, 2002).

[3] F. Green and M. P. Das, *J. Phys.: Condens. Matter* **12** 5251, 2000.

[4] C. J. Stanton, PhD Thesis, Cornell University, unpublished (1986).

[5] J. M. Ziman, *Models of Disorder* (Cambridge University Press, Cambridge, 1979), Ch 10.

[6] F. Sols, *Phys. Rev. Lett.* **67**, 2874 (1991).

[7] Ya. M. Blanter and M. Büttiker, *Phys. Rep.* **336**, 1 (2000).

[8] M. P. Das and F. Green, *J. Phys.: Condens. Matter* **15**, L687 (2003).

[9] Y. Imry and R. Landauer, *Rev. Mod. Phys.* **71**, S306 (1999).

[10] Th. Martin and R. Landauer, *Phys. Rev. B* **45**, 1742 (1992).

[11] M. Reznikov *et al.*, *Phys. Rev. Lett.* **75**, 3340 (1995).

CLUSTERING OF THE ELECTRON-HOLE LIQUID AND THE ELECTRON-PROTON MIXTURE

M. Saarela and T. Taipaleenmäki

Department of Physical Sciences, University of Oulu
P.O. Box 3000, FIN-90014 University of Oulu, Finland

F. V. Kusmartsev

Department of Physics, Loughborough University
Loughborough, Leics LE11 3TU, U.K.

1. INTRODUCTION

Quantum fluids form the basis of the condensed matter physics. The most important examples are electrons in metals, electron-hole and excitonic fluids in semi-metals and semiconductors generated by irradiation of light or by doping, electron-proton plasmas in cold stars and in high pressure and shock wave experiments performed in search of metallic hydrogen. All these fluids are usually considered as spatially homogeneous and in all of them the Coulomb potential dominates the interaction between particles. At high densities this interaction is strongly screened and the system can be treated in a simple way as it happens, for example, in many metals where electrons form the so-called Fermi liquid. However, when the density decreases the screened interaction is not any more a monotonic function of the distance between particles. At intermediate ranges the Coulomb potential is over-screened, which changes the character of the interaction. As a result the attraction between particles having different charges becomes repulsion and, vice versa, the repulsion between particles having the same charge is transformed into attraction. This may lead to formation of bound clusters of different numbers of particles and charges. Further more, due to the attractive, effective interaction between clusters and their large effective masses clusters may condensate into a new type of liquid at low temperatures.

Free electrons and holes created in semiconductors under irradiation of light may condense into the electron-hole liquid (EHL) when their density is high enough. This quantum phenomenon predicted originally by Keldysh [1] was then intensively studied theoretically [2] and experimentally [3]. At very low densities free electrons and holes are bound into excitons analogous to hydrogen atoms. The exciton gas undergoes

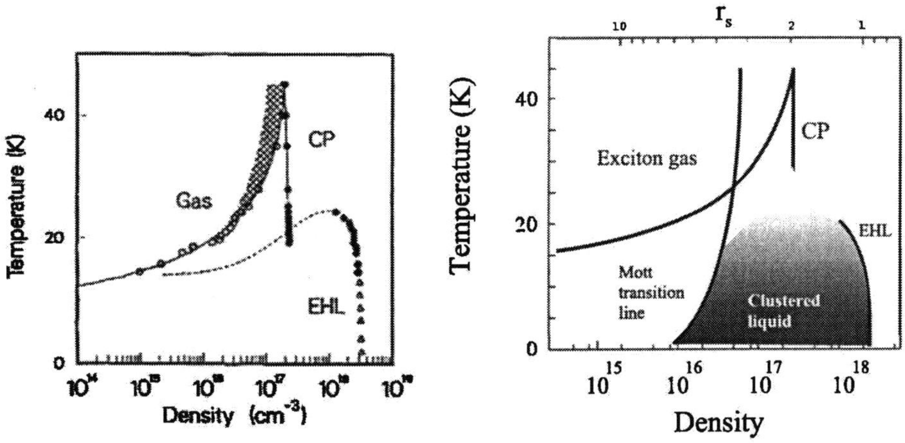

Figure 1. The phase diagram of the mixture of electrons and holes in the density-temperature plane. The horizontal axis is the density of electrons or holes per cubic centimeter excited in Si under irradiation of light. In the left figure the experimental results for three regions: the EHL, Condensed Plasma (CP) and Exciton gas are marked [3]. In the exciton gas a region of trions and polyexcitons has also been observed. In the right figure the calculated Mott transition line is shown together with the theoretical estimation of the density region at which the new liquid of the charged complexes of electrons and holes can exist.

Mott's metal-insulator phase transition at much lower density than needed for the appearance of the metallic EHL [4]. This mismatch between the critical value of the densities for the instability of free excitons and the threshold value of the density for the appearance of EHL stimulated a controversial dispute for decades of what happens in the range of densities between these two critical values. We show that in this density range a new structural liquid consisting of differently charged clusters of electrons and holes arises due to the over-screening of the Coulomb interaction. We propose a new complete phase diagram shown in Figure 1. where two established phases, the gas of free excitons and the electron-hole liquid, are complemented with a new structural liquid phase consisting of the charged clusters.

Protons and electrons mixed together form a molecular gas at the room temperature and low pressures. At zero temperature molecules solidify into a quantum crystal, which is an insulator. By increasing the pressure (or density) molecular crystal undergoes a series of phase transitions and may even melt into clustered liquid before protons form an atomic crystal. Further increase of the pressure melts the atomic crystal into the liquid metallic hydrogen. In Figure 2. we presend the complete phase diagram of the proton-electron mixture in the pressure-temperature plane. The well known molecular and plasma phases are shown together with the new phase made of charged clusters similar to the clusters in the mixture of electrons and holes. These clusters condense into a liquid state. The liquid state is very degenerate, because there are very many different configurations of clusters with the same energy. Therefore, the entropy of this state is very large and with increasing temperature the clustered liquid has a free energy lower than the competing atomic and molecular solids.

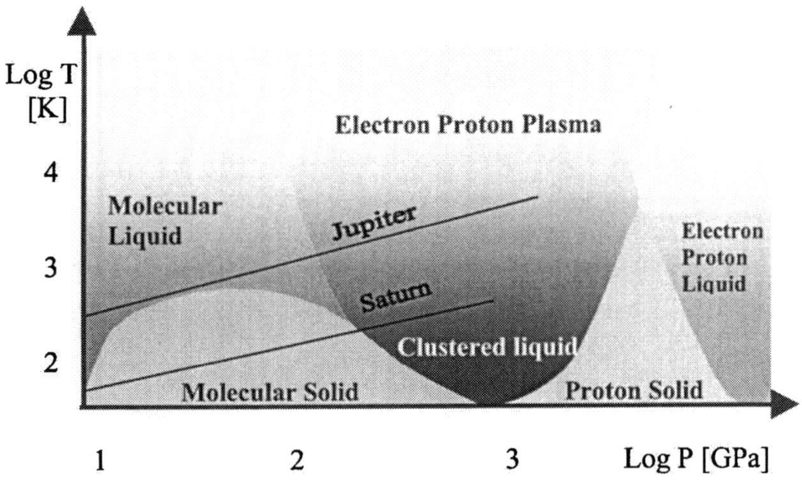

Figure 2. The phase diagram of the mixture of electrons and protons in the pressure-temperature plane. The new clustered phase is shown by the shaded area in the middle. The largest clusters form at the lowest temperatures. With increasing temperatures clusters dissociate and the clustered phase gradually transforms into the electron-proton plasma, noted by light gray at the top of the phase diagram. The straight lines describe the variation of the temperature with pressure in Jupiter and Saturn from the cool surface to the hot center of the planet.

Molecular phases are mainly insulators, but molecular solids may become metallic at high pressures due to overlap of the bands. The proton solid and liquid phases have good metallic conductivity, mainly due to free electrons. The conductivity of the clustered liquid depends strongly on the temperature and can also be associated with free electrons ionized from clusters. The ionization energy is very small and when the temperature increases the electron concentration increases rapidly from zero and therefore the conductivity of the clustered liquid increases dramatically. These phenomena have strong implications for the physics of giant planets, such as Jupiter and Saturn as well as brown dwarfs, because they are made of hydrogen. We claim that due to gravity hydrogen inside these planets is transformed into a new liquid consisting of charged clusters. In the phase diagram of Fig. 2. we show that the interior of these planets is filled with the clustered liquid. The temperature gradient creates convection flow that in turn generates the electric current and the magnetic field around these planets like in a dynamo. The strength of the generated magnetic field depends mainly on the interior temperature. The temperature inside Jupiter is higher than in Saturn and therefore the electron concentration in the clustered liquid of Saturn is of the order of a magnitude smaller than that in Jupiter. That is why the measured magnetic field on Jupiter is 20 -30 times larger than on Saturn. In the laboratory shock wave experiments metalization of the liquid molecular hydrogen has been found at temperatures of about 3000 K and at the pressure of 140 GPa [5]. High pressure experiments up to 320 GPa at low temperatures have not yet reached the metallic state.

In Fig. 3. we show the phase diagram of two-component charged mixture at zero temperature ranging from the electrons mixed with holes in semiconductors up

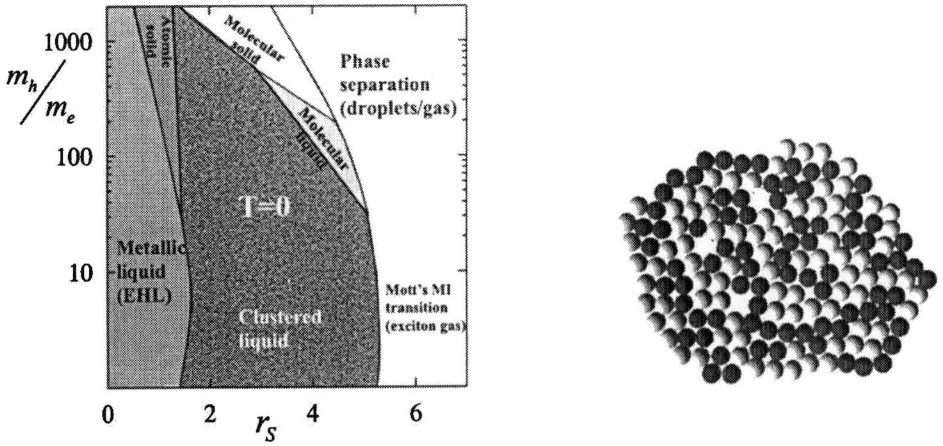

Figure 3. In the left figure is phase diagram of electrons mixed with positively charged particles at zero temperature. The vertical axis gives the mass ratio of mixed particles ranging from the typical values of hole masses up to protons mixed with electrons. In the right figure is a schematic 2-dimensional view of the clustered phase.

to electron-proton mixtures. The density range covers the homogeneous metallic liquid down to excitonic or molecular gas. When the mass of the positive charge becomes heavier the molecular liquid and atomic solid phases begin to form and further increase of the mass ratio makes the molecular solid stable as we know from the solid molecular hydrogen ground state. By increasing the pressure these molecular phases form a liquid of charged clusters. Further increase of pressure makes the atomic solid stable before everything melts into a metallic liquid of homogeneously distributed charges.

The physical origin of the new liquid of the charged electron-hole and electron-proton complexes is the over-screening of the Coulomb interaction. In Fig. 4. we show its behavior for one and two hole impurities in the electron gas [6] in the case where the masses of electrons and holes are equal. The behavior is fairly independent of the mass ratio. At large distances the Coulomb repulsion is a perfectly screened and at short distances one sees remnants of the 1/r singularity. In between there is a region of over-screening associated with the interplay between the many-body effects and bare Coulomb interaction. The maximum of the repulsion in the electron-hole interaction increases near the Mott transition indicating that the hole has collected a cluster of electrons around it. The attractive minimum of the hole-hole potential becomes deeper when the pairing instability is approached leading to the formation of a dimer.

2. VARIATIONAL THEORY OF QUANTUM FLUIDS

The microscopic description of the mixture of charged particles begins with a

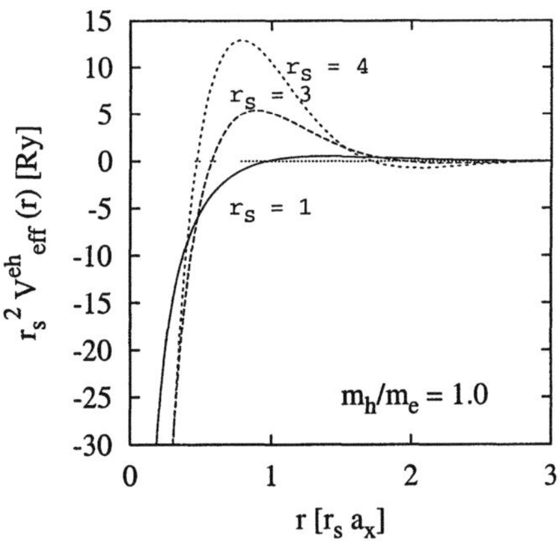

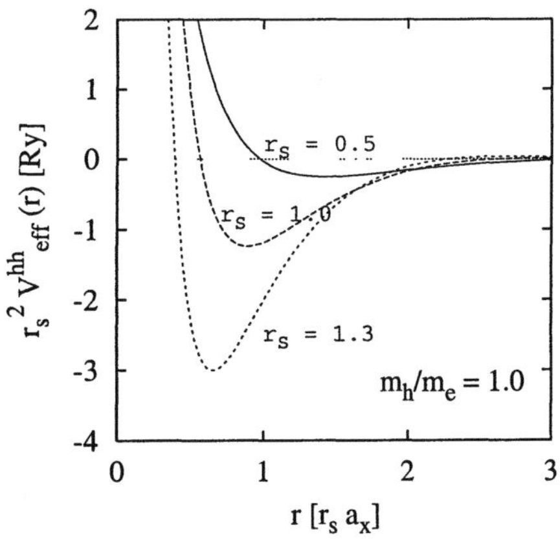

Figure 4. The effective electron-hole (left figure) and hole-hole interaction (right figure) potentials in the dilute hole concentration limit calculated for different densities indicated with the r_s-values shown in the figure. The masses of electrons m_e and holes m_h are equal.

well defined Hamiltonian,

$$H = -\sum_{\alpha=e,h}\sum_{i=1}^{N}\frac{\hbar^2}{2m_\alpha}\nabla_i^2 + \frac{1}{2}\sum_{\alpha,\beta=e,h}\sum_{i,j=1}^{N}{}' \frac{q_\alpha q_\beta}{\varepsilon|\mathbf{r}_i^\alpha - \mathbf{r}_j^\beta|}\,. \tag{1}$$

Indices α and β refer to the type of a particle (electron or hole), and subscripts i and j refer to the individual particles. We assume that the numbers of both positive and negative charges are equal to N. The prime on the summation symbol in Eq. (1) indicates that no two pairs (i,α), (j,β) can be the same. In semiconductors the masses are determined by the band structure and Coulomb forces between charges $q_e = -q_h = -|e|$ are reduced by the dielectric constant ε.

It is customary to use excitonic units where energies are measured in units of the binding energy of the electron-hole pair, called excitonic Rydberg $E_x = \mu e^4/(2\hbar^2\varepsilon^2)$ with the reduced mass $\mu = m_e m_h/(m_e + m_h)$. The length unit is then $a_x = \hbar^2\varepsilon/(\mu e^2) = a_0 m_e \varepsilon/\mu$ in terms of the Bohr radius a_0. All distances are calculated in units of $r_0 = (3V/(4\pi N))^{1/3}$, the average distance between electrons in the volume V, and all momenta in units of r_0^{-1}. The ratio $r_s = r_0/a_x$ defines the usual dimensionless density parameter. The Fermi momentum of electrons, $k_{Fe} = \left(3\pi^2\rho/\nu_e\right)^{1/3}$, depends on their density $\rho = N/V$ and the degeneracy ν_e of the conduction bands. Similarly we define the Fermi momentum of holes $k_{Fh} = \left(3\pi^2\rho/\nu_h\right)^{1/3}$, where ν_h is the degeneracy of the hole bands.

For the ground-state wave function we make the Jastrow variational ansatz

$$\begin{aligned}\Psi_0(\{\mathbf{r}_i^{(\alpha)}\}) &= e^{\frac{1}{2}U(\{\mathbf{r}_i^{(\alpha)}\})}\Phi(\{\mathbf{r}_i^{(\alpha)}\})\\ U(\{\mathbf{r}_i^{(\alpha)}\}) &= \frac{1}{2!}\sum_{\alpha,\beta}\sum_{i,j}^{N}{}' u^{\alpha,\beta}(\mathbf{r}_i,\mathbf{r}_j)\end{aligned} \tag{2}$$

with the shorthand notation $(\{\mathbf{r}_i^{(\alpha)}\}) = (\mathbf{r}_1^{(e)}, ..., \mathbf{r}_N^{(e)}, \mathbf{r}_1^{(h)}, \ldots, \mathbf{r}_N^{(h)})$. The Fermionic character is included in the Slater determinants of plane waves $\Phi_0(\{\mathbf{r}_i^{(\alpha)}\})$. The correlation functions $u^{\alpha,\beta}(\mathbf{r}_i, \mathbf{r}_j)$ are determined from the variational principle using the Euler equations [7]

$$\frac{\delta E}{\delta u^{\alpha\beta}(\mathbf{r}_i, \mathbf{r}_j)} = 0\,, \tag{3}$$

where

$$E = \frac{\langle \Psi_0 | H | \Psi_0 \rangle}{\langle \Psi_0 | \Psi_0 \rangle} \tag{4}$$

is the variational energy expectation value.

The key ingredients of the theory are, along with the correlation functions, the static structure functions $S^{\alpha\beta}(k)$ and the direct distribution functions $\tilde{\Gamma}^{\alpha\beta}(k)$. Within the single loop approximation these quantities are connected with the 2×2 matrix equation

$$\mathbf{S}(k) = \mathbf{S_F}(k) + [\mathbf{S_F}\tilde{\mathbf{\Gamma}}\mathbf{S_F}](k)\,, \tag{5}$$

where $\mathbf{S_F}(k)$ is the diagonal free Fermi–gas structure function. Without going into further details, which can be found from the original papers, we assert that the coupled Euler equations can be written in the form [8]

$$\left[\mathbf{S}^{-1}\mathbf{H_1}\mathbf{S}^{-1}\right](k) - \left[\mathbf{S_F}^{-1}\mathbf{H_1}\mathbf{S_F}^{-1}\right](k) = 2\tilde{\mathbf{V}}_{\mathrm{p-h}}(k)\,. \tag{6}$$

The matrix $\mathbf{H_1}(k)$ has simply free–particle kinetic energies in the diagonal and $\tilde{\mathbf{V}}_{\mathrm{p-h}}(k)$ is the Fourier transform of the so–called particle–hole interaction,

$$\begin{aligned} V_{\mathrm{p-h}}^{(\alpha\beta)}(r) &= \left[1 + \Gamma^{(\alpha\beta)}(r)\right] V_C^{(\alpha\beta)}(r) \\ &+ \left[\frac{\hbar^2}{2m_\alpha} + \frac{\hbar^2}{2m_\beta}\right] \left|\nabla\sqrt{1 + \Gamma^{(\alpha\beta)}(r)}\right|^2 + \Gamma^{(\alpha\beta)}(r) w_{\mathrm{I}}^{(\alpha\beta)}(r)\,, \end{aligned} \tag{7}$$

where $V_C^{(\alpha\beta)}(r)$ is the Coulomb interaction between particles α and β and $\mathbf{w}_{\mathrm{I}}(r)$ is the induced interaction matrix in coordinate space. In momentum space it has the following matrix form

$$\tilde{\mathbf{w}}_{\mathrm{I}}(k) = -\tilde{\mathbf{V}}_{\mathrm{p-h}}(k) - \frac{1}{2}\left[\mathbf{S_F}^{-1}\mathbf{H_1}\tilde{\mathbf{\Gamma}} + \tilde{\mathbf{\Gamma}}\mathbf{H_1}\mathbf{S_F}^{-1}\right](k)\,. \tag{8}$$

Equations (6), (7), and (8) form a closed set of equations that can be solved by iteration until convergence is reached. From these distribution and structure functions the variational total energy E can then be calculated. At high densities and small values of r_s the dominating terms are the Fermi kinetic energy and the exchange energy

$$\frac{T}{N} + \frac{E_{ex}}{N} = \frac{3\gamma^2\mu}{5r_s^2}\left(\frac{1}{\nu_e^{2/3}m_e} + \frac{1}{\nu_h^{2/3}m_h}\right) - \frac{3\gamma}{2\pi r_s}\left(\frac{1}{\nu_e^{1/3}} + \frac{1}{\nu_h^{1/3}}\right). \tag{9}$$

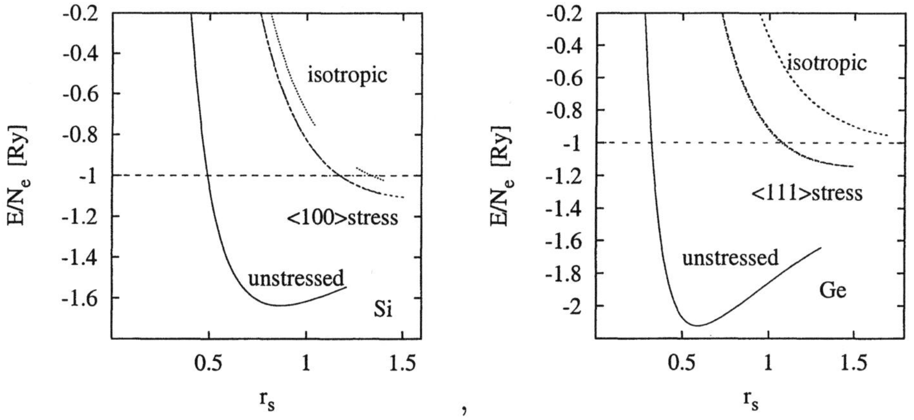

Figure 5. The total energy per electron in Si (left figure) and in Ge (right figure) is shown as a function of r_s in excitonic units. The lowest curve in both figures is the energy of the unstressed crystal structure. The curves in the middle are results when a stress in the given direction is applied to the crystals to reduce the degeneracy. For a comparison we show the results for fully isotropic, non-degenerate bands in both semiconductors.

The constant $\gamma = (9\pi/4)^{1/3}$. The correlation energy is simplest to calculate using the coupling constant integration

$$\frac{E_c}{N} = \frac{1}{\pi \varepsilon r_s} \sum_{\alpha\beta} q_\alpha q_\beta \int_0^{r_s} d\lambda \int_0^{\infty} dk \left(S^{(\alpha\beta)}(\lambda, k) - S_F^{(\alpha\beta)}(k) \right) . \tag{10}$$

A necessary condition for the existence of a solution to the Euler equation (6) is obtained by diagonalizing the Feynman–like matrix

$$\text{diag}\left(\mathbf{H_1 S^{-1}}\right) = \mathbf{D}^{1/2} \tag{11}$$

and requiring that the eigenvalues are real. The diagonal elements are the Feynman approximations of the two collective excitations in the mixture; the optical and acoustic modes. In the exact theory these would be the exact energies of the collective modes in the long wave–length limit.

3. RESULTS

We apply this theory to two semiconductors Si and Ge where the EHL-phase is well studied. The degeneracy of their band structures is essential for the stability of the EHL. Also the anisotropy of the electron bands and the difference in the effective hole masses has been included in our calculation of the kinetic and exchange energies following the method used by Combescot and Nozieres [9]. The correlation energy is fairly independent on the masses and we can safely use there the spherical approximation for electrons $m_e = 3(1/m_{||} + 2/m_{\perp})^{-1}$ and the average of the inverse masses of holes $m_h = 2(1/m_H + 1/m_L)^{-1}$. Fig. 5. summarizes our results for the

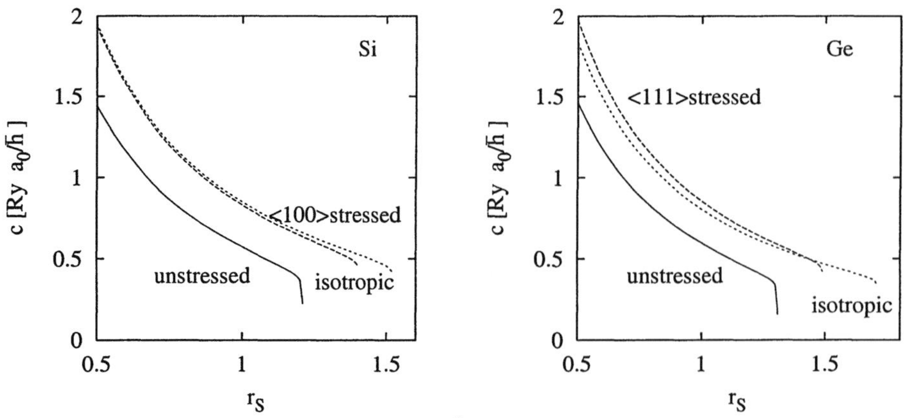

Figure 6. The speed of sound in the acoustic mode of the electron-hole liquid in unstressed and stressed Ge is shown as a function of r_s. In the top curve we have assumed isotropic band structure. At some critical density all the curves show a sharp drop of the sound velocity, which indicate the instability of the ground state associated with the electron-hole liquid and the formation of the new phase with the charged electron-hole complexes.

total energy as a function of r_s. Both equations of state show a clear minimum associated with the EHL. In Si the minimum is -1.64 Ry at $r_s = 0.87$ and in Ge -2.12 Ry at r_s =0.59 in good agreement with measurements. By applying stress on the crystals the valley degeneracy of the bands can be partially or totally removed. This shifts the energy minimum to lower density. In Ge the stress in $< 111 >$ direction removes the degeneracy completely and the minimum is barely visible with -1.15 Ry at r_s= 1.57. The stress applied in the $< 100 >$ direction in Si reduces the degeneracy from six- to two-fold and no stable EHL minimum can be reached. In the model case of fully isotropic, non-degenerate bands no stable EHL phase can exist as seen from Fig. 1.

All of the energy curves are calculated up to the density where the mixture becomes unstable against cluster formation. We see that by calculating the speed of sound of the acoustic excitation mode. The termination point depends somewhat on the degeneracy and is found between $1.1 < r_s < 1.5$. The results are shown in Fig. 6. The speed of sound drops very rapidly to zero at the critical density indicating that the homogeneous liquid is no more stable. It also suggests that phase transition is of first order. This instability shows up also in the dressed distribution function $\mathbf{\Gamma}(\mathbf{r})$. When the critical density is approached from the EHL side the nearest neighbor peaks begin to grow indicating that clusters are forming. Thus we can state that the more stable phase, which arises at lower density, consists of bound clusters. The size of these clusters is controlled by the Coulomb force (like in the Coulomb blockade) and the spin orientation. Therefore, complexes of minimal size are most favored. However, the density of the system is still so high that also larger complexes can arise. A schematic possible structure of the clustered phase is shown in Fig. 3.

Wolfe et al.[3] have made a detailed analysis of the photoluminescence spectra in Si. The contributions coming from the EHL, free excitons (FE) and small gaseous

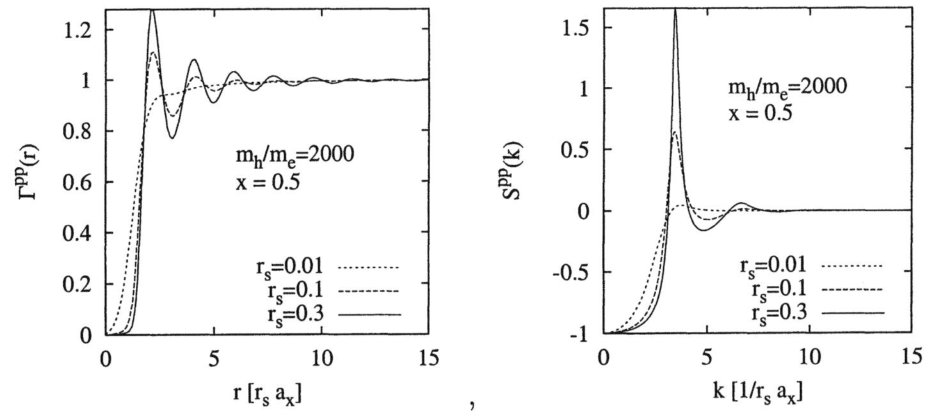

Figure 7. The proton-proton components $\Gamma^{pp}(r)$ and $S^{pp}(k)$ in the liquid metallic hydrogen for densities marked in the figure. Increasing oscillations in $\Gamma^{pp}(r)$ and increasing height of the peak in $S^{pp}(k)$ indicate that the density is approaching the solidification instability.

excitonic clusters have been identified clearly and shown in Fig. 1. The remaining luminescence intensity after subtraction of these contributions is associated with the condensed plasma phase. Our finding of the new liquid consisting of the charged complexes resolves this long-term puzzle between the interpretations of these experiments. At temperatures $T \geq 20$ K most of the charged complexes will dissociate and the luminescence from the dense electron-hole plasma will be dominating as has been identified in Si [3].

When the degeneracy and the anisotropy of the band structure are removed by stressing the crystal or by studying other non–degenerate semiconductors then the clustered liquid becomes the true ground state of the system. We can not calculate its exact structure, but the density is determined by the maximum of the depth of the inter-particle potential. Possibly, in light of our results droplets with EHL found in experiments in direct-gap CuCl semiconductors [10] may be associated with droplets of the charged complexes rather than with conventional EHL since the charged complexes arise at lower density than EHL.

In a more extreme case when we let the mass ratio m_h/m_e grow up to 2000 we reach the regime of the liquid metallic hydrogen. As seen from the phase diagram in Fig. 3. this system is at high densities in the homogeneous metallic liquid phase. The instability reached by decreasing the density does not break the system into clusters, instead we find that the new phase is a crystal of protons. The direct correlation function $\Gamma^{pp}(r)$ and structure function $S^{pp}(k)$ of the proton-proton component are shown in Fig. 7. for three densities in the approach to the instability. They clearly indicate a formation of an ordered phase. From the position of the peak of the structure function we can read the reciprocal lattice constant $k_r \approx 4/(r_s a_x)$. From the energetics we can also determine that the liquid metallic hydrogen can exist only at very high pressures before it turns into metallic atomic crystal. From this work we can not determine the metal-insulator transition density into the molecular H_2 crystal, which is the ground state of the electron-proton mixture at zero pressure and zero temperature. In the phase diagram we give only a rough estimate that if $m_h/m_e \geq 20$ then the transition from the homogeneous liquid into solid will take place instead of clustered liquid. By further decrease of the density turns the clustered phase into molecular liquid or solid depending of the mass ratio.

4. CONCLUSIONS

The formation of a new structured liquid consisting of the charged complexes described here is a very general phenomenon. The over-screening of the Coulomb interaction between charged particles can bind charged clusters in systems ranging from the electron-hole mixtures in semiconductors up to the electron-proton mixtures in Jovian planets. Clusters form a degenerate liquid at zero temperature. With increasing temperature they ionize and dissociate and gradually turn into a fully ionized plasma. Based on this idea we have proposed new phase diagrams for the electron-hole mixtures in semiconductors and for the electron-proton mixtures at high pressures. Clustered phase can have an important role in explaining the order of magnitude difference between magnetic fields in Jupiter and Saturn.

ACKNOWLEDGMENTS

The work was supported, in part, by the Academy of Finland under the project 100487 and the graduate school for Material Physics. The grant from the EPSRC (to M.S.) is gratefully acknowledged. We are grateful to V. B. Timofeev, I. Kukushkin, E. Krotscheck and P. Pietiläinen for the very illuminating discussions.

REFERENCES

[1] for review see, L. V. Keldysh and C. D. Jeffries, *Electron-Hole Droplets in Semi conductors*, (North Holland, Amsterdam) 1983.

[2] for review see, G. Beni and T. M. Rice, Phys. Rev. B **10**, 768 (1978).

[3] for review see, L. M. Smith and J.P. Wolfe, Phys. Rev. B **51**, 7521 (1995).

[4] K. V. Kulakovskii, I. V. Kukushkin and V. B. Timofeev, Sov. Phys. JETP **51**, 191 (1980).

[5] S. T. Weir, A. C. Mitchel and W. J. Nellis, Phys. Rev. Lett. **76**, 1860 (1996).

[6] M. Saarela, T. Taipaleenmäki and F. V. Kusmartsev, J. Phys. A **36**, 9223 (2003).

[7] E. Feenberg, *Theory of Quantum Liquids*, (Academic, New York) (1969).

[8] E. Krotscheck and M. Saarela, Phys. Rep. **232**, 1 (1993).

[9] M. Combescot and P. Nozieres, J. Phys. C **5**, 2369 (1972).

[10] M. Nagai, R. Shimano and M. Kuwata-Gonokami, Phys. Rev. Lett. **86**, 5795 (2001).

QUANTUM STATISTICAL THEORY OF THE FERMIONIC QUANTUM HALL EFFECT

S. Fujita and K. Ito

University at Buffalo, SUNY, Buffalo, NY 14260, USA

1. INTRODUCTION

In 1980 von Klitzing *et al.* [1] reported a discovery of the integer Quantum Hall Effect (QHE). In 1982 Tsui *et al.* [2] discovered the fractional QHE. Fig. 1 represents the data reported by Tsui [3] for the Hall resistivity $\rho_H \equiv E_H/J$ (E_H = Hall field, J = current density) and the resistivity $\rho \equiv E/J$ (E = applied field) in heterojunction GaAs/AlGaAs at 60 mK. The Quantum Hall (QH) states at the Landau Level (LL) occupation ratio (filling factor) $\nu = P/Q = 1, 2, \ldots, 5$ are visible. Each QH state with the Hall resistivity plateau (horizontal stretch) is accompanied by zero resistance (superconducting). In 1987 Willett *et al.* [4] observed the even-denominator (fermionic) QHE at $\nu = 5/2$. Their data, ref. 4, Fig. 2, show that the resistivity has clear dips at 25, 40 and 100 mK, the dips converging to a point while the Hall resistivity is linear in the magnetic field (magnitude) B and it has a value $(h/e^2)(5/2)^{-1}$ within 0.5% at $\nu = 5/2$. This behavior is distinctly different from that observed for the odd-denominator (bosonic) QHE at $\nu = 7/3$ or $\nu = 8/3$. Similar fermionic QH behavior was also observed at $\nu = 1/2,\ 3/2,\ 3/4,\ \ldots$, in later experiments [5]. The difference between the fermionic and bosonic QHE was clearly demonstrated in the surface-acoustic wave (SAW) propagation study [6], where the SAW amplitude deviation is negative (positive) for the fermionic (bosonic) QHE, suggesting different charge carriers present in the system. To summarize in the fermionic QHE (a) the resistivity ρ at $\nu = P/Q$, even Q, for a pure sample approaches a constant in the low temperature limit, (b) the Hall resistivity ρ_H is B-linear and its value is approximately equal to $(h/e^2)(Q/P)$ at $\nu = P/Q$. In contrast in the bosonic QHE at $\nu = P/Q$, odd Q, the resistivity ρ vanishes as $T \to 0$, and ρ_H has a plateau exactly equal to $(h/e^2)(Q/P)$.

The departure point for all theories for the fractional QHE is the Laughlin ground-state wavefunction [7]. Laughlin [7] and Haldane [8] showed that the qasi-particle (elementary excitation) over the Laughlin ground-state at $\nu = P/Q$, odd Q, can have the fractional charge

$$e_b = e/Q \quad \text{(c–boson)}\,. \tag{1}$$

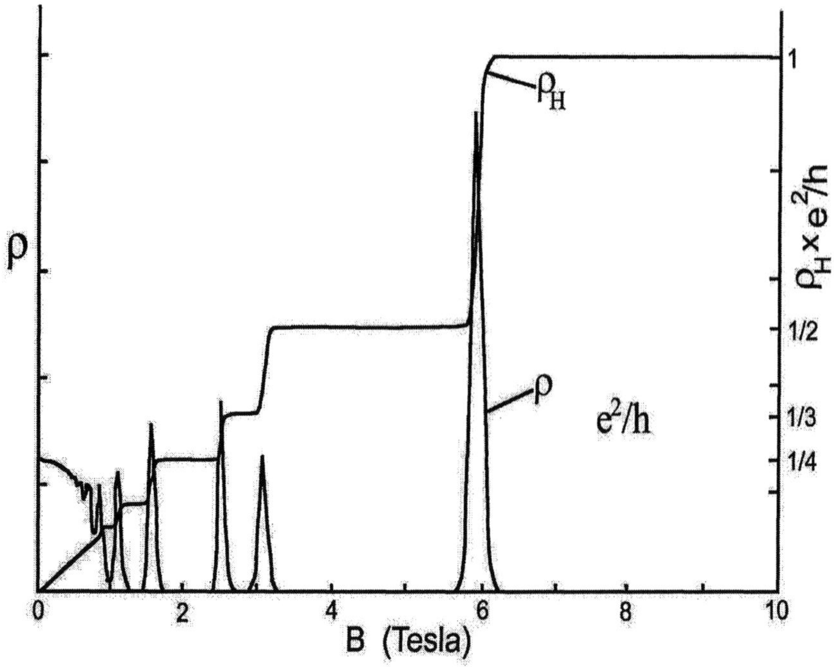

Figure 1. Observed QHE in GaAs/AlGaAs heterojunction at 60 mK, after Tsui [3]. The Hall resistivity ρ_H and the resistance ρ are shown as a function of the magnetic field B in tesla.

This surprising prediction was later confirmed by experiments [9]. The system ground state represented by Laughlin wave function does not carry a current. To interpret the magnetotransport data it is convenient to introduce composite (c-) particles (bosons, fermions). The c-boson (fermion), each containing an electron and an odd (even) number of elementary fluxes (fluxons), were introduced by Zhang *et al.* [10] and others (Jain [11]) for the description of the fractional QHE (Fermi liquid). Ezawa surveyed the theoretical and experimental QHE in his book, citing over 400 publications [12]. Halperin, Lee and Read reviewed the state of the matter at $\nu = 1/2$ in 1993 [13]. In particular they showed that the SAW amplitude sign at $\nu = 1/2$ can be explained with the assumed existence of the c-fermions. They arrived at an expression for the resistivity ρ proportional to the impurity density n_{imp} based on a c-fermionic model. More recently Read reviewed and examined the $\nu = 5/2$ puzzle from the paired-QH-state point of view [14]. Analizing the data reported by Tsui [3], Hajdu *et al.* [15] predicted that the conductivity σ in the integer QHE region is quantized: $\sigma \sim e^2/h$ at the even-denominator filling factor, see Fig. 2.

Laughlin pointed out a remarkable similarity between the QHE and the High-Temperture Superconductivity (HTSC), both occurring in two-dimensional(2D) systems [16]. Following Bardeen, Cooper and Schrieffer (BCS) [17], we regard the phonon exchange attraction as the causes of both effects. Starting with a reasonable Hamiltonian, we calculate everything using the standard statistical mechanical methods. Fujita *et al.* treated the bosonic QHE based on an electron-fluxon model [18], in which the electron and fluxons are bound by the phonon excahnge attraction. In the present work we shall show that a fermionic QH state is developed at $\nu = P/Q$, even Q, in which the conductivity $\sigma \equiv \rho^{-1}$ approaches a universal constant $(e^2/h)Q^{-1}$ as $T \to 0$ and the Hall conductivity $\sigma_H = \rho_H^{-1}$ becomes approximately equal to $(e^2/h)(P/Q)$, thus confirming the prediction by Hajdu *et al.* The resistivity widths are symmetric with respect to high and low fields. They are tmperature-dependent. The resistivity ρ smoothly approaches a constant as the field is lowered toward zero.

2. THE HAMILTONIAN

We assume the interface in AlGaAs/GaAs/AlGaAs being in (001). The planner arrays of $Ga^{3+}(A)$ and $As^{3-}(B)$ are located alternately along [100] as $ABA'B'AB\cdots$. The longitudinal phonon, proceeding in [100] can generate a density wave, which affects the electron (fluxon) motion by the lattice-ionic charge displacement (current), establishing the electron (fluxon)-phonon interaction. The phonon exchange between an electron and a fluxon generates a transition in the electron states with the effective interaction [18]:

$$V_{\rm ef} \equiv |V_q V_q'| \frac{\hbar\omega_q}{(\epsilon_{|\mathbf{k}+\mathbf{q}|s} - \epsilon_{ks})^2 - \hbar^2\omega_q^2}\,, \tag{2}$$

where $V_q(V_q')$ is the electron (fluxon)-phonon interaction strength; the Landau quantum number N_L is omitted; the bold $\mathbf{k}$ denotes the 2D guiding center momentum and the italic k the magnitude. The interaction is attractive when the electron states before and after the exchange have the same energy for the degenerate LL. Hence $V_{\rm ef} = -|V_q V_q'|(\hbar\omega_q)^{-1}$.

Following BCS [17], we start with a Hamiltonian H with the phonon variables eliminated:

$$\begin{aligned} H = {} & \sum_{\mathbf{k}}{}' \sum_{s} \epsilon_k^{(1)} n_{\mathbf{k}s}^{(1)} + \sum_{\mathbf{k}}{}' \sum_{s} \epsilon_k^{(2)} n_{\mathbf{k}s}^{(2)} + \sum_{\mathbf{k}}{}' \sum_{s} \epsilon_k^{(3)} n_{\mathbf{k}s}^{(3)} \\ & - v_0 \sum_{\mathbf{q}}{}' \sum_{\mathbf{k}}{}' \sum_{\mathbf{k}'}{}' \sum_{s} \left[B_{\mathbf{k}'\mathbf{q}s}^{(1)\dagger} B_{\mathbf{k}\mathbf{q}s}^{(1)} + B_{\mathbf{k}'\mathbf{q}s}^{(1)\dagger} B_{\mathbf{k}\mathbf{q}s}^{(2)\dagger} + B_{\mathbf{k}'\mathbf{q}s}^{(2)} B_{\mathbf{k}\mathbf{q}s}^{(1)} + B_{\mathbf{k}'\mathbf{q}s}^{(2)} B_{\mathbf{k}\mathbf{q}s}^{(2)\dagger} \right], \end{aligned} \tag{3}$$

where $n_{\mathbf{k}s}^{(j)}$ is the number operator for the "electron"(1) ["hole" (2), fluxon (3)] at momentum $\mathbf{k}$ and spin s with the energy $\epsilon_{ks}^{(j)}$. We represent the "electron" ("hole") number $n_{\mathbf{k}s}^{(j)}$ by $c_{\mathbf{k}s}^{(j)\dagger} c_{\mathbf{k}s}^{(j)}$, where c $(c^\dagger)$ are annihilation (creation) operators satisfying the Fermi anticommutation rules: $\{c_{\mathbf{k}s}^{(i)}, c_{\mathbf{k}'s}^{(j)\dagger}\} \equiv c_{\mathbf{k}s}^{(i)} c_{\mathbf{k}'s'}^{(j)\dagger} + c_{\mathbf{k}'s'}^{(j)\dagger} c_{\mathbf{k}s}^{(i)} = \delta_{\mathbf{k},\mathbf{k}'}\delta_{s,s'}\delta_{i,j}$, $\{c_{\mathbf{k}s}^{(i)}, c_{\mathbf{k}',s'}^{(j)}\} = 0$. We represent the fluxon number $n_{\mathbf{k}s}^3$ by $a_{\mathbf{k}s}^\dagger a_{\mathbf{k}s}$, with $a(a^\dagger)$, satisfying the anticommutation rules. $B_{\mathbf{k}\mathbf{q}\,s}^{(1)\dagger} \equiv c_{\mathbf{k}+\mathbf{q}/2\,s}^{(1)\dagger} a_{-\mathbf{k}+\mathbf{q}/2\,-s}^\dagger$, $B_{\mathbf{k}\mathbf{q}\,s}^{(2)} \equiv c_{\mathbf{k}+\mathbf{q}/2\,s}^{(2)} a_{-\mathbf{k}+\mathbf{q}/2\,-s}$. The prime on the summation means the restriction: $0 < \epsilon_{ks}^{(j)} < \hbar\omega_D$, ω_D = Debye frequency. If the fluxons are replaced by the conduction electrons

("electrons", "holes") our Hamiltonian H is reduced to the original BCS Hamiltonian, Eq. (24) of ref. 17. The "electron" and "hole" are generated, depending on the energy contour curvature sign [19]. For example only "electrons" ("holes"), are generated for a circular Fermi surface with the negative (positive) curvature whose inside (outside) is filled with electrons. Since the phonon has no charge, the phonon exchange cannot change the net charge. The pairing interaction terms in Eq. (3) conserve the charge. The term $-v_0 B^{(1)\dagger}_{\mathbf{k}'\mathbf{q}s} B^{(1)}_{\mathbf{kq}s}$, where $v_0 \equiv |V_q V'_q|(\hbar\omega_0 A)^{-1}$, $A =$ sample area, is the pairing strength, generates the transition in the "electron" states. Similary, the exchange of a phonon generates a transition in the "hole" states, represented by $-v_0 B^{(2)}_{\mathbf{k}'\mathbf{q}s} B^{(2)\dagger}_{\mathbf{kq}s}$. The phonon exchange can also pair-create and pair-annihilate "electron" ("hole")-fluxon composites, represented by $-v_0 B^{(1)\dagger}_{\mathbf{k}'\mathbf{q}s} B^{(2)\dagger}_{\mathbf{kq}s}$, $-v_0 B^{(2)}_{\mathbf{k}'\mathbf{q}s} B^{(1)}_{\mathbf{kq}s}$. At 0 K the system can have equal numbers of -(+)c-bosons, "electrons" ("holes") composites, generated by $-v_0 B^{(1)\dagger}_{\mathbf{k}'\mathbf{q}s} B^{(2)\dagger}_{\mathbf{kq}s}$.

3. THE FERMIONIC QUANTUM HALL EFFECT

Let us take a dilute system of electrons moving in the plane. Applying a magnetic field $\mathbf{B}$ perpendicular to the plane, each electron will be in the Landau state with the energy given by $E = (N_L + 1/2)\hbar\omega_0$, $\omega_0 \equiv |e^* B/m^*|$, $N_L = 0, 1, 2, \cdots$. In this state the electron can be viewed as circulating around the guiding center. The radius of circulation $l \equiv (\hbar/eB)^{1/2}$ for the Landau ground-state is about 81 Å at a typical field 10 T (tesla). We now apply a weak electric field $\mathbf{E}$ in the x-direction. With the scatterers (impurities, phonons) present in the system the guiding centers can jump from place to place preferentially and generate a current in the x-direction. We consider the state at $\nu = P/Q$, even Q. Applying kinetic theory to the guiding-center motion of the c-fermion, we obtain the conductivity:

$$\sigma = \frac{(e_f)^2 n}{m^*}\frac{1}{\omega}, \tag{4}$$

where n is the density, e_f the charge and ω the relaxation rate. For high-purity samples at very low temperatures ($\sim$ 60 mK) the impurity and phonon scatterings are negligible. We assume that the relaxation rate is the natural linewidth arising from the LL separation divided by $\hbar$, that is, the cyclotron frequency ω_0:

$$\omega = \omega_0 \,. \tag{5}$$

Using Eqs. (4), (5) and the flux quantization:

$$B = n_\phi(h/e), \quad n_\phi = \text{flux density}\,, \tag{6}$$

we obtain

$$\sigma = \frac{(e_f)^2 n}{m^*(e_f B/m^*)} = \frac{e_f n}{n_\phi (h/e)} = \frac{e e_f}{h}\frac{n}{n_\phi}\,. \tag{7}$$

The fluxon number conservation requires that

$$Qn = n_\phi \,. \tag{8}$$

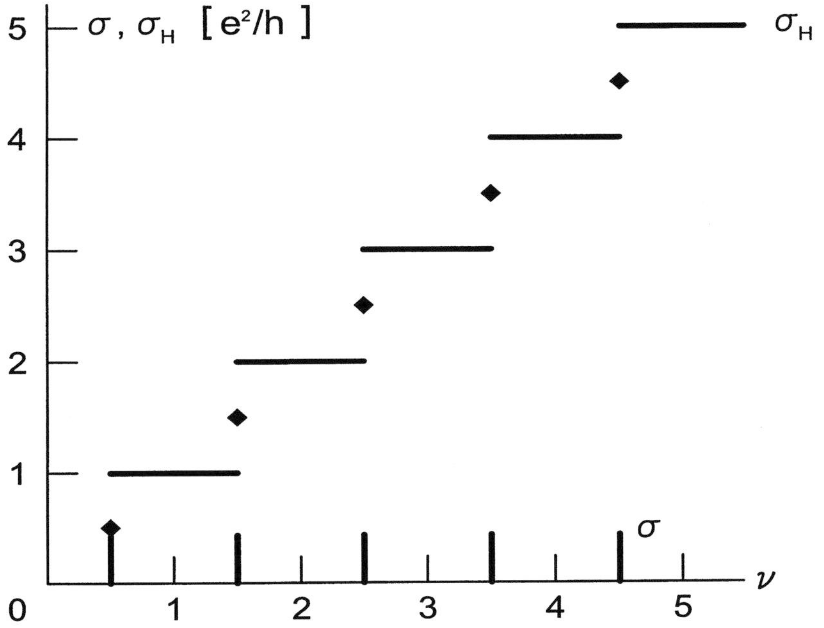

Figure 2. The conductivity σ and Hall conductivity σ_H as functions of the filling factor $\nu = P/Q$ at 0 K. $Q = 2$.

The magnetic focusing experiments by Goldman *et al.* [20] indicate that the charge magnitude of the c-fermion with two fluxons is e. We assume for any c-fermion with an even number of fluxons that

$$e_f = e \quad (\text{c}-\text{fermion}) \,. \tag{9}$$

We obtain from the last three

$$\sigma = (e^2/h)Q^{-1} \,. \tag{10}$$

In the Hall effect experimental condition we have

$$E_H = v_d B \,, \tag{11}$$

where v_d is the drift velocity. Using the standard formula for the current density:

$$J = e_f n v_d \,, \tag{12}$$

we calculate the Hall resistivity:

$$\rho_H \equiv \frac{E_H}{J} = \frac{v_d B}{e_f n v_d} = \frac{B}{e_f n} \,. \tag{13}$$

This formula indicates that ρ_H is linear in B. First let us consider the case $Q = 2$. Normalizing the field $B_{P/2}$ relative to the field $B_{1/2}$ at $\nu = 1/2$, we may write $B_{P/2} = B_{1/2}/P$. Using this and Eqs. (6), (9), (13), we obtain

$$\rho_{H,P/2} = (2/P)(h/e^2) . \tag{14}$$

The theory can simply be extended to the c-fermions at $\nu = P/Q$, even Q. The conductivity σ is given by Eq. (10), and the Hall conductivity $\sigma_H \equiv \rho_H^{-1}$ is

$$\sigma_H = (P/Q)(e^2/h) . \tag{15}$$

Our results Eq. (10) and (15) are illustrated in Fig. 2, where we chose $Q = 2$. This figure is essentially the same as Fig. 2.1 in the book by Hajdu *et al* [15]. Only the factor Q^{-1} for formula (10) is determined explicitly in the present work.

4. DISCUSSION

Willett *et al.* [4] observed that the resistivity ρ at $\nu = 5/2$ converges to a point below 100 mK. A similar behabvior was observed at $\nu = 1/2$, see ref. [5], Fig. 2. It is highly desirable to experimentally check this property in particular at $\nu = 3/2$, $7/2$ and also at $\nu = 1/4$, $3/4$. Jiang *et al.* [5] found that the strength (deviation from the background) of the resistivity minimum changes approximately linearly with temperature in $2 \sim 10$ K, where almost all features of the fractional QHE disappear. This T-linear behavior can be interpreted to arise from the phonon scattering, which we have neglected in our theory. In fact we see from Eq. (2) that the phonon scattering generates

$$\rho \propto T, \quad \omega_{\text{phonon}} \propto T \tag{16}$$

in agreement with the experiment.

Formula (10) indicates the inverse linear Q-dependence and the P-independence for the conductivity σ. Both behaviors appear to be borne out in the experimental obserbation by Jiang *et al.* [5], Fig. 1. The resistivity minima at $\nu = 1/2$ and $3/2$ are approximately equal, and they are smaller than the minimum at $\nu = 3/4$. Further detailed experimental check is required here.

Let us now turn to the Hall resistivity ρ_H. Here the difference between the fermionic and bosonic QHE becomes transparent. We have shown earlier [18] that the c-boson moves with a linear dispersion relation, and that the system of c-bosons can condense below a critical temperature T_c. The condensation is recognized by the presence of the Hall resistivity plateau. The supercurrent is generated by the c-bosons condensed monochromatically at the momentum directed along the sample length. The supercurrent density (magnitude) J, calculated by the rule: (charge e_b) $\times$ (c-boson density n_0) $\times$ (drift velocity v_d), is

$$J \equiv e_b n_0 v_d = e_b n_0 (2/\pi) |v_F^{(1)} - v_F^{(2)}| . \tag{17}$$

Using Eqs. (6), (11) and (12) we obtain from Eq. (13)

$$\rho_H \equiv \frac{E_H}{J} = \frac{v_d}{e_b n_0 v_d} n_\phi \left(\frac{h}{e}\right) = \left(\frac{h}{e_b e}\right) \frac{n_\phi}{n_0} . \tag{18}$$

Second consider the integer QHE at $\nu = P$. Since the LL degeneracy is less by the factor P^{-1}, we must consider the lowest P LL's. The Bose-Einstein Condensation (BEC) occurs at each LL. Hence we have

$$n_0 = n_e/P \,, \tag{19}$$

where n_e the electron density (constant). The fluxon density n_ϕ per LL is

$$n_\phi = n_0/P \,. \tag{20}$$

Third consider the fractional QH state at $\nu = P/Q$, odd Q. This state is formed similarly from the lowest P LL's occupied by the c-fermions, each with $Q-1$ fluxons. Eqs. (19) and (20) hold in this case. Using Eq. (20) and Eq. (1) we obtain from Eq. (18)

$$\rho_H = \frac{Q}{P}\left(\frac{h}{e^2}\right) \tag{21}$$

in agreement with the experiment. In Eq. (17), the drift velocity v_d is given by the *unaveraged* velocity differece and hence the *exact* cancellation of the v_d occurs in the calculation of ρ_H in Eqs. (18), giving risc to the extreme accuracy (10^{-8}) for the plateau value. In the presence of the supercondensate the non-condensed c-boson has an energy gap ϵ_g. The noncondensed c-boson density therefore has the activation energy type exponential temperature-dependence:

$$\exp[-\epsilon_g/(k_B T)] \,, \tag{22}$$

quite different from the phonon-generated temperature dependence. In the prevalent theories the energy gap for the fractional QHE is identified as the sum of the creation energies of a quasi-electron and a quasi-hole [12] With this view it is difficult to explain why the activation-energy type temperature dependence arises in the steady-state quantum transport. Some authors argue that the energy gap ϵ_g for the integer QHE is due to the LL separation $\hbar\omega_0$. But the LL separation is much greater than the observed ϵ_g. Besides from this view one cannot obtain the activation energy dependence observed.

In contrast the c-fermion with mass m^* moves in all directions in the plane. The drift velocity v_d is a quantity averaged over the angles. Hence the cancelation of v_d from numerator/denominator in Eqs. (13) is an approximation. After the cancelation the Hall resistivity ρ_H is B-linear and it has the value approximately equal to $(Q/P)(h/e^2)$ at $\nu = P/Q$.

Fig. 1 indicates that (a) each of the resistivity maxima at $\nu \equiv P/Q = 3/2,\ 5/2, \cdots$ is symmetric with respect to high and low fields, (b) the widths do not change much with respect to P and (c) the strength (width) of the integer QH state at $\nu = P$ decreases with P, and the resistivity curve approaches smoothly a constant as the field is reduced to zero. These features are explained as follows.

Let us consider the condition near 0 K. Only the energy matters. First, take the case at $\nu = 3/2$, where there are c-fermions with two fluxons. The system energy $E_{3/2}$ is given by

$$E_{3/2} = E_0 + C(k_B T)^2, \; C = \text{constant} \,, \tag{23}$$

where E_0 is the c-fermion system-ground-state energy; the high Fermi degeneracy is assumed. Following Jain [11], we introduce the effective magnetic field

$$B^* \equiv B - B_{3/2}, \; B_{3/2} = \text{field at } \nu = 3/2 \,. \tag{24}$$

If the field is reduced from $B_{3/2}$, the system tends to keep the same number N of the c-fermions by sucking in flux lines, since the bound c-fermion has a *negative* energy. Thus, the magnetic field becomes inhomogeneous, which generates an extra magnetic energy so that

$$E = E_0 + C(k_B T)^2 + \frac{A}{2\mu_0}(B^*)^2 \,. \tag{25}$$

If the field is raised, the system also tries to keep the same number N by expeling out flux lines. The inhomogeneous fields raise the field energy as represented by the third term in Eq. (25). This explains the high-low field symmetry.

At $\nu = 1$ there are the c-bosons, each with one fluxon. Hence there is a phase change somewhere between $\nu = 3/2$ and $\nu = 1$. The c-boson ground-state energy $E_{\rm cb}$ must enter in the arguments. We denote the energy difference by ΔE,

$$\Delta E \equiv E - E_{\rm cb} - E_0 = C(k_B T)^2 + \frac{A}{2\mu_0}(B^*)^2 \,. \tag{26}$$

We assume that the c-fermion system is stable if

$$\Delta E < E_1 = \text{constant} \,. \tag{27}$$

At the center $\nu = 3/2$, $B^* = 0$. There is a critical temperature T_c defined by

$$C(k_B T_c)^2 = E_1 \,. \tag{28}$$

Below T_c the c-fermions system is stable. The critical field B_c is

$$B_c = \sqrt{\frac{2\mu_0 C}{A} k_B^2 (T_c^2 - T^2)} \,. \tag{29}$$

This B_c may be regarded as the half-width. Eq. (29) indicates that the width B_c becomes a constant as $T \to 0$. We can simply extend the theory to the case $\nu = P/2$. The Fermi energy of the system remains the same irrespective of the field. Then Eq. (29) must hold irrespective of odd P. Here the phonon exchange attraction played an important role. The bound c-fermion needs an attraction, and cannot be derived from the repulsive Coulomb interaction, the starting Hamiltonian in the prevalent theories [12]. Jain's effective magnetic field's can be justified only with the concept of the bound c-fermion.

The BEC occurs at each LL, and therefore the c-boson density n_0 is lower for high P, see Eq. (19), and the strengths become weaker as P increases. This weakening of the c-boson minima together with the constancy of the c-fermion widths make a smooth resistivity curve for large P. The same theory explains the smooth wide resistivity minimum observed at $\nu = 1/2$ [5]. Jain's unification theory [11] gives the location of the bosonic QH states but does not allow the discussion of the states' strengths.

Moor and Read [14, 21] proposed a bosonic pair model for the 5/2 state. The bosonic model, however, yields a vanishing resistivity at 0 K in disagreement with experiment. The Halperin-Lee-Read theory [13] based on the c-fermion model yields a finite conductivity linear in the impurity density $n_{\rm imp}$, which vanishes in the limit $n_{\rm imp} \to 0$ at zero temperature. Our formula (7) remains finite at 0 K.

In the present work we calculated the transport coefficients (σ, σ_H) in the traditional way, identifying the carrier charge (e^*) and density (n). We note that the current density formula ($J = e^* n v_d$) and the Hall effect condition ($E_H = v_d B$) are exact if a single-component current is considered. We stress that the Hall resistivity $\rho_H \equiv E_H/J$ needs the measurements of two quantities (E_H, J). In the prevalent theories [12] the Hall resistivity ρ_H is calculated directly through the lowest LL projection or other methods. This is not reasonable. We must separately calculate E_H and J, and then take the ratio.

Finally the charges (e_b, e_f) of the carriers (c-boson, c-fermion) are assumed in our kinetic theory. These charges must be justified by a microscopic theory.

Eisenstein *et al.* [22] found that the QHE state at $\nu = 5/2$ collapse rapidly as the magnetic field is tilted away from the normal to the plane. This is an anomaly since the states at $\nu = 1/2$ and $\nu = 3/2$ were found not to collapse [5]. The tilting reduces the diamagnetic effect, rendering the effective g factor to vanish and making spin-mixing more important. We shall treat to the 5/2 state collapse separately.

ACKNOWLEDGMENTS

Acknowledgments are made to the US Army Research Office for travel and lodge supports.

REFERENCES

[1] K. von Klitzing, G. Dorda and M. Pepper, *Phys. Rev. Lett.* **45**, 494 (1980).

[2] D. C. Tsui, H. L. Störmer and A. C. Gossard, *Phys. Rev. Lett.* **48**, 1559 (1982).

[3] D. C. Tsui, *4. DFG-Rundgespräch über den Quanten Hall Effekt*, (Schleching, Germany, 1989).

[4] R. Willett, J. P. Eisenstein, H. L. Stormer, D. C. Tsui, A. C. Gossard, and J. H. English, *Phys. Rev. Lett.* **59**, 1776 (1987).

[5] H. W. Jiang, H. L. Stormer, D. C. Tsui, L. N. Pfeiffer and K. W. West, *Phys. Rev. B* **40**, 12013 (1989).

[6] R. L. Willett, M. A. Paalanen, R. R. Ruel, K. W. West, L. N. Pfeiffer and D. J. Bishop, *Phys. Rev. Lett.* **65**, 112 (1990).

[7] R. B. Laughlin, *Phys. Rev. Lett.* **50**, 1395 (1983).

[8] F. D. M. Haldane, *Phys. Rev. Lett.* **51**, 605 (1983).

[9] R. G. Clark, J. R. Mallett, S. R. Haynes, J. J. Harris and C. T. Foxon, *Phys.*

Rev. Lett. **60**, 1747 (1988); V. J. Goldman and B. Su, *Science* **267**, 1010 (1955); L. Saminadayar, D. C. Glattli, Y. Jin and B. Etienne, *Phys. Rev. Lett.* **79**, 2526 (1997); R. de Picciotto, M. Reznikov, M. Heiblum, V. Umansky, G. Bunin and D. Mahalu, *Nature* **389**, 162 (1997).

[10] S. C. Zhang, T. H. Hansson and S. Kivelson, *Phys. Rev. Lett.* **62**, 82 (1989).

[11] J. K. Jain, *Phys. Rev. Lett.* **63**, 199 (1989); *Phys. Rev. B* **40**, 8079 (1989); *ibid.* **41**, 7653 (1990).

[12] Z. F. Ezawa, *Quantum Hall Effects*, (World Scientific, Singapore, 2000); see also R. E. Prange and S. M. Girvin, eds., *Quantum Hall Effect*, (Springer-Verlag, New York, 1990); M. Stone, ed., *Quantum Hall Effect*, (World Scientific, Singapore, 1992); T. Chakraborty and P. Pietilainen, *Quantum Hall Effects*, 2nd. ed. (Springer-Verlag, Berlin, 1995).

[13] B. I. Halperin, P. A. Lee and N. Read, *Phys. Rev. B* **47**, 7312 (1993).

[14] N. Read, *Physica B* **298**, 121 (2001).

[15] J. Hajdu, ed., *Introduction to Theory of Integer Quantum Hall Effect* (VCH, Weinheim, Germany, 1994).

[16] R. B. Laughlin, *Science* **242**, 525 (1988).

[17] J. Bardeen, L. N. Cooper and J. R. Schrieffer, *Phys. Rev.* **108**, 1175 (1957).

[18] S. Fujita, Y. Tamura and A. Suzuki, *Mod. Phys. Lett. B* **15**, 817 (2001).

[19] S. Fujita and S. Godoy and D. Nguyen, *Found. Phys.* **25**, 1209 (1995).

[20] V. J. Goldman, B. Su and J. K. Jain, Phys. Rev. Lett. **72**, 2065 (1994)

[21] G. Moor and N. Reed, *Nucl. Phys. B* **360**, 362 (1991).

[22] J. P. Eisenstein, R. Willett, H. L. Stormer, D. C. Tsui, A. C. Gossard and J. H. English, *Phys. Rev. Lett.* **61**, 997 (1998).

EFFECTIVE HAMILTONIAN FOR CUPRATES: GLOBAL PHASE DIAGRAM

S. Capponi

Laboratoire de Physique Théorique UMR 5152, Université Paul Sabatier
118 route de Narbonne, 31062 Toulouse, France

H. D. Chen

Department of Applied Physics, McCullough Building, Stanford University
Stanford CA 94305-4045

F. Alet

Theoretische Physik & Computation Laboratory, ETH Zürich
CH-8093 Zürich, Switzerland

S. C. Zhang

Department of Physics, McCullough Building, Stanford University
Stanford CA 94305-4045

1. INTRODUCTION

On the first look, the phase diagram of the high T_c (HTSC) cuprates has a striking simplicity: there are only three *universal* phases in the phase diagram of *all* HTSC cuprates: the antiferromagnetic (AF), the superconducting (SC) and the metallic phases, which all have *homogeneous* charge distributions. However, closer inspection shows a bewildering complexity of other possible phases (with inhomogeneous charge distributions for instance), which may or may not be universally present in all HTSC cuprates. The $SO(5)$ theory unifies the AF and the SC order parameters into a single five dimensional order parameter called the superspin, and the effective quantum theory of the superspin naturally explains the phase diagram [2]. The Goldstone modes of the superspin fluctuations can be identified with the π resonance mode observed in the neutron scattering experiments [3]. This theory also predicts the AF vortex state [2,4], which has been observed in a number of experiments. The $SO(5)$ theory was initially motivated by the simplicity of the pure AF and SC states, however, given the encouraging agreements with the experiments, it is tempting to construct an unified theory of the global phase diagram of the HTSC which addresses the more complex inhomogeneous phases as well. Complexities can of course be introduced phenomenologically into the Landau-Ginzburg type of theories by simply introducing more order parameters. However, this type of approach necessarily limits the predictive power of theory. The goal of this paper is to present a single effective quantum model of the superspin degree of freedom, which can be derived systematically from the microscopic electron models, and can be investigated reliably both analytically and numerically. The global phase diagram of this model is then compared with the experimentally observed phase diagram of the HTSC cuprates. It provides a basic road-map to understand their common elements and differences.

While this paper is presented within the logical context of the $SO(5)$ theory, some of the ideas and results bear intellectual similarities to previous theoretical works. We refer the reader to [1] to have more details, including a discussion of other existing HTSC theories.

2. HAMILTONIAN OF THE MODEL

This paper mainly focuses on the zero temperature global phase diagram of the underdoped cuprates. However, it is understood that the model is valid below the pseudogap temperature, which we interpret as the temperature below which the system can be effectively described by the collective bosonic degrees of freedom, like the magnons and the hole pairs. The existence of the pseudogap temperature gives the fundamental experimental justification to investigate the global phase diagram of the underdoped cuprates by a purely bosonic model.

Projected SO(5)

When formulated on a coarse-grained lattice, with high energy charge states projected out, the projected $SO(5)$ (PSO(5)) describes five local superspin degrees of freedom per site [5]. These five states are the spin singlet state at half-filling, the spin triplet state at half-filling, and the singlet d-wave hole pair state. Using the Contractor Renormalization Group (CORE) algorithm [6], Altman and Auerbach [7] showed that the projected $SO(5)$ model can be systematically derived from the microscopic electron models, and the parameters of the effective $SO(5)$ model can be computed explicitly from the microscopic interaction parameters [8]. Restricted within the subspace of these five local states, the Hamiltonian describing their propagation and interaction is completely expressed in terms of bosonic operators.

The simplest form of the projected $SO(5)$ has been studied extensively by the Quantum Monte-Carlo (QMC) method both in two [9] and in three dimensions [10]. It describes either the direct, first order transition from the AF to the SC state, or two second order transitions with an uniform, intermediate AF/SC mixed phase in between the pure AF and the SC states. However, in the HTSC cuprates, there are other forms of charge and spin ordered states. For example, neutron scattering shows evidence for stripe formation [11]. STM experiments have revealed periodic charge modulation with period close to four lattice spacing [12,13]. Motivated by these experiments, we include extended interactions among the five bosonic states.

Effective Model

Considering a 2×2 plaquette as the basic unit and keeping only the singlet state, the three triplets $t_\alpha^\dagger$ and the hole-pair $t_h^\dagger$, the Hamiltonian of the projected SO(5) model with extended interactions is given by

$$\mathcal{H} = \mathcal{H}_0 + \mathcal{H}_{ext},$$

where $\mathcal{H}_0$ is the Hamiltonian of pure PSO(5) model [5]

$$\mathcal{H}_0 = \Delta_c \sum_i t_h^\dagger(i) t_h(i) + \Delta_s \sum_\alpha \sum_i t_\alpha^\dagger(i) t_\alpha(i)$$

$$- J_c \sum_{\langle ij \rangle} [t_h^\dagger(i) t_h(j) + H.c.] - J_s \sum_\alpha \sum_{\langle ij \rangle} [t_\alpha^\dagger(i) + t_\alpha(i)][t_\alpha^\dagger(j) + t_\alpha(j)]$$

and $\mathcal{H}_{ext}$ is the part of extended interactions

$$\mathcal{H}_{ext} = [V_c \sum_{\langle ij \rangle} + V_c' \sum_{\langle\langle ij \rangle\rangle}] n_h(i) n_h(j) - J_\pi \sum_\alpha \sum_{\langle ij \rangle} [t_h^\dagger(i) t_h(j) t_\alpha^\dagger(j) t_\alpha(i) + H.c.]$$
$$+ V_\pi \sum_\alpha \sum_{\langle ij \rangle} [n_h(i) n_\alpha(j) + n_h(j) n_\alpha(i)] + \text{ 4 triplets terms}$$

with hard-core constraints $\sum_\alpha n_\alpha(i) + n_h(i) \le 1$.

Here, $t_h(i)$ and $t_h^\dagger(i)$ are the annihilation and creation operators of hole-pair on plaquette i. $t_\alpha(i)$ and $t_\alpha^\dagger(i)$ are the annihilation and creation operators of triplet on plaquette i for $\alpha = x, y, z$. $\langle \cdots \rangle$ and $\langle\langle \cdots \rangle\rangle$ denote nearest-neighbor(nn) and next-nearest-neighbor(nnn), respectively. $n_h(i) = t_h^\dagger(i) t_h(i)$ and $n_\alpha(i) = t_\alpha^\dagger(i) t_\alpha(i)$ are the hole-pair density and triplet densities on plaquette i, respectively. The hole-pair density of n_h per plaquette corresponds to the real hole doping of $\delta = n_h/2$.

Effective parameters are obtained with CORE method. However, if one would start from a slightly different model (next-nearest neighbor hopping, extended Coulomb repulsion and so on), we would get a similar effective Hamiltonian with different parameters. Therefore, we want to focus on robust properties of this class of Hamiltonians and allow parameters to vary. We fix $J_s = 1$ as the unit of energy and, in most part of this paper, we shall consider the simplified model with $J_\pi = V_\pi = 0$.

3. SELF-SIMILARITY BETWEEN CHARGE-ORDERED STATES

First, let us ignore the triplets and consider a hard-core boson model with extended interactions. With nn interaction only, the phase diagram [14,15] has three Mott-insulating states corresponding to zero-doping, half-filling and fully-occupied, as sketched in Fig. 1.

If we integrate out the degree of freedom of the empty sublattice in the half-filled Mott-insulating state, we obtain a fully-occupied Mott-insulating state on the coarse-grained lattice. This is the self-similarity between charge-ordering states. Now, if we consider a nearest-neighbor interaction on this coarse-grained lattice, we obtain exactly the same phase diagram as previously. The zero-doping, half-filled state and fully-occupied state on the coarse-grained lattice correspond to the zero-doping, quarter-filled and half-filled state in the original lattice. Similarly, we can integrate out the degree of freedom of the occupied sublattice. In this case, the zero-doping, half-filled state and fully-occupied state on the coarse-grained lattice correspond to the half-doping, 3/4-filled and fully-occupied state in the original lattice. Combining these two parts, we obtain a phase diagram with five insulating states with doping $0/4, 1/4, 2/4, 3/4$ and $4/4$ as sketched in Fig. 1.

The above argument of self-similarity between charge-ordered states can be generalized to include more extended interactions and more insulating lobes.

As shown in Fig. 2, in the underdoped phase of the cuprates, one can drive a AF/insulator to SC transition by varying J_c/V_c with a fixed chemical potential.

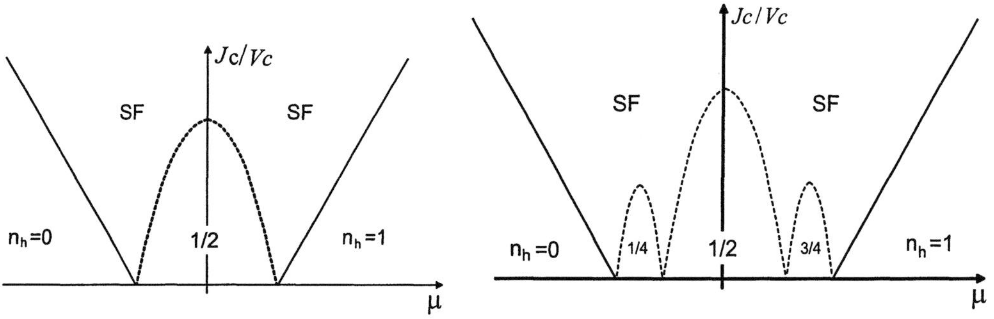

Figure 1. Left: Phase diagram of a hard-core boson model with nearest-neighbor interaction. There are one superfluid (SF) state and three insulating states: zero-doping state, half-filled state and fully-occupied state. Right: Phase diagram of a hard-core boson model with nn and nnn interactions. There are a superfluid (SF) state and five insulating states with doping $0/4, 1/4, 2/4, 3/4$ and $4/4$.

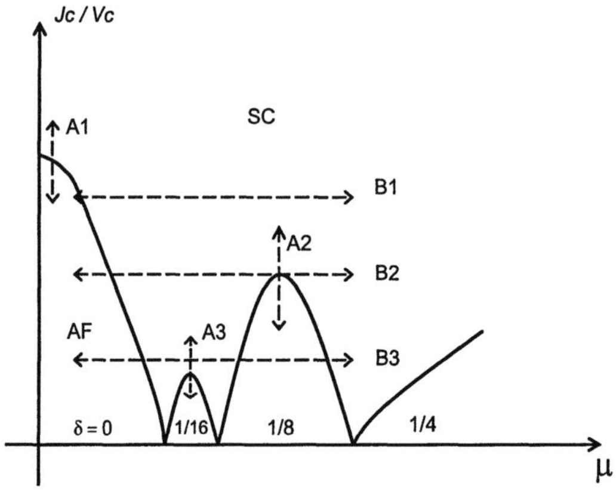

Figure 2. Illustration of typical global phase diagram of cuprates and different types transitions of cuprates (see text).

In the HTSC cuprates, the charge gap at half-filling is very large, of the order of $U \sim 6eV$, it is not possible to induce the "class A1" transition from AF to SC by conventional means. However, the charge gap at the fractional insulating states are much smaller, of the order of J_c, and it is possible to induce the "class A2" or "class A3" insulator to superconductor transition by applying pressure or magnetic field.

As the doping level is varied, a given system (constant J_c/V_c), follows a line noted $B1$, $B2$ or $B3$ in Fig. 2. For low values of J_c/V_c, the trace $B3$ encounters the $\delta = 1/8$ insulating phase. A key signature of this phase is that the SC T_c will display a pronounced minimum for this doping. Meanwhile, the AF ordering (possibly at a wave vector shifted from (π, π)) will show reentrant behavior. We believe that the AF to SC transition in the $YBCO$, $BCCO$ and the $NCCO$ systems correspond to "class B1" transition with no additional statically ordered fractional insulating phases. On the other hand, the phase transition in the $LSCO$ system, where T_c displays a pronounced dip at $\delta = 1/8$, correspond to the "class B3" transition.

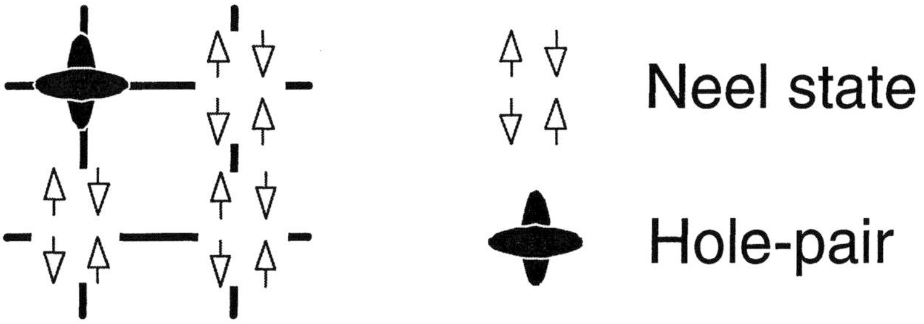

Figure 3. The schematic plot of the unit cell of a quarter-filled magnetic insulating state. Each site denotes a 2-plaquette by 2-plaquette unit cell.

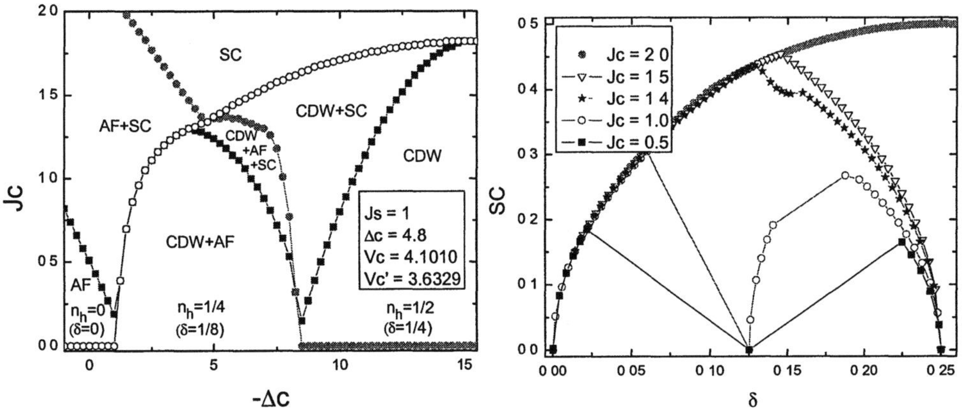

Figure 4. Left: The MF phase diagram obtained by minimizing the energy functional subjected to the hard-core constraint. J_π and V_π are taken to be zero. Right: Doping dependence of SC order parameter for different J_c. For small J_c, there is a dip around hole-pair doping $n_h = 1/4$ (real doping $\delta = 1/8$).

4. MEAN-FIELD THEORY

We introduce a four-sublattice ansatz and the energy functional is minimized, subjected to the hard-core constraint, in order to get the mean-field ground state for a given set of parameters. Fig. 4 plots the mean-field global phase diagram, for $\Delta_s = 4.8$, $V_c = 4.1010$, $V_c' = 3.6329$ and $J_\pi = V_\pi = 0$.

This phase diagram has very interesting topology, as expected. It has three insulating state: an undoped antiferromagnetic (AF) state, an insulating AF checkerboard state with hole-pair density $n_h = 1/4$ ($\delta = 1/8$) (see Fig. 3) and an insulating charge stripe state with hole-pair density $n_h = 1/2$ ($\delta = 1/4$). Besides these insulating states, it also has pure SC state, supersolid state and mixed state of coexisting AF and SC.

In Fig. 4 and Fig. 5, we plot the doping dependence of SC and AF orders for different J_c. If one follows a "class B1" trace, such as $J_c = 1.5$, the doping dependence of SC order mimics the behavior of $YBCO$ and $BSCO$ families with a underdoped region $n_h < 0.3(\delta < 0.15)$ and an overdoped region $n_h > 0.3(\delta > 0.15)$. If one follows a "class B3" trace, such as the one with fixed $J_c = 1.0$, the SC order displays a

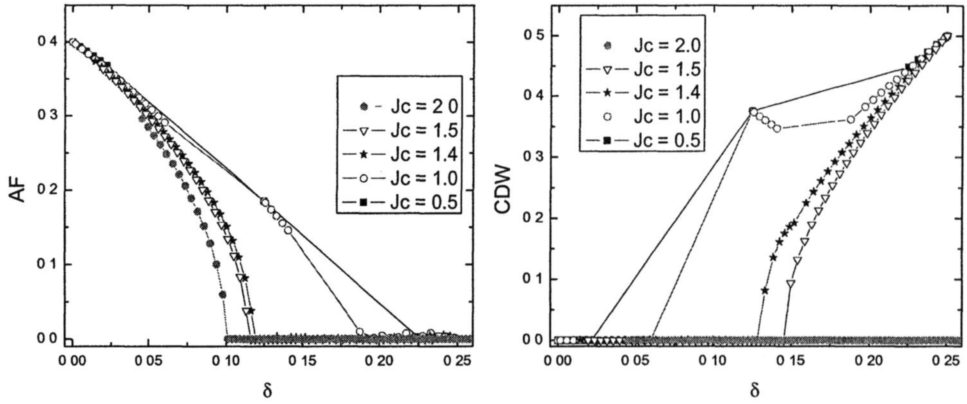

Figure 5. Left: Doping dependence of AF order parameter for different J_c. For $J_c > 1.3$, AF order decreases as doping increases and vanishes around $\delta = 0.1$. Right: Doping dependence of CDW order defined for difference J_c. For $J_c < 1.3$, a strong peak is present at $n_h = 1/4$ or real doping $\delta = 1/8$.

pronounce dip and the AF ordering is strongly enhanced around $n_h = 1/4(\delta = 1/8)$. Therefore, the $B2$-like trace mimics the behavior of $LSCO$ family.

The doping dependence of charge ordering is also plotted in Fig. 5. The charge density wave (CDW) ordering measures the charge inhomogeneity. While "class B1" trace shows no sign of charge ordering in the underdoped region, "class B3" trace displays a clear signature of charge ordering around $\delta = 1/8$.

5. QUANTUM MONTE-CARLO RESULTS

To simulate the PSO(5) model with extended interactions, we use the Stochastic Series Expansion (SSE) method [16] with operator-loop update [17]. This QMC method was shown to be efficient for simulations of harcore bosonic systems [18,19,9].

Our model has the advantage of having no sign problem. However, due to the intrinsic complexity of the PSO(5) model and to the large number of interaction types, we restricted the simulations to small lattices (from 4×4 up to 10×10 lattices) at low temperatures (typically $\beta = 10$), to mainly be in the ground state. Even using the powerful SSE method, we found that for specific points (near phase boundaries for example), autocorrelation times of different observables or tunneling times between two neighbouring phases can be long, decreasing the statistical precision.

In order to plot the phase diagram, we should compute the order parameters. The superfluid density ρ_c, used to locate SC phases, can be related to the winding numbers of the world-lines which can be directly computed in the loop algorithm [20]. In 2D, $\rho_c \sim W^2/2\beta$. We can also easily compute diagonal correlation functions such as structure factors $N(q_x, q_y)$ which, after finite-size scaling, indicate CDW phases.

The computed phase diagram is shown on Fig. 6. The qualitative features found at the mean-field level are still present in a full numerical calculation and we have a very nice overall agreement (compare Fig. 4 and 6). Of course, exact critical values of J_c for superconducting-insulator transition are different from mean-field values but this does not change the physical conclusions.

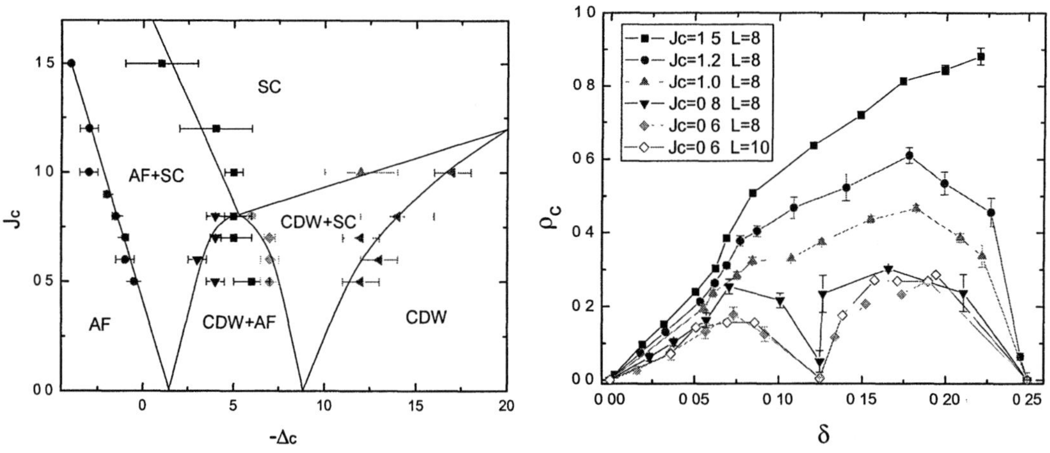

Figure 6. Left: The global phase diagram obtained by QMC. The parameters used in simulation are $\Delta_s = 4.8$, $V_c = 4.1010$, $V_c' = 3.6329$ and $J_\pi = V_\pi = 0$. The lines are guides to the eye only. Right: Superfluid density as a function of doping for various J_c. L is the linear size.

We recover the insulating phases at $n_h = 1/4$ and $n_h = 1/2$ due to extended interactions. For intermediate dopings and small J_c, we find a finite superfluid density and possibly a finite CDW order, that is a supersolid region. This phase is stable against phase separation. We cannot be conclusive about this phase and its extension in the phase diagram, due to the long autocorrelation time for some observables. This explains the large error bars in some parts of the phase diagram.

6. EXPERIMENTAL CONSEQUENCES AND PREDICTIONS

Superconducting carrier density

In cuprate system, the muon spin relaxation rate $\sigma(T \to 0)$ is proportional to n_s/m^* where n_s is the superconducting carrier density and m^* is the effective mass of hole-pairs [21]. To explain the deviation from the linear relation between σ and doping in the overdoped regime, Uemura proposed that some of the doped holes do not form hole-pairs and are phase separated from the superconducting hole-pairs, even at zero-temperature [21]. If these normal electrons existed, they should provide a channel of relaxations and thus should be observed. This is not consistent with experiments.

Under our PSO(5) scenario, we can provide a natural explanation of this doping dependence of n_s/m^*. Since localized hole-pairs do no contribute to superconductivity, as one approaches the insulating lobe with real doping $\delta = 1/4$, our theory naturally predicts a negative slope of the doping dependence of superconducting carrier density n_s in the overdoped regime. Nevertheless, the localized hole-pairs contributes to stripe-like charge ordering. This charge-ordering of hole-pairs in overdoped regime are still to be observed.

Pressure experiments

It has been demonstrated that the competition between charge order and superconducting phase in *La*-family can be controlled by pressure, either applying hydrostatic or uniaxial pressure on single crystal [22], or introducing compressive or expansive strain into thin films [23]. Enhanced T_c and disappearance of the 1/8 anomaly for compressed film and strong reduction of T_c for expanded film were observed [23].

The pressure in ab plane reduces the lattice constant, leading to the increase of the hopping term J_c. Therefore, it is equivalent to following a "class A2" trace starting from a small J_c in the global phase diagram. The doping dependence of T_c for different films given in [23] shares many common features with our doping dependence of SC order parameter ρ_c, both MF and QMC results (Fig. 4 and 6).

The destructive effect on T_c of the pressure in the c-direction can also be understood in this way. Due to the Poisson effect, when the sample is compressed in the c direction, the lattice constant in ab plane will increase. This will lead to the decrease of T_c as argued previously.

Similarly, "class A3" trace could also be realized by applying pressure. Therefore, we predict a pressure induced insulator-metal transition at $\delta = 1/16$.

Vortex phase

Recently, a striking feature is revealed in the STM experiments by Hoffman *et al.* [12], where the local density of states (DOS) near the vortex core show a two dimensional checkerboard-like modulation with a $4a \times 4a$. charge unit cell. Here a is the lattice spacing of the CuO_2 plane. This modulation decays exponentially away from the center of the vortex core, with a decay length of about $10a$. More recently, a similar pattern has also been seen in the absence of the applied magnetic field [13], possibly induced by the impurities at the surface.

The $\delta = 1/8$ insulating state was proposed as an explanation for the STM measurements [24]. In this state, the d-wave hole pairs form a Wigner crystal, dubbed a d-wave hole pair checkerboard. This state has the $4a \times 4a$ checkerboard symmetry as observed in the experiment, and the doping level for the insulating $\delta = 1/8$ state is reasonably close to the optimal doping level of the cuprates. Therefore, by forming the Wigner crystal state of the hole pairs rather than the holes themselves, the doping level can be compatible with the observed size of the charge unit cell.

This phase could also be relevant above H_{c2}.

Stripe phase

Although static and dynamic magnetic stripes around 1/8 doping are observed in LSCO family [11], there is no convincing evidence of charge stripe in cuprates yet. We would like to stress that magnetic stripe is compatible with PSO(5) with nn and nnn interactions and the anisotropic hopping terms in $LSCO$ samples might be responsible for the magnetic stripes [25]. In Fig. 7, we illustrate the coexistence of anti-phase magnetic stripe and hole-pair checkerboard state. Furthermore, for $LSCO$ family, we believe that the interactions more extended than nnn cannot be neglected. If these more extended interactions are strong enough, charge stripe in $\delta = 1/8$ state is favored over the checkerboard state. However, we want to emphasize that our theory predicts the charge stripes of hole-pairs not holes and the charge stripes are always competing with SC state.

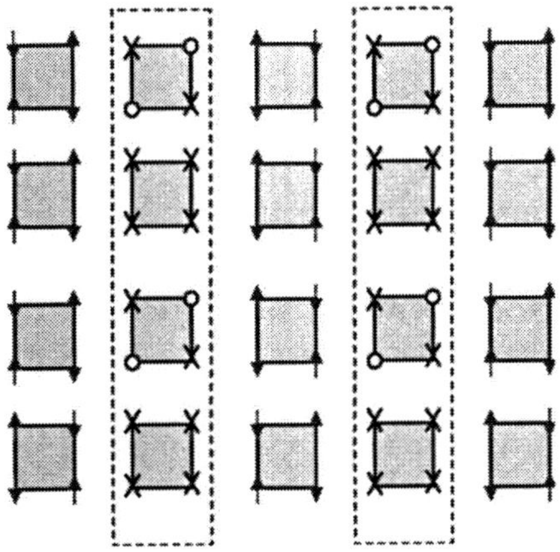

Figure 7. The illustration of anti-phase magnetic stripe and hole-pair checkerboard state with 1/8 real doping as sketched in real lattice. Circles denote holes and arrows denote spins while black crosses denote frustrated spins.

Coexistence

In the global phase diagram of Fig. 4 and Fig. 6, there is a large region of coexisting AF and SC. After considering the interactions of J_π and V_π, the coexistence region can be much smaller. As suggested by CORE method, J_π is negative. We also assume V_π is positive. Thus, at mean-field level, both J_π and V_π terms induce a repulsion between AF and SC in the mixed state of coexisting AF and SC. Therefore, one would expect a smaller region of mixed state of AF+SC in the phase diagram.

In a real system, the Gossamer effect [26] at very low doping might reduce the coexistence region further.

7. CONCLUSIONS

A bosonic effective Hamiltonian is proposed to explain the features of HTSC cuprate systems. The projected $SO(5)$ model with extended interactions support a complex phase diagram, obtained both by mean-field study and extensive QMC simulations. In particular, there are insulating phases at fractional filling factors where the charges form a commensurate lattice. A crucial aspect of this model is that all charge ordered states are formed by the Cooper pairs of the holes, rather than the holes themselves [24]. The CDW state of the hole pairs can either take the form of stripes or checkerboards, depending on the ratios of the extended interaction parameters in the model.

Based on this result, a simple picture emerges for the global phase diagram of underdoped cuprates. The phase diagram consists of islands of insulating states immersed in the background of SC states (see Fig. 2). The height of the Mott insulator lobes vary depending on the filling fraction and the range of extended interactions, but in principle, they are all self-similar, and similar to the parent AF insulator at half-filling.

Different families of cuprates are attributed to different traces in the global phase diagram. Some experimental consequences and predictions have been discussed. A more detailed discussion is available in [1].

ACKNOWLEDGMENTS

We would like to acknowledge useful discussions with Drs. A. Auerbach, E. Demler, W. Hanke, J.P. Hu, M. Troyer and C.J. Wu.

REFERENCES

[1] H.D. Chen, S. Capponi, F. Alet and S.C. Zhang, in preparation.

[2] S. C. Zhang, *Science* **275**, 1089 (1997).

[3] E. Demler and S. C. Zhang, *Nature* **396**, 733 (1998).

[4] D. P. Arovas, A. J. Berlinsky, C. Kallin and S. C. Zhang, *Phys. Rev. Lett.* **79**, 2871 (1997).

[5] S. C. Zhang, J. P. Hu, E. Arrigoni, W. Hanke and A. Auerbach, *Phys. Rev. B* **60**, 13070 (1999).

[6] C. J. Morningstar and M. Weinstein, *Phys. Rev. D* **54**, 4131 (1996).

[7] E. Altman and A. Auerbach, *Phys. Rev. B* **65**, 104508 (2002).

[8] S. Capponi and D. Poilblanc, *Phys. Rev. B* **66**, 180503 (2002).

[9] A. Dorneich, W. Hanke, E. Arrigoni, M. Troyer and S. C. Zhang, *Phys. Rev. Lett.* **88**, 057003 (2002).

[10] M. Jöstingmeier, A. Dorneich, E. Arrigoni, W. Hanke and S. C. Zhang, cond-mat/0207528.

[11] J. M. Tranquada *et al*, *Nature* **375**, 561 (1995).

[12] J. E. Hoffman *et al*, *Science* **295**, 466 (2002).

[13] C. Howald *et al*, *Phys. Rev. B* **67**, 014533 (2003).

[14] M. P. A. Fisher, P. B. Weichman, G. Grinstein and D. S. Fisher, *Phys. Rev. B* **40**, 546 (1989).

[15] C. Pich and E. Frey, *Phys. Rev. B* **57**, 13712 (1998).

[16] A. W. Sandvik and J. Kurkijarvi, *Phys. Rev. B* **43**, 5950 (1991).

[17] A. W. Sandvik, *Phys. Rev. B* **59**, 14157 (1999).

[18] F. Hébert *et al*, *Phys. Rev. B* **65**, 014513 (2001).

[19] G. Schmid, S. Todo, M. Troyer and A. Dorneich, *Phys. Rev. Lett.* **88**, 167208 (2002).

[20] E. L. Pollock and D. M. Ceperley, *Phys. Rev. B* **36**, 8343 (1987).

[21] Y. J. Uemura, *Solid State Communications* **120**, 347 (2001).

[22] S. Arumugam *et al*, *Phys. Rev. Lett.* **88**, 247001 (2002).

[23] H. Sato, A. Tsukada, M. Naito, A. Matsuda, *Phys. Rev. B* **62**, R799 (2000).

[24] H. D. Chen, J. P. Hu, S. Capponi, E. Arrigoni and S. C. Zhang, *Phys. Rev. Lett.* **89**, 137004 (2002).

[25] F. Becca, L. Capriotti and S. Sorella, *Phys. Rev. Lett.* **87**, 167005 (2001).

[26] R. B. Laughlin, cond-mat/0209269.

APPLICATION OF LSDA TO THE STUDY OF STRONGLY LOCALIZED 2D ELECTRON SYSTEMS

A. Emperador

Department of Physics, University of Trento
I-38050 Povo, Italy

1. INTRODUCTION

This work analizes the reliability of the Local Spin Density Approximation in the case in which the electrons in a semiconductor quantum well are strongly localized. Localization in a two-dimensional electron gas (2DEG) occurs at very low electronic densities, when the kinetic energy is weak compared to the potential energy due to the Coulomb repulsion between electrons. The electrons tend to keep constant distances forming the so-called Wigner crystal in the homogeneous system. Quasi-one-dimensional quantum rings have been taken as a case of study, due to the fact that in these finite systems the localization can be inferred experimentally from measurements of the persistent currents that appear when a magnetic field is applied perpendicular to the plane of the ring. In the following of this introduction it will be explained the correspondence between the phenomenon that is experimentally observed, called Fractional Aharonov-Bohm effect, and the localization of the electrons in the ring.

Very recently InGaAs and GaAlAs/GaAs quantum rings with a radius of the order of 20-100 nm have been fabricated [1,2]. These nanorings bind only a few electrons, in contrast with the previously available mesoscopic rings on GaAs [3], containing a number of electrons two or three orders of magnitude larger. The low number of electrons and the dimensions of the nanoring make such systems a new kind of artificial atoms, that exhibit a richer variety of physical phenomena compared to quantum dots. In fact, the perimeter of the rings is tipically smaller than the mean free path in the semiconductor substrate, so that the phase of the electrons is conserved.

A very interesting quantum interference effect occurring in quantum rings is the Aharonov-Bohm (AB) effect, consisting in a series of periodic oscillations in the energy of the electronic system as the flux of magnetic field across the ring is varied. The AB effect gives rise to oscillations of the persistent currents in the rings [4,5] that can be measured by conductance experiments. AB oscillations have been also experimentally observed in larger GaAlAs/GaAs microscopic rings, with a diameter of less than half μm, by direct measurement of the conductance across the ring for a given intensity of the magnetic field [3], or from addition spectroscopy [6].

The oscillations in the persistent current are related to the oscillations of the ground state energy. In the case of non-interacting systems, the period of the AB oscillations is the flux quantum $\Phi_0 = hc/e$ for an even electron number N, and approximately a half flux quantum for an odd number of electrons [7,8]. However, the situation observed by experiments is rather different. Hansen et al. [9] found a large weight of the $\Phi_0/2$ component in the Fourier transform of the current oscillations in a ring with a diameter smaller than 1μm. Keyser et al. [2] reported measurements in which oscillations of the persistent current with a period of $\Phi_0/4$ are observed. Their work gave for the first time clear evidence of the existence of a fractional AB effect in a nanoscopic quantum ring.

The fractional AB effect is due to the electron–electron interaction, whose importance increases as the electronic density decreases. Its effects are manifested in two ways: with the removal of the degeneracy between states with different total spin due mainly to the exchange interaction [10]; and with a strong localization of the electrons in the two–body density (often reported as the formation of a "Wigner molecule") at very low electronic densities where the kinetic energy of the electrons is much lower than the interaction energy. This is the case of study of this work. In the next section it is explained the physics of the system for only one particle or for several particles if the interaction between electrons is neglected. In section 3 is dicussed the effect of the interaction on the internal symmetry of the ground state, in section 4 it is explained the LSDA, and in section 5 we show the results of this method and compare with the exact ones.

2. INDEPENDENT ELECTRON PHENOMENOLOGY

When a magnetic field is applied to an electrically charged particle its dinamics is descrived by the Pauli Hamiltonian:

$$H = \frac{1}{2m^*}\left(\vec{p} - \frac{e}{c}\vec{A}\right)^2 + V(\vec{r}) + \frac{1}{2}g^*\mu_B B\sigma_z$$

In this work we consider the case in which the magnetic field is perpendicular to the orbit of the electrons in the ring. In the case of a circular ring, it is useful to choose the symmetric gauge

$$\vec{A} = \frac{1}{2}(\vec{B} \times \vec{r}) = -\frac{1}{2}Br\hat{e}_\theta \qquad \vec{B} = B\hat{z}$$

In this gauge the Pauli equation becomes

$$H = \frac{1}{2m^*}\left(-i\hbar\vec{\nabla} + \frac{eB}{2c}r\hat{e}_\theta\right)^2 + V(\vec{r}) + \frac{1}{2}g^*\mu_B B\sigma_z$$

From this equation it can be deduced that the component of the linear momentum along the azimuthal direction (that is the angular momentum in a two-dimensional system) is coupled with the magnetic field. This originates the Aharonov-Bohm effect.

For an electron descriving a closed orbit of length L the periodic condition for the wavefunction must be verified:

$$\phi(L) = \phi(0) \Rightarrow e^{ikL} = 1 \Rightarrow kL = 2\pi l$$

When a magnetic field is applied, it is added the so-called Aharonov-Bohm phase, due to the coupling between the momentum and the magnetic field in the Pauli Hamiltonian:

$$e^{i(kL+2\pi\Phi/\Phi_0)} = 1 \Rightarrow kL = 2\pi(l - \Phi/\Phi_0)$$

where $\Phi = AB$ is the flux of magnetic field through the area A closed by the orbit, and $\Phi_0 = \frac{hc}{e}$ is the flux quantum. The kinetic energy of the particle then becomes

$$E = \frac{k^2}{2m} = \frac{2\pi^2}{mL^2}\left(l - \frac{\Phi}{\Phi_0}\right)^2$$

Suppose the electron is constrained to move in a circle of radius R_0. In this limit all the motion is along the azimuthal direction, and the energy of the one electron ring is:

$$E_L(\Phi) = E_0 + \frac{\hbar^2}{2m^* R_0^2}\left(L - \frac{\Phi}{\Phi_0}\right)^2$$

where L is now the angular momentum, and the magnetic flux across the ring is $\Phi = \pi R_0^2 B$. In the one-dimensional limit the potential energy does not depend on the magnetic field, so the parabolic dependence with the magnetic field is fully descrived by the equation above.

At $\Phi = \left(L + \frac{1}{2}\right)\Phi_0$, $E_L = E_{L+1}$ and there is a ground state transition. The ground state energy oscillates with a period Φ_0. This leads to the so-called Aharonov-Bohm oscillations in the persistent current $I = -c\frac{\partial E}{\partial B}$ that is measured in the experiments.

3. INTERACTING ELECTRONS

In reference [11] it has been found that in the limit of very low electronic density the energy of the system is

$$E_L(\Phi) = E_0^{loc} + \frac{\hbar^2 N}{2m^* R_0^2}\left(\frac{L}{N} - \frac{\Phi}{\Phi_0}\right)^2 = E_0^{loc} + \frac{\hbar^2}{2m^* N R_0^2}\left(L - \frac{\Phi}{\Phi_0}N\right)^2$$

The period of the oscillations becomes Φ_0/N, and this is called fractional Aharonov-Bohm effect. Comparing this equation with that of the noninteracting case, it can be understood that all the N electrons have the same angular momentum L/N, so they keep their distances fixed and the only motion is the rotation of the whole electron

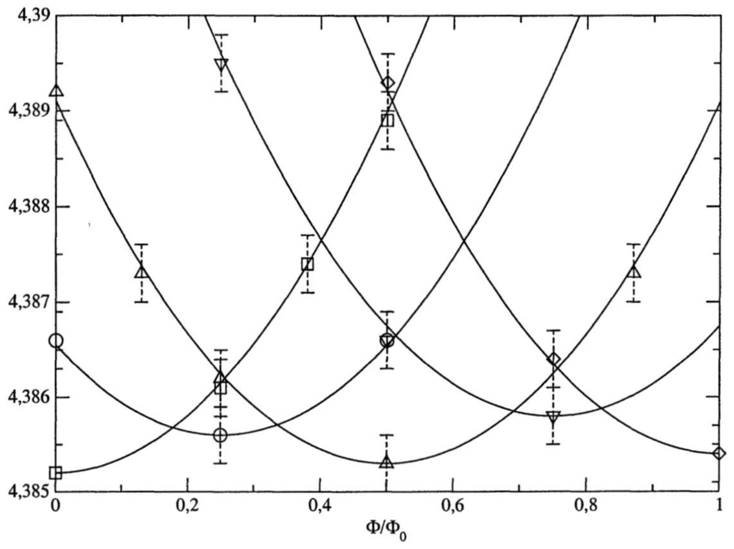

Figure 1. Energy of the lowest energy configurations as a function of the magnetic field flux across the ring in the $N = 4$, $r_s = 9$ quasi one-dimensional ring calculated with DMC in reference [11]. It can be observed that the period of the energy oscilations is $\Phi_0/4$.

system as a rigid body. The first two figures show the fractional periodicity of the energy and the angular correlation function showing the localization.

The localization appears due to the fact that the ground state is a multiconfiguration wavefunction, i.e. the sum of many different Slater determinants with the same angular momentum and spin

$$\Psi^{L,S} = \sum_{\alpha=1}^{m} a_\alpha \Phi_\alpha^{L,S}$$

although Ψ keeps the circular symmetry of the Hamiltonian. One speaks of localization in the sense that the electrons keep their distances constant, forming a Wigner molecule that rotates to form a circularly symmetric density. The exact calculations in this work are made finding the total wave function as expressed above by means of a configuration-interaction (CI) method. Details about this method, also known as exact diagonalitation, can be found in reference [12] and references therein.

In reference [11] the multiconfiguration wavefunction has been expressed as a product of the so called Jastrow factor and a Slater determinant

$$\Psi(\mathbf{R})_{L,S} = J(\mathbf{R})\Phi^{L,S}(\mathbf{R})$$

and in this case the angular correlations are explicitly introduced in the Jastrow factor, that is optimized by means of Monte Carlo methods, widely explained in this reference.

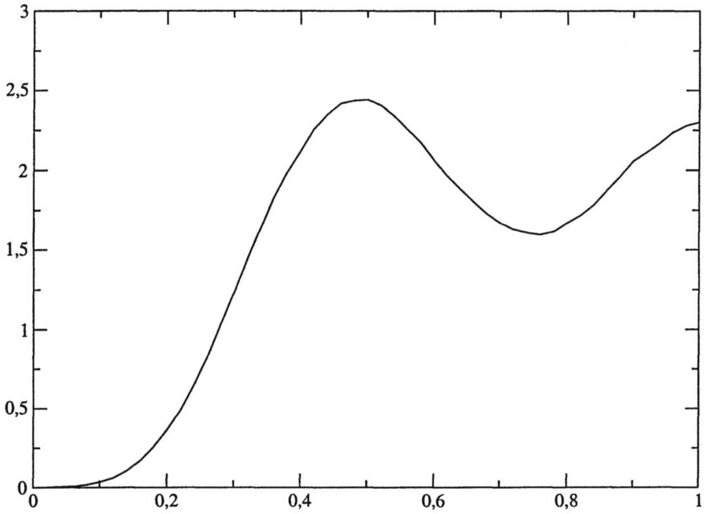

Figure 2. Angular correlation function of the same system as in figure 1. The angle is in units of π rad. The clear maxima at $\pi/2$ and π demonstrate that the electrons are located forming a square.

In a mean field calculation it is assumed that the wavefunction is a single Slater determinant. The only way to introduce angular correlations into such a kind of wavefuntion is allowing the single particle orbitals to be non circularly symmetric. The mean field Hamiltonian is constructed from the single-particle wavefunctions ϕ_i, via the density $n = \sum |\phi_i|^2$, and therefore this can lack the circular symmetry of the real Hamiltonian. It will be shown that this strongly affects the results.

4. THE LOCAL-SPIN-DENSITY APPROXIMATION

In this special type of Density Functional Theory the exchange and correlation energy is calculated with an energy density function ϵ_{xc} that depends on the total density and the spin magnetization

$$E_{xc}[n] = \int \epsilon_{xc} n(\vec{r}) d\vec{r}$$

The total energy in the DFT is a function of the density: $E[n] = T[n] + E_c[n] + E_{ext}[n] + E_{xc}[n]$, where T is the kinetic energy, E_C the direct Coulomb energy and E_{ext} the energy due to the external confinement. As one assumes that the wavefunction is a single Slater determinant, the density is $n = \sum |\phi_i|^2$

Minimizing the total energy with respect to the ϕ_i^* one gets the Kohn-Sham equations:

$$H_{KS}\phi_i(\vec{r}) = \epsilon_i \phi_i(\vec{r})$$

$$H_{KS} = \frac{1}{2m^*}\left(-i\hbar\vec{\nabla} - \frac{e}{c}\vec{A}\right)^2 + V_{ext} + V^C + V^{xc} + (W^{xc} + \frac{1}{2}g^*\mu_B B)\sigma_z$$

Where

$$V^C = \int d\vec{r}\,' \frac{n(\vec{r}\,')}{|\vec{r} - \vec{r}\,'|}$$

is the direct Coulomb potential and

$$V_{xc} = \frac{\partial(n\epsilon_{xc})}{\partial n}, W_{xc} = \frac{\partial(n\epsilon_{xc})}{\partial m}$$

are the spin-independent and the spin dependent parts of the exchange-correlation potential. $m(r) = n_\uparrow(r) - n_\downarrow(r)$ is the spin magnetization, and $\xi(r) = m(r)/n(r)$ is the spin polarization.

The exchange-correlation energy density depends on the polrization as $\epsilon_{xc}[n, \xi] = \epsilon_{xc}^P[n] + (\epsilon_{xc}^F[n] - \epsilon_{xc}^P[n])f(\xi)$ and therefore

$$W_{xc} = (\epsilon_{xc}^F - \epsilon_{xc}^P)\frac{\partial f(\xi)}{\partial \xi}$$

where $f(\xi)$ is the Von Barth and Hedin interpolation formula, that is consistent with the dependence of the exchange enegy with the polarization in a Hartree-Fock calculation for the homogeneous system

$$f(\xi) = \frac{(1+\xi)^{3/2} + (1-\xi)^{3/2} - 2}{2^{3/2} - 2}$$

ϵ_{xc}^F and ϵ_{xc}^P are the values of ϵ_{xc} in the 2DEG in the ferromagnetic and paramagnetic cases, respectively. We have used the functional form for the exchange and correlation energy density that is given in reference [13]. It is important to point out that the wavefunctions found with the LSDA method are eigenfunctions of the mean field hamiltonian H_{KS}, but not of the real Hamiltonian

$$H = \sum_i \left(\frac{1}{2m^*}\left(\vec{p}_i - \frac{e}{c}\vec{A}(\vec{r}_i)\right)^2 + V(\vec{r}_i) + \frac{1}{2}g^*\mu_B B\sigma_i + \sum_{j>i} \frac{e^2}{|\vec{r}_i - \vec{r}_j|} \right)$$

5. RESULTS

We define the ring with the external potential $V_{ext} = \frac{1}{2}m^*\omega_0^2(r - R_0)^2$, and we study an $N = 2$ electron ring with different values of R_0. The one-dimensional electron density can be parametrized with the Wigner-Seitz radius $r_s = \pi R_0/N$ that is the mean distance between electrons in the ring. We have first made the calculation for a ring with $r_s = 0.6$, finding a circularly symmetric LSDA density. This is consistent with the results for a $N = 10$ ring of the same density calculated in reference [11], where the circular symmetric LSDA calculation coincided with DMC calculations (regarded to be exact), implying that the exact wavefunction has actually

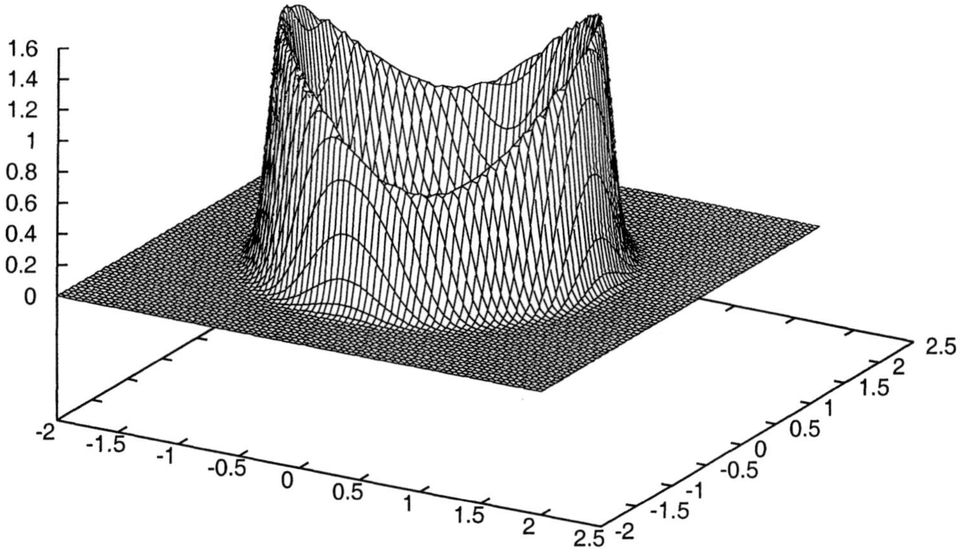

Figure 3. Density of a quasi one-dimensional two electron ring of $r_s = 1.8$ obtained with a non-circular symetric LSDA calculation.

intrinsic circular symmetry (no localization). The density for a lower density ring, with $r_s = 1.8$, shows that the system is already localized, although there is still an appreciable overlapping between the single-particle wavefunctions of each electron. In these one-dimensional systems localization appears at a much higher density than in the 2DEG. This is due to the fact that the effect of the electron-electron repulsion is enhanced by the low dimensionality of the system. In other words, the channel where the electrons move is so narrow that they have not enough space to avoid each other.

The Pauli equation with the confining potential V_{ext} and in the symmetric gauge becomes

$$H = -\frac{\hbar^2\vec{\nabla}^2}{2m^*} - i\frac{1}{2}\omega_c\frac{\partial}{\partial\theta} + \frac{1}{8}m^*\omega_c^2r^2 + \frac{1}{2}m^*\omega_0^2(r-R_0)^2 + \frac{1}{2}g^*\mu_B B\sigma_z$$

The cyclotron frequency $\omega_c = \frac{eB}{m^*c} = \frac{h}{\pi m^* R_0^2}\frac{\Phi}{\Phi_0}$ has its origin in the magnetic field, that generates an additional confinement that compresses the electronic density as B increases. If $\omega_0 >> \omega_c$, the single-particle wavefunctions are not significantly compressed when B increases and then the potential energy is independent of B, so the kinetic is the only part of the energy that depends of the magnetic field, with the parabollic dependence shown in section 2. As far as the external confinement ω_0 is very strong, its value does not change the oscillations of the energy, shifting only in a constant value the energy of the ground state.

Observing the plot of $E(B)$ in figure 4 and comparing with the results of the exact calculation one finds that the LSDA does not show the oscillations. We have included just to compare the results of circularly symmetric LSDA, that shows oscillations but lacking the fractional periodicity of the exact calculation. In fact, the ground

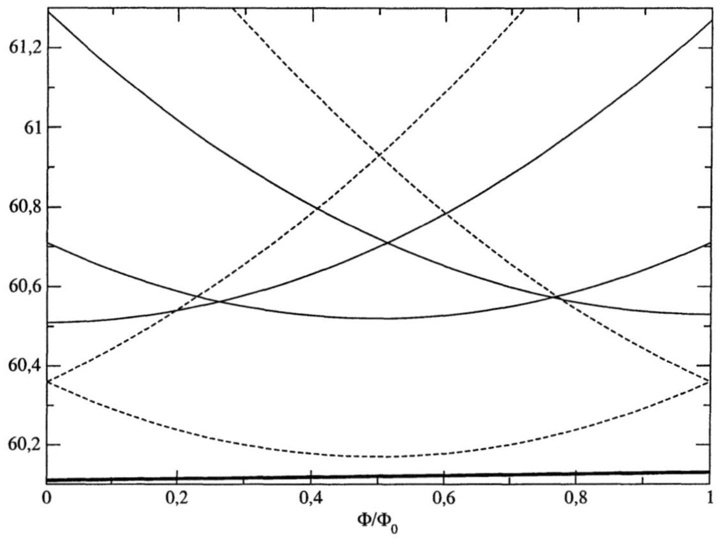

Figure 4. For the same system as in Fig. 3, exact energies obtained with a CI calculation (narrow solid lines), energies obtained from a circularly symmetric LSDA calculation (dashed lines), and ground state energy obtained from the non-circularly symmetric LSDA calculation (thick solid line)

state wavefunctions given by the LSDA calculation without circular symmetry are not eigenfunctions of the angular momentum, because the LSDA Hamiltonian H_{KS} does not conmute with L when the single particle wavefunctions do not have circular symmetry. The value of the angular momentum changes continuously as the magnetic field increases, so there are no sharp transitions from a given L ground state to another one, and the energy oscillations disappear. It would be necessary to impose any constraint to the total wavefunction to fix its angular momentum.

In the case of a $r_s = 1$ ring it can be appreciated a smooth oscillation of the LSDA ground state energy. We have expanded the energy scale in the lower part of figure 5 in order to make evident this oscillation. A more detailed observation reveals that the energy difference between the minima and the maximum is similar to the energy difference between the minima of each angular momentum configuration obtained in the exact calculation.

For each magnetic field B, the mean field calculation gives the ground state energy of the many particle state whose kinetic energy cancels at B, therefore it gives the energy E_{LS} of the state with integer angular momentum L when the magnetic flux is $\Phi_L = L\Phi_0/N$. If the system is strongly one-dimensional, the energy of a configuration (L, S) must depend on the magnetic field as:

$$E(\Phi) = E_{LS} + \frac{\hbar^2}{2m^* N R_0^2}\left(L - \frac{\Phi}{\Phi_0}N\right)^2$$

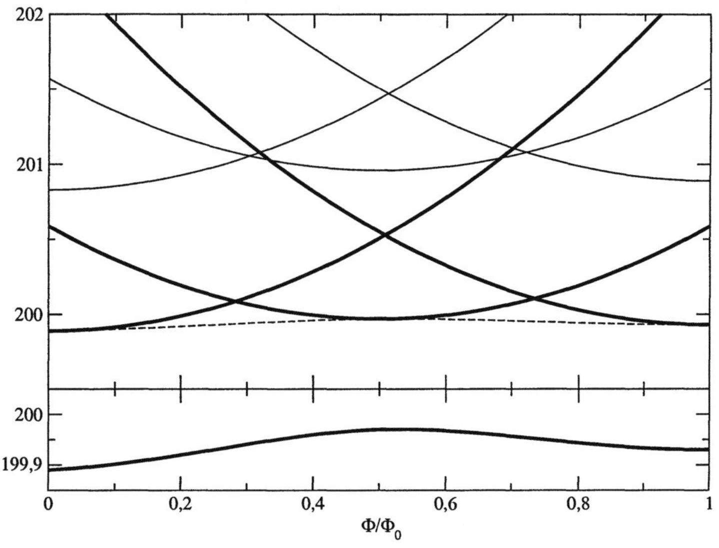

Figure 5. *Upper pannel:* For a quasi one-dimensional two electron ring with $r_s = 1$, exact energies (thin solid lines), energy obtained from the non-circular LSDA calculation (dashed line) and energies extrapolated from the value of the LSDA energy at $\Phi = 0, \Phi_0/2$ and Φ_0 with the method explained in the text (thick solid lines) *Lower pannel:* higher scale plot of the non-cicular LSDA ground state energy, where it can be observed a maximum at $\Phi = \Phi_0/2$.

Assuming that this dependence is accurate for the system that we are considering, the energy of this configuration can be extrapolated to any magnetic field flux different from Φ_L using the equation above, valid while $\omega_c << \omega_0$. Figure 5 shows that the $E(B)$ dependence obtained in this way gives the same result as the exact calculation, apart of a constant shift, due to the fact that LSDA is only exact in the 2DEG, and the physical conditions for a narrow ring are totally different from that for the homogeneus system. This constant difference does not affect the calculated persistent current, that is the derivative respect to the magnetic field. The same extrapolation has been applied to the $r_s = 1$ system and it has been found an excelent agreement with the exact results.

6. CONCLUSIONS

It has been shown that LSDA calculations made without imposing circular symmetry give good results for the ground state energy of strongly localized electron systems in quasi one-dimensional quantum rings at values of the magnetic field such that the angular momentum of the solution of the mean field calculation is integer. The method does not give the right energy for any value of the magnetic field because the many-particle wavefunction that is solution of the LSDA Hamiltonian is not an eigenfunction of the angular momentum, as this mean field Hamiltonian has lost the circular symmetry of the true Hamiltonian. In the case of quasi one-dimensional quantum rings it is proposed a sound method to extrapolate the ground state energy for the other values of magnetic field, and it is found that the results obtained in this way are equivalent to the exact ones, apart of a constant that does not influence the persistent current, that is the magnitude that can be experimentally measured.

7. ACKNOWLEDGMENTS

The author thanks Llorenç Serra and Antonio Puente for useful discussions and for providing the non circularly symmmetric mean field code.

REFERENCES

[1] A. Lorke, R. J. Luyken, A. O. Govorov, J. P. Kotthaus, J. M. Garcia and P. M. Petroff, *Phys. Rev. Lett.* **84**, 2223 (2000).

[2] U. F. Keyser, C. Führer, S. Borck, R. J. Haug, M. Bichler, G. Abstreiter and W. Wegscheider, Phys. Rev. Lett. **90**, 196601 (2003).

[3] D. Mailly, C. Chapelier and A. Benoit, Phys. Rev. Lett. **70**, 2020 (1993).

[4] T. Chakraborty and P. Pietiläinen, Phys. Rev. B **50**, 8460 (1994).

[5] S. Viefers, P. Singha Deo, S. M. Reimann, M. Manninen and M. Koskinen, Phys. Rev. B **62**, 10668 (2000).

[6] A. Fuhrer, S. Lüscher, T. Ihn, T. Heinzel, K. Ensslin, W. Wegscheider and M. Bichler, Nature **413**, 822 (2001).

[7] D. Loss and P. Goldbart, Phys. Rev. B **43**, 13762 (1991).

[8] K. Niemelä, P. Pietiläinen, P. Hyvönen, and T. Chakraborty, Europhys. Lett. **36**, 533 (1996).

[9] A. E. Hansen, A. Kristensen, S. Pedersen, C. B. Sorensen and P. E. Lindelof, Physica E **12**, 770 (2002).

[10] A. Emperador, M. Pi, M. Barranco and E. Lipparini, Phys. Rev. B **64**, 155304 (2001)

[11] A. Emperador, F. Pederiva and E. Lipparini, Phys. Rev. B **68**, 115312 (2003)

[12] M. Koskinen, M. Manninen, B. Mottelson and S. M. Reimann, Phys. Rev. B **63**, 205323 (2001)

[13] B. Tanatar and D. M. Ceperley, Phys. Rev. B **39**, 5005 (1989)

MULTISTABILITY AND FRACTAL PROPERTIES OF HAMILTONIAN LATTICE MODELS

Karl E. Kürten

Institute for Experimental Physics, University of Vienna
5, Boltzmanngasse, A-1090 Vienna, Austria

Christian Krattenthaler

Institut Girard Desargues, Université Claude Bernard Lyon-I,
21, avenue Claude Bernard, F-69622 Villeurbanne Cedex, France

1. INTRODUCTION

Numerous condensed matter systems are effectively discrete by nature because the relevant length scales are of the order of the interparticle distance. Such systems are described by a Hamiltonian that is discrete in space, while their time evolution is considered as continuous. Their remarkable behavior, exemplified in models of charge-density waves, magnetic spirals, disordered crystals, magnetic multilayers or adsorbed monolayers, stems from a competition between two or more forces that leads to multistable spatially modulated structures [1–5]. One other prominent example is modeling proton dynamics in hydrogen bonded chains [6]. Spatial disorder is associated with a highly complex energy landscape in configuration space, where the number of locally stable configurations typically increases exponentially with the size of the system. The simplest model system can be envisioned as a one-dimensional chain of N particles with nearest-neighbour interactions, each particle, which is considered as a classical spin, also subject to an external multi-well potential field. Specifying the displacement of particle i at time t from its lattice site by the variable x_i, and assuming periodic boundary conditions, the total energy of the system is given by the N-particle Hamiltonian

$$\mathbf{H}(x_1, x_2, \ldots, x_N) = \sum_{i=1}^{N} \left(\frac{1}{2}\dot{x}_i^2 + E_I(x_{i-1}, x_i, x_{i+1}) + U(x_i) \right). \tag{1}$$

The first term is the kinetic energy, the second term defines the inter-site energy, specified by nearest-neighbour interactions, while the last term is the potential energy due to an external on-site potential.

A standard harmonic inter-site potential is given by

$$E_I(x_{i-1}, x_i, x_{i+1}) = \frac{1}{4}(x_i - x_{i-1})^2 + \frac{1}{4}(x_i - x_{i+1})^2,$$

while the on-site potential is specified by the Φ^4 double-well potential

$$U(x_i) = \frac{\alpha}{4}(1 - x_i^2)^2, \tag{2}$$

depicted in Fig. 1. It is often used for the description of displacive and order-disorder transitions. Here, the control parameter α specifies the height of the barrier $U(0) = \frac{\alpha}{4}$ which separates the two symmetrical sinks of the two potential wells.

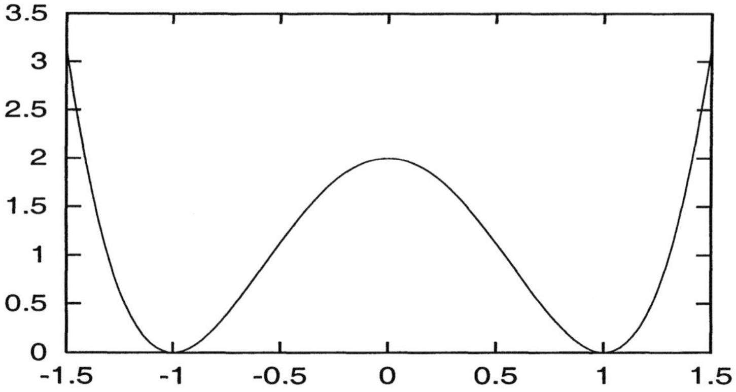

Figure 1. Symmetric Φ^4 double-well potential for $\alpha = 8$.

Based on the Φ^4 potential, the total energy Eq. (4) takes the form

$$\mathbf{E} = \sum_{i=1}^{N} \left(\frac{1}{2}\dot{x}_i^2 + \frac{1}{4}(x_i - x_{i-1})^2 + \frac{1}{4}(x_i - x_{i+1})^2 + \frac{\alpha}{4}(1 - x_i^2)^2 \right). \tag{3}$$

The ground state with zero energy is obtained, when all particles are placed in one of the two sinks of the double-well potential. According to the variational principle, stationary configurations obey the set of N non-linear coupled equations

$$-x_{i-1} + 2x_i - x_{i+1} - \alpha x_i(1 - x_i^2) = 0, \qquad i = 1, \ldots, N. \tag{4}$$

However, solutions $\mathbf{x}^* = (x_1^*, x_2^*, \ldots, x_N^*)$ specify a local minimum only if the eigenvalues of the triangular Hessian $\nabla^2\mathbf{H}(\mathbf{x})_{|\mathbf{x}=\mathbf{x}^*} = (\frac{\partial^2\mathbf{H}(\mathbf{x})}{\partial x_i \partial x_j})_{|\mathbf{x}=\mathbf{x}^*}$ are all positive. Since the diagonal entries are $2 + U''(x_i^*)$ and the two off-diagonal entries take the value -1, Gershgorin's disk theorem provides a sufficient stability condition $U''(x_i^*) > 0$, where all particles occupy the convex part of the potential well. For the double well potential this condition is satisfied for $x_i^2 > \frac{1}{3}$.

There are two macroscopic quantities of interest. First, the total energy, which takes the simple form, reminiscent of the virial theorem in the continuous counterpart of the nonlinear Klein-Gordon equation,

$$E = \frac{\alpha}{4}\sum_{i=1}^{N}(1 - x_i^4), \tag{5}$$

which is obtained after insertion of the equilibrium condition Eq. (4). Second, the average displacement

$$M = \frac{1}{N}\sum_{i=1}^{N} x_i, \tag{6}$$

reminiscent of the total magnetization of a classical spin chain of interacting magnetic particles, a macroscopic variable, which is often experimentally accessible. In this case the intersite energy E_I specifies the exchange interaction between two neighbouring particles, while the on-site potential plays the role of the uniaxial anisotropy energy with strength parameter α [7].

2. FEW PARTICLE CASE

Let us first consider the situation for $N = 2$ particles, where the energy takes the symmetric form

$$E(x_1, x_2) = (x_1 - x_2)^2 + \frac{\alpha}{4}\left((1 - x_1^2)^2 + (1 - x_2^2)^2\right).$$

The set of coupled equations

$$\begin{aligned} -x_2 + 2x_1 - x_2 - \alpha x_1(1 - x_1^2) &= 0, \\ -x_1 + 2x_2 - x_1 - \alpha x_2(1 - x_2^2) &= 0. \end{aligned}$$

has 9 real valued solutions representing stationary configurations. Fig. 2 shows the energy landscape $E(x_1, x_2)$ for $\alpha = 8$ characterized by one relative maximum (0,0) and four local minima $\pm(1,1)$, and $\pm\left(\sqrt{1 - 4/\alpha}, -\sqrt{1 - 4/\alpha}\right)$. The first two minima represent the two degenerate ground states with energy $E = 0$, while the latter represent two energetically higher lying antiferromagnetic states with energy per particle $E/2 = 2\left(1 - \frac{2}{\alpha}\right)$. Note that these four local minima are separated by four saddle points with energy per particle $E/2 = (2 + \alpha)^2/(8\alpha)$.

The saddle points act as energy barriers, whose height increases linearly with increasing control parameter α. It is important to note that the height of the barriers is of the order of α, while the energy values of the local minima are all of the order of one. Accordingly, the energy difference between these states is much smaller than the energy required to overcome the barrier in order to switch to another state of equilibrium.

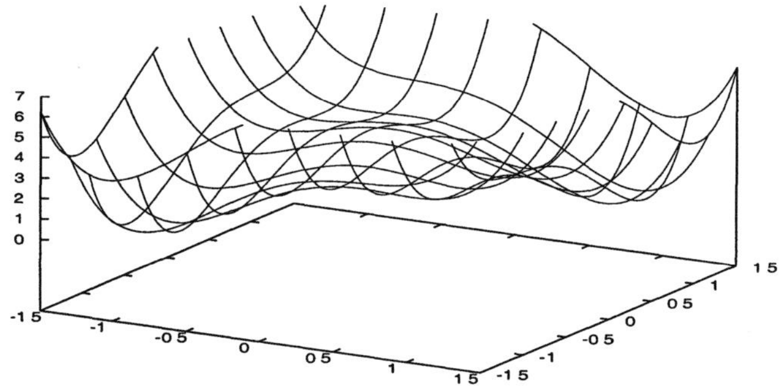

Figure 2. Energy landscape $E(x_1, x_2)$ for $\alpha = 8$.

The same arguments hold for larger values of N, where we will show in Section 3 that the energy landscape exhibits an extremely complicated multi-valley structure with an exponentially increasing number of local minima and saddle points that also allows the appearance of structural disorder.
For $N = 3$ we have a "soliton" solution

$$\mathbf{x}^* = \{x_1, x_2, x_1\},$$

with

$$x_1 = \left[\frac{2}{3} - \frac{1}{\alpha} + \frac{2}{3}\left(1 - \frac{3}{\alpha}\right)^{\frac{1}{2}} \cos\frac{\phi + \pi}{3}\right]^{1/2} \quad \text{and} \quad x_2 = x_1(1 - \alpha + cx_1^2),$$

and with

$$\cos\phi = \frac{1 - \frac{9}{2\alpha} + \frac{27}{\alpha^3}}{(1 - \frac{3}{\alpha})^{\frac{3}{2}}}.$$

This solution represents a local minimum only for $\alpha > 3 + \sqrt{9 + 6\sqrt{3}} \approx 7.40367$ with the expansion $x_1 = 1 - \frac{2}{\alpha} - \cdots$ and $x_2 = -1 + \frac{1}{\alpha} - \cdots$, respectively.

3. EXACT ENUMERATION OF ALL LOCALLY STABLE STRUCTURES

Let us now further concentrate on large values of α, where the on-site potential is sufficiently strong. One might ask: which kind of landscape- or domain structures can evolve due to the competition between the exchange- and the on-site energy? Depending on the number of particles N, how many distinct non-equivalent structures can there exist? When the control parameter α is varied, the energy balance is changed such that a rearrangement of the energy landscape can take place. Stationary configurations of the Hamiltonian (1) are described by the N non-linear coupled equations

$$-x_{i-1} + 2x_i - x_{i+1} - \alpha x_i(1 - x_i^2) = 0, \qquad i = 1, \ldots, N. \tag{7}$$

In order to determine all possible locally stable spatial structures we first consider the system for large values of α. In the large α-limit, Eq. (7) reduces to

$$x_i(1 - x_i^2) = 0, \qquad i = 1, \ldots, N. \tag{8}$$

Ignoring the solutions $x_i = 0$, which correspond to saddle point configurations, this coupled set of equations has exactly 2^N distinct solutions consisting of N-dimensional binary strings

$$\mathbf{x}^* = (x_1^*, x_2^*, \ldots, x_N^*) \tag{9}$$

with components $x_i^* \in \{-1, 1\}$. Provided that α is sufficiently large, the implicit function theorem guarantees the existence of all these solutions of Eq. (7) in a neighbourhood of any of these binary strings. (Experimentally, the critical α depends weakly on the particle number N, however, numerical calculations suggest that in fact **all** 2^N locally stable solutions of Eq. (7) exist in a neighbourhood of any of these binary strings provided that $\alpha \approx> 8$.) If these are expressed in terms of a power series expansion about the asymptotic strings $\mathbf{x}^*$, then the first order correction term

$$\Delta x_i^{(1)} = \frac{x_{i-1}^* - 2x_i^* + x_{i+1}^*}{2\alpha} \tag{10}$$

is proportional to $1/\alpha$. The particular form of the first- and the higher order correction terms then implies that $|x_i| \leq 1$ rigorously holds. It should be noted however that, depending on a specific solution, the stability range can vary widely.

Since the particles reside on a circle, we will consider configurations that only differ by a rotation $(x_i \to x_{s+i})_{1 \leq i \leq N}$ (for some fixed s with $1 \leq s \leq N$) or by a reflection $(x_i \to x_{s-i})_{1 \leq i \leq N}$ (for some fixed s with $1 \leq s \leq N$) as equivalent. Together, these rotations and reflections form the dihedral group $\mathcal{D}_N$. Since for large α, the stable solutions of (7) can be identified with the 2^N strings of 1s and -1s of length N (for example, the "soliton" solution for $N = 3$ presented in Section 2 would be identified with the string $(-1, 1, -1)$), the number of inequivalent solutions will be equal to the number of orbits of these (circular) strings under the action of the dihedral group $\mathcal{D}_N$. In more colloquial terms, we want to count the number $F_D(N)$ of different necklaces one can make out of N beads, each of them either coloured white or black. It follows from Redfield-Pólya theory (see for example [8]), that the number of these orbits (or necklaces), and thus the number of inequivalent stable solutions to (7), is

$$F_D(N) = \frac{1}{2N} \sum_{d|N} \varphi(d)\, 2^{N/d} + \begin{cases} \frac{3}{4} 2^{N/2} & \text{for } N \text{ even,} \\ 2^{(N-1)/2} & \text{for } N \text{ odd,} \end{cases} \tag{11}$$

where $\varphi(x)$ is the Euler totient function. For $N = 1, 2, 3, \ldots$ this is the sequence $\{2, 3, 4, 6, 8, 13, 18, 30, 46, 78, 126, 224, \ldots\}$. Since $\varphi(1) = 1$, the number $F_D(N)$ is asymptotically equal to $2^{N-1}/N$ as N tends to ∞.

In order to enumerate the orbits of strings that are invariant under reflections and those which are not separately, we also count the number $F_C(N)$ of different necklaces made out of N beads, each of them coloured white or black, *which are embedded in the plane*, that is, the orbits of strings of 1s and -1s of length N under the action of the cyclic group $\mathcal{C}_N$ of rotations $(x_i \to x_{s+i})_{1\leq i\leq N}$. Redfield–Pólya theory again shows that

$$F_C(N) = \frac{1}{N}\sum_{d|n} \varphi(d)2^{N/d}.$$

The first few terms of this sequence are $\{2, 3, 4, 6, 8, 14, 20, 36, 60, 108, 188, 352, \ldots\}$.

As is easy to see, the number of orbits *under the action of the dihedral group* $\mathcal{D}_N$ which are *not* invariant under reflection is then $F_C(N) - F_D(N)$, while the number of the orbits under the action of the dihedral group $\mathcal{D}_N$ which are is $2F_D(N) - F_C(N)$.

The spectrum of the total magnetizations M as well as the energy spectrum, consisting of 8267 distinct values, both reminiscent of Cantor-set structures, are depicted in Fig. 3 and Fig. 4, respectively.

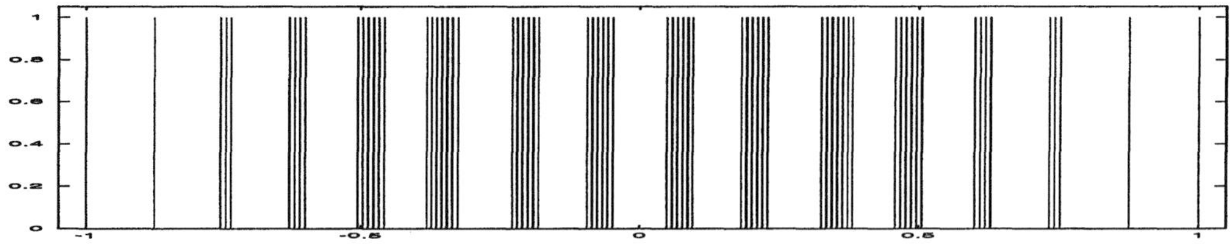

Figure 3. Spectrum of the total magnetizations Eq. (6) for $N = 15$ and $\alpha = 8$.

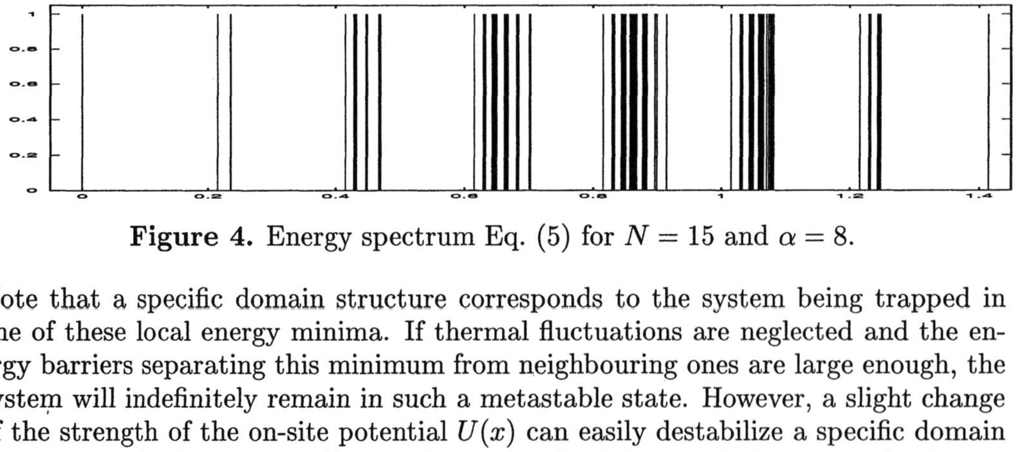

Figure 4. Energy spectrum Eq. (5) for $N = 15$ and $\alpha = 8$.

Note that a specific domain structure corresponds to the system being trapped in one of these local energy minima. If thermal fluctuations are neglected and the energy barriers separating this minimum from neighbouring ones are large enough, the system will indefinitely remain in such a metastable state. However, a slight change of the strength of the on-site potential $U(x)$ can easily destabilize a specific domain structure such that it is sufficient that a local minimum of the energy landscape is transformed into a saddle point and the system can evolve towards some other metastable configuration.

4. EXACT ENUMERATION OF ALL DISPLACEMENTS

In order to determine the distribution or the "spectrum" of all possible displacements $|x_i|$, $i = 1, 2, \ldots, N$, as a function of the particle number N, we exploit the fact that two-dimensional maps allow us to represent any stationary configuration of a Hamiltonian of the form (1) by a trajectory of a dynamical system. Therefore, the mathematical situation is *identical* to that of temporal evolution, although the problem has been formulated in terms of spatial arrangements. Introducing the auxiliary variable $y_{n+1} = x_n$, Eq. (7) takes the form of a two-dimensional iterative map in discrete time,

$$\begin{pmatrix} x_{n+1} \\ y_{n+1} \end{pmatrix} = \mathbf{F}(x_n, y_n) = \begin{pmatrix} -y_n + 2x_n - \alpha x_n(1 - x_n^2) \\ x_n \end{pmatrix} \tag{12}$$

Due to the periodic boundary conditions, we have to determine all $F_D(N)$ inequivalent periodic orbits of the map equation. These can be easily calculated, once the fixed points

$$\begin{pmatrix} x^* \\ y^* \end{pmatrix} = \mathbf{F}^{(N)}(x^*, y^*) \tag{13}$$

of the N-th iterate of the map are known. Since periodic orbits of the map equation can be shown to be unstable with respect to iterating the map [9], we solve the nonlinear set Eq. (13) with a standard Newton-Raphson procedure, where the asymptotic strings Eq. (9) serve as initial conditions.

We first calculate all possible displacements as the length N of the chain is varied, where we first concentrate on N odd. Fig. 5 shows the displacement spectrum for odd $N = 3, 5, 7, 9$. Experimentally, with increasing number of particles, the spectrum evolves by consecutive tripling and quadrupling of spectral substructures. It obviously grows in a quasi self-similar manner, where structures replicate themselves on successively smaller scales with respect to their statistical properties. Triplets split into a quadruplet surrounded by two triplets, while quadruplets split into four quadruplets. Hence, it seems that the spectrum grows according to

$$S(N) = 2S(N-2) + 4^{\frac{N-3}{2}}. \tag{14}$$

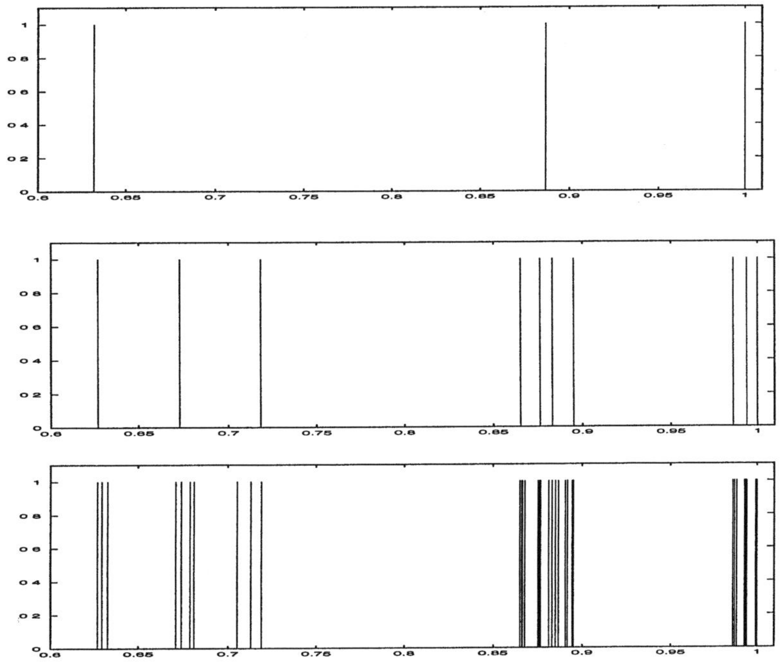

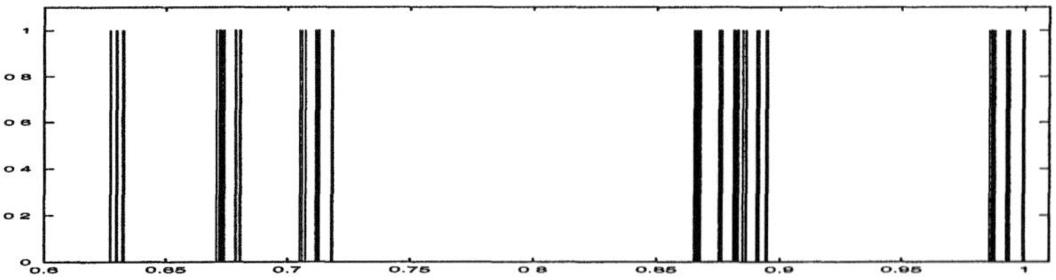

Figure 5. Spectrum of the displacements for $N = 3$, $N = 5$, $N = 7$, and $N = 9$ (from above) for $\alpha = 8$.

For $N = 3, 5, 7$, and $N = 9$, we have $3, 10, 36$, and 136 distinct values, respectively. An estimate for the fractal dimension can be obtained by using a box counting algorithm, and it yields the value $d_f = 0.58$.

A rigorous verification of the recurrence (14) is equivalent to rigorously determine the numbers $S(N)$ of distinct displacements. We shall be able to do this under the hypothesis, which is confirmed by our experiments, that displacements in one orbit are distinct from the displacement in another orbit, and that the number of distinct displacements in an orbit is equal to the minimal period s under rotation of the corresponding binary string $\mathbf{x}^* = (x_1^*, x_2^*, \dots, x_N^*)$ if the orbit is not invariant under reflection, and equal to $(s+1)/2$ otherwise. Thus, one way to determine $S(N)$ is to calculate the sum $\frac{1}{2}\sum_{\mathbf{x}^*} w(\mathbf{x}^*)$, where the sum is over all orbits $\mathbf{x}^*$, and $w(\mathbf{x}^*) = s$, respectively $w(\mathbf{x}^*) = (s+1)/2$, depending on the two cases described above. (The factor $\frac{1}{2}$ results from the invariance $x_i \to -x_i$ in Eq. (7)). There is a similar weighted sum for even N.

It is possible to do this calculation directly. There is, however, an elegant way around this. Consider the set of all binary strings constructed in the following manner: For any orbit, let $\mathbf{x}^* = (x_1^*, x_2^*, \dots, x_N^*)$ be the corresponding binary string, with weight $w(\mathbf{x}^*) = w$, say. List the strings

$$
\begin{array}{l}
(x_1^*, x_2^*, \dots, x_{N-1}^*, x_N^*) \\
(x_2^*, x_3^*, \dots, x_N^*, x_1^*) \\
(x_3^*, x_4^*, \dots, x_1^*, x_2^*) \\
\dots\dots\dots\dots\dots\dots\dots\dots \\
(x_w^*, x_{w+1}^*, \dots, x_{w-2}^*, x_{w-1}^*).
\end{array}
$$

Finally form the union of all these strings over all orbits. The upshot is that this set of strings is a set of representatives of orbits of strings of 1s and -1s of length N under the action of the group generated by the two operations of reversal of strings $r : (x_i^*) \to (x_{N-i+1}^*)$, and the operation of simultaneous exchange of 1s and -1s $e : (x_i^*) \to (-x_i^*)$. This group consists only of 4 elements, the identical operation $(x_i^*) \to (x_i^*)$, the reversal r, the exchange e, and the composition re : $(x_i^*) \to (-x_{N-i+1}^*)$ of reversal and exchange. Thus, with the help of Redfield-Pólya theory, we arrive at the explicit expression

$$
S(N) = 2^{N-2} + \begin{cases} 2^{(N-2)/2} & \text{for } N \text{ even,} \\ 2^{(N-3)/2} & \text{for } N \text{ odd,} \end{cases} \tag{15}
$$

which had been empirically found earlier in [7] and confirms indeed the empirically observed recurrence Eq. (14).

4. DISCUSSION

We have shown that the energy surface of our model consists of exponentially many locally stable minima separated by large barriers specified by unstable saddle points. With the aid of Redfield-Pólya theory we give the exact number of inequivalent locally stable configurations as well as the exact number of distinct values of the displacement spectrum. Both quantities increase exponentially with increasing particle number N. As N tends to ∞ they are asymptotically $2^{N-1}/N$ and 2^{N-2} , respectively. The spectrum, which grows exponentially in a quasi self-similar manner is shown to be a fractal with fractal dimension $d_f = 0.55$.

The model with slight modifications can also describe the formation of magnetic structures in physical novel systems such as antiferromagneticly coupled magnetic multilayers, where modulated structures arise due to the competition between the exchange energy, the anisotropic on-site energy and an additional external magnetic field [7]. Here the fractal structure is intimately connected with the experimentally observed Barkhausen jumps which exhibit fractal properties associated with random Cantor dust of a fractal dimension d_f depending on the strength of the external magnetic field [10].

ACKNOWLEDGMENTS

The first author thanks S. Charpentier, M. Olivier and P. Martin for helpful computer assistance and F.V. Kusmartsev for various useful discussions.

REFERENCES

[1] W. Selke, in *Phase Transitions and Critical Phenomena*, Vol. 15,1, (Academic Press Limited, 1992).

[2] P. Bak, Rep. Prog. Phys. **45**,587 (1982).

[3] S. Aubry, Physica **D 7**,240 (1983).

[4] K. E. Kürten, in *Condensed Matter Theories*, Vol. **13**, edited by B. Malik and J. da Providencia , (Nova Science Publisher, New York, 1998), p.473.

[5] F. V. Kusmartsev and K. E. Kürten, in *Lecture Notes in Physics*, Vol. 284 (1997), edited by J. W. Clark and M. L. Ristig, Springer-Verlag, New York Heidelberg Berlin.

[6] R. Grauer, K.H. Spatschek and A.V. Zolotaryuk, Phys.Rev. **E 47**,1,236 (1993).

[7] K. E. Kürten, in *Condensed Matter Theories*, Vol. **15**, edited by J. da Providencia , (Nova Science Publishers, New York, 2003).

[8] E. N. Gilbert and J. Riordan, *Illinois J.Math.* **5**, 657–665 (1961).

[9] K. E. Kürten, in *Condensed Matter Theories*, Vol. **14**, edited by D. Ernst, I. Perakis, and S. Umar (Nova Science Publishers, New York, 1999).

[10] G. Durin, A. Magni, and G. Bertotti, *J. Magn. Magn. Mater.* **140–144**, 1835–1836 (1995).

Superconductivity, Superfluidity and Bose Condensate

COOPER PAIRING REVISITED

V.C. Aguilera-Navarro,[a] *M. Fortes,*[b] *M. de Llano,*[c] *and F.J. Sevilla*[b]

[a]Depto. de Física, UNICENTRO,
85015, Guarapuava, PR, Brazil

[b]Instituto de Física, UNAM,
01000 México, DF, Mexico

[c]Instituto de Investigaciones en Materiales, UNAM,
04510 México, DF, Mexico

1. INTRODUCTION

Doubtlessly the most central notion in *superconductivity*, for both low and high transition temperatures T_c, is that of Cooper pairs (CPs) [1] that form among the underlying electron (or hole) charge carriers of the many-electron system. And yet, it is perhaps the least understood concept. Shortly after the publication of the BCS theory [2] of superconductivity, charged pairs observed in magnetic flux quantization experiments with 3D conventional [3][4], and much later with quasi-2D cuprate [5] superconductors, suggested CPs as an indispensable ingredient, regardless of the inability of BCS theory *per se* to describe high-T_c superconductivity, as now seems an almost universal consensus. Cooper pairing is no less central, albeit with a different interfermion interaction, to *neutral-atom superfluidity* as in liquid ^3He [6], and presumably also to ultracold *trapped alkali Fermi gases* such as ^6Li [7] and ^{40}K [8] where pairing is expected to occur as well. More recently, studies of quantum degenerate Fermi gases consisting of neutral ^{40}K atoms and their so-called Feshbach "resonance superfluidity" have appeared [9]-[13], but assuming quadratically-dispersive CPs and ignoring hole pairs—two fundamental shortcomings as we now illustrate.

In Sec. 2 we recall how the Bethe-Salpeter (BS) many-body equation (in the ladder approximation), treating both 2p and 2h pairs on an equal footing, implies that the ordinary CP problem [based on an ideal Fermi gas (IFG) ground state (the usual "Fermi sea")] does *not* possess stable energy solutions; in Sec. 3 we sketch how CPs based not on the IFG-sea but on the BCS ground state survive, along with the usual trivial sound mode, as nontrivial "generalized" or "moving" CPs, linear in total or center-of-mass-momentum (CMM) in leading order, that are *positive* energy resonances with an imaginary energy term implying *finite-lifetime* effects. The nontrivial "moving CP" solution, though often confused [14] with it, is physically *distinct* from the trivial sound mode solution sometimes called the Anderson-Bogoliubov-Higgs (ABH) [15], ([16] p. 44), [17][18] collective excitation mode. The ABH mode is also linear in CMM in leading order, and reduces to the IFG ordinary sound mode in zero coupling. All this occurs in both the 3D study outlined in Ref. [19] as well as in 2D [20]. Sec. 4 offers conclusions.

Provided CPs are bosons, as they indeed [21] turn out to be, our results will in general be crucial for Bose-Einstein condensation (BEC) scenarios employing BF models of superconductivity, not only *in exactly 2D* as with the Berezinskii-Kosterlitz-Thouless [22][23] transition, but also down to $(1+\epsilon)$D which characterize the quasi-1D organo-metallic (Bechgaard salt) superconductors [24]-[26]. This is contrary to well-entrenched perceptions (see, e.g., Ref. [27]) that BEC is impossible in 2D.

2. Ordinary Cooper pairing

The *original* "ordinary" CP problem [1] (with the BCS model two-electron interaction) is defined in an N-electron system for two electrons above the Fermi energy E_F but within a thin shell of energy $\hbar\omega_D$. Only there do they suffer a constant attraction $-V < 0$, giving rise to the familiar result for the *negative* energy of the pair, relative to the energy $2E_F$ of the interactionless pair,

$$\mathcal{E}_0 = -\frac{2\hbar\omega_D}{e^{2/\lambda}-1} \underset{\lambda\to 0}{\longrightarrow} -2\hbar\omega_D e^{-2/\lambda}. \tag{1}$$

Here $\lambda \equiv g(E_F)V$ is a dimensionless coupling constant with $g(E_F)$ the density of fermionic states (for each spin) evaluated at E_F. The equality in (1) is *exact* in 2D for all coupling—as well as in 1D or 3D provided only that $\hbar\omega_D \ll E_F$ so that $g(\epsilon) \simeq g(E_F)$, a constant that can be taken outside an energy integral.

However, the original CP problem neglects the effect of two-hole (2h) CPs treated *simultaneously* on an equal footing with two-electron, or two-particle (2p), CPs—as Green's functions [28] can naturally guarantee. On the other hand, the BCS condensate consists of *equal numbers of 2p and 2h Cooper correlations.* This was already evident, though scarcely emphasized, from the perfect symmetry about μ, the electron chemical potential, of the well-known Bogoliubov [29] $v^2(\epsilon)$ and $u^2(\epsilon)$ coefficients [see just below (10) later on], where ϵ is the electron energy. Indeed, our prime motivation comes from the fact established recently [30] that the BCS condensate is a BEC condensate for equal numbers of 2p and 2h pairs, in the limit of weak coupling. Additional empirical motivation comes from the unique but unexplained role played by *hole* charge carriers in the normal state of superconductors in general [31]. Even further motivation stems from the ability of the "complete (in that both 2h- and 2p-CPs are allowed in varying proportions) BF model" of Refs. [30],[32]-[33] to "unify" both BCS and BEC theories as special cases, and to predict substantially higher T_c's than BCS theory without abandoning electron-phonon dynamics. Compelling evidence for a significant presence of this dynamics in high-T_c cuprate superconductors from angle-resolved photoemission spectroscopy data has recently been reported [34].

In dealing with the many-electron system we assume the BCS model interaction in the form with double Fourier transform

$$\nu(|\mathbf{k}_1 - \mathbf{k}_1'|) = -(k_F^2/k_1k_1')V \quad \text{if } k_F - k_D < k_1,\ k_1' < k_F + k_D, \tag{2}$$

and $= 0$ otherwise. As before $V > 0$, $\hbar k_F \equiv mv_F$ the Fermi momentum, m the effective electron mass, v_F the Fermi velocity, and $k_D \equiv \omega_D/v_F$ with ω_D the Debye frequency. The usual physical constraint $\hbar\omega_D \ll E_F \equiv \hbar^2k_F^2/2m$ then implies that $k_D/k_F \equiv \hbar\omega_D/2E_F \ll 1$.

The bound-state BS wavefunction equation [19] in the ladder approximation with both particles and holes for the original IFG-based CP problem using an interaction such as (2) is

$$\Psi(\mathbf{k},E) = -\left(\frac{i}{\hbar}\right)^2 G_0\left(\mathbf{K}/2+\mathbf{k},\mathcal{E}_K/2+E\right)G_0\left(\mathbf{K}/2-\mathbf{k},\mathcal{E}_K/2-E\right)\times$$
$$\times\frac{1}{2\pi i}\int_{-\infty}^{+\infty}dE'\,\frac{1}{L^d}\sum_{\mathbf{k}'}v(|\mathbf{k}-\mathbf{k}'|)\Psi(\mathbf{k}',E') \tag{3}$$

where L^d is the "volume" of the d-dimensional system; $\mathbf{K} \equiv \mathbf{k}_1 + \mathbf{k}_2$ is the CMM and $\mathbf{k} \equiv \frac{1}{2}(\mathbf{k}_1 - \mathbf{k}_2)$ the relative wavevectors of the 2e bound state whose wavefunction is $\Psi(\mathbf{k},E)$; $\mathcal{E}_K \equiv E_1 + E_2$ is the energy of this bound state while $E \equiv E_1 - E_2$, and $G_0\left(\mathbf{K}/2+\mathbf{k},\mathcal{E}/2+E\right)$ is the bare one-fermion Green's function given by

$$G_0(\mathbf{k}_1,E_1) = \frac{\hbar}{i}\left\{\frac{\theta(k_1-k_F)}{-E_1+\epsilon_{\mathbf{k}_1}-E_F-i\varepsilon}+\frac{\theta(k_F-k_1)}{-E_1+\epsilon_{\mathbf{k}_1}-E_F+i\varepsilon}\right\} \tag{4}$$

where $\epsilon_{\mathbf{k}_1} \equiv \hbar^2k_1^2/2m$ and $\theta(x) = 1$ for $x > 0$ and $= 0$ for $x < 0$, so that the first term refers to *electrons* and the second to *holes*. Figure 1 shows all Feynman diagrams for the 2p, 2h and ph wavefunction ψ_+, ψ_- and ψ_0, respectively, that emerge in the general (BCS-ground-state-based) problem to be discussed later. For the present IFG-based case, diagrams in shaded rectangles do *not* contribute. Since the energy dependence of $\Psi(\mathbf{k},E)$ in (3) is only through the Green's functions, the ensuing energy integrals can be evaluated directly in the complex E'-plane and yield, for interaction (2),

$$(2\xi_k - \mathcal{E}_0)\psi_{\mathbf{k}} = V{\sum_{\mathbf{k}'}}'\psi_{\mathbf{k}'} - V{\sum_{\mathbf{k}'}}''\psi_{\mathbf{k}'} \tag{5}$$

where $\psi_{\mathbf{k}}$ is the resulting wavefunction after the energy integration. Here $\xi_k \equiv \hbar^2k^2/2m - E_F$ while $\mathcal{E}_0$ is the (unknown) eigenvalue energy. The single prime over the first (2p-CP) summation term denotes the restriction $0 < \xi_{k'} < \hbar\omega_D$ (i.e., *above* the IFG "sea") while the double prime in the last (2h-CP) term means $-\hbar\omega_D < \xi_{k'} < 0$ (i.e., *below* the IFG sea). Without this latter term we have Cooper's Schrödinger-like equation [1] for 2p-CPs whose implicit wavefuncion solution is clearly $\psi_{\mathbf{k}} = (2\xi_k - \mathcal{E}_0)^{-1}V{\sum_{\mathbf{k}'}}'\psi_{\mathbf{k}'}$. Since the summation term is constant, performing that

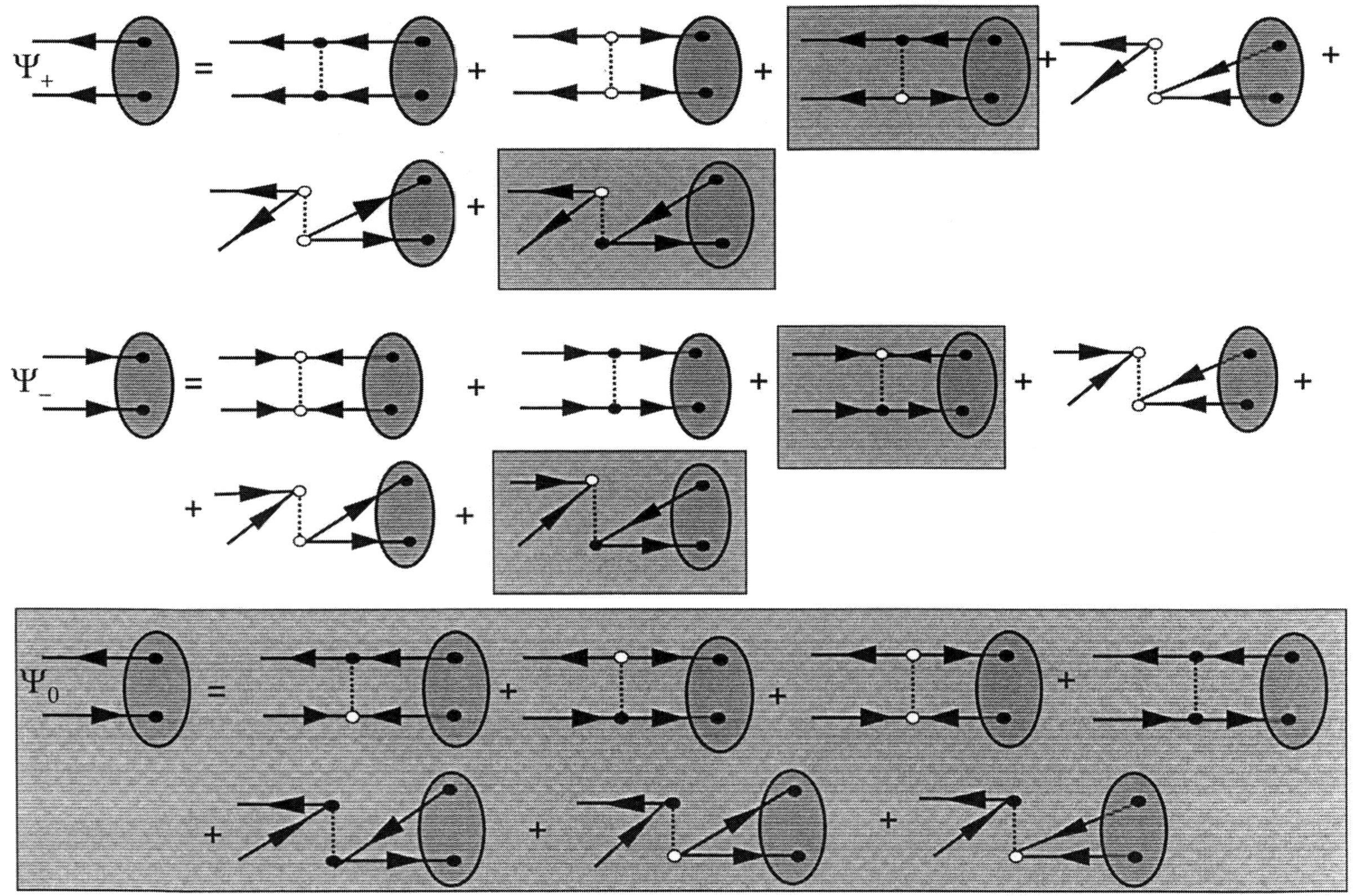

Figure 1. Wavefunction Feynman diagrams for 2p (ψ_+), 2h (ψ_-) and ph (ψ_0) bound states arising from the BS equations. Shaded rectangles designate diagrams that do not contribute in the IFG-based case.

summation on *both* sides allows canceling the $\psi_{\mathbf{k}}$-dependent terms, leaving the eigenvalue equation $\sum_{\mathbf{k}}{}'(2\xi_k - \mathcal{E}_0)^{-1} = 1/V$. This is one equation in one unknown $\mathcal{E}_0$; transforming the sum to an integral over energies immediately gives (1). This corresponds to the usual negative-energy, infinite-lifetime stationary-state bound pair. For $K \geq 0$ the CP eigenvalue equation is just $\sum_{\mathbf{k}}{}'(2\xi_k - \mathcal{E}_K + \hbar^2K^2/4m)^{-1} = 1/V$. Since a CP state of energy $\mathcal{E}_K$ is characterized only by a definite K but *not* definite $\mathbf{k}$, in contrast to a "BCS pair" defined [Ref. [2], Eqs. (2.11) to (2.13)] with fixed $\mathbf{K}$ and $\mathbf{k}$ (or equivalently definite $\mathbf{k}_1$ and $\mathbf{k}_2$). This renders CPs legitimate bosons [21]. Without the first summation term in (5) the same result in $\mathcal{E}_0$ (1) for 2p-CPs follows for 2h-CPs (apart from a sign change).

In contrast with Cooper's equation neglecting hole-pairs, the *complete* CP equation (5) *cannot* be derived from an ordinary (non-BS) Schrödinger-like equation in spite of its simple appearance. A more general technique such as the BS equation that includes both particles (in this case electrons) and holes is needed. To solve it for the unknown energy $\mathcal{E}_0$, let the rhs of (5) be defined as $A - B$, with A relating to the 2p-pair term and B to the 2h-pair term. Then the unknown $\psi_{\mathbf{k}}$ becomes

$$\psi_{\mathbf{k}} = (A-B)/(2\xi_k - \mathcal{E}_0) \quad \text{or equivalently} \quad \psi(\xi) = (A-B)/(2\xi - \mathcal{E}_0) \tag{6}$$

whence

$$\begin{aligned} A &\equiv \lambda \int_0^{\hbar\omega_D} d\xi\psi(\xi) = \tfrac{1}{2}(A-B)\lambda \int_{-\mathcal{E}_0}^{2\hbar\omega_D-\mathcal{E}_0} dz/z \equiv (A-B)x, \\ B &\equiv \lambda \int_{-\hbar\omega_D}^{0} d\xi\psi(\xi) = \tfrac{1}{2}(A-B)\lambda \int_{-2\hbar\omega_D-\mathcal{E}_0}^{-\mathcal{E}_0} dz/z \equiv (A-B)y. \end{aligned} \tag{7}$$

The integrals are readily evaluated giving $x \equiv \frac{1}{2}\lambda \ln(1-2\hbar\omega_D/\mathcal{E}_0)$ and $y \equiv -\frac{1}{2}\lambda\ln(1+2\hbar\omega_D/\mathcal{E}_0)$. As A and B still contain the unknown $\psi(\xi)$ let us eliminate them. Note that equations (7) are equivalent to *two* equations in two unknowns A and B, or $[(1-x)A + xB = 0 \quad \text{and} \quad -yA + (1+y)B = 0.]$ These readily lead to the single equation $1 - x + y = 0$, which on inserting the definitions for x and y becomes

$$1 = \frac{1}{2}\lambda\ln[1 - (2\hbar\omega_D/\mathcal{E}_0)^2] \quad \text{which gives} \quad \mathcal{E}_0 = \pm i2\hbar\omega_D/\sqrt{e^{2/\lambda}-1}. \tag{8}$$

As the CP energy is pure-imaginary, there is an obvious instability of the CP problem when both particle- and hole-pairs are included. This transcendant result dates back to the late 50's and early 60's and was reported in Refs. [16] p. 44 and [35] Sec. 33, where, however, the well-known pure 2p and 2h special cases just stressed was not discussed. Clearly then, the original CP picture *is meaningless if particle- and hole-pairs are treated on an equal footing*, as consistency demands. Curiously, this result has been largely ignored in the entire literature since then.

A dramatic analogue of the nontriviality of such consistency is found in the very high temperature treatment of relativistic BEC [36], where pair production becomes possible and creates *antibosons* in addition to more bosons. Here, BEC *must* take into account $\bar{N}$ antibosons of charge, say, $-q$ along with the N bosons of charge q. In units such that $\hbar \equiv c \equiv k_B \equiv 1$ the boson energy is $\varepsilon_K = (K^2 + m_B^2)^{1/2}$. Charge conservation requires that not only $N \equiv N_0(T) + \sum_{\mathbf{K}\neq\mathbf{0}}[\exp\beta(\varepsilon_K - \mu_B) - 1]^{-1}$ be constant but rather $N - \bar{N}$, where $\bar{N}$ is the same as N but with $+\mu_B$ instead of $-\mu_B$.

If $\rho \equiv q(N-\bar{N})/L^3 \equiv qn$ is the net conserved charge density, it is shown in Ref. [36] that $T_c = (3|n|/m_B)^{\frac{1}{2}}$ and that the condensate fraction $n_0/n = [1-(T/T_c)^2]$. This is *qualitatively* different from the better-known results assuming only N constant, which are the mass-independent $T_c = [\pi^2 n/\zeta(3)]^{1/3}$ and $n_0/n = [1-(T/T_c)^3]$. This example exhibits the strikingly dramatic effect of including or not antiparticles (analogous to holes in the nonrelativistic case).

3. Generalized Cooper pairing

However, a BS treatment not about the IFG sea but about the BCS ground state (which we refer to as "generalized" Cooper pairing) *vindicates the CP concept*, and adds something new. This is equivalent to starting not from the IFG unperturbed Hamiltonian but from the BCS one. Thus, (4) is replaced by

$$\mathbf{G}_0(\mathbf{k}_1, E_1) = \frac{\hbar}{i}\left\{\frac{v_{k_1}^2}{-E_1 + E_{k_1} - i\varepsilon} + \frac{u_{k_1}^2}{-E_1 + E_{k_1} + i\varepsilon}\right\} \tag{9}$$

where $E_{\mathbf{k}} \equiv \sqrt{\xi_k{}^2 + \Delta^2}$ with Δ the fermionic gap, $v_k^2 \equiv \frac{1}{2}(1-\xi_k/E_{\mathbf{k}})$ and $u_k^2 \equiv 1 - v_k^2$ are the Bogoliubov functions [29]. As $\Delta \to 0$ these three quantities become $|\xi_k|$, $\theta(k_1 - k_F)$ and $\theta(k_F - k_1)$, respectively, making (9) become (4) as expected. Substituting $G_0(\mathbf{k}_1, E_1)$ by $\mathbf{G}_0(\mathbf{k}_1, E_1)$ corresponds to rewriting the total Hamiltonian so that the pure-kinetic-energy unperturbed Hamiltonian is replaced by the BCS one. The remaining terms are then assumed suitable to a perturbation treatment. Experimental support for this can be found precisely in Refs. [3]-[5], and its physical justification lies in recovering both the expected ABH sound mode (which contains the BCS $T = 0$ gap equation) and the finite-lifetime effects of moving CPs. In either 3D [19] or 2D [20] the BCS-based BS equation yields *two distinct solutions*: a) the usual trivial ABH sound solution and b) a highly nontrivial "moving CP" solution. In either case the BS formalism consists of a set of three coupled equations, one for each (2p, 2h and ph) channel wavefunction for any spin-independent interaction such as (2). However, the ph channel decouples, leaving only two coupled wavefunction equations for the ABH solution in 2D which we consider first. We focus here on 2D because of its interest [37] for quasi-2D cuprate superconductors.

The equations involved are too lengthy even in 2D and will be derived in detail elsewhere, but for the trivial or ABH sound solution they boil down to the single expression

$$\frac{1}{2\pi}\lambda\hbar v_F \int_{k_F-k_D}^{k_F+k_D} dk \int_0^{2\pi} d\varphi \{u_{\mathbf{K}/2+\mathbf{k}} u_{\mathbf{K}/2-\mathbf{k}} + v_{\mathbf{K}/2+\mathbf{k}} v_{\mathbf{K}/2-\mathbf{k}}\}\times$$

$$\times\left[\frac{v_{\mathbf{K}/2+\mathbf{k}} v_{\mathbf{K}/2-\mathbf{k}}}{\mathcal{E}_K + E_{\mathbf{K}/2+\mathbf{k}} + E_{\mathbf{K}/2-\mathbf{k}}} + \frac{u_{\mathbf{K}/2+\mathbf{k}}\, u_{\mathbf{K}/2-\mathbf{k}}}{-\mathcal{E}_K + E_{\mathbf{K}/2+\mathbf{k}} + E_{\mathbf{K}/2-\mathbf{k}}}\right] = 1 \tag{10}$$

where φ is the angle between $\mathbf{K}$ and $\mathbf{k}$. Here k_D is defined as below (2) and as before $\lambda \equiv Vg(E_F)$ with $g(E_F) \equiv m/2\pi\hbar^2$ the constant 2D electronic DOS and V is defined in (2). The *ABH collective excitation mode* energy $\mathcal{E}_K$ must then be extracted from this equation. For $\mathbf{K}=0$ it is just $\mathcal{E}_0=0$ (Ref. [16] p. 39) and (10) rewritten as an integral over $\xi \equiv \hbar^2k^2/2m - E_F$ reduces to the familiar BCS $T=0$ gap equation $\int_0^{\hbar\omega_D} d\xi/\sqrt{\xi^2+\Delta^2} = 1/\lambda$ for interaction (2) which gives $\Delta = \hbar\omega_D/\sinh(1/\lambda)$. Returning to the ABH energy $\mathcal{E}_K$ equation (10) and Taylor-expanding $\mathcal{E}_K$ about $K=0$, and then taking Δ small, leaves

$$\mathcal{E}_K = \frac{\hbar v_F}{\sqrt{2}} K + O(K^2) + o(\lambda) \tag{11}$$

where $o(\lambda)$ refers to interfermion interaction terms that vanish as $\lambda \to 0$. Note that the leading term is just the ordinary sound mode in an IFG whose sound speed $c = v_F/\sqrt{d}$ in d dimensions. This result also follows (trivially) on solving for c in the familiar thermodynamic relation $dP/dn = mc^2$ involving the zero-temperature IFG pressure $P = n^2[d(E/N)/dn] = 2nE_F/(d+2) = 2C_d n^{2/d\,+1}/(d+2)$ where the constant C_d will drop out. Here the IFG ground-state energy $E = dNE_F/(d+2)$ was used along with $E_F \equiv \hbar^2k_F^2/2m = C_d n^{2/d}$ while $n \equiv N/L^d = k_F^d/d2^{d-2}\pi^{d/2}\Gamma(d/2)$ is the fermion-number density. The derivative dP/dn finally gives $c = \hbar k_F/m\sqrt{d} \equiv v_F/\sqrt{d}$ which in 2D is just the coefficient of the first term of (11).

The nontrivial or *moving CP* solution of the BCS-ground-state-based BS treatment, which is *entirely new,* leads to the pair energy $\mathcal{E}_K$ which in 2D is contained in the equation

$$\frac{1}{2\pi}\lambda\hbar v_F \int_{k_F-k_D}^{k_F+k_D} dk \int_0^{2\pi} d\varphi\, u_{\mathbf{K}/2+\mathbf{k}} v_{\mathbf{K}/2-\mathbf{k}} \times$$

$$\times \{u_{\mathbf{K}/2-\mathbf{k}} v_{\mathbf{K}/2+\mathbf{k}} - u_{\mathbf{K}/2+\mathbf{k}} v_{\mathbf{K}/2-\mathbf{k}}\} \frac{E_{\mathbf{K}/2+\mathbf{k}} + E_{\mathbf{K}/2-\mathbf{k}}}{-\mathcal{E}_K^2 + (E_{\mathbf{K}/2+\mathbf{k}} + E_{\mathbf{K}/2-\mathbf{k}})^2} = 1, \tag{12}$$

In addition to the pp and hh wavefunctions (depicted diagrammatically in Ref. [19] Fig. 2), diagrams associated with the ph channel give zero contribution at $T=0$. A third equation for the ph wavefunction describes the ph bound state but turns out to depend only on the pp and hh wavefunctions. Taylor-expanding $\mathcal{E}_K$ in (12) in powers of K around $K=0$, and introducing a possible damping factor by adding an imaginary term $-i\Gamma_K$ in the denominator, yields to order K^2 for small λ

$$\pm\mathcal{E}_K \simeq 2\Delta + \frac{\lambda}{2\pi}\hbar v_F K + \frac{1}{9}\frac{\hbar v_F}{k_D} e^{1/\lambda} K^2 - i\hbar v_F K \left[\frac{\lambda}{\pi} + \frac{1}{12k_D} e^{1/\lambda} K\right] + O(K^3) \tag{13}$$

where the upper and lower sign refers to 2p- and 2h-CPs, respectively. A linear dispersion in leading order again appears, but now associated with the bosonic moving CP. Figure 2a graphs the exact moving CP *real* energy (full curves) extracted from (12), along with its leading linear-dispersion term (short-dashed) and this plus the next (quadratic) term (long-dashed) from (13). The interaction parameter values used for (2) were $\hbar\omega_D/E_F = 0.05$ (a typical value for cuprates) and the two values $\lambda = \frac{1}{4}$ (lower set of curves) and $\frac{1}{2}$ (upper set), so that $\mathcal{E}_0/E_F \equiv 2\Delta/E_F = 2\hbar\omega_D/E_F \sinh(1/\lambda)$.This has values $\simeq 0.004$ (for $\lambda = \frac{1}{4}$) and 0.028 (for $\lambda = \frac{1}{2}$), (marked as dots in the figure). Remarkably enough, the linear approximation (short-dashed lines in figure) is better over a wider range of K/k_F values for weaker coupling in spite of a larger and larger partial contribution from the quadratic term in (13).

This peculiarity also emerged from the ordinary CP treatment with the BCS model interaction [38] in both 2D and 3D, and with a (regularized) delta interaction in 2D [39] and in 3D [40], and might suggest the expansion in powers of K to be an asymptotic series that should be truncated after the linear term. For reference we also plot the linear term $\hbar v_F K/\sqrt{2}$ of the sound solution (11) (thick long-dashed line starting at origin). The *positive*-energy 2p-CP resonance of width Γ_K has a lifetime from (13) of $\tau_K \equiv \hbar/2\Gamma_K = \hbar/2\left[(\lambda/\pi)\hbar v_F K + (\hbar v_F/12k_D)e^{1/\lambda}K^2\right]$ diverging only at $K=0$, and falling to zero as K increases; see Fig. 2b. Thus, "faster" moving CPs are shorter-lived and eventually break up, while "non-moving" ones are (infinite-lifetime) stationary states. The real linear term $(\lambda/2\pi)\hbar v_F K$ in (13) contrasts sharply with the *coupling-independent* leading-term $(2/\pi)\hbar v_F K$ that follows [38] from the *original* CP problem neglecting holes, which if graphed in Fig. 2a would almost coincide with the ABH term $\hbar v_F K/\sqrt{2}$ and have a slope about 90% smaller. Fig. 2c depicts analogies of a 3D potential problem for the original CP energy (top), as well as for $K>0$ (middle) and $K=0$ (bottom) BCS-based BS CPs.

As in Cooper's [1] original equation, our BCS-based BS moving CPs are characterized by a definite $\mathbf{K}$ and *not* also by definite $\mathbf{k}$ as the pairs discussed by BCS [2]. Hence, the objection does not apply that CPs are not bosons because BCS pairs with definite $\mathbf{K}$ and $\mathbf{k}$ (or equivalently definite $\mathbf{k}_1$ and $\mathbf{k}_2$) have creation/annihilation operators that do *not* obey the usual Bose commutation relations [Ref. [2], Eqs. (2.11) to (2.13)]. In fact, (12) shows that a given "generalized" CP state labeled by either $\mathbf{K}$ or $\mathcal{E}_K$ can accommodate (in the thermodynamic limit) an indefinitely many possible BCS pairs with different $\mathbf{k}$'s; see Ref. [21]. A recent electronic analog [41] of the Hanbury Brown-Twiss photon-effect experiment suggests electron pairs to be definitely bosons.

4. Conclusions

Hole pairs treated on a par with electron pairs play a vital role in determining the precise nature of nontrivial CPs even at zero temperature—only when based not on the usual IFG "sea" but on the BCS ground state. Their treatment with a Bethe-Salpeter equation gives purely-imaginary-energy CPs when based on the IFG, and when based on the BCS ground state gives positive-energy, resonant-state CPs with a finite lifetime for nonzero CMM. This is instead of the more familiar negative-energy stationary states of the original IFG-based CP problem that neglects holes, as sketched just below (5). The BS "moving-CP" dispersion relation (13), on the other hand, is gapped by twice the BCS energy gap, followed by a *linear* leading term in the CMM expansion about $K=0$. This linearity is distinct from the better-known but trivial one (11) associated with the sound or ABH collective excitation mode whose energy vanishes at $K=0$.

Thus, instead of the quadratic $\hbar^2K^2/2(2m)$ assumed for CPs in Refs. [9]-[13],[30],[32],[42]-[44], among many others, BF models based on the correct CP linearity for the boson component can give BEC for all $d>1$, including exactly 2D, and thus in principle address not only quasi-2D cuprate but also quasi-1D organo-metallic superconductors.

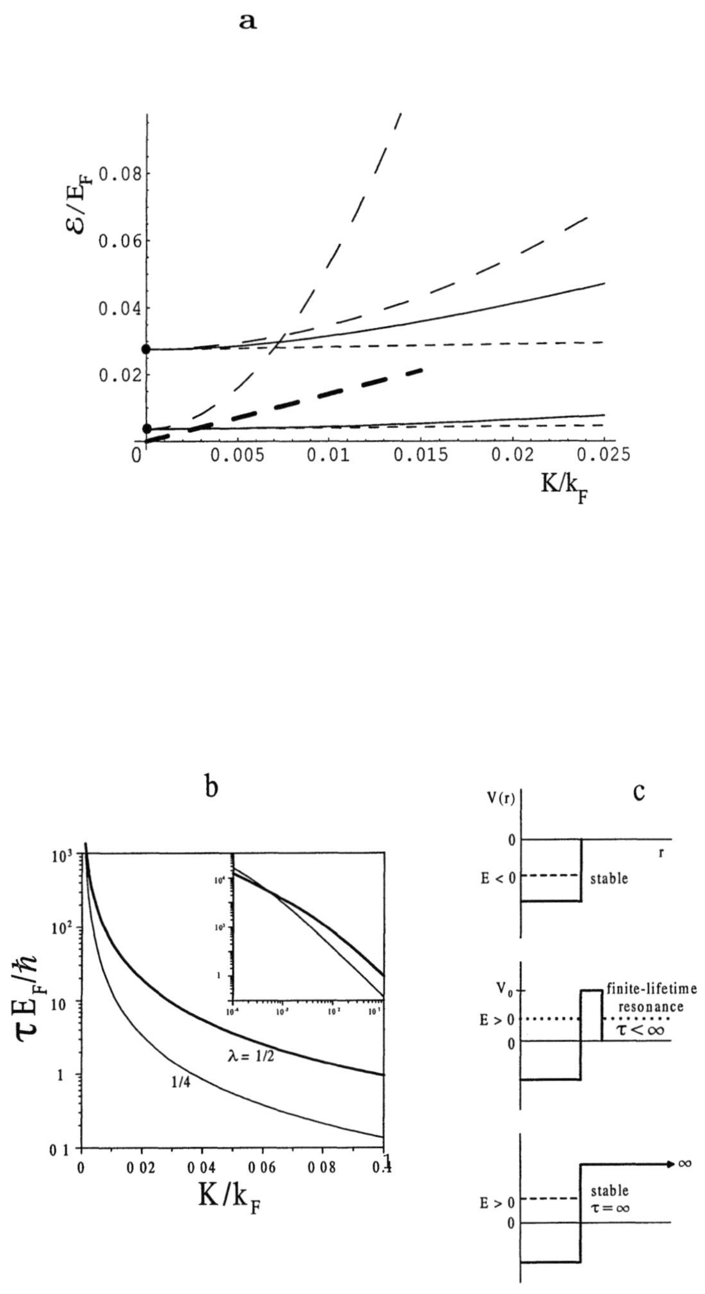

Figure 2. a) Exact "moving" 2p-CP (real) energy $\mathcal{E}_K$ (in units of E_F) in 2D from (12) (full curves), compared with its linear leading term (short-dashed lines) and its linear plus quadratic expansion (long-dashed curves) both from (13), *vs.* CMM wavenumber K (in units of k_F), for interaction (2) parameters $\lambda = \frac{1}{4}$ (lower set of curves) and $\frac{1}{2}$ (upper set of curves), and $\hbar\omega_D/E_F = 0.05$. For reference, leading linear term (11) of trivial ABH sound mode is also plotted (lower thick dashed line). b) 2p-CP lifetime as defined in text. c) Analogy of BCS-based BS 2p-CPs with various states in a 3D potential problem, as discussed in text.

Acknowledgments

MdeLl and MF thank UNAM-DGAPA-PAPIIT (Mexico), grant # IN106401, and CONACyT (Mexico), grant # 27828 E, for partial support. MdeLl is grateful for travel support through a grant to Southern Illinois University at Carbondale from the U.S. Army Research Office.

REFERENCES

[1] L.N. Cooper, Phys. Rev. **104**, 1189 (1956).

[2] J. Bardeen, L.N. Cooper and J.R. Schrieffer, Phys. Rev. **108**, 1175 (1957).

[3] B.S. Deaver, Jr. and W.M. Fairbank, Phys. Rev. Lett. **7**, 43 (1961).

[4] R. Doll and M. Näbauer, Phys. Rev. Lett. **7**, 51 (1961).

[5] C.E. Gough, *et. al.,* Nature **326**, 855 (1987).

[6] D. Vollkardt and P. Wölfle, *The Superfluid Phases of Helium 3*, (Taylor & Francis, London, 1990).

[7] K.E. Strecker, *et. al.*, Phys. Rev. Lett. **91**, 080406 (2003).

[8] M. Holland, *et. al.,* Phys. Rev. A **61**, 053610 (2000), and refs. therein.

[9] M.J. Holland, *et. al.,* Phys. Rev. Lett. **87**, 1204061 (2001).

[10] E. Timmermans, *et. al.,* Phys. Lett. A **285**, 228 (2001).

[11] M.L. Chiofalo, *et. al.,* Phys. Rev. Lett. **88**, 090402 (2002).

[12] Y. Ohashi and A. Griffin, Phys. Rev. Lett. **89**, 130402 (2002).

[13] L. Pitaevskii and S. Stringari, Science **298**, 2144 (2002).

[14] M. Randeria, asserted at CMT20 Workshop (Poone, India, 1996).

[15] P.W. Anderson, Phys. Rev. **112**, 1900 (1958).

[16] N.N. Bogoliubov, V.V. Tolmachev and D.V. Shirkov, Fortschr. Phys. **6**, 605 (1958); and *A New Method in the Theory of Superconductivity* (Consultants Bureau, NY, 1959).

[17] P.W. Higgs, Phys. Lett. **12**, 132 (1964).

[18] L. Belkhir, M. Randeria, Phys. Rev. B **49**, 6829 (1994).

[19] M. Fortes, *et. al.,* Physica C **364-365**, 95 (2001).

[20] V.C. Aguilera-Navarro, *et. al.,* to be published. Cond-mat/0306726.

[21] M. de Llano, F.J. Sevilla, S. Tapia and J.R. Clem, to be published. Cond-mat/0307258.

[22] V.L. Berezinskii, Sov. Phys. JETP **34,** 610 (1972).

[23] J.M. Kosterlitz and D.J. Thouless, J. Phys. **C6**, 1181 (1973).

[24] D. Jérome, Science **252**, 1509 (1991).

[25] J.M. Williams, *et. al.*, Science **252**, 1501 (1991).

[26] H. Hori, Int. J. Mod Phys. B **8,** 1 (1994).

[27] A.A. Abrikosov, asserted at CMT26 Workshop (Luso, Portugal, 2002).

[28] A.L. Fetter and J.D. Walecka, *Quantum Theory of Many-Particle Systems* (McGraw-Hill, New York, 1971).

[29] N.N. Bogoliubov, N. Cim. **7**, 794 (1958).

[31] V.V. Tolmachev, Phys. Lett. A **266**, 400 (2000).

[32] J. Hirsch, Physica C **341-348**, 213 (2000) and also www.iitap.iastate.edu/htcu/forum.html#Q3.

[33] M. de Llano and V.V. Tolmachev, Physica A **317**, 546 (2003).

[33] J. Batle, *et. al.,* Cond. Matter Theories **18** (in press) (2003); *BCS and BEC Finally Unified: A brief review.* Cond-mat/0211456.

[34] A. Lanzara, *et. al.,* Nature **412**, 510 (2001).

[35] A.A. Abrikosov, L.P. Gorkov, and I.E. Dzyaloshinskii, *Methods of Quantum Field in Statistical Physics* (Dover, NY, 1975) § 33.

[36] H.E. Haber and H.A. Weldon, Phys. Rev. Lett. **46**, 1497 (1981).

[37] B.D. Brandow, Phys. Repts. **296**, 1 (1998).

[38] M. Casas, *et. al.,* Physica C **295**, 93 (1998).

[39] S.K. Adhikari, *et. al.,* Phys. Rev. B **62**, 8671 (2000).

[40] S.K. Adhikari, *et. al.,* Physica C **351**, 341 (2001).

[41] P. Samuelsson and M. Büttiker, Phys. Rev. Lett. **89**, 046601 (2002).

[42] J.M. Blatt, *Theory of Superconductivity* (Academic, New York, 1964).

[43] R. Friedberg and T.D. Lee, Phys. Rev. B **40**, 6745 (1989).

[44] R. Friedberg, T.D. Lee, and H.-C. Ren, Phys. Lett. A **152**, 417 and 423 (1991).

STUDY OF GROUND STATE PROPERTIES AND VACANCIES IN SOLID p-H_2 WITH A SHADOW WAVE FUNCTION

Francesco Pederiva and Francesco Operetto

Dipartimento di Fisica and INFM, Università di Trento
via Sommarive 14, I-38050 Povo, Trento, Italy

1. INTRODUCTION

From the theoretical point of view, the simulation approach is the most effective in analyzing inhomogeneous phases of quantum systems. In this work we extend to the study of p-H_2 a technique that revealed extremely powerful in the description of inhomogeneous phases of ^{4}He with large numbers of particles: Variational Monte Carlo calculations based on Shadow Wave functions (SWF)[1,2]. The main property of SWF is the capability of describing the crystalline and the disordered phase of a quantum system with the same translationally invariant form. In the past this technique was applied to the study of coexisting liquid–solid[3] and liquid–vapor[4] ^{4}He as well as to finite systems like ^{4}He clusters with and without impurities[5]. This method, although not exact, gives quantitatively significant results, as for instance a realistic estimate of the interface energy of solid ^{4}He[3], in situations where other methods, like Path Integral MC or Diffusion MC, are harder to apply. Inhomogeneous phases of p-H_2 are of special interest due to the peculiar behavior of this molecular system at very low temperatures. In fact, the light mass of the molecule, and its Bosonic nature would made p-H_2 an ideal candidate for observing superfluid behavior. However, the very strong intermolecular attraction (about 32K/molecule, to be compared with the analogous 10K/atom in ^{4}He), makes its ground state to be a crystal. There are clues, mostly coming from Path-Integral Monte Carlo simulations, that in strongly inhomogeneous situations, like small droplets with $N<30$ molecules[6], or two-dimensional puddles deposited on graphite substrates[7,8], p-H_2 should remain in the liquid phase. Recently this behavior has been qualitatively explained in terms of the high cost of creating a solid-liquid interface in a small system[9]. Recent experiments by Grebenev et al.[10], measuring rotational spectra of a linear OCS molecule surrounded by a few molecules of para-hydrogen, and embedded in a liquid He droplet, show that the friction opposed by the p-H_2 molecules to the rotation of the OCS molecule disappears when the temperature of the system drops from 0.38K (corresponding to having only ^{4}He in the cluster) to 0.15K (corresponding to the case in which ^{3}He coats the ^{4}He). This was the first clean experimental evidence of a superfluid transition occurring in a finite system of p-H_2. While our goal is to be able in the future to simulate the complete He–p-H_2-OCS compound, a number of preliminary steps is necessary, the first of which is to set up a Shadow Wave Function capable to describe bulk properties of molecular hydrogen. Some early calculations using SWF for small p-H_2 clusters (N$\leq$7) were performed by Rama Krishna and Whaley[11]. However, the form of the wave function used there cannot be immediately extended to bulk systems. In this paper we introduce a SWF optimized and parametrized in a form directly usable in calculations where the parameters become functions of the *local* density of the system[3], therefore employable in calculations for strongly inhomogeneous systems. We also present results for an estimate of the vacancy formation energy in p-H_2 as a function of the crystal density as a byproduct of our preliminary calculations.

2. METHODS

Molecular para-hydrogen can be described as a collection of N point-like particles interacting via a two-body potential:

$$\hat{H} = -\frac{\hbar}{2m}\sum_{i=1}^{N} + \sum_{i<j} v(r_{ij}). \tag{1}$$

The model potential we chose is the Silvera-Goldman (SG)[12] potential, consisting in an interpolation between an exponential repulsive core, and a multipolar expansion describing a van der Waals-like interaction between the molecules. A term proportional to $1/r^9$ is also introduced as an effective many–body force, assuming that the leading term is a triple-dipole contribution. This parameterization is effective for studying isotropic properties of the system, and the replacement of the three-body term with a pair term is a second order effect due to the fact that the p-H_2 molecule at T=0 is always found in the $J = 0$ rotational state, which guarantees that anisotropy effects can be effectively treated averaging over the angles.

Variational Monte Carlo calculations by Norman et al.[13], using a Bijl-Jastrow-Nosanow trial wave function, showed that within this model the SG potential is in qualitative agreement with experiments in a wide range of densities; other model interactions (like the Schaefer-Watts potential[14] or the Buck et al. potential[15]) give better values around the equilibrium density, but become worse at higher pressure. In any case, the situation for as regards the knowledge of the p-H_2–p-H_2 interaction is far from being satisfactory. An accurate analysis of the several potentials available in the literature by means of exact calculations (like Diffusion Monte Carlo) is therefore necessary.

Shadow Wave Function

We use as trial solution for the N-molecules Hamiltonian at T=0K a Shadow Wave Function[1,2], having the following general form:

$$\Psi(R) = \int K(R,S)\phi(S)\, dS, \tag{2}$$

where $R = \{\mathbf{r}_1 \ldots \mathbf{r}_N\}$ and $S = \{\mathbf{s}_1 \ldots \mathbf{s}_N\}$ are the molecular and auxiliary ("shadow") degrees of freedom respectively. The kernel K is written as the product of a Jastrow–pair wavefunction involving the molecular degrees of freedom, times a term coupling molecular and shadow positions:

$$K(R,S) = \prod_{i<j} \exp\left[-\frac{1}{2}\left(\frac{b}{r_{ij}}\right)^5\right] \prod_{i=1}^{N} \exp\left[-C\left(\mathbf{r}_i - \mathbf{s}_i\right)^2\right] \tag{3}$$

The shadow degrees of freedom are also correlated by $\phi(s)$, a Jastrow product of the same form of the one used for the molecules. The correlation pseudopotential is taken in the form of a rescaled intermolecular interaction[16]:

$$\phi(s) = \exp\left[-\delta \sum_{i<j} v(\alpha s_{ij})\right]. \tag{4}$$

The parameters b, C, δ, α appearing in the SWF are determined variationally, by minimizing the variance of the expectation value of the Hamiltonian

$$\langle \Delta E^2 \rangle = \frac{\langle \Psi(R)|(H - E_0)^2 \Psi(R)\rangle}{\langle \Psi(R)|\Psi(R)\rangle}. \tag{5}$$

As already mentioned, SWF provides a stable crystalline phase despite its translationally invariant form, due to the implicitly induced many–body correlations. The stable phase, ordered or disordered, is determined by the variational principle only.

Simulations

All simulations have been performed for a cell of constant volume V containing a number N of molecules such that $\rho = N/V$, and imposing periodic boundary conditions in order to reduce finite–size effects. Calculations have been performed for two different crystal geometries: face-centered cubic (fcc) and hexagonal close-packed (hcp). Most of the results for the fcc crystal were obtained using N=108 molecules arranged on 3x3x3 elementary cubic cells of side $a_{cell} = (4/\rho)^{\frac{1}{3}})$. For simulations in the hcp phase we considered N=180 molecules in a cell made up of 5x3x3 elementary cells. In order to check the magnitude of finite size effects (in particular for the vacancy formation energy) simulations in the fcc crystal with N=256 (4x4x4 elementary cubic cells) and N=500 (5x5x5 elementary cubic cells) have also been performed.

The expectation values of the observables of interest have been computed by means of the Variational Monte Carlo method. When using SWF, the expectation value of a local operator $\hat{O}(R)$ is given by:

$$\langle \hat{O} \rangle = \frac{1}{\mathcal{N}} \int\int\int \pi(R,S,S')\hat{O}(R) dR\, dS\, dS', \tag{6}$$

where $\mathcal{N}$ is the normalization of the wave function. This integral can be computed sampling the joint probability distribution for the molecular and shadow degrees of freedom:

$$\pi(R,S,S') = K(R,S)\phi(S)K(R,S')\phi(S'). \tag{7}$$

Table 1

Coefficients of eq. (10) fitted on the variationally optimized values of the shadow–shadow correlation parameters α and δ of eq. (4) at various densities. The values δ_n are given in K^{-1}.

Parameter	Value
α_0	1.2049±0.0872
α_1	-21.961±2.984
δ_0	-0.0047±0.0008
δ_1	0.3717±0.0370

The optimization of the variational parameters appearing in the SWF was performed using the optimization program by C.J. Umrigar and P. Nightingale implementing a modified Levemberg-Marquardt algorithm. The optimization of the parameters of the shadow–shadow correlation pseudopotential of eq. (4) is particularly demanding from the computational point of view. In fact the local energy does not depend, configuration by configuration, on the value of δ and α, but on the statistical weight of the configuration $\pi(R, S, S')$ only.

3. PARAMETRIZATION OF THE SWF

As previously mentioned, one of the most interesting properties of the Shadow Wave Function is the capability of describing phases of different symmetry within the same functional form. This property can be exploited in order to obtain a single wave function that can be used to study the system at different densities, the Local-Density SWF (LD-SWF)[3]. In the LD-SWF the parameters α and δ used in computing the pair correlation pseudopotential between shadows i and j are made functions of the local density of shadows:

$$\alpha \to \alpha(\hat{\rho}_{ij})$$

$$\delta \to \delta(\hat{\rho}_{ij}).$$

The local density operator $\hat{\rho}$ is defined as:

$$\hat{\rho}_{ij} = \frac{1}{2}(\hat{\rho}_i + \hat{\rho}_j), \tag{8}$$

where

$$\hat{\rho}_i = \frac{1}{A}\sum_{l \neq i}^{N} \frac{1}{1 + e^{\mu(s_{il} - r_C)}}, \tag{9}$$

and A is a normalization factor. This operator gives a value proportional to the average density seen by the pair of shadows ij. The parameters μ and r_C are to be

Table 2

Energies and average local densities for a p-H_2 crystal at density $\rho = 0.02604\text{Å}^{-3}$ as function of the parameters μ and r_C in eq. (9).

r_C (Å)	μ (Å^{-1})	E (K)	$\langle\hat{\rho}\rangle$ (Å^{-3})
5.0	0.5	-86.15(3)	0.02552(1)
5.0	4.0	-86.61(2)	0.02626(1)
5.0	5.0	-86.61(1)	0.02604(1)
5.0	6.0	-86.58(2)	0.02580(1)
5.0	10.0	-86.55(2)	0.02521(1)
4.6	5.0	-40.70(15)	0.02552(1)
4.8	5.0	-38.32(22)	0.02626(1)
5.0	5.0	-86.61(1)	0.02604(1)
5.2	5.0	-86.59(2)	0.02580(1)
5.4	5.0	-81.74(2)	0.02521(1)

determined in order to correctly reproduce the average density in the homogeneous system. In order to parametrize a LD-SWF to be used in the coexistence region, the optimization of the parameters in the standard SWF has to be carried out accurately in the region close to the equilibrium density (which is experimentally found at $\rho_0 = 0.02595\text{Å}^{-3}$[17]), and lower. In this range The parameters b, connected to the width of the correlation hole of the molecules, and C, giving the inverse of the mean square displacement between particles and shadows, show a weak dependence on the density. In particular the parameter C is nearly constant and equal to 1Å^{-2} throughout the density range considered. The parameter b tends to saturate at high densities around a value 3.35Å, while at equilibrium density its value is $b = 3.25$Å. For densities lower than the equilibrium density the parameter b shows some oscillations, contained within 5% of the value at equilibrium value. Such oscillations might be due to the fact that the system and autocorrelations between configurations become very large, making the optimization difficult.

For such reasons the choice in the LD-SWF of keeping the parameters b and C constant at the value optimal at the equilibrium density, and of varying only α and δ, is reasonable. The parameters α and δ show indeed a stronger density dependence. From the results of the simulations it turns out that such dependence can be safely assumed to be linear:

$$\alpha(\rho) = \alpha_0 + \alpha_1 \rho, \tag{10a}$$

$$\delta(\rho) = \delta_0 + \delta_1 \rho. \tag{10b}$$

The coefficients of the linear fits are given in Table 1. The differences between energies computed with the optimal values of the parameters and the values for the LD-SWF parameterization are less than 1%. While the following results have been obtained with the optimized standard wave function, we performed some preliminary calculations in order to fix the parameters μ and r_C in the LD-SWF. The computed average local density as function of μ and r_C is reported in Table 2.

4. GROUND STATE PROPERTIES

With the optimized SWF we computed the equation of state molecular p-H_2 both in the crystal phase, and in the disordered metastable phase found at densities below the equilibrium value. The results are plotted in Figure 1. As already mentioned, when using shadow wavefunctions, the stable phase (crystalline or disordered) is determined entirely from the variational principle. Therefore, given a set of variational parameters, we do not know *a priori* if the molecules will stay localized on a lattice. In order to determine the phase of the system, we need to compute a crystalline order parameter of this form:

$$O = \frac{1}{NM} \sum_{i=1}^{N} \sum_{\alpha=1}^{M} \left| e^{-i\mathbf{k}_\alpha \cdot \mathbf{r_i}} \right|, \tag{11}$$

where the $\mathbf{k}_\alpha, \alpha = 1...M$ are vectors of the reciprocal lattice for which the order is monitored. This quantity is exactly 1 if all the molecules are sitting on top of a lattice site, while in a disordered system its value is about $1/\sqrt{N}$, where N is the number of particles. The value we find at the equilibrium density is $\langle O \rangle \sim 0.72$ for the molecular degrees of freedom. This value slightly increases with the density of the system as the molecules become more and more localized. At the highest density considered we found $\langle O \rangle \sim 0.76$. The limit of stability for the crystal phase is found at a density $0.0172\text{Å}{-3} < \rho < 0.0194\text{Å}^{-3}$. In the inset of Figure 1 we also report the results of a calculation performed with a JN wave function, and the DMC results computed at density $\rho = 0.02600\text{Å}^{-3}$. As it can be noticed, the SWF definitely improves the simple two-body wavefunction, but it still misses about 1K from the exact Diffusion Monte Carlo result. A better structure of the particle-particle and shadow–shadow would greatly improve the situation.

In order to compute the value of the equilibrium density and pressure, it is convenient to fit the results for the ground state energy per particle by means of the following expression:

$$E(\rho) = E_0 + a\rho + b\rho^\gamma. \tag{12}$$

The estimate of the equilibrium density obtained from the fit, $\rho_0 = 0.02603\text{Å}^{-3}$ for the hcp lattice, and $\rho_0 = 0.02601\text{Å}^{-3}$ for the fcc lattice, is in good agreement with the experimental finding $\rho_0^{exp} = 0.02595\text{Å}^{-3}$[17]. The pressure as a function of density is then obtained from the following expression:

$$P(\rho) = \frac{1}{\rho^2} \frac{\partial E(\rho)}{\partial \rho}. \tag{13}$$

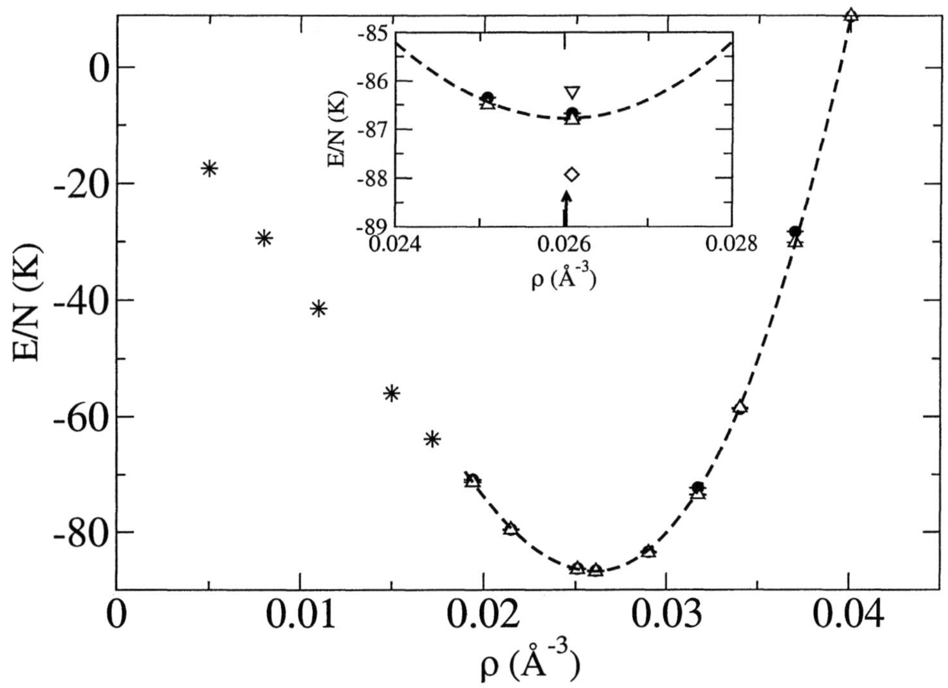

Figure 1. Estimated energy per molecule in solid and liquid p-H_2. Filled circles: SWF results for the fcc crystal; empty triangles: SWF results for the hcp crystal; stars: SWF results in the disordered phase. The inset gives an expanded view around the equilibrium density. Triangle down: JN result; diamond: DMC result. The dashed line is a plot of the fit with Eq. (12). The arrow indicates the equilibrium density obtained by the fit.

In Figure 2 the computed pressure for the fcc and hcp solid phases is compared to the experimental curve extrapolated to T=0[17]. The SWF result is lower than the experiment near the equilibrium density, while the pressure tends to be overestimated at high densities. We also compare our results with results of Norman et al.[13] for the same Silvera-Goldman potential and for other intermolecular interactions.

5. VACANCIES

The vacancy formation energy at constant pressure in a system of N particles and N_l lattice sites at a given density ρ can be defined as[19,20]:

$$\Delta E_{vac} = E(V', N = N-1, N_l = N) - \frac{N-1}{N} E(V, N, N_l = N). \tag{14}$$

The volumes V and V' are related by the requirement that the density of the system remains constant, i.e., $N/V = (N-1)/V'$. In a quantum crystal ΔE_{vac} has contributions from three different effects. The main contribution is given by the energy of formation of a vacancy in a rigid crystal, which can be expressed, at constant

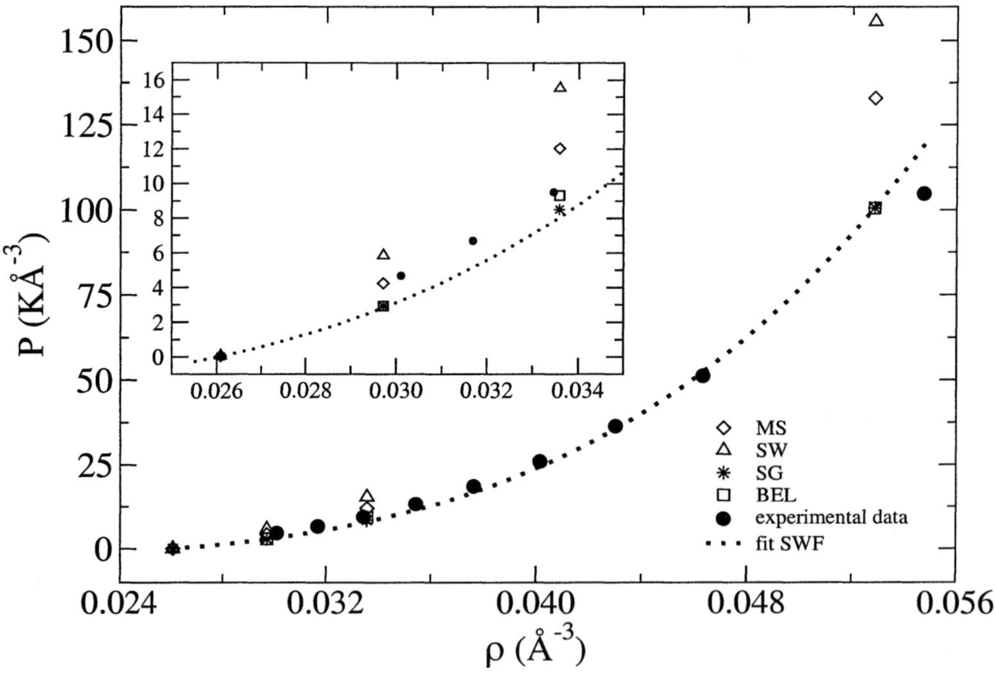

Figure 2. Pressure as a function of density in solid p-H_2. Dotted line: SWF result computed from Eq. (13) from the fit of the ground state energy. Filled circles are experimental data from ref. [17]. Points are values computed in ref. [13] with different intermolecular potentials (MS: Meyer and Schaefer[18]; SW: Schaefer and Watts[14]; SG: Silvera and Goldman[12]; BEL: Buck *et al.*[15]). In the inset we expand the same data near the equilibrium density.

pressure and in the thermodynamic limit, as:

$$\Delta E^0_{vac} = \frac{1}{\rho} P(\rho) - \frac{V(\rho)}{N}. \tag{15}$$

Another important contribution comes from the relaxation of the crystal around the empty site. This term lowers the vacancy formation energy due to the fact that the kinetic energy of the molecules surrounding the vacancy is reduced. This contribution is more important at lower densities, and can be well described only within a model that allows lattice sites to be displaced from their original positions, as happens for SWF where no *a-priori* lattice is assumed[21]. The third contribution comes from the motion of the vacancy through the crystal, and it is likely to be small in p-H_2, due to the high degree of localization of the molecules.

In Figure 3 we report the results obtained for ΔE_{vac} as a function of the density for the fcc crystal (obtained with N=108 molecules), and for the hcp crystal (obtained with N=180 molecules). The values are compared with the corresponding estimate of ΔE^0_{vac}. As it can be seen, there is a strong dependence of ΔE_{vac} on the density. For low densities the contribution from lattice relaxation, which can be estimated by the difference $E_{rel} = \Delta E_0^{vac} - \Delta E^{vac}$, is $E_{rel} \sim 9K$. This value decreases when the

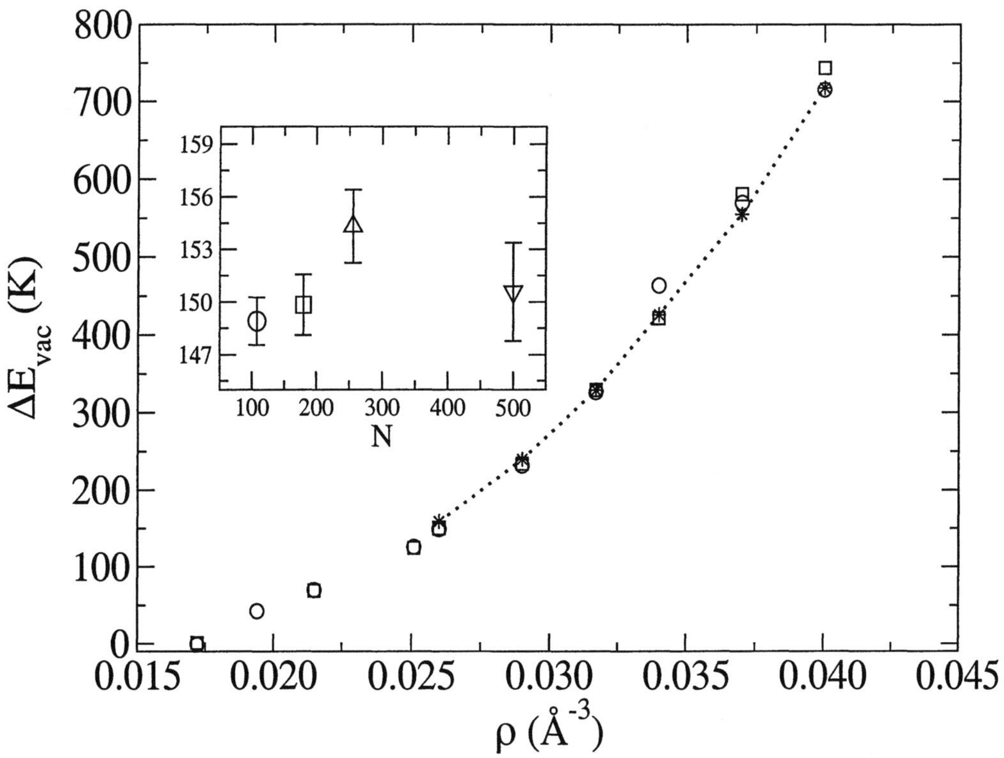

Figure 3. Vacancy formation energy ΔE_{vac} from SWF calculations as a function of the molecular density. Circles: fcc crystal (108/107 particles); squares: hcp crystal (180/179 particles). The dotted line represents the estimated energy for a vacancy without relaxation effects, obtained from the fitted equation of state. In the inset we plot the vacancy formation energy at density $\rho = 0.02609\text{Å}^{-3}$ as a function of N, the number of particles used in the simulation.

density increases. For high densities E_{rel} does not show a systematic behavior, due probably to much larger finite size effects in the calculations. The use of periodic boundary conditions implies that the presence of one vacancy in the simulation cell corresponds to a density 1/N of vacancies in the infinite crystal. The local deformation of the crystal due to the relaxation of the atoms around the empty site might induce deformations to the next shells, which might translate into a vacancy-vacancy interaction. In order to check if such interaction affects the estimate of the vacancy formation energy, we performed simulations at different numbers of molecules at the equilibrium density (where relaxation effects are large), and recomputed the vacancy formation energy. Results are plotted in the inset of Figure 3. As it can be seen, the differences are within two standard deviations, suggesting that no sizeable effects of relaxation can be observed beyond the second shell of neighbors (which is contained in the simulation box with 108 molecules). This is also confirmed by the fact that at density ρ_0 no significant difference is observed for the vacancy formation energy in the fcc and the hcp crystals, that have the same structure for the first shell of neighbors.

ACKNOWLEDGMENTS

We thank G.V. Chester, M.H. Kalos, S. Fantoni and L. Reatto for useful discussions. This work has been partly supported by the Italian MIUR under a COFIN grant. Calculations were performed on the ALPS cluster at ECT* in Trento, and on the Beowulf cluster at CINECA under a INFM grant for supercomputing initiatives.

REFERENCES

[1] S. Vitiello, K. Runge, and M. H. Kalos, *Phys. Rev. Lett.* **60**, 1970 (1988).

[2] L. Reatto and G. L. Masserini, *Phys. Rev. B* **38**, 4516 (1988).

[3] F. Pederiva, A. Ferrante, S. Fantoni, and L. Reatto, *Phys. Rev. Lett.* **72**, 2589 (1994).

[4] D. E. Galli and L. Reatto, *J. Low Temp. Phys.* **113**, 223 (1998).

[5] D. E. Galli, M. Buzzacchi, and L. Reatto, *J. Chem. Phys.* **115**, 10239 (2001).

[6] P. Sindzingre, D. M. Ceperley, and M. L. Klein, *Phys. Rev. Lett.* **67**, 1871 (1991).

[7] K. Nho and E. Manousakis, *Phys. Rev. B* **65**, 115409 (2002).

[8] M. C. Gordillo and D. M. Ceperley, *Phys. Rev. B* **65**, 174527 (2002).

[9] A. C. Levi and R. Mazzarello, *J. Low. Temp. Phys.* **122**, 75 (2001).

[10] S. Grebenev, B. Sarkatov, J. P. Toennis, and A. F. Vilesov, *Science* **289**, 1532 (2000).

[11] M. V. R. Krishna and K. B. Whaley, *Z. Phys. D* **20**, 223 (1991).

[12] I. F. Silvera and V. V. Goldman, *J. Chem. Phys.* **69**, 4209 (1978).

[13] M. J. Norman, R. O. Watts, and U. Buck, *J. Chem. Phys.* **81**, 3500 (1984).

[14] J. Schaefer and R. O. Watts, *Mol. Phys.* **47**, 933 (1982).

[15] U Buck, F. Huisken, A. Kohlhase, D. Otten, and J. Schaefer, *J. Chem. Phys.* **78**, 4439 (1983).

[16] T. MacFarland, S. A. Vitiello, L. Reatto, G. V. Chester, M. H. Kalos, *Phys. Rev. B* **50**, 13577 (1994).

[17] J. van Straaten and I. F. Silvera, *Phys. Rev. B* **37**, 1989 (1988).

[18] J. Schaefer and W. Meyer *J. Chem. Phys.* **70** 344 (1979).

[19] R. A. Guyer, *J. Low Temp. Phys.* **8**, 427 (1972).

[20] F. Pederiva, F. Dalfovo, S. Fantoni, L. Reatto, and S. Stringari, *Phys. Rev. B* **55**, 3122 (1997).

[21] B. Chaudhuri, F. Pederiva, and G. V. Chester, *Phys. Rev. B* **60**, 3271 (1999).

MICROSCOPIC CALCULATIONS OF SMALL MIXED HELIUM DROPLETS

J. Navarro
Instituto de Física Corpuscular (CSIC Universidad de Valencia)
Edificio Institutos Paterna, Apdo. 22085, E-46071 Valencia, Spain

R. Guardiola
Depto. Física Atómica y Nuclear, Universidad de Valencia
Avda. Dr. Moliner 50, E-46100 Burjassot, Spain

1. INTRODUCTION

Helium bound systems are dominated by quantum effects. The large zero-point motion of He atoms, combined with the weak van der Waals interaction between them, causes helium to have the lowest boiling point of all substances and to remain liquid down to the absolute zero. A pressure higher than 25 bar has to be applied in order to solidify the liquid. One may thus expect that Clusters made by a small number of He atoms are thus weakly bound quantum systems.

From the theoretical side, various properties of the bosonic ^4He_N clusters have been studied employing a great variety of microscopic many-body techniques [1-8], as well as density functional methods [9-11]. All calculations predict that ^4He_N clusters are bound for any number N of atoms. The direct solution of the Schrödinger equation employing modern He-He interactions predict for the dimer $^4He_2$ a binding energy between 1 and 2 mK, depending on the specific interaction, and a size of about 60 Å. In contrast, neither $^3He_2$ nor $^4He^3He$ are bound. No "exact" results have yet been obtained for the fermionic ^3He_N clusters, whose properties have been investigated by means of Variational Monte Carlo techniques [2,12] and density functional methods [13-14]. In contrast with the bosonic clusters, it turns out that because of the smaller ^{3}He atomic mass plus the repulsion related to Pauli principle, a minimum number $N_{\rm min} > 2$ of ^{3}He atoms is required so as to form a bound system. In Ref. [14] a shell-model calculation based on a finite-range density functional was used to estimate that minimum number in 30 atoms. The microscopic variational Monte Carlo calculations of Refs. [12] and [15] predicted 34 and 35, respectively for such a number. The actual value of $N_{\min}$ is still an open question.

From the experimental side, beams of helium clusters are produced by expanding the high purity gas at high pressure and low temperature into a vacuum through a nozzle. The number of atoms in the droplet is measured in scattering experiments, crossing the beam of droplets with a secondary beam of a heavy rare gas, usually krypton. Varying the conditions at the source it is possible to adjust the average cluster size in the beam. For instance, source conditions of 20 bar and 12-15 K produce clusters with $3 \cdot 10^3 - 10^4$ atoms. Increasing T at fixed pressure yields smaller sizes, and viceversa. An alternative, non-destructive method has been employed to select very small sizes, based on the diffraction by a transmission grating [16]. Since the velocity v of the cluster beam is sharply peaked, the quantal wavelength λ of the clusters is also well defined. In the case of a pure cluster the de Broglie wavelength is inversely proportional to the number N of atoms in the cluster

$$\lambda = \frac{h}{Nmv} \tag{1}$$

where m is the atomic mass. Typically, λ is about $0.1/N$ in nm. Pure $^4\mathrm{He}_N$ clusters, with $N \leq 8$, and mixed $^4\mathrm{He}_N{-}^3\mathrm{He}$ clusters, with $2 \leq N \leq 6$, have been detected using a grating with 100 nm period [17]. In Ref. [18], a bond length of 52 ± 4 Å was determined for the dimer $^4\mathrm{He}_2$, and a binding energy of $1.1 + 0.3 - 0.2$ mK was estimated from that size. These values are in agreement with the results obtained by solving the Schrödinger equation with the modern He-He interactions.

Mixed clusters containing N_B atoms of ^{4}He and N_F atoms of ^{3}He are particularly interesting, since they are made of bosons and fermions with different mass interacting through the same potential. The case of a single fermion with a variable number of bosons has been studied using a density functional approach [19] and microscopic methods [20-22]. It turns out that such clusters form bound states for $N_B \geq 2$. The larger zero-point motion of the ^{3}He atom pushes it to the surface, where its wave function becomes quasi two-dimensional, similar to the Andreev state describing one ^{3}He impurity in ^{4}He bulk. Recently, we have investigated the stability of small mixed clusters with $N_B \leq 8$ and $N_F \leq 20$ by means of a variational Monte Carlo (VMC) calculation [23-24] as well as a diffusion Monte Carlo (DMC) calculation [25]. DMC techniques have also been used by Bressanini and collaborators [26-27] to analyze systems with $N_B = 2 - 17$ and $N_F = 1 - 3$. Compounds with large number of both ^{3}He and ^{4}He atoms have been studied employing a non-local finite range density functional [28-29]. The functional is determined by fitting some selected bulk properties, both static and dynamic, as well as to the surface tension. Once the free parameters are completely fixed, the functional is used to analyze finite systems.

The study of the lightest clusters is a challenge for theoretical methods due to their very small binding energy. Microscopic many-body methods have to be used for this purpose. Indeed, the use of a density functional should be *a priori* avoided for studying very small clusters, due to both the uncertainties related to the extrapolation to small systems, and the approximated treatment of the center-of-mass. From the experimental point of view one may expect in the near future the improvement of the detection systems, so as to resolve clearly clusters of mass up to 100 amu [30].

Some intriguing questions motivate the studies of small mixed clusters, as in our previous works VMC [23-24] and DMC [25] calculations. For instance, knowing that a fermionic system of $N_F < 30$ is not bound, which is the minimum number of bosons able to bound them? Notice that from the fermionic viewpoint, the presence of bosons will provide an external field to bind the fermions, and hence the whole system. Conversely, given a pure boson cluster with few constituents, how many ^{3}He atoms may be added up and still having a bound state? How bosons and fermions are distributed in the cluster? In Section 2 we detail the trial wave function employed in our VMC. In Section 3 we give some details on the DMC method. The results will be presented and discussed in Section 4.

2. A VARIATIONAL WAVE FUNCTION FOR MIXED CLUSTERS

Our VMC calculation [23,24] is based on the following trial function

$$\Psi(\mathbf{R}) = \Phi_{BB}\Phi_{BF}\Phi_{FF}D_{\uparrow}D_{\downarrow}\Phi_{CI} \tag{2}$$

where $\mathbf{R}$ stands for the coordinates of all particles, and the labels B, F mean refer to bosons and fermions. The first three factors, depending on boson-boson, boson-fermion and fermion-fermion coordinates, have the same form

$$\Phi_{MN} = \prod_{i\in N, j\in M} \exp\left(-\frac{1}{2}\left[\frac{b_{MN}}{r_{ij}}\right]^{\nu} - \alpha_{MN} r_{ij}\right) \tag{3}$$

where indices M, N refer to labels B, F and r_{ij} is the relative distance between particles i and j. The so-defined two-body correlations contain a short-range McMillan form [32] plus a long-range confining exponential term. The factors $D_{\uparrow(\downarrow)}$ are Slater determinants, referred to spin-up (spin-down) particles, to take into account the required antisymmetry for fermions. These determinants are built up with harmonic polynomials in the fermionic Cartesian coordinates

$$\{1, x, y, z, x^2, y^2, z^2, xy, xz, yz\} \tag{4}$$

so that they are translationally invariant. These Cartesian single-particle orbitals are filled up within each shell by requiring the maximum allowable value for the spin, according to our findings for the pure ^{3}He case. In the case of fermions, we have included the Feynman-Cohen backflow [33] using transformed coordinates $\tilde{\mathbf{r}}_i$ in both the exponential factor and the Slater determinants. The transformed coordinates are defined as

$$\tilde{\mathbf{r}}_i = \mathbf{r}_i + \sum_{i\neq j} \frac{\lambda}{r_{ij}^3}(\mathbf{r}_i - \mathbf{r}_j) \tag{5}$$

with the parameter λ fixed to the value 5 Å^3, according to Ref. [2]. Finally, the last factor in Eq. (2) contains linear two-body correlations

$$\Phi_{CI} = 1 + \sum_{i<j} f(r_{ij}) \tag{6}$$

coming from a translationally invariant configuration interaction (hence the subindex CI), with the role of incorporating fine details at medium and long ranges, as we have seen in our previous works for pure clusters (see eg Ref. [34]).

We have fixed the values $\nu = 5.2$, $b_{BB} = 2.95$ Å, $b_{FF} = 2.85$ Å, as used in pure clusters, and $b_{BF} = 2.90$ Å. The parameters α_{BB}, α_{FF} and α_{BB}, as well as the unknown pair correlation function f are optimally determined by minimizing the ground state expectation value of the Hamiltonian.

3. THE DIFFUSION MONTE CARLO METHOD

The basic idea is to solve the imaginary-time Schrödinger equation for a function $f(\mathbf{R}, t)$ which is the product of a trial wave function Φ_{var} and the true ground-state wave function $\Psi(\mathbf{R})$. The resulting equation can be written as

$$-\frac{\partial f(\mathbf{R}, \mathbf{t})}{\partial t} = -\sum_i D_i \nabla_i^2 f + \sum D_i \nabla_{\mathbf{i}} \cdot (\mathbf{F}_{\mathbf{i}} f) + (E_L(\mathbf{R}) - E) f, \tag{7}$$

where the index i runs over all particles, and the diffusion constants D_i are $\hbar^2/2m_i$, with m_i equal to the ^{3}He or ^{4}He mass. The so-called dritf force $\mathbf{F}_{\mathbf{i}}(\mathbf{R})$ is related to the logarithmic derivative of the importance-sampling wave function

$$F_i(\mathbf{R}) = 2\nabla_i \ln \Phi_{\text{var}}(\mathbf{R}) \tag{8}$$

and the local energy $E_L(\mathbf{R})$ is related to the action of the Hamiltonian on the importance-sampling wave function

$$E_L(\mathbf{R}) = \frac{1}{\Phi_{\text{var}}} H \Phi_{\text{var}}(\mathbf{R}). \tag{9}$$

In the DMC method one solves the above equation by means of an approximate small-time Green funtion $G(\mathbf{R}, \mathbf{R}', \tau)$

$$f(\mathbf{R}', t + \tau) = \int d\mathbf{R} G(\mathbf{R}', \mathbf{R}, \tau) f(\mathbf{R}, t). \tag{10}$$

In our DMC calculations [25] we have chosen the $O(\tau^3)$ time-dependent Green function

$$G(\mathbf{R}, \mathbf{R}', \tau) = \frac{1}{(4\pi\tau)^{3N/2} \prod_i D_i^{3/2}} \exp\{-\tau[(E_L(\mathbf{R}) + E_L(\mathbf{R}')/2 - E]\} \tag{11}$$
$$\exp\left\{-\sum_i [[\mathbf{r}_i' - \mathbf{r}_i - D_i\tau(\mathbf{F}_{\mathbf{i}}(\mathbf{R}) + \mathbf{F}_{\mathbf{i}}(\mathbf{R}'))/2]^2/4D_i\tau]\right\},$$

as described for instance in Refs. [35-36].

The Monte Carlo solution of the differential equation consists in creating a set of walkers $\{\mathbf{R}_1, \mathbf{R}_2, \mathbf{R}_3, \ldots \mathbf{R}_{N_w}\}$ to represent the function at the initial time, $f(\mathbf{R}, 0)$, and applying a large number of times the short-time approximate Green function.

After a long series of applications all components of the starting wave function orthogonal to the ground state one disappear and the set of walkers is a representation of the quantity

$$f(\mathbf{R}, t \to \infty) \to \Phi_{\text{var}}(\mathbf{R})\Psi_0(\mathbf{R}), \tag{12}$$

i.e., the product of the exact ground-state wave function and the driving starting wave function Φ_{var}. From this converged product one may compute mixed estimators of physically interesting quantities, like e.g. the energy

$$E = \frac{\int f(\mathbf{R}, t \to \infty) E_L(\mathbf{R}) d\mathbf{R}}{\int f(\mathbf{R}, t \to \infty) d\mathbf{R}} \tag{13}$$

Given that we want to represent a system with both bosons and fermions with the corresponding requirements associated to the statistics, the ground state wave function cannot be positive definite, with the obvious exceptions of a single fermion or a pair of fermions, one spin up and the other spin down. This will not be a problem if we were solving the differential equation, or the equivalent integral equation, by analytic methods. However, it is a serious difficulty if the equation is solved by the Monte Carlo technique. In this case instead of having a function we deal with a set of random points which should be related to a probability distribution function. This requires to deal with positive functions and a way to do it is to introduce the importance-sampling function. The product of the importance-sampling wave function and the time-dependent ground state wave function will remain positive if they have (at any time) the same nodal surfaces. To accomplish that requirement any walker which attempts to cross a nodal surface is killed. To recognize that a nodal surface is going to be crossed is a simple as to check if the sign of the fermionic part changes sign or not. This way of carrying out the Monte Carlo process is known as the fixed node approximation, and actually solves a problem different to that one required, because of the boundary conditions imposed at the nodal surfaces. It has been proved [37] that the solution is really an upper bound to the fermionic ground state. As importance sampling function we have used the wave function of Eq. (2) with $\Phi_{CI} = 1$, ie without the two-body CI linear term.

4. RESULTS AND DISCUSSION

In Figure 1 are plotted the ground state energies as obtained within our variational Monte Carlo (VMC) and diffusion Monte Carlo (DMC) calculations. As a general rule, we see that, for a given number of bosons, the binding energy regularly increases with the number of fermions. The exceptions to this trend correspond to metastable clusters, whose binding energy is smaller or equal, within statistical error bars, than the system with one or more less fermions. We can also notice an indication of shell closure at $N_F = 2, 8$, manifested by a slope change of the energies as a function of N_F. As expected, DMC energies are substantially lower than VMC ones and, in fact, some clusters which appear not bound in a VMC calculation are definitely bound after the DMC improvement.

Some special DMC results are of particular relevance. For example, the case of a single boson, which is able to bind 20 fermions. Also of interest is the cluster

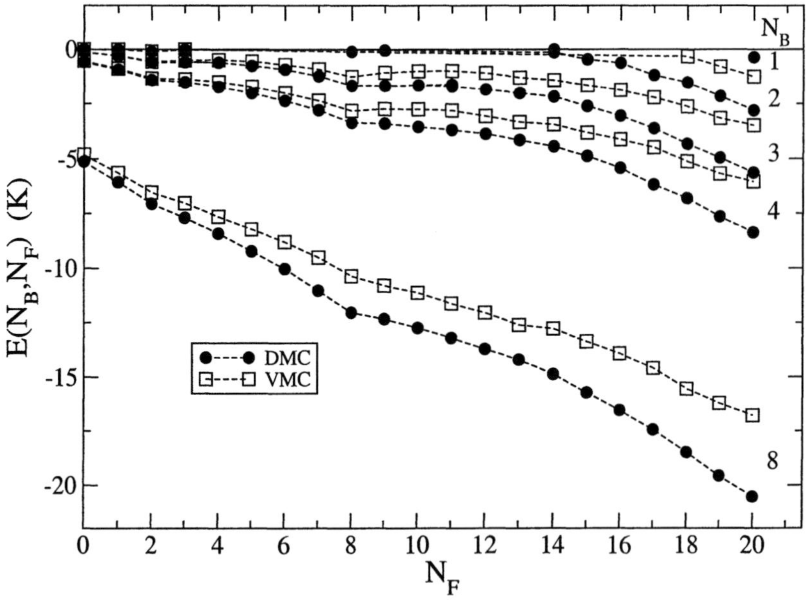

Figure 1. Ground state energies per particle (in K) as a function of the number of atoms N in the cluster, as obtained from a variational Monte Carlo calculation (open squares) and a diffusion Monte Carlo calculation (solid circles). The Aziz HFD-H interaction [] has been used in both calculations.

$^4He_2{}^3He_8$, which turns out to be an isolated bound cluster, having a metastable neighbour $^4He_2{}^3He_9$. The cluster $^4He^3He_{20}$ is probably also as an isolated system, but we have not studied the case with 21 or more fermions. We shall mention later on other metastable states or regions.

Another interesting point coming out from this Figure is that there are no significant differences between VMC and DMC energies in the smaller clusters region $(N_B, N_F \leq 4)$. That means tha a trial wave function combining Jastrow-type short-range correlations and medium- and long-range correlations, coming from a translationally invariant configuration interaction description, is a very efficient approach to describe light clusters. In fact, we have previously shown [7] that including three-body correlations in this scheme, the resulting ground state energies for pure ^4He_N with $N \leq 40$ are at worst within 3% of the exact DMC ones, for N close to 40.

Shell effects are magnified in Figure 2, where we have plotted the fermion separation energies

$$E(N_B, N_F - 1) - E(N_B, N_F) \tag{14}$$

or chemical potentials, as a function of the number of fermions in the clusters containing 3, 4 and 8 bosons. There are sudden droppings after $N_F = 2$ and 8, which

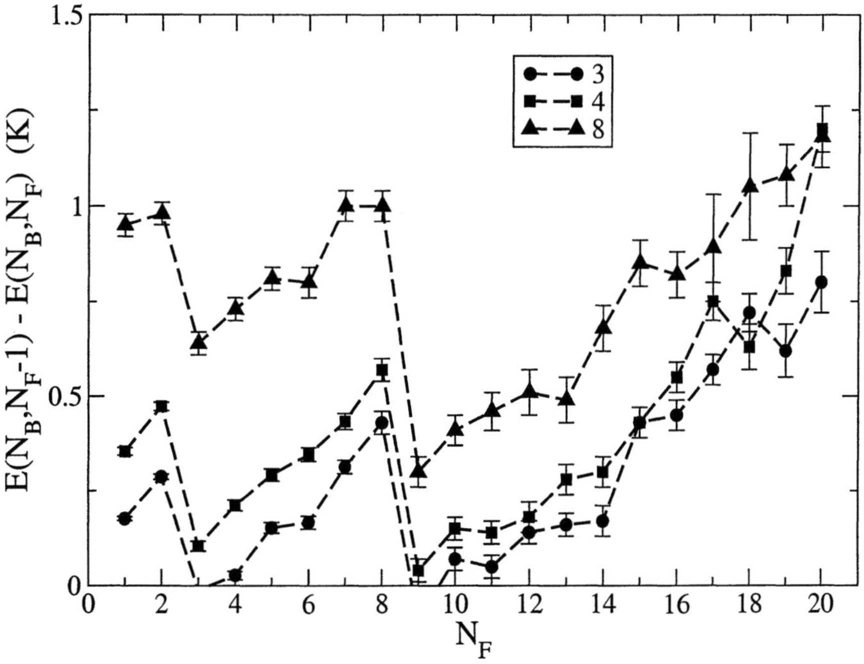

Figure 2. Fermion separation energies $E(N_B, N_F - 1) - E(N_B, N_F)$ (in K) as a function of N_F for several fixed numbers of bosons N_B. are the thicker lines. All energies are in K.

Table 1

Stability chart of mixed clusters ${}^4\mathrm{He}_{N_B}{}^3\mathrm{He}_{N_F}$. Symbols • and o mean stable and metastableclusters, respectivley. No symbol means an unbound cluster.

4	•	•	•	•	•	•	•	•	•	o	•	•	•	•	•	•	•	•	•	•	•
3	•	•	•	o	o	•	•	•	•	o	o	o	•	•	•	•	•	•	•	•	•
2	•	•	•	o					•	o					o	•	•	•	•	•	•
1																					•
0																					
N_B/N_F	0	1	2	3	4	5	6	7	8	9	10	11	12	13	14	15	16	17	18	19	20

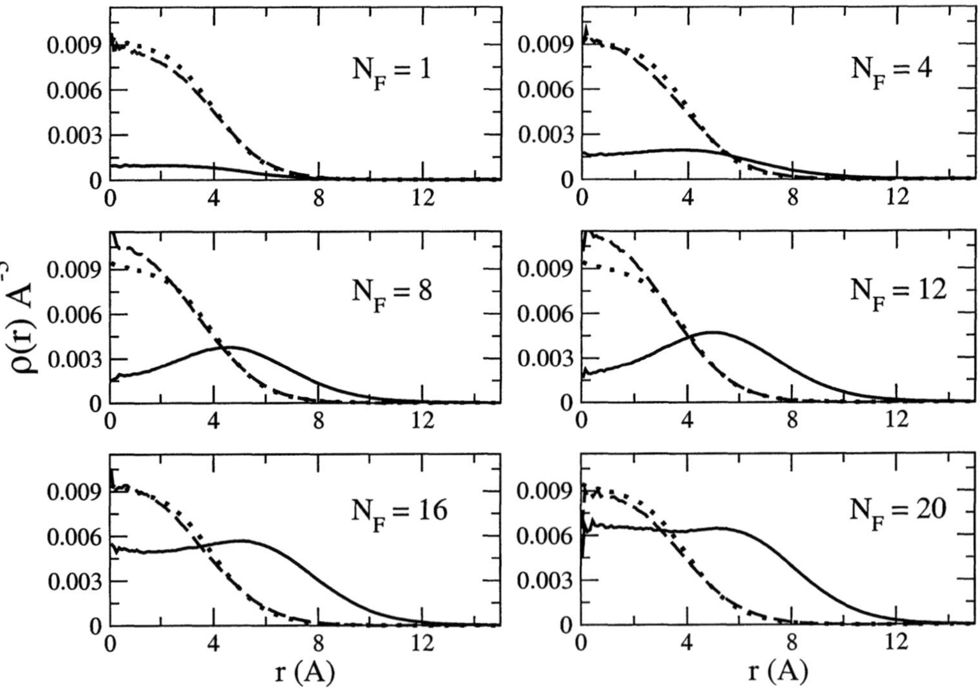

Figure 3. One-body distribution densities (in Å^{-3}) as a function of the distance r (in Å) to the center of mass of a mixed cluster with $N_B = 4$. Dashed and solid lines correspond to boson and fermion densities, respectively. In all panels, dotted lines correspond to the pure $N_B = 4$ case.

correspond to the filling of 1s and 1p shells, and afterwards a steady growing within the active shells.

Our DMC results concerning the stability of mixed clusters are summarized in Table 1, where rows and columns respectively correspond to the number N_B, N_F of bosons and fermions. The symbols • and ∘ stand for stable and metastable states, respectively. The absence of any of these symbols means that the system is unboud. The lower row, with $N_B = 0$, is empty. According to the discussion in the Introduction, we know that around 30-34 fermions are required to form a self-bound system. In the upper row, it is indicated that a single boson is able to bind 20 fermions. Systems with 2 bosons are bound if $N_F \leq 2$, $N_F = 8$, and $N_F \geq 11$. Otherwise, the systems are either metastable ($N_F = 3, 9$) or unbound. Clusters with 3 bosons and $N_F = 3, 4, 9, 10, 11$ are metastable, as well as the cluster with 4 bosons and 9 fermions. The fact that clusters with 9 fermions are metastable is an evidence of the particular stability related to the magic number $N_F = 8$. However, it is worth to keep in mind that our present DMC calculations are not exact, but only provide upper variational bounds to the ground state energies, due to the fixed node approximation we have used. Therefore, it is not excluded that some of these metastable states will appear as stable in an exact calculation.

The last question we want to investigate refers to the spatial distribution of bosons and fermions in the cluster. In Figure 3 are plotted the one-body density profiles $\rho(r)$ as a function of the distance r to the center-of-mass of a mixed cluster with $N_B = 4$, and $N_F = 0, 4, 8, 12, 16$, and 20. As a reference, we have also displayed the density profile of the pure $N_B = 4$ cluster (dotted line). The density probability distributions have been normalized to their respective number of bosons and fermions. The general trend of these profiles can be understood as the result of a balance between the weak attractive interaction and the zero-point motion. A single fermion stays mainly inside the cluster. Keeping in mind the normalization of the densities, we can see from the figure that, as compared with the bosons, the fermion has a larger probability to be located at the exterior of the cluster, as a consequence of its smaller atomic mass. When N_F is increased, the fermions are expelled to the surface of the drop, until N_F is much larger than N_B, in whose case fermions are located both in the center and the surface of the cluster. Increasing the number of fermions produces an expulsion of bosons from the center of the drop, with the surface of the boson one-body density remaining unchanged, and practically the same as that of the pure case.

ACKNOWLEDGMENTS

This work has been supported by MCyT/FEDER (Spain), grant number BFM2001-0262, and Generalitat Valenciana, grant number GV01-216.

REFERENCES

[1] V.R. Pandharipande, J.G. Zabolitzky, S.C. Pieper, R.B. Wiringa, and U. Helmbrecht, Phys. Rev. Lett **50**, 1676 (1983).

[2] V.R. Pandharipande, S.C. Pieper and R.B. Wiringa, Phys. Rev. B **34**, 4571 (1986).

[3] M.V. Rama Krishna and K.B. Whaley, J. Chem. Phys. **93**, 6738 (1990).

[4] S.A. Chin and E. Krotscheck, Phys. Rev. Lett. **65**, 2658 (1990).

[5] S.A. Chin and E. Krotscheck, Phys. Rev. B **45**, 852 (1992).

[6] M. Lewerenz, J. Chem. Phys. **106**, 4596 (1997).

[7] R. Guardiola, M. Portesi and J. Navarro, Phys. Rev. B **60**, 6288 (1999).

[8] R. Guardiola, M. Portesi and J. Navarro, Phys. Rev. B **63**, 224519 (2001).

[9] S. Stringari and J. Treiner, J. Chem. Phys. **87**, 5021 (1987).

[10] F. Dalfovo, A. Lastri, L. Pricaupenko, S. Stringari, and J. Treiner, Phys. Rev. B **52**, 1193 (1995).

[11] M. Casas and S. Stringari, J. Low Temp. Phys. **79**, 135 (1990).

[12] R. Guardiola and J. Navarro, Phys. Rev. Lett. **84**, 1144 (2000).

[13] M. Barranco, D.M. Jezek, E.S. Hernández, J. Navarro, and Ll. Serra, Z. Phys. D **28**, 257 (1993).

[14] M. Barranco, J. Navarro and A. Poves, Phys. Rev. Lett. **78**, 4729 (1997).

[15] R. Guardiola, Phys. Rev. B **62**, 3146 (2000).

[16] W. Schöllkopf and J.P. Toennies, Science **256**, 1345 (1993).

[17] W. Schöllkopf and J.P. Toennies, J. Chem. Phys. **104**, 1155 (1996); J.P. Toennies, private communication (1999).

[18] R.E. Grisenti, W. Schöllkopf, J.P. Toennies, T. Köhler, and M. Stoll, Phys. Rev. Lett. **85**, 2284 (2000).

[19] F. Dalfovo, Z. Phys. D **14**, 263 (1989).

[20] A. Belić, F. Dalfovo, S. Fantoni, and S. Stringari, Phys. Rev. B **49**, 15253 (1994).

[21] D. Bressanini, M. Zavaglia, M. Mella, and G. Morosi, J. Chem. Phys. **112**, 717 (2000).

[22] E. Krotscheck and R. Zillich, J. Chem. Phys. **115**, 10161 (2001).

[23] R. Guardiola and J. Navarro, Phys. Rev. Lett. **89**, 193401 (2002).

[24] R. Guardiola and J. Navarro, Few-Body Syst. Suppl. **14**, 223 (2003).

[25] R. Guardiola and J. Navarro, Phys. Rev. A, in press (2003).

[26] D. Bressanini, G. Morosi, L. Bertini, M. Mella, Few-Body Syst. **31**, 199 (2002).

[27] D. Bressanini and G. Morosi, Phys. Rev. Lett. **90**, 133401 (2003).

[28] M. Barranco, M. Pi, S.M. Gatica, E.S. Hernández, and J. Navarro, Phys. Rev. B **56**, 8997 (1997).

[29] M. Pi, R. Mayol and M. Barranco, Phys. Rev. Lett. **82**, 3093 (1999).

[30] J.P. Toennies and O. Kornilov, private communication (2003).

[31] R.A. Aziz, F.R. McCourt, and C.C.K. Wong, Mol. Phys. **61**, 1487 (1987).

[32] W.L. McMillan, Phys. Rev. **138**, A442 (1965).

[33] R.P. Feynman and M. Cohen, Phys. Rev. **102**, 1189 (1956).

[34] See, e.g., J. Navarro, R. Guardiola and I. Moliner, in *Introduction to Modern Methods of Quantum Many-Body Theory and their Applications*, edited by A. Fabrocini, S. Fantoni and E. Krotscheck, Vol. 7 of Series in Advances in Quantum Many-Body Theory (World Scientific, Singapore, 2002).

[35] J. Vrbik and S.M. Rothstein, J. Comp. Phys. **63**, 130 (1986).

[36] S.A. Chin, Phys. Rev. A **42**, 6991 (1990).

[37] P.J. Reynolds, D.M. Ceperley, B.J. Alder and W.A. Lester Jr., J. Chem. Phys. **77**, 5593 (1982).

ON THE KELVIN-HELMHOLTZ INSTABILITY IN A PHASE-SEPARATED ^{3}He-^{4}He LIQUID MIXTURE

S.Burmistrov [a], *L.Dubovskii* [a], *and T.Satoh*[b]

[a] Kurchatov Institute, Moscow 123182, Russia
[b] Tohoku University, Sendai 980, Japan

1. INTRODUCTION

The Kelvin-Helmholtz instability (KHI) is well-known in the common classical hydrodynamics. The dispersion law of waves on the water surface is complex-valued [1] on the neglection of gravity acceleration and interfacial tension:

$$\omega = qv\frac{\rho_1 \pm i\sqrt{\rho_1\rho_2}}{\rho_1 + \rho_2}$$

The both signs before imaginary unit show the unstable behavior of the system. Here ρ_1 and ρ_2 are the densities of air and water, ω and q are the frequency and the momentum of the waves induced by the tangential flow of the air with the velocity v along the air-water interface.

Here we apply this consideration of the common classical hydrodynamics to the quantum superfluid systems. We study the behavior of the interface between the c- and d-phases of a phase-separated ^{3}He-^{4}He liquid mixture in the presence of superflow in the d-phase. The superflow can produce the KHI for the c-d interface as well. Here we consider several types of possible instability: (i) quantized vortex in the superfluid liquid beside the superfluid-normal interface; (ii) the tangential flow of the superfluid component with respect to the normal fluid in the direction parallel to the flat interface; (iii) quantized vortex line parallel to the interface in the field of gravity. In these cases the HKI has a threshold character due to the surface tension and acceleration normal to the interface. The acceleration is of the centrifugal type in (i) and gravitational type in (ii) and (iii). The presence of the threshold results in the quite different scales of the typical distances. The centrifugal acceleration induces the scale of the order of the core radius b of several Angstroems. The acceleration of gravity yields the scale of the capillary length $\lambda = \sqrt{\alpha/(\Delta\rho g)} \sim 1.3mm$. In the cases (i) and (iii) we obtain the groove at the interface producing the instability of the vortex at a critical distance h_{cr}, being $h_{cr} = b\rho/(\rho - \rho')$ for the case (i) and $h_{cr} = \lambda$ for the case (iii). The vortex at the distances smaller than h_{cr} proves to be unstable and the vortex should merge with the interface. In (ii) the interface becomes unstable provided the superfluid component flows in the direction tangential to the interface at the velocity exceeding the critical one of about 6.3cm/s, resulting in the ripple structure with the wavelength of the order of the capillary constant λ.

2. QUANTIZED VORTEX IN THE SUPERFLUID LIQUID BESIDE THE SUPERFLUID-NORMAL INTERFACE

The quantized vortex in the superfluid ^{4}He is a circular flow of a superfluid component around a core of atomic dimensions with a constant and quantized circulation. Outside the core the superfluid velocity $v_s(r)$ decays slowly with the distance r from the axis of the core [2]:

$$v_s(r) = \kappa/(2\pi r),$$

Here κ is the circulation $\kappa = 2\pi\hbar/m_4 = 9.97 \cdot 10^{-4} cm^2/s$, m_4 is the mass of ^{4}He atom. For simplicity, we consider the cylindrical geometry of the system with the vortex at the axis of a cylinder. In this geometry the superfluid velocity is parallel to the interface which is located at distance R from the core axis. So, beside the interface we have the tangential flow with the superfluid velocity $v_s(R) = \kappa/(2\pi R)$. In this case we have the KHI as well. The instability has a threshold. The reason for this threshold is connected with the surface tension α at the c-d interface and the centrifugal acceleration $a = v_s^2/R$ in the flow of superfluid component around the vortex:

$$V_{cr} = \left[\frac{4\alpha a(\rho_d - \rho_c)(\rho_d + \rho_c)^2}{\rho_s^2(\rho_n + \rho_c)^2}\right]^{1/4}$$

Here ρ_c and ρ_d are the densities of the normal (c-phase) and superfluid (d- phase). In addition, $\rho_d = \rho_s + \rho_n$, ρ_s and ρ_n being the supefluid and normal components of the d-phase.

Using $a = v_s^2/R$ for the the centrifugal acceleration, we arrive at the critical size $R_{cr} \sim b\rho_4/(\rho_4 - \rho_3)$, $b = \rho_s\kappa^2/(8/\pi^2\alpha)$ being the core radius. At $R < R_{cr}$ the system is unstable, at $R > R_{cr}$ the system becomes stable. Since core radius b in ^{3}He-^{4}He mixture is about 6.8 Å [3], the typical distance $R_{cr} \sim 15$Å. So, the instability under consideration does not manifest in the experiments of macroscopic scale.

3. TANGENTIAL FLOW OF THE SUPERFLUID COMPONENT PARALLEL TO THE FLAT INTERFACE

Now we consider another system where the typical distances are much larger. We consider the tangential flow of the superfluid component with respect to the normal fluid in the direction parallel to the flat interface in the field of gravity. To analyze the stability of the system, we impose a small perturbation periodic along the horizontal x-axis. The z-coordinate of the interface reads

$$z = \zeta(x, t) = a \exp[i(qx - \omega t)]$$

We have three velocities in the system. In the normal c-phase we have one velocity of a fluid $v_c(x,z,t)$ and the potential as

$$\phi_3(x,z,t) = A_3 exp(-qz)exp[i(qx-\omega t)], \quad z>0$$

The behavior ϕ_c as a function of x and z follows from the usual equation for the potential $\Delta\phi_c = 0$. In the d-phase we have the velocities of the normal and the superfluid components v_n and v_s with the appropriate potentials

$$\phi_n(x,z,t) = A_n exp(qz)exp[i(qx-\omega t)],$$

$$\phi_s(x,z,t) = A_s exp(qz)exp[i(qx-\omega t)], \quad z<0$$

The displacement of the interface ζ and the potentials ϕ_c, ϕ_n, ϕ_s include four constants which we must determine from the boundary conditions for velocities and pressure at the interface:

$$\partial\phi_c/\partial z = \partial\zeta/\partial t,$$

$$\partial\phi_n/\partial z = \partial\zeta/\partial t,$$

$$\partial\phi_s/\partial z = \partial\zeta/\partial t + U_s\partial\zeta/\partial x,$$

U_s being the velocity of flow of the superfluid component along the the superfluid-normal interface. Here we used the approximation of immiscible liquids, neglecting possible phase conversion between the phases at the interface cf.[4]. The equality of the pressures in both fluids at the interface reads

$$\rho_s\dot{\phi}_s + \rho_n\dot{\phi}_n + \rho_s(v_s^2 - U_s^2)/2 + (\rho_d - \rho_c)g\zeta = \rho_c\dot{\phi}_c + \alpha\zeta_{xx}$$

The last term is the Laplace pressure. The other terms involves the Bernoulli pressure and the pressure of gravity [1]. Due to above boundary conditions in the linear approximation on a, A_c, A_n and A_n the dispersion equation becomes

$$\left[\omega - qU_s\frac{\rho_s}{\rho_d+\rho_c}\right]^2 = \frac{\rho_d-\rho_c}{\rho_d+\rho_c}qg + \frac{\alpha q^3}{\rho_d+\rho_c} - q^2U_s^2\left[1-\frac{\rho_s}{\rho_d+\rho_c}\right].$$

The threshold for the instability is determined by the critical velocity

$$U_{cr} = \left[4\alpha g\frac{\rho_d-\rho_c}{\rho_s^2}\left(\frac{\rho_d+\rho_c}{\rho_n+\rho_c}\right)^2\right]^{1/4}$$

If $U_s > U_{cr}$, we arrive at the usual HK tangential instability for the case of superfluid flow. The wavelength q_0 at which the ripple shape of the interface develops is given by the length corresponding to the capillary constant:

$$q_0 = 2\pi/\lambda_0, \ \lambda_0 = 2\pi(\alpha/g(\rho_d-\rho_c))^{1/2}.$$

Using the experimental value of surface tension [5] for zero pressure $\alpha = 23.9 mdyne/cm$, we get $U_{cr} = 6.3 cm/s$ and $\lambda_0 = 1.3 mm$.

4. QUANTIZED VORTEX LINE PARALLEL TO THE INTERFACE IN THE FIELD OF GRAVITY

We consider a quantized straight-line vortex parallel to the interface between normal fluid c- and superfluid d-phases of a separated ^{3}He-^{4}He liquid mixture. The d-phase liquid is treated as incompressible and the velocity of the superfluid component satisfies the continuity equation [1] $div\vec{v} = 0$. Provided the superfluid velocity depends on the x and y coordinates alone, we can represent the velocity field as $\vec{v} = rot\vec{A} = \{\partial A/\partial y, -\partial A/\partial x\}$, $\vec{A}$ being vector-potential directed along the third axis perpendicular to the interface. In a standard way the potential $\vec{A}$ can be derived from the imaginary part of the complex potential $U = \Phi + iA$. The straight-line vortex at the point $z = 0$ is described by the complex potential $U = (\kappa/2\pi i)\log z$ where $z = x + iy$ and $\kappa = 2\pi/m_4$ is the circulation quantum.

For the vortex line parallel to the flat interface, the complex potential is given by $U = (\kappa/2\pi i)log(z - z_0)/(z - \bar{z}_0)$. Here $z_0 = ih$ where h is the distance of vortex line from the interface. The energy of a vortex per unit length reads [4]

$$E = \rho_s/2 \int \vec{v}^2 dxdy = (\rho_s\kappa^2/2\pi)\ln(2h/b)$$

b being the vortex core radius.

Now we turn to the case of an arbitrarily curved interface. Let complex function $w = w(z)$ map the upper half-plane confined in its lower part by the curve L onto the upper half-plane. The curve L is determined by $y = \zeta(x)$ where $\zeta(x)$ is the deviation of the interface from the flat one. Hence the complex potential for a vortex at point z_0 is given by

$$U = \frac{\kappa}{2\pi i} log \frac{w(z) - w(z_0)}{w(z) - w(\bar{z}_0)}.$$

Unexpecting large and sharp distortions of the interface due to the presence of vortices, we below assume a weak and smooth bending of the interface. The corresponding conformal mapping can be found from, e.g., [6] :

$$w = z + \pi^{-1} \int_{-\infty}^{\infty} \frac{\zeta(t)dt}{z - t}$$

Expressing an integral for the kinetic energy of the superfluid component over the bulk of the d-phase with the exception of vortex core as

$$E = (\rho_s/2) \int \vec{v}^2 dxdy = (\rho_s/2) \int \vec{A} \cdot rot\vec{v}\, dxdy + (\rho_s/2) \oint (\vec{A} \times \vec{v})\vec{n}dl$$

we find that the vortex core surface alone contributes into the integral. The contribution from the interface surface $\zeta = \zeta(x)$ vanishes as $A = 0$ at the interface due to condition $w(z) = 0$ if $z \in L$. Correspondingly, we arrive at the energy of a vortex beside the interface

$$E = \rho_s \frac{\kappa^2}{4\pi} \log \left| \frac{w(z_0) - w(\bar{z}_0)}{w'(z_0)} \frac{1}{b} \right|$$

Substituting $w(z_0)$, we represent the vortex energy as a sum of two terms

$$E_v = E_{flat} + \Delta E_v.$$

The second term is associated with the bending of the interface and equals to

$$\Delta E_v = \rho_s \frac{\kappa^2}{4\pi} \log \left[\frac{1 - \frac{1}{\pi}\int_{-\infty}^{\infty} \frac{\zeta(t)}{h^2+t^2} dt}{1 - \frac{1}{\pi}\int_{-\infty}^{\infty} \frac{\zeta(t)(t^2-h^2)}{(h^2+t^2)^2} dt} \right].$$

The variation of the energy of the interface as a functional of its symmetric deformation $\zeta(x)$ in the presence of a single vortex line at point $(0, h)$ reads

$$\Delta E\left[\zeta(x)\right] = \alpha \int_{-\infty}^{\infty} \left(\sqrt{1+\zeta'^2(x)} - 1\right) dx + \Delta E_v + \frac{1}{2}\Delta\rho g \int_{-\infty}^{\infty} \zeta^2(x) dx.$$

Here α is the interface tension, $\Delta\rho$ is the difference in densities of c- and d-phases, and g is the gravity acceleration. The three terms correspond to the variation of the surface, vortex, and gravitational energies as compared with the flat interface. The physical reason for the deformation of the interface beside vortex line is obvious and lies in the competition between the vortex energy and the other two terms. In fact, as the deformation $\zeta(x)$ grows in the direction to the vortex line, the vortex energy decreases and, on the contrary, surface and gravitational energies increase.

For the problem on the whole, it is convenient to introduce two natural length scales. The first one is the capillary length $\lambda = \sqrt{\alpha/(\Delta\rho g)}$ and the second the core radius $b = \rho_s\kappa^2/(8\pi^2\alpha)$ calculated within the hollow core model of a vortex. For the c-d interface in a separated ^{3}He-^{4}He liquid mixture at low temperature, this means $\lambda = 0.2mm$ and $b = 6.8\mathring{A}$. The values near the tricritical $T_t = 0.87K$ point and other examples of possible interfaces can be found elsewhere [3]. Below we imply $b/\lambda \ll 1$.

Varying the energy ΔE with respect to $\zeta(x)$, we obtain the integro-differential equation $\delta\Delta E/\delta\zeta = 0$ for the profile of the interface

$$\frac{d}{dx}\left(\frac{\zeta'}{\sqrt{1+\zeta'^2(x)}}\right) - \frac{\zeta(x)}{\lambda^2} =$$

$$= -\frac{2b}{(x^2+h^2)^2}\left[\frac{x^2+h^2}{1 - \frac{1}{\pi}\int_{-\infty}^{\infty} \frac{\zeta(x)}{h^2+x^2} dx} - \frac{x^2-h^2}{1 - \frac{1}{\pi}\int_{-\infty}^{\infty} \zeta(x)\frac{x^2-h^2}{(h^2+x^2)^2} dx}\right].$$

Due to the parameter $b/\lambda \ll 1$, the deflection $\zeta(x)$ can be found in the analytical form. The most interesting case is that, when the vortex line approaches the interface. The bending deflection $\zeta(0)$ increases and becomes comparable $\zeta(0) \sim \lambda$ with the spacing between interface and vortex line at the distances $h \sim \sqrt{\pi b\lambda} = 0.65\mu m$. In this most interesting case, corresponding $h \ll \lambda$, the integro-differential can be reduced to the linear differential equation with the constant coefficients

$$\zeta''(x) - \frac{\zeta(x)}{\lambda^2} = -\frac{4bh^2}{(x^2+h^2)^2} - \frac{2b}{x^2+h^2}\frac{\zeta(0)/h}{1-\varsigma(0)/h}.$$

The solution can readily be represented by the integral

$$\zeta(x) = \frac{\lambda}{2}\int_{-\infty}^{\infty} dt \exp\left(-\frac{|x-t|}{\lambda}\right)\left\{\frac{4bh^2}{(t^2+h^2)^2} + \frac{2b}{t^2+h^2}\frac{\zeta(0)/h}{1-\zeta(0)/h}\right\}.$$

Then we can obtain the equation for self-consistent determination of $\zeta(0)$

$$\zeta(0) = \frac{\pi b\lambda}{h}\frac{1}{1-\zeta(0)/h}.$$

The solution of the equation yields two roots

$$\zeta(0) = h/2 \pm \sqrt{(h/2)^2 - \pi b\lambda}$$

Thus we have two positions of equilibrium. The positive sign corresponds to the maximum value of energy ΔE and, therefore, such deflection is absolutely unstable. The second root of the negative sign is associated with the minimum value of energy ΔE and such curved shape of the interface in the presence of a vortex line can exist.

One can easily see that there is no solution for $\zeta(0)$ provided the vortex line is located at the distance closer than the critical one $h_{cr} = 2\sqrt{\pi b\lambda} = 1.3\mu m$. From the physical point of view this means that no stable or metastable states can exist in the system of the interface and vortex line for distances of $h < h_{cr}$, i.e., vortex should disappear, merging with the interface. The bending deflection at the critical distance reaches $\zeta_{cr}(0) = \sqrt{\pi b\lambda} = 0.65\mu m$.

The qualitative features of the phenomenon can be traced with the aid of the probe function, e.g., $\zeta(x) = \zeta_0 e^{-|x|/l}$ where ζ_0 and l are the variational parameters satisfying $\zeta_0 \ll l$ and $h \ll l$. For ΔE, we have readily

$$\Delta E = \alpha\left\{\zeta_0^2/2a + 2\pi b\log(1-\frac{\zeta_0}{h}) + \zeta_0^2 l/2\lambda^2\right\}.$$

Minimizing ΔE with respect to l yields $l = \lambda$. Using the condition $\zeta_0 \ll h$ we get

$$\Delta E = \alpha\left\{\zeta_0^2/2\lambda + 2\pi b\log(1-\frac{\zeta_0}{h})\right\}.$$

Depending on h compared with h_{cr}, energy ΔE has neither extremum or two ones.

5. QUANTIZED VORTEX IN THE TANGENTIAL FLOW OF THE SUPEFLUID COMPONENT

Let the superfluid component of the d-phase flow along the interface and the velocity of the flow parallel to the x axes at the infinity be V_∞. The complex potential for the velocity field in the case of the flat interface of $y = 0$ reads

$$U = V_\infty z + \frac{\kappa}{2\pi i}\log\frac{z - z_0}{z - \bar{z}_0}.$$

If the equation of the interface surface is $y = \zeta(x)$ and function $w(z)$ performs the conformal mapping into the upper half-plane, the complex potential is given by

$$U = V_\infty w(z) + \frac{\kappa}{2\pi i}\log\frac{w(z)-w(z_0)}{w(z)-w(\bar{z}_0)}.$$

At the interface $y = \zeta(x)$ the vector-potential $A = ImU$ vanishes and $A \to V_\infty y$ corresponding to $\vec{V} \to (V_\infty, 0)$ at $|z| \to \infty$.

In the presence of the superfluid flow at the velocity V_∞ playing a role of external parameter the shape of the interface should be found from minimizing the functional [2]

$$\tilde{E} = E - \vec{P}\vec{V}_\infty$$

where $\vec{P}$ is the momentum of a fluid. We start first from the kinetic energy of the liquid, representing it as an integral over the surface of a fluid

$$E = (\rho_s/2)\oint \vec{A}(-\vec{n}\times\vec{v})dl$$

Here $\vec{n}$ is the outward normal. We are interested only in the contribution associated with the deformation of the interface. The contribution from the infinitely distant surface is independent of the interface and coincides with the case of the flat interface. The interface surface does not contribute and the only contribution from the vortex core surface can be represented as

$$E_v = (\rho_s/2)\,\vec{A}(z_0)\vec{\kappa}$$

Calculating $A(z)$ in the vicinity of z_0, we find the energy due to the presence of vortex line

$$E_v = \frac{\rho_s}{2}\kappa V_\infty\frac{w_0-\bar{w}_0}{2i} + \rho_s\kappa^2 4\pi\log\frac{w-w_0}{w_0'}\frac{1}{b} = E_v^{(1)} + E_v^{(2)}.$$

The second term in E_v is completely analogous to that considered in Sect.4. The first one $E_v^{(1)}$ describes the interaction between vortex line and superfluid flow. The calculation with the help of function $w(z)$ yields

$$E_v^{(1)} = E_{flat}^{(1)} + \Delta E_v^{(1)} = \frac{\rho_s}{2}\kappa V_\infty h - \frac{\rho_s h}{2\pi}\kappa V_\infty\int_{-\infty}^{\infty}\frac{\zeta(x)}{x^2+h^2}dx$$

The last term is due to bending the interface compared with the flat shape.

Let us turn now to the momentum of a fluid

$$\vec{P} = \rho_s\int\vec{V}dxdy = \rho_s\oint_L Ad\vec{l}$$

where L is the contour enclosing the fluid. Since the vector-potential A vanishes at the interface, the contribution into the integral comes from the infinitely distant semicircle. In what follows, we are interested only in the difference $\Delta\vec{P} = \vec{P} - \vec{P}_{flat}$

of the momentum for the curved and flat interfaces. From the symmetric speculation it is obvious that $\Delta P_y = 0$ and ΔP_x is given by

$$\Delta P_x = -\frac{\rho_s h}{2\pi}\kappa \int_{-\infty}^{\infty} \frac{\zeta(x)}{x^2+h^2}dx$$

We are now in the position to write the variation of energy $\Delta\tilde{E} = \Delta E_v - V_\infty \Delta P_x$ in order to find the profile of the interface in the presence of a vortex line at the distance h

$$\Delta\tilde{E}\left[\zeta(x)\right] = \alpha \int_{-\infty}^{\infty}\left(\sqrt{1+\zeta'^2(x)}-1\right)dx + \rho_s\frac{\kappa^2}{4\pi}\log\frac{1-\frac{1}{\pi}\int_{-\infty}^{\infty}\frac{\zeta(x)}{h^2+x^2}dx}{1-\frac{1}{\pi}\int_{-\infty}^{\infty}\zeta(x)\frac{x^2-h^2}{(h^2+x^2)^2}dx}$$

$$+\frac{1}{2}\Delta\rho g\int_{-\infty}^{\infty}\zeta^2(x)dx - \frac{\rho_s\kappa}{\pi}V_\infty\int_{-\infty}^{\infty}\frac{\zeta(x)}{x^2+h^2}dx.$$

The last term, originating from the interaction between vortex line and superfluid flow, depends on the direction of circulation with respect to superfluid flow. For the opposite $\kappa < 0$ circulation, the effect of superfluid flow on the flexure of the interfaces smaller. Below we concentrate on the case of the clockwise $\kappa > 0$ circulation providing a stronger effect.

Here it is convenient to introduce the natural scale of velocity equal to $V_\kappa = 4\pi\alpha/(\rho_s\kappa) = \kappa/(2\pi b)$, $V_\kappa = 23m/s$ being the superfluid velocity at the vortex core surface for the hollow core model of a quantum vortex. As usual, variation of $\delta\tilde{E}/\delta\zeta = 0$ yields the interface profile

$$\frac{d}{dx}\left(\frac{\zeta'}{\sqrt{1+\zeta'^2(x)}}\right) - \frac{1}{\lambda^2}\zeta(x) = -\frac{4V_\infty}{V_\kappa}\frac{h}{x^2+h^2} -$$

$$-\frac{2b}{(x^2+h^2)^2}\left[\frac{x^2+h^2}{1-\frac{1}{\pi}\int_{-\infty}^{\infty}\frac{\zeta(x)}{x^2+h^2}dx} - \frac{x^2-h^2}{1-\frac{1}{\pi}\int_{-\infty}^{\infty}\zeta(x)\frac{x^2-h^2}{(x^2+h^2)^2}dx}\right]$$

Let us consider the values of the bending deflection close to the distance h which satisfies $h \ll \lambda$. From the speculations completely analogous to the previous section, we have for the profile

$$\zeta(x) = \frac{\lambda}{2}\int_{-\infty}^{\infty}dt\exp(-\frac{|x-t|}{\lambda})\left\{\frac{4bh^2}{(t^2+h^2)^2} + \frac{2b}{(t^2+h^2)^2}\frac{\zeta(0)/h}{1-\zeta(0)/h} + \frac{2V_\infty}{V_\kappa}\frac{h}{t^2+h^2}\right\}.$$

The self-consistent equation for $\zeta(0)$ reads

$$\zeta(0) = \frac{\pi b\lambda}{h}\frac{1}{1-\zeta(0)/h} + 2\pi\lambda\frac{V_\infty}{V_\kappa}$$

yielding the roots

$$\zeta(0) = \frac{1}{2}\left(h + 2\pi\lambda V_\infty/V_\kappa\right) \pm \sqrt{\left(h - 2\pi\lambda V_\infty/V_\kappa\right)^2/4 - \pi\lambda b}$$

The negative sign corresponds to the minimum of energy and stable bending of the interface. As it seen from equation, no stable configuration of the interface shape can exist if $h < h_{cr}$. The critical distance h_{cr} is determined from

$$(h_{cr} - 2\pi\lambda V_{\infty}/V_{\kappa})^2 = 4\pi\lambda b$$

and $h_{cr} = 2\pi\lambda V_{\infty}/V_{\kappa} + 2\sqrt{\pi\lambda b}$. The solution with the negative sign in front of the square root does not satisfy condition $\zeta(0) < h$. The corresponding deflection at $h = h_{cr}$ reaches $\zeta(0) = 2\pi\lambda V_{\infty}/V_{\kappa} + \pi\lambda b$.

On the other hand, if the velocity of superflow increases and $h > h_{cr}(0) = 2\sqrt{\pi\lambda b}$, the bending deflection enhances too and such profile becomes absolutely unstable at the critical velocity $V_{cr}(h)$ equal to

$$V_{cr}/V_{\kappa} = \sqrt{b/(\pi\lambda)}\,(h/h_{cr}(0) - 1)$$

The magnitude of the bending deflection at $V = V_{cr}(h)$ reaches $\varsigma(0) = h - h_{cr}/2$. Thus, for sufficiently large velocities, the deflection can be large and comparable with h.

6. ON THE EXPERIMENT

Recently, the successful experiments on KHI in superfluid ^{3}He at the interface of A and B phases have been fulfilled [7,8]. It is known that the core diameter of a typical vortex is 10^3 larger in the A phase than in the B phase. Correspondingly, the vortex energy in the A phase is lower and vortices do not easily penetrate from the A to B phase. To obtain a two-phase sample of superfluid ^{3}He, the A-B interface is stabilized in a gradient of magnetic field. Vortices are created by rotating the sample at angular velocity Ω around the axis z perpendicular to the interface. In the A-phase section the vortices are formed at low critical velocity v_{cA}. The vortices have a large "soft vortex core" region for which the length scale $\xi_d \sim 10\mu m$. The vortex line is doubly quantized in units of the circulation $\kappa = \hbar/2m_3$ (m_3 is ^{3}He atom mass). The B phase vortices, in turn, are singly quantized and have a narrow "hard vortex core" with a radius comparable to the superfluid coherent length $\xi \sim 10nm$. Their smaller core radius causes the B-phase critical velocity to be at least one order of magnitude larger. Thus, the B-phase remains in a metastable vortex-free state, where its superfluid fraction is stationary in the laboratory frame. In the experiment, as the rotation velocity Ω, increases, the events are recorded when the A-B phase boundary becomes unstable, i.e., when some circulation from the A phase crosses the A-B interface and vortex lines are introduced into the initially vortex-free B phase.

The KHI of the superfluid liquid free surface was considered in [9] in relation with experiments [10]. The simpliest situation, when an equilibrium difference in velocities can be maintained at the surface of a liquid, is the relative motion of the superfluid and normal components in superfluid ^{4}He. The counterflow can be induced by a heat flow $\vec{q}$ parallel the surface of ^{4}He, which is connected with the flow of entropy of the normal component

$$\vec{q} = ST\vec{v}_n$$

As the whole current $\vec{j} = \rho_n \vec{v}_n + \rho_s \vec{v}_s = 0$, we have for the flow of the superfluid component $v_s \sim \rho_n \vec{q}/(ST\rho_s$. So, for Bernulli pressure we arrive at $\Delta P = \rho_n \vec{v}_n^2/2 + \rho_s \vec{v}_s^2/2$, yielding the threshold [9]

$$w_{c0}^2 = 2((\rho_n + \rho_s)^3 \alpha g)^{1/2}/\rho_n \rho_s.$$

The instability threshold is found to be independent of the value of viscosity, but turns out lower than in absence of dissipation. The result is analogous to obtained for the interface between two sliding superfluids [11] with different mechanism of dissipation and confirmed by the experimental observation of KHI at the interface between A and B phases of ^{3}He [7,8]. The cylindrical faceting of ^{4}He-crystals induced by a flow of superfluid component [12] is another impressive example of KHI.

CONCLUSIONS AND ACKNOWLEDGMENTS

The ^{3}He-^{4}He separated system is promising for the HKI investigation. The reason is that the typical velocity of the flow of superfluid component is rather small and is of the order of 6 cm/s. The typical distance is of the order of $\sim 1mm$. Whereas at the surface of the pure ^{4}He the typical velocity enhances by factor of 3 and the typical distance reduces by the same factor. The difference in the behavior of these systems is due to small surface tension at ^{3}He-^{4}He interface and small value of $\rho_d - \rho_c$.

We are thankful to RFBR, Grants 04-02-17363, 02-02-16772, and Grant for the Promotion of Universities of Russia.

REFERENCES

[1] S. Chanrasekhar *Hydrodynamic and hydromagnetic stability* (Oxford, Clarendon Press, 1961)

[2] R. J. Donelly, *Quantized Vortices in He II* (Cambridge Univ. Press, 1991).

[3] E. B. Sonin, A. J. Manninen, *Phys. Rev. Lett.* 70, 2585 (1993); L. Senbetu, *J. Low Temp. Phys.* 32, 3/4, 571 (1978).

[4] S. N. Burmistrov and T. Satoh, *Physica* B284-288, 329 (2000)

[5] A. Sato, K. Ohishi and M. Suzuki, *J.Low Temp.Phys.* 107, 165 (1997)

[6] M. L. Lavrenťev and B. V. Shabat, *Methods of the theory on the complex function variables* (Fiz-Mat, Moscow) (1958), p. 359 (in Russian).

[7] R. Blaauwgeers et al, *Phys. Rev. Lett.* 89, 155301 (2002).

[8] R. Haenninen et al, *Phys. Rev. Lett.* 90, 225301 (2003).

[9] S. E. Korshunov, *Europhys. Lett.* 16, 673 (1991); *cond-mat/0203374* v2 21 Mar (2002).

[10] P. W. Egolf et al *Physica* 169, 673 (1991).

[11] G. E. Volovik *cond-mat/02022445* v4 4 Apr (2002).

[12] A. F. Andreev *JETP* 106, 1219 (1994).

MEAN-FIELDS, SCATTERING LENGTHS AND OBSERVED RESONANCES IN BOSE-EINSTEIN CONDENSATES

F. Bary Malik

Physics Department, Southern Illinois University
Carbondale, Illinois 62901, USA

1. INTRODUCTION

In 1998, Courteille et.al. [1] observed sharp resonances in the collision of ^{85}Rb atoms in the presence of a tunable magnetic field at Bose-Einstein Condensate (BEC) at nK temperature. This observation was immediately confirmed by other groups [2,3]. The sharpness of these observed resonances is reminiscence of sharp resonances seen in the scattering of thermal neutrons by nuclei in 1930s, widely known as Breit-Wigner resonances [4]. The starting point in many theoretical investigations of physical properties of BEC, has been the Gross-Pitaevskii equation (GPE) [5,6] which is basically a mean-field Hartree equation [7,8,9] where two-particle potential is related to a repulsive Dirac δ-function, the strength of which is then replaced by a positive energy-independent scattering length, a, the magnitude of which is determined from low energy scattering data. In this investigation, we show that the observed resonances in the scattering dictates that (a) the mean-field cannot be entirely repulsive, (b) the use of a single energy-independent scattering length is not sufficient as the sole characteristic parameter to describe BEC, as already noted by Geltman and Bambini [10]. However, a momentum or energy dependent scattering length is a good measure to describe the resonant behavior, (c) an alternative to (b) is to use a proper potential that reflects the appropriate analytic properties of scattering length, a, either in energy or in momentum plane commensurate with the data and (d) the nature of mean-field within the context of a reaction theory that attributes these resonances to residual interaction or pair correlation, cannot be purely repulsive.

2. THE MEAN-FIELD CASE

The self-consistent Hartree equation for the wave function, $\psi(\vec{r})$, of a condensate is given by [7-9]

$$\left[T(\vec{r}) - E + \int d^3r'\psi(\vec{r}')v(\vec{r}-\vec{r}')\psi(\vec{r}')\right] = 0 \tag{1}$$

In (1), $T(\vec{r})$ is composed of the kinetic energy operator, $(\hbar^2/2\mu)\nabla^2$ and the one body trap potential, taken to be that of harmonic oscillator, $(1/2)Kr^2$. E is the energy of the incident boson.

Setting

$$V(\vec{r}) = \int d^3r'v(\vec{r}-\vec{r}')|\psi(\vec{r}')|^2 \tag{2}$$

and assuming it to be spherically symmetric, one can obtain the following equation for r times the radical wave function, $U_{nl}(r)$:

$$[d^2/dr^2 - q^2(r) - l(l+1)/r^2]U_{nl}(r) = 0 \tag{3}$$

where, in the absence of any external trap potential

$$q^2(r) = (2\mu/\hbar^2)V(r) - k^2 \tag{4a}$$

with $\hbar^2k^2/(2\mu) = E$ and in the presence of a harmonic trap

$$q^2(r) = (2\mu/\hbar^2)[V(r) + (K/2)r^2] - k^2 \tag{4b}$$

As noted by Malik and Sabatier [11], the integral form of (3) is the following Volterra equation that is regular at the origin:

$$U_{nl}(r) = r^{l+1} + \frac{1}{(2l+1)r}\int_0^r [(r/x)^{l+1/2} - (x/r)^{l+1/2}](rx)^{1/2}q^2(x)U_{nl}(x)dx \tag{5}$$

The derivative of (5) is given by

$$\begin{aligned}\frac{dU_{nl}(r)}{dr} =&(l+1)r^l \\ &+\frac{1}{(2l+1)r}\int_0^r [(l+1)r/x)^{l+1/2} + l(x/r)^{l+1/2}](rx)^{1/2}q^2(x)U_{nl}(x)dx\end{aligned} \tag{6}$$

$U_{nl}(r)$ and $dU_{nl}(r)/dr$ are known upto a multiplicative constant which is set here to be 1. Since the collision is at a very low energy, the prevalent angular-orbital is likely to be s-wave. In that case (5) and (6) reduce to the following simple forms:

$$U_{no}(r) = r + \int_0^r (r-x)q^2(x)U_{no}(x)dx \tag{7}$$

and

$$dU_{no}(r)/dr = 1 + \int_0^r U_{no}(r) q^2(x) dx \tag{8}$$

The characteristic features of a wave function near a resonance are that (a) it exhibits a sharp maximum at the resonant energy and (b) the signature of its derivative must change near this maximum. In case, $v(\vec{r}-\vec{r}')$ in (2) is purely repulsive, $V(r)$ is purely repulsive. In that case, $q^2(x)$ defined in (4a) and (4b) is positive everywhere in (5), (6), (7), and (8) since k^2 is nearly zero. Hence, the wave function in (5) and (7) cannot have a maximum and its derivatives (6) and (8) cannot change sign. For a purely repulsive mean-field, one cannot, therefore, have a resonance. This is, also, true for $v(\vec{r}-\vec{r}') = V_o\delta(\vec{r}-\vec{r}')$ where V_o is repulsive characterized by a positive scattering length. This is, already, concluded in [12]. In short, the Gross-Pitaevskii equation is not suitable to describe the resonant behavior.

3. SCATTERING LENGTH AND RESONANCE

This topic has been dealt with extensively in the literature on nuclear physics (see *e.g.* [13]). The total cross-section, σ, for elastic scattering is related to phase shifts λ_l, for a partial wave e by

$$\sigma = (4\pi/k^2) \sum (2l+1) \sin^2 \lambda_l$$

In the following, we consider only s-wave but the treatment can be extended to any partial wave. The relation between phase-shift $\lambda(k)$ (dropping the subscript o) for s-wave is related to scattering length, a, as follows:

$$-\frac{1}{a} = \lim_{k\to o} k \cot \lambda \tag{9}$$

To describe a resonance, one may define a momentum dependent scattering length $a(k)$ as follows:

$$k \cot \lambda(k) = -\frac{1}{a(k)} \tag{10}$$

The s-wave cross-section in that case is given by

$$\sigma = (4\pi/k^2)\sin^2\lambda = 4\pi/\left|ik + 1/a(k)\right|^2 \tag{11}$$

$a(k)$, being a function of k, is also a function of E. Let $\frac{1}{a(E)}$ is zero, at $E = E_R$. Expanding this around E_R and keeping only the first derivative, we get

$$\frac{1}{a(E)} = 0 + (E - E_R) \left.\frac{d}{dE}\left(\frac{1}{a(E)}\right)\right|_{E=E_R} \tag{12}$$

Setting

$$\frac{2k}{\Gamma} = \left.\frac{d}{dE}\left(\frac{1}{a(E)}\right)\right|_{E=E_R}, \tag{13}$$

one gets

$$\sigma = (\pi/k)^2 \frac{\Gamma^2}{(E - E_R)^2 + \Gamma^2/4} \tag{14}$$

(14) exhibits a resonance at $E = E_R$, with a width Γ. (14) is termed in nuclear physics usually as Breit-Wigner resonance [13]. Thus, the necessary criteria for scattering length to generate a resonance are (a) it is infinite at the resonant energy and (b) it admits an analytic expansion (13). For a constant scattering length, as is the case in the Gross-Pitaevskii equation, or in using scattering length for a hard sphere, one cannot do the expansion (13) and have a resonance. A single value of, a, is insufficient to describe resonance. Its analytic form must be specified. As noted in Bethes effective range theory, in the presence of potentials dropping asympototically to zero faster than a power series potential, the analytic behavior of $-1/a(k)$ is simply given by

$$k \cot \lambda(k) = -1/a(o) + (r_o/2)k^2 \tag{15}$$

where r_o is a constant, known as scattering length. Its actual value depends on the choice of the potential. Analytic behavior of phase-shift plays a key role in determining the location and width of a resonance. A proper choice of a potential can determine the appropriate analyticity. In the next section, we present an example of the resonance in the presence of a potential.

4. RESONANCE IN A NON-MONOTONIC POTENTIAL

The analysis done in section 2, indicates that a purely repulsive potential is incapable of generating any resonances. We, therefore, consider here a potential having an infinite repulsion followed by an attractive square well which is a poor mans way to concoct the actual, molecular potential and has been successful in describing many general properties of bosonic and fermionic systems near zero temperature. Thus, the potential $V(r)$ in (2) or (4) is chosen to be

$$V(r) = \begin{cases} +\infty & \text{for } r < c \\ -V & \text{for } c < r < R \\ o & \text{for } r > R \end{cases} \tag{16}$$

As noted in [14], the analytic property of the scattering length $a(k)$ for this potential is determined by its range and the depth as follows

$$a(k) = -\tan \lambda(k)/k = \frac{(1/k)\tan(kR) - (1/\alpha)\tan[\alpha(R-c)]}{1 + (k/\alpha)\tan(kR)\tan[\alpha(R-c)]} \tag{17}$$

where

$$\alpha^2 = (2\mu/\hbar^2)[V + E] \tag{18}$$

In the limit $k \to o$, $a(k) \to a(o)$ which is given by

$$a(o) = c\left[1 + \frac{R-c}{c}\left\{1 - \frac{\tan\beta}{\beta}\right\}\right] \tag{19}$$

where

$$\beta = \sqrt{2\mu V}(R - c)/\hbar \tag{20}$$

In the limit of $R = c$, $a(o) = c$ and also in limit of $V(o) \to o$, $a(o) = c$. Both of these limits describe the hard sphere case. Since c is finite, $1/a(o)$ cannot be zero. Thus, the system cannot exhibit resonances. However, in case $V > o$, $1/a(o)$ has poles whenever $\beta = (n + \frac{1}{2})\pi$ (with $n = 0, 1, 2, \ldots$). Thus, one can generate resonances near these poles. One can also show that for this potential,

$$\frac{1}{a(k)} = -\frac{1}{a(o)} + \frac{r_o}{2}k^2 + O(k^4) \tag{21}$$

Thus, the cross section exhibits resonance like behavior at very low energies for $\beta = (n + 1/2)\pi$. This means that a potential with a depth and a range can generate the appropriate analyticity of $a(k)$ necessary for generating resonances.

5. MEAN-FIELD AND RESONANCES IN COMPOSITE SYSTEMS

The above sections have primarily dealt with scattering by a purely mean-field or a potential. The scattering of a boson by a system of bosons involves the collision between composite systems and is similar to the collision between two nuclei, except that the Pauli principle may not be invoked. We consider this case within the context of the reaction theory of Mustafa and Malik [15] and Haider and Malik [16] which is based on the Feshbach theory, [17]. [15] and [16] also have their roots in the early theory of Trefftz [18] dealing with electron recombination process in atomic ions. The Hamiltonian of a system of $(n + 1)$ bosons, $H(1, 2 \ldots i - 1, i, i + 1 \ldots n + 1)$ can be written in terms of the Hamiltonian where the i-th boson is omitted, $H_o(\bar{i})$ as follows

$$H(1, 2 \ldots i - 1, i, i + 1 \ldots n + 1) = H_o(\bar{i}) + t(i) + \frac{1}{2}\sum_{i \neq j = 1}^{n} v(ij) \tag{22}$$

The total wave function $\Psi(1, 2 \ldots i - 1, i, i + 1 \ldots n + 1)$ may be expanded in terms of the eigenfunctions of $H_o(\bar{i})$, which form an orthonormal set, and the wave function of the scattered boson, ϕ_α

$$\Psi(1, 2 \ldots i - 1, i, i + 1 \ldots n + 1) = \sum_{\alpha\beta} \phi_\alpha(i)\Phi_\beta(1, 2 \ldots i - 1, i + 1 \ldots n + 1) \tag{23}$$

with

$$H_o\Phi_\beta = E_\beta\Phi_\beta \tag{24}$$

and

$$H\Psi = E\Psi \tag{25}$$

Taking scalar product of (25) with respect to Φ_β, one get the following set of coupled equations

$$[t(i) - (E - E_\alpha) + V_{\alpha\alpha}(i)]\phi_\alpha(i) = \sum_{\beta \neq \alpha} V_{\beta\alpha}(i)\phi_\beta(i) \tag{26}$$

where

$$V_{\beta\alpha}(i) = \left(\Phi_\beta, \sum_{i\neq j} v(ij)\Phi_\alpha\right) \tag{27}$$

$t(i)$ in (26) represents kinetic energy operator and any other external potential due to a trap. The integration in (27) is over all coordinates but the i-th one [A similar equation can also be obtained for a fully symmetrized expansion instead of (23)]. In the case (27) is spherically symmetric, r times the radical wave function, $X_\alpha(i)$ satisfies the following set of coupled integro-differential equation

$$\begin{aligned}(h(i) + k_\alpha^2)X_\alpha(i) &= \left[\frac{d^2}{dr_i^2} + V(i) + k_\alpha^2 - U_{\alpha\alpha}(i) - \frac{l(l+1)}{r_i^2}\right] X_\alpha(i) \\ &= \sum_{\beta\neq\alpha} U_{\beta\alpha}(i)X_\beta(i)\end{aligned} \tag{28}$$

where $k_\alpha^2 = (2\mu/\hbar^2)(E - E_\alpha)$ and $U_{\beta\alpha}(i) = (2\mu/\hbar^2)V_{\beta\alpha}(i)$

The S-matrix for the incident α-channel to the same or any other channel β is given by

$$S_{\beta\alpha} = \delta_{\beta\alpha} - (2i/k_\alpha)\int drU_\alpha(r)\sum_\beta U_{\beta\alpha}(r)X_\beta(r) \tag{29}$$

In (29) $U_\alpha(r)$ is the solution of

$$\left(d^2/dr_i^2 + V(i) + k_\alpha^2\right) U_\alpha(r) = 0 \tag{30}$$

The summation in (29) runs over all channels including, the $\alpha = \beta$ one, which is the elastic channel. To investigate the condition leading to resonances, we expand $X_\beta(r)$ in terms of the basis states defined by the homogenous part of (28) for any β-channel

$$X_\beta(r) = \sum_n \alpha_{n\beta}X_{n\beta}(r) + \int dk\, \alpha_{k\beta}X_{k\beta}(r) \tag{31}$$

In (31), the summation and integrations are over discreet and continuum states, respectively, which satisfy the following equations

$$[h(i) - k_{n\beta}^2]X_{n\beta}(r) = 0 \tag{32a}$$

and

$$[h(i) + k_{k\beta}^2]X_{k\beta}(r) = 0 \tag{32b}$$

The negative sign in (32a) and positive sign in (32b) reflect the bound and continuum character of respective wave function. Equations (31), (32a) and (32b) lead to the following equations determining the coefficients

$$\left(k_{n\beta}^2 - k_\beta^2\right)\alpha_{n\beta} = \sum_{\gamma\neq\beta}\int drX_{n\beta}(r)U_{\beta\gamma}(r)X_\gamma(r) \tag{33a}$$

and

$$- \left(k_{k\beta}^2 + k_\beta^2\right) \alpha_{k\beta} = \sum_{\gamma \neq \beta} \int dr X_{k\beta}(r) U_{\beta\gamma}(r) X_\gamma(r) \tag{33b}$$

Clearly, the only amplitudes given by (32a) could exhibit resonant behavior of the wave function $X_\beta(r)$ and generate resonances in S-matrix in (29). Resonances occur whenever $k_\beta^2 = k_{n\beta}^2$. In case $\alpha = \beta$, the resonances occur whenever the energy of the α-channel is equal to the bound states of (32a). As indicated already, $\alpha = \beta$ represents the elastic case. As noted in section 2, for a purely repulsive mean potential in any channel including the α-channel, there is no bound state and hence, (32a) does not exist. Resonances in α-channel could also be generated by coupling it to β-channel wave function that exhibits resonant behavior, as done in [19]. For that to occur, $U_{\beta\beta}$ in (32a) must be capable of generating at least one bound state. A purely repulsive $U_{\beta\beta}$ cannot do that. It is easy to show that the consideration of a single bound and no continuum state in the expansion (31) leads to the following expression for the S-matrix

$$S_{\alpha\beta} = \frac{-i\Gamma_{\beta\alpha}}{(E - E_R) + i\Gamma_{\beta\beta}/2} \tag{34}$$

where widths $\Gamma_{\beta\alpha}$ and $\Gamma_{\beta\beta}$ and resonance energy E_R related to matrix elements noted on the right hand sides of (32a) and (32b) and are explicitly noted in [15,16]. Clearly, $|S_{\alpha\beta}|^2$ exhibits the resonant behavior, of the Breit-Wigner type. In this particularly case, a resonance occurs when a bound state in β-channel is embedded in the continuum of α-channel.

6. CONCLUSION

This investigation conclusively establishes that a purely repulsive mean-field within the context of a single or multiple channels cannot generate resonant structure. A necessary condition for the resonance in a single or multiple channel theory to occur is the existence of at least one bound state in the mean-field. Moreover, a single energy independent scattering length is insufficient to generate resonances, for which one needs the information on its analytic properties in energy plane. The latter can be generated by a proper choice of a potential.

ACKNOWLEDGEMENT

It is a pleasure to thank Professor Henry Glyde and Mr. Sakhel for many discussions on the subject, Dr. M.Dinh for editing the manuscript and Ms. Laniya Moore for the preparation of this manuscript. I acknowledge with thanks a travel grant from the U.S. Army Research Office.

REFERENCES

[1] Ph. Courteille, R.S. Freeland, D. Heinzen, F.A. Van Abulen and B.J. Verhaar, Phys. Rev Lett. **81**, 69 (1998).

[2] J.L. Roberts, N.R. Claussen, J.P. Burke, Jr., C.H. Green, E.A. Cornell and C.E. Wieman, Phys. Rev. Lett. **81**, 5109 (1998).

[3] J. Strenger, S. Inouye, M.R. Andrew, H.J. Miesner, D.M. Stàmper-Kurn and W. Ketterle, Phys. Rev. Lett. **82**, 2422 (1999).

[4] G. Breit and E.P. Wigner, Phys. Rev. **48**, 519, 642 (1936).

[5] E.P. Gross, Nuovo Cimento **20**, 454 (1961).

[6] L.P. Pitaevskii, Sov. Phys. JETP **40**, 451 (1961).

[7] E.P. Gross, Ann. Phys. (N.Y.) **4**, 57 (1958).

[8] E.P. Gross, J. Math. Phys. **4**, 195 (1963).

[9] A.L. Fetter and J.D. Walecka, Quantum Theory of Many Particle Systems (McGraw Hill Book Co. 1971).

[10] S. Geltman and A. Bambini, Phys. Rev. Lett. **86**, 3276 (2001).

[11] F.B. Malik and P. Sabatier, Helv. Phys. Acta **46**, 303 (1973).

[12] J. da Providencia, A. Sakhel, F.B. Malik and H.R. Glyde, Phys. Rev. C (submitted).

[13] J.M. Blatt and V.F. Weisskopf, Theoretical Nuclear Physics (John Wiley, New York, 1952).

[14] R.M. Carter, M. Casas, J.M. Getino, M. de Llano, A. Puente, H. Rubio and D.M. van der Walt, Phys. Rev. B **52**, 16149 (1995).

[15] M.G. Mustafa and F.B. Malik, Ann. Phys. (N.Y.), **83**, 340 (1974).

[16] Q. Haider and F.B. Malik, Phys. Rev. C **28**, 2328 (1983).

[17] H. Feshbach, Ann. Phys. (N.Y.) **5**, 357 (1958); *ibid.* **19**, 287 (1962).

[18] E. Trefftz, Z. Astrophysik, **65**, 299 (1967).

[19] F.H. Mies, E. Tissinga and P.S. Julienne, Phys. Rev. A, **61**, 022721 (2000).

TRACTABLE CROSSING SYMMETRIC EQUATIONS, NON-LOCAL INTERACTIONS AND PAIRING IN 3D FERMI SYSTEMS

Khandker F. Quader
Department of Physics, Kent State University
Kent, Ohio 44242, USA

and

T. L. Ainsworth
Naval research Laboratory
Washington, D. C., U.S.A.

1. INTRODUCTION

In quantum many-electron systems, novel electronic behavior is generally achieved by fine-tuning of density, composition or competing electronic interactions. Situation favorable to an instability of the existing quantum state can be created as a consequence. At the brink of quantum instabilities, competing low-energy excitations of varied nature can give rise to fundamentally new types of electronic correlations, and eventually endow materials with novel phases. Superconductivity and exotic magnetic states are examples of such phases. In recent years exotic magnetic and unconventional superconducting phases have been discovered in weak ferromagnets (FM) (e.g. UGe_2 [1], $ZrZn_2$ [2], $URhGe$ [3], heavy fermion compounds (e.g. UPt_3, $CePd_2Si_2$ [4]), and high temperature superconductors (e.g. $YBaCuO$, $LaSrCuO$). The nature of these phases are not well understood.

While we are interested quite generally in the study of novel phases and quantum fluctuations, in this paper, we study the general nature of fermion pairing in strongly interacting 3D systems with underlying *finite-range local*, as well as. *non-local* interactions. For this we utilize a microscopic theory that allows for the consideration of the full momentum dependence of the renormalized many-body interactions: the diagrammatic *crossing symmetric technique* [5]. Since it proves to be extremely difficult to calculate excited state properties of a Fermi system using the full scheme, we use a *tractable* version [6,7,8,9,10], and the ideas of a generalized Fermi Liquid Theory (defined for finite momentum). This allows us to obtain renormalized quasiparticle interaction functions, $F_l(q)$ and *pairing amplitudes* with various angular momentum content (s, p, d, etc).

Among the key finding in the paramagnetic state, is the remarkable role of the non-local interaction in switching from p-wave pairing (for small, *local*, finite-range interaction) to s-wave pairing for repulsive non-local interaction; and to a narrow region of d-wave pairing for an attractive one. The s-wave pairing, accompanied by large effective mass enhancements, is driven by transverse current fluctuations competing with ferromagnetic spin fluctuations; the d-wave pairing by "antiferromagnetic-like" spin fluctuations.

2. CROSSING SYMMETRIC EQUATIONS

At the core of our tractable scheme is the "parquet" method [5] that sums a large class of important Feynman diagrams, namely, the 2-body planar diagrams. The parquet equations for the fully reducible 2-body vertex, Γ, in the particle-particle (S), particle-hole (T), and the exchange particle-hole (U) are shown schematically in Fig. 1. On considering the s (particle-particle), t (particle-hole), and u (exchange particle-hole) channels in a conserving, self-consistent fashion, and using crossing symmetry, one is led to the crossing symmetric non-linear coupled integral equation(s) for the fully reducible 4-point vertex function Γ (Fig. 1).Here I denotes a set of completely irreducible diagrams, and G_i the fermion Green's function in the respective S, T, U channels.

The diagram forms for the parquet equations for the 2-body vertex in the 3 channels are shown schematically in Fig. 2. Each of the "boxes" represent a large set of Feynman diagrams, and the lines with arrows the relevant fermion particle and hole Green's functions.

3. TRACTABLE CROSSING-SYMMETRIC EQUATIONS

It has proved difficult to solve the full "parquet" equations and/or the resulting crossing-symmetric equation for the full vertex self-consistently to obtain excited state properties. However, a judicious exploitation of the p-h processes near the fermi surface, partial resummation of certain diagrams, quasiparticle renormalization, and the imposition of crossing symmetry leads to a *tractable* version of the coupled non-linear integral equations [6,7,8,9,10]. The renormalized quasiparticle interactions in the Fermi liquid retain the full crossing symmetry of the underlying Hamiltonian while reproducing the low energy physics of a Fermi liquid. The approach insures that the Ward identities for charge, spin, current, etc. are satisfied. Thus, this reformulation in terms of Landau interaction functions, scattering amplitudes, and a fully 1p-1h irreducible part, is exact on the Fermi surface.

We extrapolate away from the the Fermi surface by summing the p-h diagrams to all orders in both the t and u channels with renormalized, fully *momentum-dependent* interaction functions [7]. This necessarily requires non-diagonal phase space func-

4-POINT VERTEX: CROSSING SYMMETRIC EQUATIONS

Parquet Equations for 2-body Vertex Function, Γ

$$1.\ S = (I + T + U) G_s G_s \Gamma$$

$$2.\ T = (I + S + U) G_t G_t \Gamma$$

$$3.\ U = (I + S + T) G_u G_u \Gamma$$

$$4.\ \Gamma = I + S + T + U$$

Crossing-symmetric Non-linear Integral Equation:

$$\Gamma = I + \sum_{i=s,t,u} \frac{\Gamma}{1 + G_i G_i \Gamma} G_i G_i \Gamma$$

Figure 1. Crossing-symmetric non-linear integral equation from parquet equations for the 4-point vertex function in the s, t, u channels. I represents a set of completely irreducible diagrams.

tions, $\chi(q), \chi(q')$, in addition to diagonal Lindhard-type functions. The formulation is particularly well-suited for calculations of different quantum fluctuations because the renormalized interaction can be separated into a part that is fully 1p-1h irreducible, termed the "direct" interaction, $D(q)$, and a part that includes 1p-1h reducible processes, termed the "induced" interaction, $F_{\text{ind}}(q)$. The resulting equations for the interaction functions, $F(q)$, scattering amplitudes, $A(q)$, and the "direct", and their diagrammatic contents are shown in Fig. 3.

In physical terms, the "induced" part represent exchange of competing quantum fluctuations, such as density, spin-density, current, spin-current, and higher order fluctuations. The "direct" part contains p-p diagrams to all order (e.g. t-matrix) as well as processes that reflect possible non-locality of the underlying Hamiltonian. We have contributed substantively to a comprehensive understanding of the technique, and extended it to include the full momentum and spin polarization dependence of the interaction functions [7.11].

Within this formulation of the theory, given a "direct" interaction $D(q)$, one can

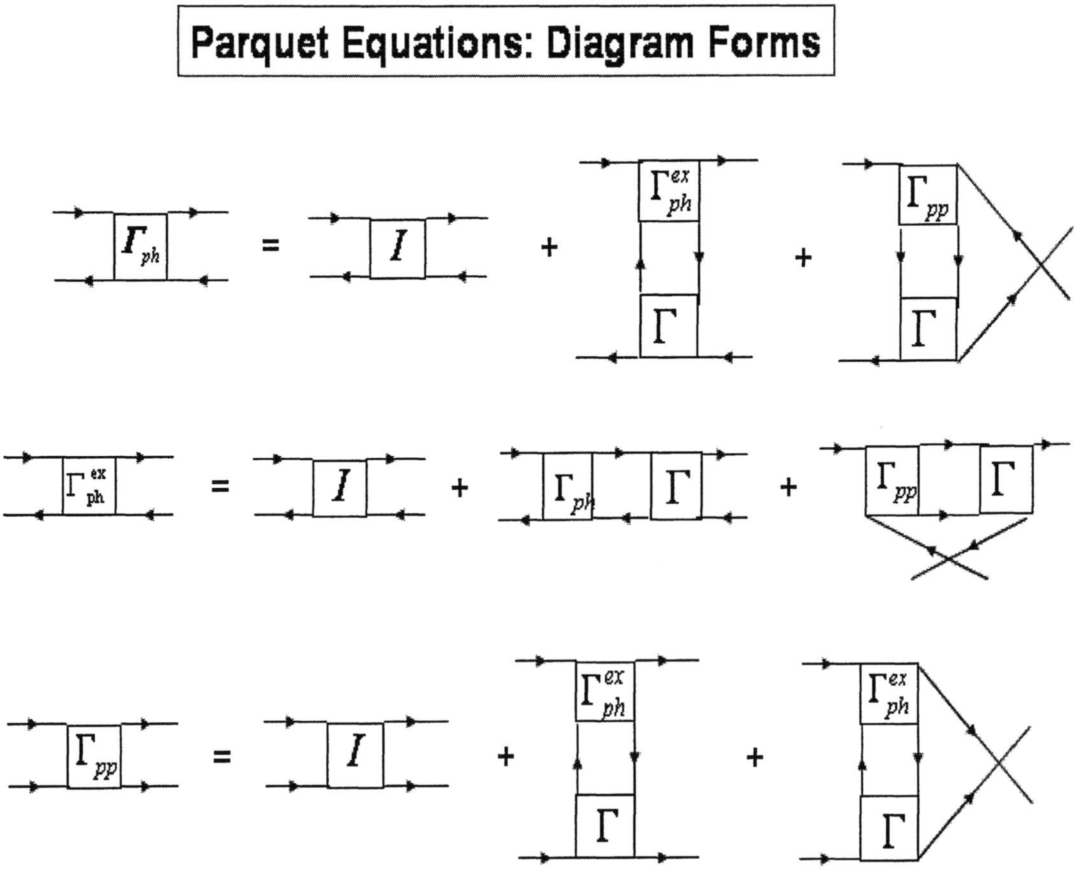

Figure 2. Schematic Diagrammatic Representations of the Parquet Equations in the 3 channels in Fig. 1 .

obtain the renormalized interactions, $F(q)$, the scattering amplitudes $A(q)$ and the effective mass m^*/m. Thus the chief approximation is in the choice of $D(q)$. It is important, however, to ensure that $D(q)$ is properly antisymmetrized so as to preserve crossing symmetry. For a properly constructed "direct" term projected in orthogonal channels (e.g. angular momentum, ℓ, and spin-symmetric(s)/antisymmetric(a) channels), one obtains a set of coupled non-linear integral equations for $F_l^{s,a}(q)$'s and $A_l^{s,a}(q)$'s in different angular momentum channels that have to be solved self-consistently. The dimensionality of the problem to be solved depends on the number of moments retained for $F(q)$ and $A(q)$.

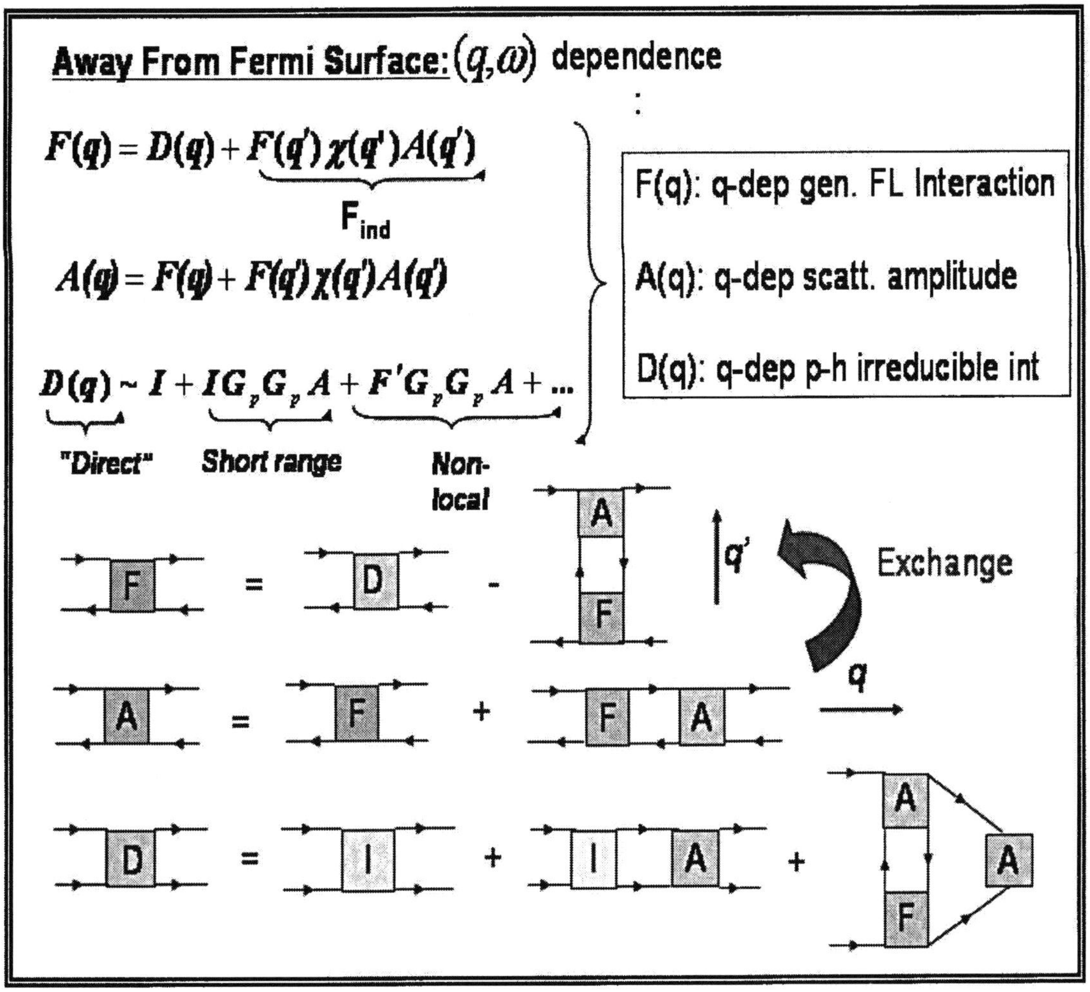

Figure 3. Tractable crossing symmetric equations for $F(q)$, $A(q)$, and $D(q)$, and their diagram forms away from the Fermi surface.q and q' are the momentum transfers in the p-h and exchange p-h channels respectively.

4. MODEL CALCULATIONS

In our present calculation, for the "direct" term, $D(q)$, we use the following two approximations: (i) t-matrix (s-channel ladder diagrams); (ii) Fourier transform of an effective quasiparticle interaction. Since we allow for the intermediate states to be *off* the Fermi surface, the scattering processes are necessarily a function of two indepenedent variables, viz., (q, q'), or two angular variables that depend on the interaction channel, s, t, u. This requires a *double Legendre expansion* of $D(q), F(q), A(q)$. Accordingly the phase space functions can be *non-diagonal* Lindhard-type functions..

The antisymmetrized form of he $D(q)$ is parametrized by a zero-range interaction term, U_o between up ($\uparrow$) and down ($\downarrow$) -spin quasiparticles; a finite-range interaction

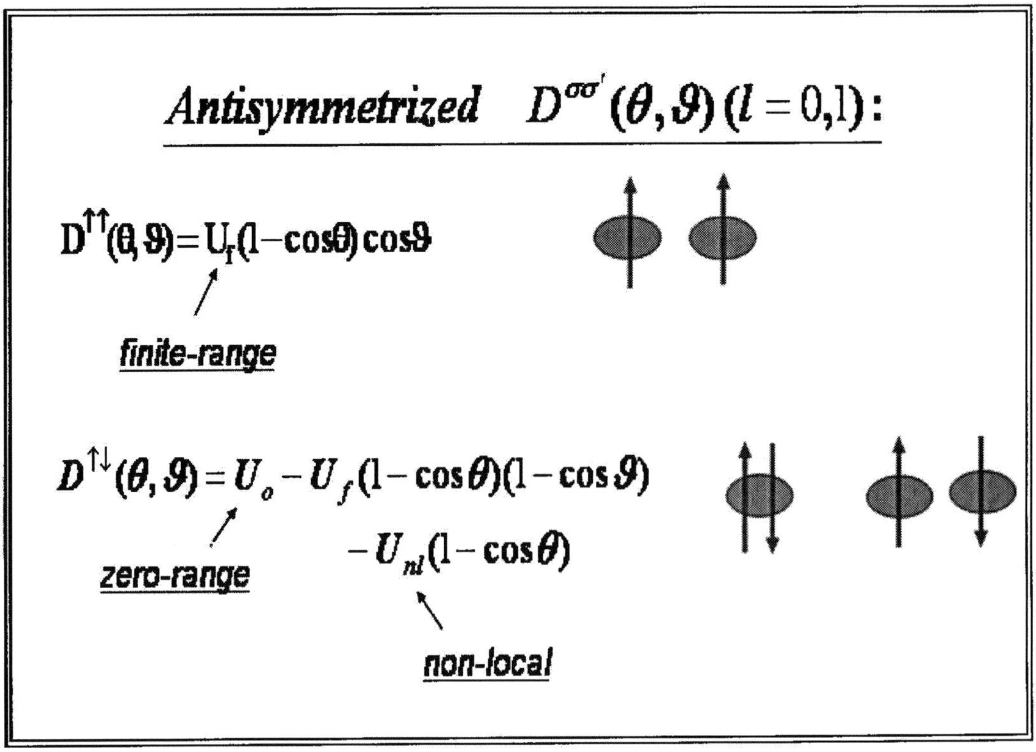

Figure 4. Antisymmetrized "Direct" interaction showing zero-range (U_o), finite-range (U_f), and the non-local (U_{nl} components used in our model calculations.

term U_f between two up (↑) -spin quasiparticles; and a non-local term, U_{nl} between up (↑) and down (↓) -spin quasiparticles. The $\ell = 0, 1$ terms in $D^{\sigma,\sigma'}(\theta, \phi)$ are shown in Fig. 4; θ, ϕ are the scattering angles in the s-channel. . In the Landau limit: $q \to 0$, $q' \to 0$, $\cos\theta \to \cos\Theta_L = \cos\Theta'_L$, and $\cos\phi \to 1, -1$, where Θ_L and Θ'_L are the generalized Landau angles in the t and u -channel respectively. The range of our 3 parameters are such that $U_f, U_{nl} \sim O(0.1)U_o$.

4.1 Pairing Interactions

Pair-couplings, λ_ℓ, in different angular momentum channels, can be classified as *singlets* or *triplets*, depending whether ℓ is *even* or *odd.* To obtain the pair-couplings, we first construct the *triplet* and *singlet* pairing channel scattering ampli-

Pairing Channel Scattering Amplitudes

$$T^{t,s}(\theta,\vartheta) = \sum_{l,m} T^{s,t}_{l,m}(\theta = \pi, \vartheta)\,(-1)^l P_m \cos(\vartheta)$$

$$T^{t}(\theta,\vartheta) = A^{s}(\theta,\vartheta) + A^{a}(\theta,\vartheta) \;:\text{Triplet}$$

$$T^{s}(\theta,\vartheta) = A^{s}(\theta,\vartheta) - 3A^{a}(\theta,\vartheta) \;:\text{Singlet}$$

Pairing Interaction in Angular Momentum Channels

$$\lambda_l = \frac{1}{8}\int_{-1}^{+1} d(\cos\vartheta)\,T^{t,s}(\theta = \pi, \vartheta)\,P_l(\cos\vartheta)$$

Figure 5. Construction of the pairing interactions, λ_ℓ from the scattering amplitudes, $A^{s,a}(\theta,\phi)$ obtained from our calculations.

tudes, $T^{t,s}(\theta,\phi)$ from the scattering amplitudes $A^{s,a}(\theta,\phi)$, obtained by solving our coupled non-linear equations. The construction of pairing interactions is shown in Fig. 5.

5. SOLUTION AND RESULTS

For our calculations, we found that retaining between 10 and 15 moments in the double moment Legendre expansions of $F(q), A(q)$ were sufficient for stable results; higher moments were found to be not significant.

For most of the calculations, we kept the finite-range interaction fixed at $U_f \sim O(0.1)U_o$, and varied the strength of the zero-range interaction, U_o and the non-local interaction, U_{nl}. Fig. 6 shows 3D plots of the s, p, d pairing interaction strengths,

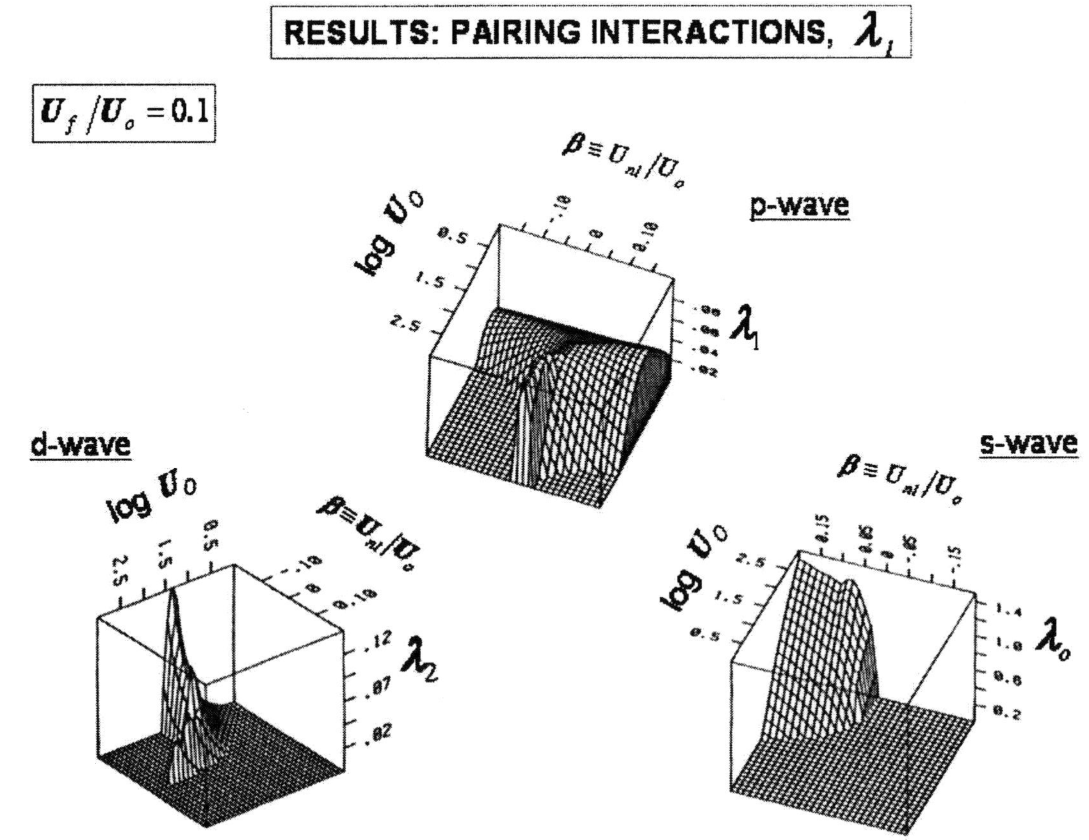

Figure 6. 3D plots of our results for the s-wave (λ_0), p-wave (λ_1), and d-wave (λ_2) pairing interactions shown as functions of zero-range (U_o) and nono-local (U_{nl}) interactions, and a fixed finite-range (U_f) interaction.

$\lambda_o, \lambda_1, \lambda_2$ as functions of U_o and U_{nl}.

The results are summarized in a schematic phase diagram in Fig. 7. We believe that the *p-wave* pairing is driven mainly by ferromagnetic spin fluctuations ("paramagnons"), F_0^a, for both repulsive and attractive values of the non-local interaction. We find that the strength of transverse current fluctuations (and consequently the effective mass) *increase* as the U_o is increased for repulsive U_{nl}. This competes with diminishing strength of spin fluctautions to favor *s-wave* pairing. For attractive U_{nl} and a narrow region of U_o, we find *d-wave* pairing. We believe that this is due to the development of strong anti-ferromagnetic type spin fluctuations accompanied by very small current fluctuations. We deduce this from our result that in this regime, $F_0^a(q)$ is peaked at large momenta, q, rather than zero momenta. We were also not able to obtain stable solutions for large values of U_o for attractive U_{nl}. This may suggest possibly some other instability (perhaps a magnetic one) driven by attractive non-local interactions.

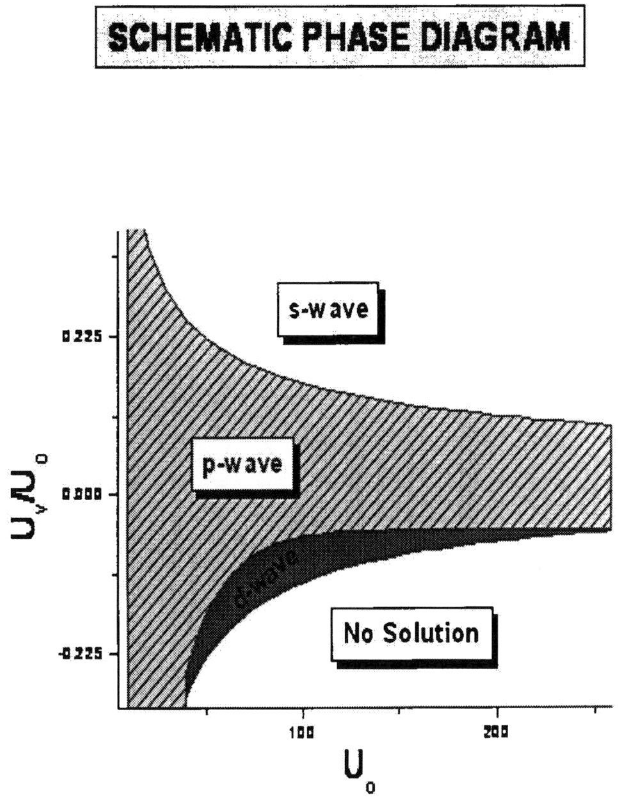

Figure 7. Schematic Phase Diagram of our pairing results shown for different values of repulsive zero-range interaction, U_o, and repulsive and attractive values of the non-local interaction, U_{nl}. The finite-range interaction, U_f is fixed at $\approx O(0.1)U_o$.

ACKNOWLEDGMENTS

We would like to acknowledge the support of the US Department of Army Research Office. We would like to thank K. S. Bedell, S. Trugman and E. Y. Andrei for several illuminating discussions.

REFERENCES

[1] N S. Saxena, et al., Nature (London) **406**, 587 (2000).

[2] D.N. Aoki, et al., Nature (London) **413**, 613 (2001).

[3] C. Pfleiderer et al., Nature **412**, 59 (2001).

[4] N. D. Mathur et al., Nature **394**, 39 (1998).

[5] A. D. Jackson, A. Lande, and R. A. Smith, Phys. Reports **86**, 55 (1982); N. E. Bickers and D. J. Scalapino, Ann. Phys. **193**, 206 (1989).

[6] K. F. Quader, "The Induced Interaction Way to Quasiparticle Interactions: Minimal Fermion Parquet", in **Windsurfing the Fermi Sea**, eds. T. T. S. Kuo, and J. Speth (Elsevier, 1987), Vol. 2, p. 390.

[7] T. L. Ainsworth and K. S. Bedell, Phys. Rev. **B35**, 8425 (1987).

[8] S. Babu and G. E. Brown, Ann. Phys. 78, 1 (1973).

[9] T. L. Ainsworth, K. S. Bedell, G. E. Brown, and K. F. Quader, J. Low Temp. Phys. **50**, 315 (1983).

[10] K. F. Quader, K. S. Bedell, G. E. Brown, Phys. Rev. **B36**, 156 (1987).

[11] K. F. Quader and K. S. Bedell, J. Low Temp. Phys., **58**, 89 (1985).

ONSET OF MOTION AND DEPINNING OF A BRAGG GLASS

Guohong Li and Eva Y. Andrei
Department of Physics and Astronomy,Rutgers University
Piscataway, New Jersey 08855, USA

P. Shuk and M. Greenblatt
Department of Chemistry, Rutgers University
Piscataway, New Jersey 08855, USA

1. INTRODUCTION

The response of vortices to applied currents or fields has been a topic of intense study for almost half a century. Surprisingly, in spite of enormous progress in our understanding of vortex physics, many of the outstanding questions identified by Anderson and Kim in 1964, are still unsolved[1]. Their statement " we have made no progress in studying the transient solutions ... when one quickly applies an external field or currents to a superconductor" is still valid today. Most experimental studies on the dynamics of vortices have focused on the evolution of the magnetization to an applied field in the limit of long time scales[2-4]. The much faster initial transients occurring in magnetization experiments have received less attention. Similarly few experiments have focused on the response of a superconductor to a suddenly applied current.

Standard transport experiments measuring the steady state response to an applied current provide information on the degree of order of the vortex state. For clean samples where pinning is absent vortices are expected to form an ordered state, the Abrikosov lattice[5] at low temperatures and fields. Pinning arising in the presence of any amount of material defects destroys the long-range order[6] of the vortex lattice. In the limit of weak pinning however, the Abrikosov lattice can maintain its topological integrity, forming a so-called Bragg glass [7-12] with quasi long-range order. As thermal fluctuations or the strength of pinning are increased, the Bragg glass undergoes a transition into a less ordered liquid or glassy state. As shown by Pippard [13] and Larkin- Ovchinninkov[14], the transport signature of this transition is an increase in the critical current density, $J \propto R_c^{-1/2}$ where R_c is the size of a coherent Larkin domain[6]. This may be the origin of the peak effect, a sharp rise in critical current observed just below the superconducting transition in weak pinning superconductors[15,16].

The critical current I_c is determined from standard transport measurements as the current for which a small longitudinal voltage drop, typically $1\mu V$, is detected. The voltage drop signals the onset of vortex motion and the loss of superconductivity. The temperature and field dependence of I_c contain information on the collective properties of the vortex lattice. Further information on the vortex dynamics is gained from the shape of the $V(I)$ curves. If in response to the applied current I,the vortices move uniformly, the voltage $V = \rho_{ff}(I - I_c)$ is linear in the applied current with $\rho_{ff} = \rho_n H/H_{c2}$, H the applied field, H_{c2} the upper critical field and ρ_n the normal state resistivity. This regime known as free flux flow is generally expected at high current levels. The situation is more complex close to I_c at the onset of vortex motion where the $V(I)$ is non-linear. Various models have been developed to describe this onset in term of thermal activation across bulk pinning barriers[1-3,17,18]. Recently it was shown that in clean $NbSe_2$ samples the non- linear $V(I)$ are a result of the surface rather than bulk barriers[19,20]. The surface barrier inhibits vortex motion in and out of the sample and causes a non-uniform distribution of the transport current due to the excess force needed to introduce vortices into the sample [21]. By separating the contributions of surface and bulk to the $V(I)$ characteristics these experiments demonstrated that thermal activation across the surface barrier is the sole origin of non linearity while the bulk contribution remains linear down to the experimental resolution.

Going beyond the steady state $V(I)$ characteristics, pulsed transport measurement [22, 23] revealed rich dynamics in the vortex response near the peak effect. These experiments showed strong metastabillity, nonlinear dynamics and clear evidence of reordering in the vortex state resulting from its motion and from its interaction with boundaries. Below the peak effect transport measurements on a field cooled (FC) vortex lattice revealed that the FC state is metastable and that it decays to a stable state if perturbed by an applied current, a change in field or mechanically. The resulting stable state had a lower I_c which was close to that of the ZFC (Zero Field Cooled) state. These results were interpreted in terms of a supercooled disordered state that reorganizes into a more ordered state or Bragg glass when driven by a current[24,26].

Here we describe time resolved transport measurements that probe the response of the vortex lattice in $NbSe_2$ samples to an applied current pulse over a wide range of fields and temperatures. The response was characterized by two quantities: asymptotic voltage V_0 and rise time τ. We identified a region of the phase diagram where τ depends only on the asymptotic vortex velocity, derived from V_0. Despite the fact that pinning, vortex-vortex interactions and temperature varied the rise time remained the same if the velocity was sufficiently high. The region of phase diagram where this universal behavior is present coincides with that of the Bragg glass state identified in other experiments. This unique feature disappears when the Bragg glass becomes unstable at high temperatures or magnetic fields.

2. EXPERIMENTS

A pure single crystal of 2H-$NbSe_2$ (4.41 mm x 0.83 mm x 6 μm) was used

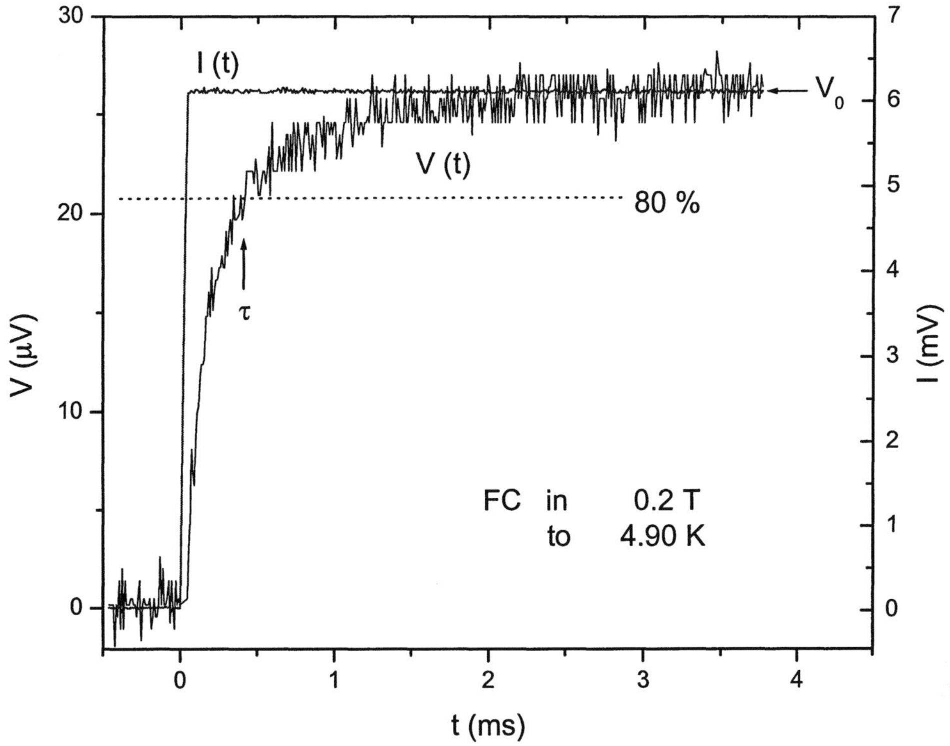

Figure 1. Response to transport current pulse. The vortex state was prepared by field-cooling. Definitions of the asymptotic voltage V_0 and the rise time τ are shown.

in this study. The thin platelet sample has a T_c of 7.2 K with a width of 130 mK in zero magnetic field. Standard four probe technique was employed in the pulsed measurements. The contacts were prepared by depositing Au/Ti film on cleaved sample surface, and the distance between voltage contacts was 3.43 mm. The magnetic field were applied along the c-axis, and currents were in the a-b plane. An external measurement and control system, Adwin-Gold was used for the pulse experiments because of its fast data acquisition and deep memory. Its analog output generated the current pulse and its analog input collected the response of the sample. The voltage response was amplified by a low noise fast amplifier before it was passed to the Adwin-Gold. For low level experiments, a Keithley 2400 source-meter and 2182 nanovoltmeter were used in order to increase the sensitivity.

In this paper we focus on the field-cooled (FC) vortex states whereby the sample is cooled below the superconducting transition in the presence of a constant magnetic field. The field was generated by a superoconducting magnet working in persistent mode. The sample was first warmed up into its normal state and then slowly cooled down to a temperature where the pulsed measurement was made. A low temperature response curve is shown in Fig.1. No voltage was detectable when the current is just turned on. This feature is typical for the low temperature data. At higher temperatures, above the peak effect the initial response is finite. With time the voltage increases gradually toward an asymptotic value V_0. The rise time τ is defined as the time to reach 80% of the asymptotic value. Similar response curves to a current pulse [25, 26] were seen in previous measurements.

3. RESULTS

The temperature dependence of the response to transport current pulses is shown in Fig. 2. Every data point was taken on a freshly prepared FC vortex state as described above. The vortex response is characterized by two quantities, V_0 and τ. Both are strong functions of the current pulse level I. The voltage current characteristics $V_0(I)$ obtained from the asymptotic response to pulses of varying amplitude coincides with the conventional $V(I)$ obtained in a standard slow transport measurement. V_0 increased linearly with I at high levels, and the slope is consistent with the free flux flow resistance. We note some rounding of the $V_0(I)$ at low levels close to the critical currents, which could reflect thermal activation over bulk barriers (creep) [1- 3]or over a surface the barrier [21]. The rise time τ increases sharply with decreasing I, consistent with previous studies [25, 26]. Both $V_0(I)$ and $\tau(I)$ depend on temperature for a given magnetic field as shown in the figure. This is not surprising in view of the fact that the competition between vortex-vortex interactions, pinning strength, surface barrier and thermal fluctuations ultimately determines not only the vortex state but also the dynamics. However what *is* surprising is the fact that the temperature dependence disappears when plotting τ versus V_0. In other words in this regime the rise time τ is determined by the asymptotic voltage V_0 alone, and is insensitive to applied current or temperature.

The results of the same experiment carried out in different magnetic fields are shown in Fig. 3. Here again we note that $\tau(V_0)$ is independent of temperature but does depend on the value of the magnetic field. If the curves at various fields represent the same physical phenomenon it should be possible to obtain a further collapse by plotting the response in terms of intrinsic physical parameters. Clearly τ is intrinsic to the dynamics and so is the velocity v, but the voltage $V_0 \sim nv$ is not because it depends on the density of moving vortices n which varies with field. We therefore plot τ against the vortex velocity $v \propto V_o/B$ in the lower panel of Fig. 3. We find that the entire data set collapses onto a single curve that corresponds to a power law curve $\tau \propto v^{-3/2}$. This simple law holds at high vortex velocities over a range of temperature and fields. At low velocities, deviations appear [27] (hints of the deviation can also be seen in Fig. 3). The fact that this universal behavior holds over a wide range of velocities, fields and temperatures is even more remarkable in view of the fact that in the same regime the critical current depends strongly on field and temperature.

Of course this universality cannot persist throughout the entire phase space. To study the region of phase space where this behavior holds we repeated the experiments over a range of fields and temperatures. In Fig. 4 we display the field and temperature dependence of the rise time corresponding to the same asymptotic vortex velocity, $36mm/s$. Note that in order to drive the vortices toward the same asymptotic velocity the driving currents, which have strong field and temperature dependence, had to be adjusted accordingly. The universal behavior shown above is evident here for a range of fields and temperatures where $\tau = 0.6ms$. Beyond this regime as the field or temperature are increased we note a sharp drop in τ. The onset temperature of this drop is quite well defined since it is almost independent of the vortex velocity. In fact, the whole τ(v) curve shifts downward at this temperature (data not shown here).

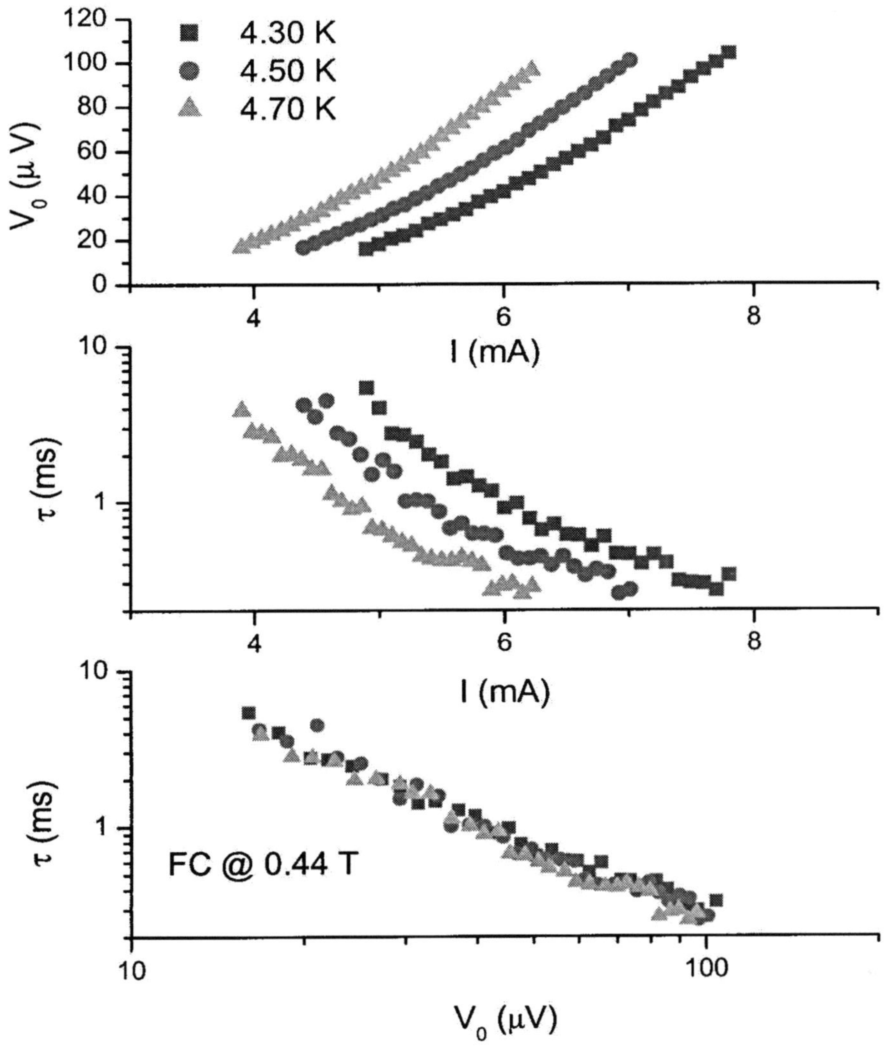

Figure 2. (top) Asymptotic voltage versus current pulse level at various temperatures. (middle) Rise time versus current pulse level at various temperatures. (bottom) Curves of asymptotic voltage versus rise time for various temperatures collapse onto the same line. No adjustable parameters or normalization were used.

In Figure 5 we plot the vortex phase diagram. In addition to the usual lines representing the upper critical field H_{c2}, the positions of the peak H_p and the onset of the peak effect H_o we show the region of the phase space where the measured $\tau(v)$ is independent of field and temperature by hatched bars. The boundary of the regime where this new dynamic behavior is observed coincides with that of a stable Bragg glass (to be published elsewhere) shown by the dotted line in Fig. 5.

4. DISCUSSION

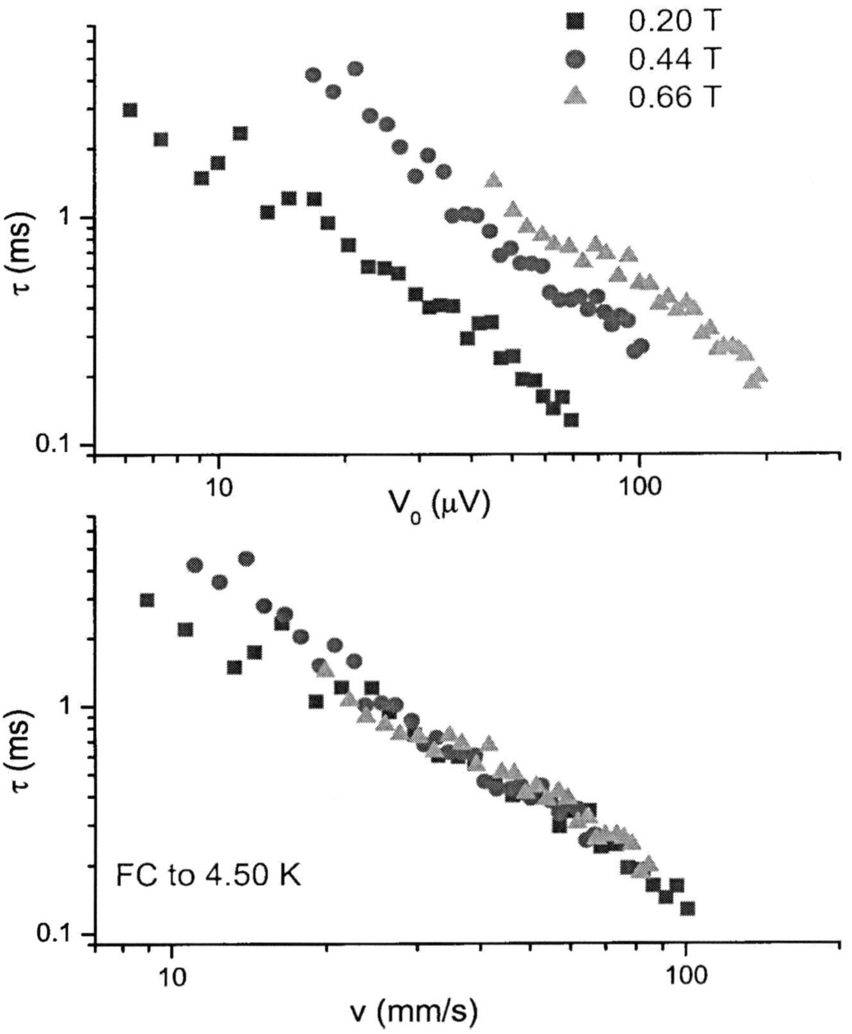

Figure 3. Rise time dependence on asymptotic voltage for three values of magnetic field (top) collapse onto the same line when the rise time is plotted against the vortex velocity (bottom).

We now discuss possible origins of the rise time in the regime where it is uniquely described by the asymptotic velocity.

a. The inertial mass of vortices contributes little to τ because it is too small [28-30].

b. Thermal activation above a pinning barrier is commonly associated with long logarithmic response times in magnetization experiments arising from vortex creep. But the response times of vortex creep are strongly temperature and field dependent. By contrast in the regime described here low temperatures, low fields and free flux flow - the response time is independent of temperature.

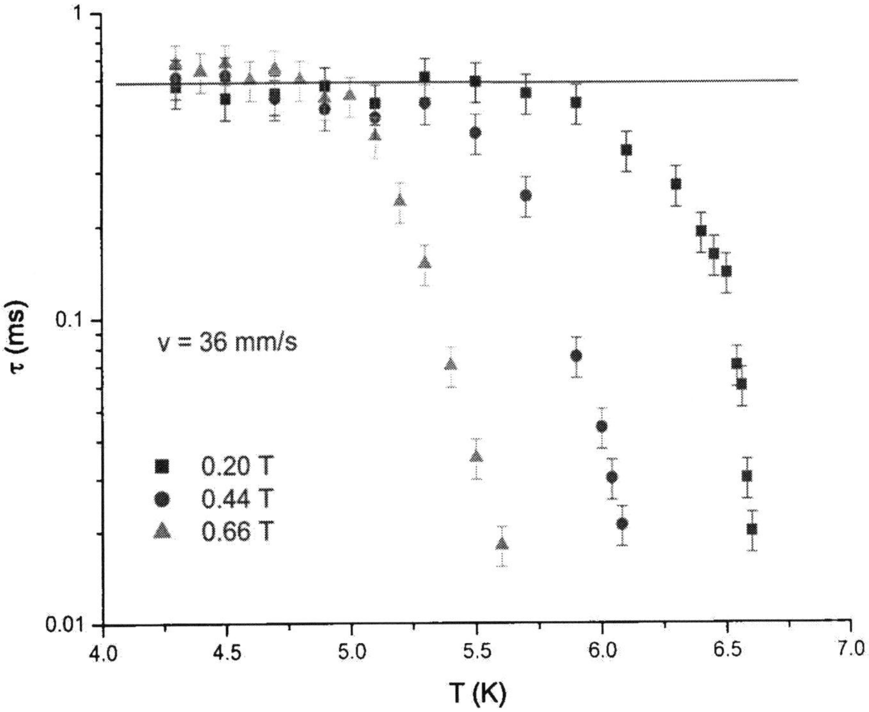

Figure 4. Temperature dependence of the rise time τ for vortices driven toward the same asymptotic velocity, 36 mm/s by a current pulse. At the lowest temperatures τ is uniquely defined by the asymptotic velocity.

c. Thermo-magnetic instability. Experiments following the vortex motion in response to an intense laser pulse [31] or to a small applied field [32-34] in thin superconducting film showed that the response is dominated by a thermo-magnetic instability which gives rise to field penetration into the sample via dendritic growth patterns. Within the dendritic regions the vortex lattice was found to be in a disordered or liquid state. The thermo-magnetic instability was not observed for thick samples or in large magnetic fields exceeding several Gauss. Since the samples used in our experiments were thick ($> 6\mu m$) and the fields large ($> 0.1T$) it is unlikely that this instability is responsible for the observed behavior.

d. Establishment of field gradient. Current penetration into the superconducting sample requires a simultaneous rearrangement of vortices according to $\nabla \times H \propto J$. Therefore, when a current pulse is applied to an FC state, the initial flat vortex density profile has to evolve in order to produce a density gradient consistent with the applied current. The final density gradient is proportional to the asymptotic vortex velocity. In a sense the approach to the asymptotic velocity resembles that of a self organized critical state[35]. These systems reach the critical state through a succession of avalanches generated by a redistribution of energy between moving particles and their neighbors. Such mechanism quite naturally can result in a power law dependence of the rise time on the asymptotic velocity. The dynamics of self organized criticality could take place in a vortex system if the energy of moving vortices is shared with neighboring vortices faster than it is lost to the environment.

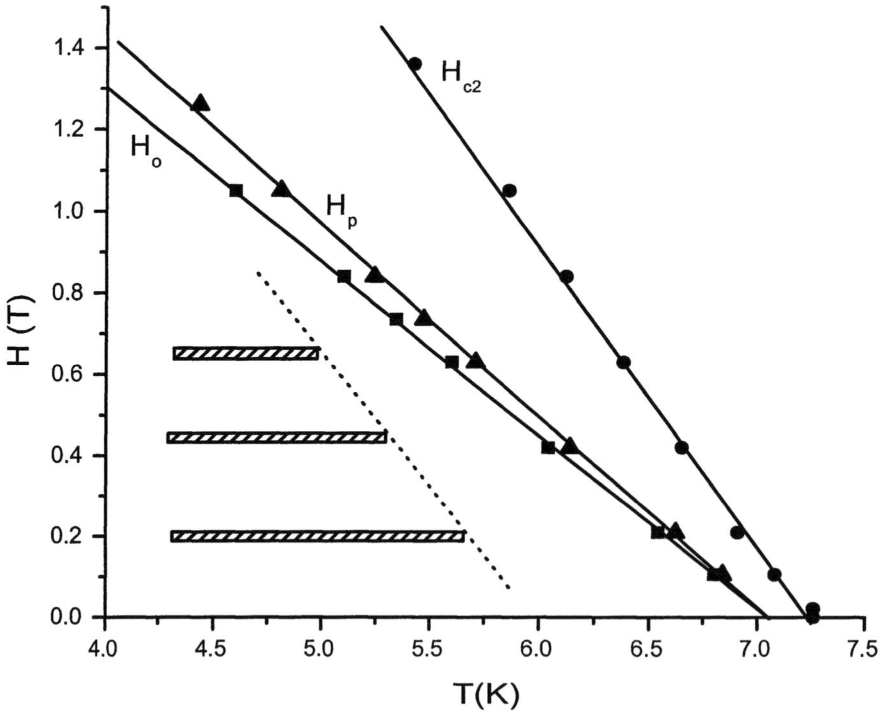

Figure 5. Vortex phase diagram for NbSe2. The upper critical field line H_{c2} separates the normal from the superconducting state. The peak effect is marked by the onset H_o and the peak H_p. The hatched bars represent the region in phase space were the response to a current pulse is uniquely defined by the asymptotic vortex velocity as seen in Fig. 3. The Bragg glass can be reached by field-cooling at temperatures lower than the dotted line (to be published). The solid lines are guides to the eye.

This would require a fairly coherent vortex lattice were the motion occurs in chunks rather than individual vortices or interstitials. In the Bragg glass regime were it is energetically unfavorable to form vacancies or interstitial that could facilitate sliding of individual vortices or small bundles these conditions are satisfied. By contrast outside the Bragg glass regime were vortex motion is less correlated the dynamics is governed by single vortex motion where the times scales are too fast to be measurable in our experiments.

e. Vortex reorganization. Rearrangement of the vortex lattice leading to a change in the critical current or a change in the number or distribution of moving vortices gives rise to a change in the voltage response. If the rearrangements occur within the experimental time scales they will naturally result in an evolution of the response to an applied current. Current induced rearrangements of the FC vortex lattice from a disordered metastable state to an ordered stable state with a lower critical current were previously reported in this system[24- 26] as well as in high T_c samples[36]. These rearrangements from a disordered to an ordered lattice can delay the current penetration into the sample if the rearrangement times are slower than the dynamic penetration times discussed in (d). In this case the local current density would initially correspond to the disordered state. As rearrangements occur throughout the sample reducing the value of the local critical current density the voltage response would grow until the entire sample is in the ordered state. The strong correlation between the reordering time and the asymptotic velocity observed at low fields and temperatures is a new and intriguing feature that could be a dynamic signature of the moving Bragg glass[27,37-39].

5. CONCLUSIONS

We have described a series of pulsed transport measurements to study vortex dynamics of over a wide range of temperature and magnetic field. Our experiments revealed that the two aspects of the response, asymptotic vortex velocity and the rise time are strongly correlated to each other in a region of phase diagram that coincides with the Bragg glass. Outside this region the response develops a strong dependence on field and temperature and can no longer be uniquely characterized by the asymptotic velocity. Our results strongly suggest that this novel feature is a dynamic signature of the Bragg glass. Clearly more work is needed, both theoretical and experimental, in order to make progress on the transient solutions when one quickly applies an external current to a superconductor.

ACKNOWLEDGMENTS

We would like to acknowledge a stimulating discussion with V. Vinokur, Y.M. Galperin and N. B. Kopnin. The research described herein was supported by the National Science Foundation underGrant NSF-DMR-0102692 and the US Department of Energy under grant DE-FG02- 99ER45742 and by the US Office of Army Research.

REFERENCES

[1] P.W. Anderson and Y.B. Kim Rev. Mod. Phys. **36** , 39 (1964)

[2] M. R. Beasley , R. Labusch, and W. W. Webb, Phys. Rev. 181, 682 (1969)

[3] Y. Yeshurun, A. P. Malozemoff , and A. Shaulov , Rev. Mod. Phys. 68, 911 (1996).

[4] G. Blatter et. al., Rev. Mod. Phys. 66, 1215 (1994).

[5] A.A. Abrikosov, Sov. Phys. JETP 5, 1174 (1957).

[6] A.I. Larkin, Sov. Phys. JETP 31, 784 (1970).

[7] T. Giamarchi and P. Le Doussal, Phys. Rev. B 52, 1242 (1995).

[8] D.S. Fisher, Phys. Rev. Lett. 78, 1964(1997).

[9] E. Zeldov et. al., Nature 375, 373 (1995).

[10] A. Schilling et. al., Nature 382, 791 (1996).

[11] X.S. Ling et. al., Phys. Rev. Lett. 86, 712 (2001).

[12] T. Klein et al. Nature 413, 404 (2001).

[13] A. B. Pippard, Philos. Mag. **19**, 217 (1969).

[14] A. I. Larkin and Yu. N. Ovchinnikov, J. Low Temp. Phys. **34**, 409(1979).

[15] S. H. Autler, E. S. Rosenblum, and K. H. Gooen, Phys. Rev. Lett. **9**,489 (1962); W. DeSORBO, Rev. Mod. Phys. **36**, 90 (1964).

[16] M.J. Higgins, S. Bhattacharya, Physica C 257, 232 (1996).

[17] M.V. Feigelman et. al., Phys. Rev. Lett. **63**, 2303 (1989).

[18] T. Nattermann, Phys. Rev. Lett. 64, 2454 (1990).

[19] Y. Paltiel et al., Phys. Rev. Lett. 85, 3712 (2000).

[20] Z.L. Xiao et. al., Phys. Rev. B 65, 094511 (2002).

[21] C.P. Bean Rev. Mod. Phys. **36** , 31 (1964)

[22] W. Henderson, E.Y. Andrei and M.J. Higgins, Phys. Rev. Lett. **81**, 2352 (1998)

[23] Z.L. Xiao et. al., Phys. Rev. Lett. 85, 3265 (2000).

[24] U. Yaron et. al., Phys. Rev. Lett. 73, 2748 (1994).

[25] W. Henderson et. al., Phys. Rev. Lett. 77, 2077 (1996); E. Y. Andrei, Z. L. Xiao, W. Henderson, M. J. Higgins, P. Shuk, and M. Greenblatt, J. Phys. IV 10, 5 (1999).

[26] Z.L. Xiao, et. al., Phys. Rev. Lett. 86, 2431 (2001).

[27] Guohong Li et. al., Physica C (to be published).

[28] H. Suhl, Phys. Rev. Lett. 14, 226 (1965).

[29] J.M. Duan, and A.J. Leggett, Phys. Rev. Lett. 68, 1216 (1992).

[30] E.M. Chudnovsky and A.B. Kuklov, Phys. Rev. Lett. 91, 067004 (2003).

[31] P. Leiderer et al., Phys. Rev. Lett. 71, 2646 (1993);

[32] C. A. Duran et al., Phys. Rev. B 52, 75 (1995)

[33] R. Surdeanu et al., Phys. Rev. Lett. 83, 2054 (1999).

[34] E. R. Nowak et al., Phys. Rev. B 55, 11 702 (1997).

[35] P. Bak, C. Tang and K. Wiesenfeld, Phys. Rev. A 38, 364 (1988).

[36] F. Portier et. al.,Phys. Rev. B 66, 140511 (2002)

[37] A.C. Shi and A.J. Berlinskii, Phys. Rev. Lett. 67, 1926 (1991).

[38] A.E. Koshelev and V.M. Vinokur, Phys. Rev. Lett. 73, 3580 (1994).

[39] P. Chauve, T. Giamarchi and P. Le Doussal, Phys. Rev. B 62 6241-6267 (2000).

Quantum Information

ENTANGLEMENT AS AN OBSERVER-DEPENDENT CONCEPT: AN APPLICATION TO QUANTUM PHASE TRANSITIONS

G. Ortiz, R. Somma, H. Barnum, E. Knill, and L. Viola

Los Alamos National Laboratory
Los Alamos, New Mexico 87545, USA

1. INTRODUCTION

In 1935 Einstein, Podolsky, and Rosen [1] published a Gedanken-experiment that still surprises us today [2]. Their main observation highlighted a key feature of quantum phenomena in which a pure state of a composite quantum system may cease to be determined by the states of its constituent subsystems. It is this non-classical behavior that Schrödinger later termed *entanglement* [3]. Entangled states are joint states of two or more distinguishable quantum systems that cannot be expressed as a mixture of products of states of each system. To establish whether or not a state is entangled requires knowledge of the correlations between subsystems, and measurement of one subsystem may affect the results of measurements on another even when the system is in a pure state, something which is against classical intuition. In Schrödinger's words [3]: "[The] Best possible knowledge of a *whole* does not necessarily include the same for its *parts*." Today we know that entanglement is the defining resource for quantum communications (e.g., allowing quantum teleportation protocols), it provides non-local correlations between subsystems that admit no local classical interpretation (quantum non-locality), and it is believed to be an essential ingredient to understanding and unlocking the power of quantum computation [4].

Until very recently, most studies concentrated on how the entanglement of a number of *distinguishable* quantum subsystems differs from classical correlations. Typically these studies focus on two subsystems (the bipartite or "Alice and Bob" setting). A notion of entanglement emerged from these investigations that we will term *conventional* entanglement. This paper addresses the following question: Do we have a theoretical understanding of entanglement applicable to a full variety of physical settings? It is clear that not only the assumption of distinguishability (which is natural and useful in standard quantum information processing (QIP) situations), but also the few-subsystem scenario, are too narrow to embrace all possible physical settings. In particular, the need to go beyond this subsystem-based framework becomes manifest when one tries to apply the conventional concept of entanglement to the physics of matter, since the constituents of a quantum many-body system are *indistinguishable* particles. We shall discuss here a notion of *generalized entanglement*

(GE), which can be applied to any operator language (fermions, bosons, spins, etc.) used to describe a physical system and which includes the conventional entanglement settings introduced to date in a unified fashion. This is realized by noticing that entanglement is an *observer-dependent* concept, whose properties are determined by the expectations of a *distinguished set of observables* without reference to a preferred subsystem decomposition, i.e., it depends on the physically relevant point of view. This viewpoint depends in turn upon the relationship between different sets of observables that determine our ability to control the system of interest. Indeed, the extent to which entanglement is present depends on the observables used to measure a system and describe its states. It is worthwhile noting that the role of observables and control in distinguishing subsystems such as qubits and determining the emergence of a preferred tensor product structure has been stressed before by various authors (see e.g., [5,6]). However, our present approach is conceptually new and more general in that the observable sets need *not* be associative algebras, thus the resulting entanglement notion is capable of going beyond the identification of factorizations of a system into subsystems. This represents a most conspicuous advantage as will be highlighted by the condensed-matter application we will discuss.

On the other hand, novel materials display complex phase diagrams as a result of competing interactions with complex orderings (states of matter) which are believed to be influenced by being in proximity to quantum critical points (high-T_c, heavy fermion compounds, frustrated magnets, etc.). And the truth is that our understanding of the nature of these transitions is very poor. Since entanglement is a property inherent in quantum states and is strongly related to quantum correlations, one would expect that the entanglement present in the ground state of the system changes substantially at a quantum phase transition (QPT), i.e., when there is a qualitative change in the behavior of the correlations between constituents. Can we use concepts and tools borrowed from QIP to better understand QPTs? What is the nature and role of entanglement in a QPT? Can one quantify entanglement in a physically meaningful way? What properties distinguish between broken- and non-broken-symmetry QPTs? These are some of the questions we are going to address by example. (See also Refs. [7-10] for recent work in similar directions.)

Before we describe the concept of GE, let us start by recalling the standard framework for conventional entanglement. Given a quantum system with state space $\mathcal{H}$, it can a priori support inequivalent tensor product structures; for instance, $\mathcal{H} \simeq \mathcal{H}_1 \otimes \mathcal{H}_2 \otimes \cdots \otimes \mathcal{H}_N$, or ($N$ even) $\mathcal{H} \simeq \mathcal{H}_{12} \otimes \mathcal{H}_{34} \otimes \cdots \otimes \mathcal{H}_{(N-1)N}$, where $\mathcal{H}_{ij} \simeq \mathcal{H}_i \otimes \mathcal{H}_j$. Entanglement of states in $\mathcal{H}$ is unambiguously defined only once a *preferred subsystem decomposition* is chosen: $\mathcal{H} \simeq \bigotimes_j \mathcal{H}_j$. Relative to the selected multipartite structure, a pure state $|\Psi\rangle$ is entangled iff $|\Psi\rangle$ induces at least some mixed subsystem states. For example: if $\mathcal{H} \simeq \mathcal{H}_A \otimes \mathcal{H}_B$, where the Hilbert spaces for *A*lice and *B*ob, $\mathcal{H}_A, \mathcal{H}_B$, are two-dimensional ($|\psi\rangle_{A,B} = a_0^{A,B}|0\rangle_{A,B} + a_1^{A,B}|1\rangle_{A,B}$), and

$$|\Psi\rangle = \frac{|0\rangle_A \otimes |1\rangle_B + |1\rangle_A \otimes |0\rangle_B}{\sqrt{2}} \;, \text{ then } \begin{cases} \rho_A = \mathrm{tr}_B|\Psi\rangle\langle\Psi| \\ \rho_B = \mathrm{tr}_A|\Psi\rangle\langle\Psi| \end{cases} \text{are mixed} \;, \tag{1}$$

whereas if

$$|\Psi\rangle = |0\rangle_A \otimes |1\rangle_B \;, \text{ then } \rho_A \text{ and } \rho_B \text{ are pure} \;. \tag{2}$$

Thus, in the conventional approach, entangled pure states look *mixed* to at least some *local* observers, while unentangled pure states still look pure. In standard QIP settings the choice of preferred subsystem is usually not problematic, as there is a notion of locality in *real space*. Indeed, spatially separated local parties are often taken as synonymous with distinguishable quantum subsystems.

However, as mentioned above, the distinguishability assumption is too narrow for a generic physical setting, and yet many questions remain open:

i) What does entanglement mean for indistinguishable particles?

It has been known since the early days of quantum mechanics that particles in Nature are either bosons or fermions in the three-dimensional space. Indistinguishability places an additional constraint on the space of admissible states which manifests itself in their symmetry properties. The physically accessible state space is the symmetric(bosons)/antisymmetric(fermions) subspace of the full tensor product state space. For example, consider the free electron gas (Fermi liquid) in the real-space x-representation (k_j is a label of momentum), described by a many-body wavefunction of the form

$$\langle x_1, x_2, \cdots |\Psi\rangle \sim \text{Det} \begin{pmatrix} e^{ik_1x_1} & e^{ik_1x_2} & \cdots \\ e^{ik_2x_1} & e^{ik_2x_2} & \cdots \\ \vdots & \vdots & \cdots \end{pmatrix}, \langle x_1, x_2, \cdots |\Psi\rangle = -\langle x_2, x_1, \cdots |\Psi\rangle. \quad (3)$$

Exchange correlations are present but are not, in principle, a usable resource in the usual QIP sense. (Other recent work on generalizing entanglement to indistinguishable fermions may be found in [11] and references therein.)

ii) Particle or mode entanglement?

The state $\langle x_1, x_2, \cdots |\Psi\rangle$ given above exhibits mode entanglement with respect to the set of momentum modes; yet, the electrons are non-interacting. A set of modes provides a factorization into a distinguishable-subsystem structure, but in principle inequivalent factorizations (e.g., position modes and momentum modes) may occur on the same footing for a given system.

iii) What is the most appropriate operator language?

The algebraic language (fermions, bosons, anyons, gauge fields, etc.) used to describe an interacting quantum system may be intentionally changed by mappings such as the Jordan-Wigner transformation and its generalizations [12].

The bottom line is that nontrivial quantum statistics, or other physical restrictions, can make the choice of preferred subsystem problematic. Our generalized approach can overcome such difficulties, by removing the need for a subsystem decomposition from the start. Even when a subsystem partition exists, we would like to emphasize that from the viewpoint of GE, ordinary separable pure states (i.e., states that can be written as a tensor product of normalized subsystem states, $|\Psi\rangle_s = |\psi\rangle_1 \otimes |\phi\rangle_2 \otimes \cdots \otimes |\varphi\rangle_N$) are not necessarily equivalent to generalized unentangled states. We will illustrate this issue by example in section 3.2.

2. ENTANGLEMENT AS AN OBSERVER-DEPENDENT CONCEPT

Our approach to tackle these issues will be to reformulate entanglement as a *subsystem-independent* property that depends on the physically relevant point of view. The formal development of GE may be found in Refs. [13,14]. Here we will simply recall the key concepts and further illustrate them by example.

The notions of Hilbert space and linear maps or operators are central to the formulation of quantum mechanics. Pure states are elements of a Hilbert space and physical observables are associated to Hermitian (self-adjoint) operators which act on that space, and whose eigenvalues are selected by a measuring apparatus. The role of linear operators in quantum mechanics is not restricted to the representation of physical observables. Non-Hermitian operators are very often used as well, for instance in the context of describing non-unitary quantum dynamics. Linear operators form a complex vector space under the sum and the multiplication by a scalar over the field of complex numbers. If we augment this vector space with a bilinear operation, the set forms an *algebra*. Quantum mechanics also requires that this operation be non-commutative and associative. A *Lie algebra* $\mathfrak{h}$ is a vector space endowed with a bilinear map $[\cdot,\cdot]$ satisfying antisymmetry and the Jacobi identity

$$[x,x]=0,\quad [x,[y,z]]+[y,[z,x]]+[z,[x,y]]=0,\quad \forall\, x,y,z\in\mathfrak{h}\ . \tag{4}$$

An ideal I in a Lie algebra is a subalgebra fixed by the commutator map: For $x \in I$ and arbitrary $h \in \mathfrak{h}$, $[h,x] \in I$. A simple Lie algebra is one with no proper ideals. $\mathfrak{h}$ is said to be semisimple iff it is the direct sum of simple Lie algebras. A Cartan subalgebra (CSA) $\mathfrak{c}$ of a semisimple Lie algebra $\mathfrak{h}$ is a maximal commutative subalgebra. A vector space carrying a representation of $\mathfrak{h}$ decomposes into orthogonal joint eigenspaces V_λ of the operators in $\mathfrak{c}$. That is, each V_λ consists of the set of states $|\psi\rangle$ such that for $x \in \mathfrak{c}$, $x|\psi\rangle = \lambda(x)|\psi\rangle$. The label λ is therefore a linear functional on $\mathfrak{c}$, called the weight of V_λ. The subspace of operators in $\mathfrak{h}$ orthogonal in trace inner product to $\mathfrak{c}$ can be organized into orthogonal *raising* ($\mathfrak{e}_\mu$) and *lowering* ($\mathfrak{e}_{-\mu}$) operators, which connect different weight spaces. For a fixed CSA, the weights form a convex polytope; a lowest (or highest) weight is an extremal point of such a polytope, and the one-dimensional weight-spaces having those weights are known as *lowest-weight states*. The set of lowest-weight states for all CSAs is the orbit of any one such state under the Lie group generated by $\mathfrak{h}$. These are the group-theoretic generalized coherent states (GCSs) [15], which may be formally represented as

$$|\text{GCS}\rangle = e^{\sum_\mu(\eta_\mu \mathfrak{e}_\mu - \bar{\eta}_\mu \mathfrak{e}_{-\mu})}|\text{ext}\rangle\ ,\ \text{ where } |\text{ext}\rangle \text{ is an extremal state}\ . \tag{5}$$

The GCSs attain *minimum uncertainty* in an appropriate invariant sense [16], thus providing a natural generalization of the familiar harmonic-oscillator coherent states.

Our notion of GE is relative to a distinguished subspace of observables Ω of the quantum system. The basic idea is to generalize the observation that standard entangled pure states are those that look mixed to local observers. Given a pure state of a system, we remind the reader that the associated *reduced state*, or Ω-state, is obtained by only considering the expectation values of the distinguished observables Ω. In other words, an Ω-state is a linear and positive functional ω on the operators of Ω induced by a density matrix ρ according to $\omega(x) = \text{tr}(\rho x)$. The set of reduced states is convex. We then have the following

Definition :

A pure state $|\Psi\rangle$ is generalized unentangled relative to the distinguished set of observables Ω, if its reduced state is pure (extremal), and generalized entangled otherwise. Similarly, a mixed state is generalized unentangled relative to Ω, if it can be written as a convex combination of generalized unentangled pure states.

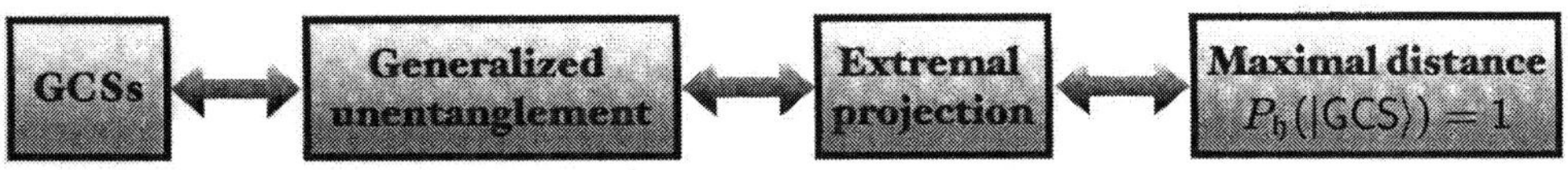

Figure 1. Equivalent statements in the irreducible Lie-algebraic setting.

When Ω is an irreducibly represented Lie algebra $\Omega \simeq \mathfrak{h}$, the set of unentangled pure states is identical to the set of GCSs. Another, more physically transparent, characterization of generalized-unentangled states is as the set of states that are unique ground states of a distinguished observable (e.g., a Hamiltonian).

2.1 Measure of generalized entanglement

One would like to have a way to quantify how entangled a given state is. In our theory of GE (as well as in conventional entanglement theory), no single measure is able to uniquely characterize the entanglement properties of a state. Indeed, a hierarchy of characterizations of quantum correlations is necessary. In order to connect the notions of generalized unentanglement and coherence, a natural way is to introduce the quadratic purity $P_{\mathfrak{h}}$ relative to the distinguished subspace of observables $\mathfrak{h}$.

Definition :

Let $\{x_i\}$ be a Hermitian ($x_i^\dagger = x_i$), and commonly-normalized orthogonal basis for $\mathfrak{h}$ ($\mathrm{tr}(x_i x_j) \propto \delta_{ij}$). For any $|\Psi\rangle \in \mathcal{H}$, the purity of $|\Psi\rangle$ relative to $\mathfrak{h}$, $\mathfrak{h}$-purity, is

$$P_{\mathfrak{h}}(|\Psi\rangle) = \sum_i |\langle\Psi|x_i|\Psi\rangle|^2 . \tag{6}$$

This measure has the following geometric meaning: $P_{\mathfrak{h}}(|\Psi\rangle)$ is the square-distance from 0 of the projection of $|\Psi\rangle\langle\Psi|$ onto $\mathfrak{h}$ according to the usual trace-inner-product norm. If $\mathfrak{h}$ is a Lie algebra, it is invariant under group transformations, $\tilde{x}_i = \mathfrak{g}^\dagger x_i \mathfrak{g}$, where $\mathfrak{g} \in e^{i\mathfrak{h}}$.

So far, $\mathfrak{h}$ has been assumed to be a *real* Lie algebra of Hermitian operators. These may be thought of as a preferred family of Hamiltonians, which generate (via $\mathfrak{h} \mapsto e^{i\mathfrak{h}}$) a Lie group of unitary operators, or as a preferred family of observables.

The following characterizations of unentangled states (proven in Ref. [9]) demonstrate the power of the Lie-algebraic setting (Fig. 1 summarizes equivalent statements for generalized unentangled states).

Theorem :

The following statements are equivalent for an irreducible representation of a Lie algebra $\mathfrak{h}$ on $\mathcal{H}$ and state ρ

(1) ρ is generalized unentangled relative to $\mathfrak{h}$.

(2) $\rho = |\Psi\rangle\langle\Psi|$ with $|\Psi\rangle$ the unique ground state of some Hamiltonian H in $\mathfrak{h}$.

(3) $\rho = |\Psi\rangle\langle\Psi|$ with $|\Psi\rangle$ a lowest-weight vector of $\mathfrak{h}$.

(4) ρ has maximum $\mathfrak{h}$-purity.

3. A FEW EXAMPLES

3.1 Alice and Bob revisited

As mentioned above, this example corresponds to a bipartite situation with preferred distinguishable subsystems A and B. The total Hilbert space $\mathcal{H} \simeq \mathcal{H}_A \otimes \mathcal{H}_B$, such that dim $\mathcal{H}_A = m$, and dim $\mathcal{H}_B = n$. Physical access is restricted to *local* observables acting on one subsystem i.e., observables in the set

$$\Omega_{\text{loc}} = \{\hat{A} \otimes \mathbb{1} \oplus \mathbb{1} \otimes \hat{B}\} , \tag{7}$$

with $\hat{A}$ and $\hat{B}$ Hermitian and traceless. For each pure state $|\Psi\rangle \in \mathcal{H}$, the reduced state ρ_{red} is then determined by the pair of reduced density operators ρ_A and ρ_B.

Theorem:

An Ω_{loc}-state is pure iff it is induced by a pure product state, meaning that *conventional* bipartite entanglement is equivalent to GE relative to Ω_{loc}.

For the particular case of two S=1/2 parties ($m = n = 2$), and $\Omega = \mathfrak{h} = su(2) \oplus su(2) = \{S^j_x, S^j_y, S^j_z |\ j = 1, 2\}$, where the three generators

$$S^j_x = \frac{1}{2}\begin{pmatrix} 0 & 1 \\ 1 & 0 \end{pmatrix}_j , S^j_y = \frac{1}{2}\begin{pmatrix} 0 & -i \\ i & 0 \end{pmatrix}_j , S^j_z = \frac{1}{2}\begin{pmatrix} 1 & 0 \\ 0 & -1 \end{pmatrix}_j \tag{8}$$

satisfy the $su(2)$ algebra $[S^i_\alpha, S^j_\beta] = i\delta_{ij}\varepsilon_{\alpha\beta\delta}S^j_\delta$ ($\varepsilon_{\alpha\beta\delta}$ being the totally antisymmetric tensor, with $\alpha, \beta, \delta = x, y, z$) and a generic normalized state $|\Psi\rangle = a_1|\uparrow\uparrow\rangle + a_2|\uparrow\downarrow\rangle + a_3|\downarrow\uparrow\rangle + a_4|\downarrow\downarrow\rangle$, the purity relative to $\mathfrak{h}$ is

$$P_{\mathfrak{h}}(|\Psi\rangle) = 2\sum_{j,\alpha}\langle\Psi|S^j_\alpha|\Psi\rangle^2 \ , \text{ with the result} \begin{cases} P_{\mathfrak{h}} = 1 & \text{product states} \\ \vdots & \vdots \\ P_{\mathfrak{h}} = 0 & \text{Bell states} \end{cases} . \tag{9}$$

However, when physical access is unrestricted (such as $\Omega = \mathfrak{h}' = su(4)$), *all* pure states have maximal purity meaning that all of them are generalized unentangled.

To understand the relevance of the operator language used to describe our physical system, let us consider a maximally entangled (Bell) state

$$|\text{Bell}\rangle = \frac{|\uparrow\downarrow\rangle - |\downarrow\uparrow\rangle}{\sqrt{2}} = \frac{S^1_+ - S^2_+}{\sqrt{2}}|\downarrow\downarrow\rangle , \tag{10}$$

where $S^j_\pm = S^j_x \pm iS^j_y$, and change our spin into a fermionic description. After a Jordan-Wigner isomorphic mapping

$$\begin{cases} S^1_+ = c^\dagger_1 \\ S^2_+ = (1 - 2n_1)c^\dagger_2 \end{cases} , \text{ the Bell state turns into } |\text{Bell}\rangle = \frac{c^\dagger_1 - c^\dagger_2}{\sqrt{2}}|0\rangle_F , \tag{11}$$

where $|0\rangle_F$ is the fermionic vacuum. Written in the fermionic language this is a single-particle state which can only display *mode* entanglement relative to the local spin algebra $\mathfrak{h}$. However, had we asked whether $|\text{Bell}\rangle$ is entangled relative to the algebra $\mathfrak{h}'' = u(2) = \{(c^\dagger_1 c_2 + c^\dagger_2 c_1)/\sqrt{2}, i(c^\dagger_1 c_2 - c^\dagger_2 c_1)/\sqrt{2}, n_1 - \frac{1}{2}, n_2 - \frac{1}{2}\} = \{(S^1_x S^2_x + S^1_y S^2_y)/\sqrt{2}, (S^1_x S^2_y - S^1_y S^2_x)/\sqrt{2}, S^1_z, S^2_z\}$, the answer would be **No**. The message is that the property of entanglement is independent of the operator language used to describe a state, and only dependent on the observer.

3.2 A single spin $S = 1$

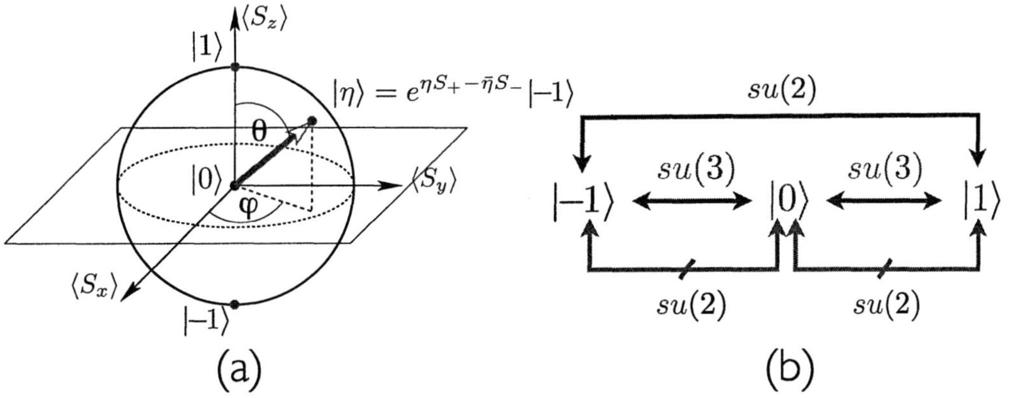

Figure 2. (a) A ball in $\mathbb{R}^3$ of radius one, whose points (vectors of expectations values of the $S = 1$ operators S_x, S_y, and S_z) represent the reduced states. The points on the surface, the extremal ones, are the *spin-coherent* states $|\eta\rangle$ ($\eta \in \mathbb{C}$, and $\bar{\eta}$ is its complex conjugate), or the GCSs of SU(2). These states are generalized unentangled. Notice that the state $|0\rangle$ is at the center of the ball indicating minimal distance and, therefore, maximal generalized entanglement. (b) Schematics of the connections between weight states $|{-1}\rangle, |0\rangle, |1\rangle$ by means of group rotations with elements in the algebras $su(2)$ and $su(3)$. The broken lines indicate that no group element exists in SU(2), able to connect either maximal or minimal weight vectors with $|0\rangle$. On the other hand, there are group elements in SU(3) connecting them.

The extent to which our viewpoint extends the subsystem-based definition may be appreciated in situations where no physically natural subsystem partition exists and conventional entanglement is not directly applicable. Consider a single spin S=1 system, whose three-dimensional state space $\mathcal{H}$ carries an irreducible representation of $su(2)$, with generators S_x, S_y, S_z. Suppose that operational access to the system is restricted to observables in the given representation of $su(2)$

$$S_x = \frac{1}{\sqrt{2}} \begin{pmatrix} 0 & 1 & 0 \\ 1 & 0 & 1 \\ 0 & 1 & 0 \end{pmatrix}, S_y = \frac{1}{\sqrt{2}} \begin{pmatrix} 0 & -i & 0 \\ i & 0 & -i \\ 0 & i & 0 \end{pmatrix}, S_z = \frac{1}{\sqrt{2}} \begin{pmatrix} 1 & 0 & 0 \\ 0 & 0 & 0 \\ 0 & 0 & -1 \end{pmatrix}. \quad (12)$$

The reduced states can be identified with vectors of expectation values of these three observables (see Fig. 2(a)) which form a unit ball in $\mathbb{R}^3$, $\langle S_x \rangle^2 + \langle S_y \rangle^2 + \langle S_z \rangle^2 \leq 1$, and the extremal points are those on the surface, having maximal spin component 1 for some linear combination of S_x, S_y, S_z. These are the *spin coherent states* $|\eta\rangle$, or GCSs for SU(2). For any choice of spin direction, $\mathcal{H}$ is spanned by the $|1\rangle, |0\rangle, |{-1}\rangle$ eigenstates of that spin component; the first and last are GCSs (i.e., unentangled), but $|0\rangle$ is *not*, characterizing $|0\rangle$ as a generalized (*maximally*) entangled state relative to $\mathfrak{h} = su(2)$. Note, however, that all pure states appear generalized-unentangled if access to the full algebra $\mathfrak{h}' = su(3)$ is available (that is, $su(3)$ is distinguished). This is pictorially illustrated in Fig. 2(b).

To appreciate the distinction between separability and generalized unentanglement, let us consider the case of two spins $S = 1$. The only product states that are generalized unentangled with respect to $\mathfrak{h} = su(2) \oplus su(2)$ are those that are products of local SU(2) spin coherent states, e.g., the state $|1\rangle \otimes |1\rangle$. Instead, product states such as $|0\rangle \otimes |0\rangle$ will be entangled (in particular, this state is maximally entangled).

4. QUANTUM PHASE TRANSITIONS AND ENTANGLEMENT

QPTs occur at zero temperature due to changes in the interactions among the constituents of the system. Each quantum phase is characterized by different behaviors of appropriate correlation functions (such as, long-range order, algebraic or exponential decay). Since the notions of entanglement and quantum correlations are intimately related, it becomes quite natural to look for a good measure of entanglement as a way to characterize the QPT.

In this section we study the paramagnetic-to-ferromagnetic QPT present in the one-dimensional ($S = 1/2$) anisotropic XY model in a transverse magnetic field, applying the concepts of GE described in the previous sections (a more expanded discussion is also given in [17]). Fortunately, this model is exactly solvable and the ground state properties are well known, allowing for a better understanding of the entanglement properties at and across the transition point.

The model Hamiltonian for an N (N even) spin system is given by

$$H = -g\sum_{j=1}^{N}[(1+\gamma)\sigma_x^j\sigma_x^{j+1} + (1-\gamma)\sigma_y^j\sigma_y^{j+1}] + \sum_{j=1}^{N}\sigma_z^j \ , \tag{13}$$

where the Pauli spin operators $\sigma_\alpha^j = 2S_\alpha^j$ (see Eq. (8)), $g \in [0,\infty)$ is the ratio between the spin-spin exchange coupling and the external magnetic field, and $\gamma \in [0,1]$ is the anisotropy in the xy-plane. Periodic boundary conditions will be assumed (i.e., $\sigma_\alpha^{N+1} = \sigma_\alpha^1$). The operator $Z_2 = \prod_{j=1}^N \sigma_z^j$ that maps $(\sigma_x^j, \sigma_y^j, \sigma_z^j) \rightarrow (-\sigma_x^j, -\sigma_y^j, \sigma_z^j)$,$\forall j$, is a global ($\mathbb{Z}_2$) symmetry of the model, leaving the Hamiltonian invariant ($[H, Z_2] = 0$). Therefore, for finite N, the energy eigenstates $|E\rangle$ satisfy $Z_2|E\rangle = z_2|E\rangle$, where $z_2 = \pm 1$. The ground state $|G\rangle$ belongs to the sector $z_2 = +1$. For $\gamma = 1$ the model reduces to the Ising model in a transverse magnetic field. In this case and for $g \rightarrow 0$ the spins align in the direction of the external magnetic field (z-direction), so the ground state is $|G\rangle = |\downarrow\downarrow \cdots \downarrow\rangle$. On the other hand, when $g \rightarrow \infty$ the external field becomes irrelevant and the spins align in the x-direction: $|G\rangle \simeq |\rightarrow\rightarrow \cdots \rightarrow\rangle + |\leftarrow\leftarrow \cdots \leftarrow\rangle$, which becomes degenerate with $|G_-\rangle \simeq |\rightarrow\rightarrow \cdots \rightarrow\rangle - |\leftarrow\leftarrow \cdots \leftarrow\rangle$ in the thermodynamic limit ($N \rightarrow \infty$). Therefore, the system undergoes a QPT at some critical value g_c such that for $g > g_c$ a long range order in the x-direction develops ($\langle\sigma_x^1\sigma_x^{N/2}\rangle = M_x^2 \neq 0$, where M_x is the total magnetization in the x-direction) and the global $\mathbb{Z}_2$ symmetry breaks spontaneously. In other words, for $g > g_c$ the quantum phase is ferromagnetic (see Fig. 3).

The situation is similar for other anisotropies γ. In principle, one would expect that the critical point g_c depends on the anisotropy. Remarkably, this is not the case and $g_c = 1/2$, $\forall\gamma$ such that $1 \geq \gamma > 0$. (No QPT occurs for $\gamma = 0$.)

4.1 The hydrogen atom of QPT

As mentioned before, the anisotropic XY model in a transverse magnetic field is exactly solvable. Finding its ground state is a simple task if we first map the Pauli spin operators into spinless fermionic operators through the Jordan-Wigner formula

$$S_+^j = \frac{\sigma_x^j + i\sigma_y^j}{2} = \left(\prod_{k=1}^{j-1} -\sigma_z^k\right) c_j^\dagger \ , \ \sigma_z^j = 2n_j - 1 \ , \tag{14}$$

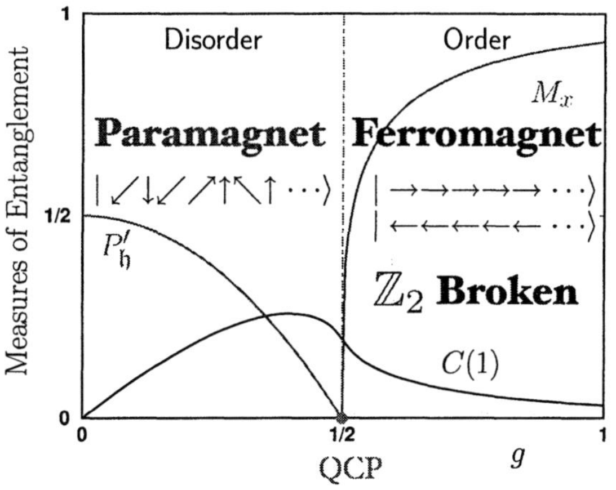

Figure 3. Measures of entanglement for the Ising model in a transverse magnetic field ($\gamma = 1$). The blue line represents the magnetization in the x-direction M_x (order parameter), the black line is the nearest neighbors concurrence $C(1)$, and the red line identifies the purity relative to the $u(N)$ Lie algebra, $P'_{\mathfrak{h}} = P_{\mathfrak{h}} - 1/(1+\gamma)$. QCP stands for quantum critical point.

where the operators $c_j^\dagger$ and $c_j = (c_j^\dagger)^\dagger$, create and destroy a fermion at site j, respectively, and $n_j = c_j^\dagger c_j$ is the fermionic number operator.

Since the model exhibits translational symmetry, it is useful to map the fermionic operators in the site representation to the Fourier-transformed operators; i.e., to

$$c_k^\dagger = \frac{1}{\sqrt{N}} \sum_{j=1}^{N} e^{-ikj} c_j^\dagger \,, \tag{15}$$

where the operator $c_k^\dagger$ ($c_k = (c_k^\dagger)^\dagger$) creates (destroys) a fermion in the mode k. In the fermionic language the sector $z_2 = +1$ corresponds to fermionic anti-periodic boundary conditions and thus $k \in K = K_+ + K_- = \left[\pm\frac{\pi}{N}, \pm\frac{3\pi}{N}, \cdots, \pm\frac{(N-1)\pi}{N}\right]$. Since the ground state $|G\rangle$ belongs to this sector we will only consider these 2^{N-1} states. In this new operator algebra, the Hamiltonian possess terms that correlate the k and $-k$ modes (Cooper pairs). At this point, the Hamiltonian can be diagonalized by performing a Bogoliubov transformation; that is, by defining a new set of fermionic (quasiparticle) operators $\gamma_k^\dagger = u_k c_k^\dagger + i v_k c_{-k}$, with $u_k^2 + v_k^2 = 1$, $u_k = u_{-k}$, and $v_k = -v_{-k}$. The transformed Hamiltonian reads

$$H = \sum_{k \in K} \epsilon_k (\gamma_k^\dagger \gamma_k - 1/2) \,, \tag{16}$$

where $\gamma_k^\dagger \gamma_k$ is the quasiparticle number operator. Since the energy per mode $\epsilon_k = 2\sqrt{(-1+2g\cos k)^2 + 4g^2\gamma^2 \sin^2 k} > 0 \;\forall k \in K$, the ground state of the system contains no quasiparticles: $\gamma_k|G\rangle = 0$. Thus, $|G\rangle = |\mathrm{BCS}\rangle = \prod_{k \in K_+} (u_k + i v_k c_k^\dagger c_{-k}^\dagger)|0\rangle_F$, where $|0\rangle_F$ is the fermionic vacuum state (i.e., $c_k|0\rangle_F = 0$), and the name $|\mathrm{BCS}\rangle$ refers to the Bardeen-Cooper-Schrieffer superconducting state.

4.2 $\mathfrak{h}$-Purity as an indicator of the QPT

Figure 3 displays the behavior of the concurrence $C(1)$ (a measure of bipartite entanglement) between nearest neighbors for the case $\gamma = 1$ (Ising model in a transverse magnetic field) as a function of g (see also [8]). Although it is possible to show that its derivative, $\partial_g C(1)$, diverges at the critical point ($g_c = 1/2$), the function itself has a smooth behavior across g_c, thus it does not directly characterize the QPT. Moreover, one also finds that for $\gamma = 0$ (isotropic case) where no QPT occurs, $\partial_g C(1)$ still shows a singularity, thus being an incorrect indicator of a QPT in this case.

The relevant question is whether GE may be able to characterize the QPT, and to what extent. In order to answer this question we first have to identify the relevant algebra $\mathfrak{h}$ of observables that should be considered. Since in terms of fermionic operators (after the Jordan-Wigner transformation) the Hamiltonian of the system is a linear combination of quadratic operators belonging to the Lie algebra $so(2N) = \{c_k^\dagger c_{k'}, c_k^\dagger c_{k'}^\dagger, c_k c_{k'} | \ \forall \ k, k' \in K\}$, the ground state (if not degenerate) must be a GCS of this algebra. In other words, the $|\text{BCS}\rangle$ state can be obtained by applying $so(2N)$ group operations to the fully polarized state (which is also a GCS of $so(2N)$): $|\text{BCS}\rangle = \prod_{k \in K_+} e^{i\phi_k c_k^\dagger c_{-k}^\dagger} |0\rangle_F$, with $u_k = \cos\phi_k$ and $v_k = \sin\phi_k$. In this way, the $\mathfrak{h}$-purity relative to this algebra is always maximum ($P_\mathfrak{h} = 1, \ \forall \ g, \gamma$) and does not give information about the QPT.

The $|\text{BCS}\rangle$ state has no longer the property of being GCS and becomes generalized entangled ($P_\mathfrak{h} < 1$) when we choose a Lie subalgebra of $so(2N)$ that does not contain operators of the form $c_k^\dagger c_{-k}^\dagger$. This is the case if we consider the subalgebra that conserves the number of fermions; that is $u(N) = \{c_k^\dagger c_{k'} | \ \forall k, k' \in K\}$. In particular, in the $|\text{BCS}\rangle$ state the expectation values of the operators in $u(N)$ are $\langle c_k^\dagger c_{k'}\rangle = \delta_{kk'} v_k^2$. The $\mathfrak{h}$-purity becomes

$$P_\mathfrak{h}(|\text{BCS}\rangle) = \frac{4}{N} \sum_{k \in K} \langle c_k^\dagger c_k - 1/2\rangle^2 = \frac{4}{N} \sum_{k \in K} (v_k^2 - 1/2)^2 \ , \tag{17}$$

where the constant $1/2$ has been subtracted for normalization reasons. Then, any fermionic product state of the form $|\psi\rangle = c_{k_1}^\dagger c_{k_2}^\dagger \cdots c_{k_m}^\dagger |0\rangle_F$ is a GCS of this algebra, thus, it has maximum purity ($P_\mathfrak{h} = 1$).

The $\mathfrak{h}$-purity relative to the $u(N)$ algebra for the $|\text{BCS}\rangle$ state can be exactly calculated in the thermodynamic limit (where the sum becomes an integral), yielding

$$P_\mathfrak{h}(|\text{BCS}\rangle) = \begin{cases} \frac{1}{1-\gamma^2}\left[1 - \frac{\gamma^2}{\sqrt{1-4g^2(1-\gamma^2)}}\right] & \text{for } g \leq g_c \\ \frac{1}{1+\gamma} & \text{for } g > g_c \end{cases} . \tag{18}$$

Obviously, $P_\mathfrak{h} = 1$ for $g = 0$, where the state $|\text{BCS}\rangle$ reduces to $|0\rangle_F \equiv |{\downarrow\downarrow} \cdots {\downarrow}\rangle$. On the other hand, the $\mathfrak{h}$-purity can be related with the fluctuations in the total number of fermions in this model,

$$P_\mathfrak{h}(|\text{BCS}\rangle) = 1 - \frac{2}{N}(\langle \hat{N}^2\rangle - \langle \hat{N}\rangle^2) \ , \ \text{where } \hat{N} = \sum_{k \in K} c_k^\dagger c_k \ . \tag{19}$$

Figure 4(a) shows the (shifted) $\mathfrak{h}$-purity vs g, for different anisotropies γ. Remarkably, this function behaves as a *disorder parameter*, being 0 in the ferromagnetic (ordered) phase and different from 0 in the paramagnetic (disordered) phase, sharply identifying the QPT. Moreover, for $\gamma = 0$, where there is no QPT, the $\mathfrak{h}$-purity remains constant as one would expect for a good QPT indicator.

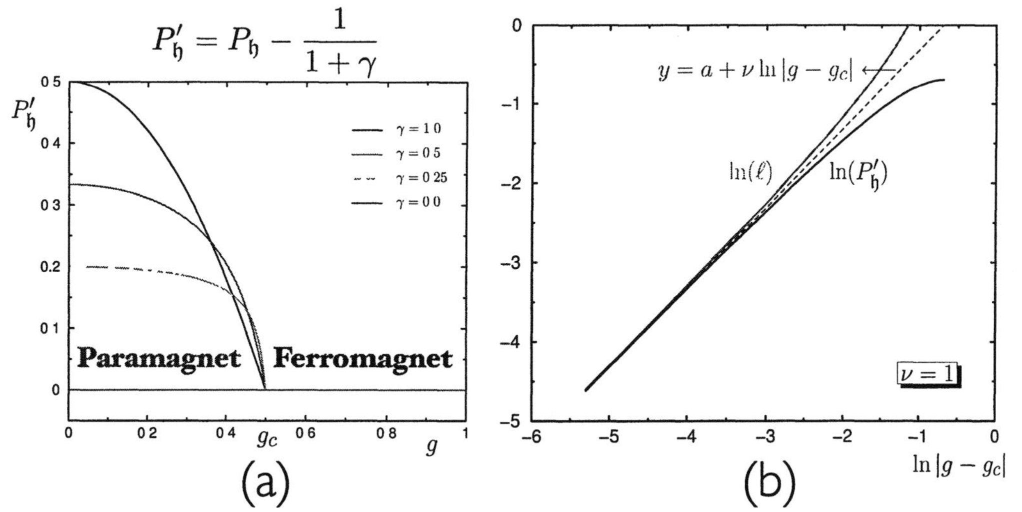

Figure 4. (a) Purity (shifted) relative to the $u(N)$ algebra in the ground state $|\text{BCS}\rangle$ of the anisotropic XY model in a transverse magnetic field. (b) Scaling behavior of the purity relative to the $u(N)$ algebra.

The critical behavior of the $\mathfrak{h}$-purity can also be extracted by performing a Taylor-expansion near the critical point (in the disordered phase). One finds $P_{\mathfrak{h}} \sim (g_c - g)^\nu$ (Fig. 4(b)), with $\nu = 1$ being the critical exponent that characterizes the Ising universality class; that is, the correlation length ℓ in this model diverges with the same exponent (Fig. 4(b)): $\ell \sim (g_c - g)^{-\nu}$.

All these interesting features make the quadratic purity measure of GE a physically appealing measure that characterizes the QPT. In principle, for other kinds of systems one could think in terms of different algebras of observables. However, identifying the appropriate algebra remains in general an open problem.

5. CONCLUSIONS

Entanglement is of one of the key features of quantum mechanics, and consequently a deep understanding of its properties and physical implications is essential not only to fundamentally advance our understanding of how Nature works, but also to design more powerful technologies. In this work we have described a generalization of conventional entanglement which is applicable to arbitrary physical settings, going beyond the standard distinguishable-subsystem approach. It is clear from our formulation that entanglement is a (relative) context-dependent notion, whose properties are determined by the expectations of a distinguished set of observables Ω of the system of interest, thus being observer-dependent. The concept is independent of the operator language used to describe the system but depends upon the way we can physically access information. (In the QIP setting locality is usually involved.) Most importantly, we have tied together the theory of entanglement and the theory of generalized coherent states in those cases where the set Ω forms a Lie algebra $\mathfrak{h}$, thus establishing that generalized unentangled states are the (highest-weight) generalized coherent states of $\mathfrak{h}$. We have also introduced measures of generalized entanglement. In particular, we introduced the purity relative to a subalgebra which can represent a global measure of entanglement. Different choices of observable subalgebras may provide different information on the hierarchical structure of quantum correlations.

In the second part of the paper we discussed an application of our theory of generalized entanglement to the study of quantum phase transitions. We showed that the purity relative to a subalgebra can be used as a quantum phase transition indicator. Indeed, it is a useful diagnostic tool playing the role of a disorder (or order [7]) parameter for broken-symmetry quantum phase transitions. Several important open questions remain. In particular: Given the model Hamiltonian describing a physical system, what is the minimum number of observable algebras $\mathfrak{h}$ one needs to fully characterize a quantum critical point in arbitrary space dimensions? How would one choose them?

The research described herein was sponsored by the US DOE. GO is grateful to the US Army Research Office for travel support.

REFERENCES

[1] A. Einstein, B. Podolsky, and N. Rosen, Phys. Rev. **47**, 777 (1935).

[2] J. S. Bell, *Speakable and Unspeakable in Quantum Mechanics*, (Cambridge Univ. Press, Cambridge, 1993).

[3] E. Schrödinger, Naturwissenschaften **23**, 807 (1935), *ibid* 823 (1935), *ibid* 844 (1935).

[4] M. A. Nielsen and I. L. Chuang, *Quantum Computation and Quantum Information* (Cambridge Univ. Press, Cambridge, 2000).

[5] L. Viola, E. Knill, and R. Laflamme, J. Phys. A: Math. Gen **34**, 7067 (2001).

[6] P. Zanardi, Phys. Rev. Lett. **87**, 077901 (2001).

[7] T. J. Osborne and M. A. Nielsen, Quant. Inf. Process. **1**, 45 (2002); Phys. Rev. A **66**, 032110 (2002).

[8] A. Osterloh, L. Amico, G. Falci, and R. Fazio, Nature **416**, 608 (2002).

[9] M. Arnesen, S. Bose, and V. Vedral, Phys. Rev. Lett. **87**, 290 (2001).

[10] G. Vidal, J. I. Latorre, E. Rico, and A. Kitaev, Phys. Rev. Lett. **90**, 227902 (2003).

[11] K. Eckert, J. Schliemann, D. Bruß, and M. Lewenstein, Ann. Phys. **299**, 88 (2002).

[12] C. D. Batista and G. Ortiz, Phys. Rev. Lett. **86**, 1082 (2001); Adv. Phys. (in press) and cond-mat/0207106; G. Ortiz and C. D. Batista in *Recent Progress in Many-Body Theories*, Eds. R. F. Bishop, T. Brandes, K. A. Gernoth, N. R. Walet, and Y. Xian (World Scientific, Singapore, 2002), p. 425.

[13] H. Barnum, E. Knill, G. Ortiz, and L. Viola, Phys. Rev. A **68**, 032308 (2003).

[14] H. Barnum, E. Knill, G. Ortiz, R. Somma, and L. Viola, Phys. Rev. Lett. (submitted) and quant-ph/0305023.

[15] A. Perelomov, *Generalized Coherent States and their Applications*, (Springer Verlag, Berlin, 1986).

[16] R. Delbourgo and J. R. Fox, J. Phys. A, **10** L233 (1977); R. Delbourgo, J. Phys. A **10**, 1837 (1977).

[17] R. Somma, G. Ortiz, H. Barnum, E. Knill, and L. Viola (unpublished preprint).

A SYSTEMATIC NUMERICAL SURVEY OF THE SEPARABILITY CRITERIA FOR BIPARTITE QUANTUM SYSTEMS

M. Casas[1], *J. Batle*[1], *A. R. Plastino*[1,2,3] *and A. Plastino*[3]

[1] Departament de Física and IMEDEA-CSIC, Universitat de les Illes Balears, 07122 Palma de Mallorca, Spain

[2] Physics Department, University of Pretoria, Pretoria 0002, South Africa

[3] National University La Plata and CONICET, C. C. 727, 1900 La Plata, Argentina

1. INTRODUCTION

Quantum entanglement is the basic resource required to implement quantum information processes [1]. One of the most important challenges in both science and technology is that posed by quantum computation [1]. In classical computers the information is recorded in macroscopic two-level systems called bits and, for instance, given the problem of evaluating a function f at N points, the computational time grows exponentially with the number of steps required. In addition, the classical information can be read, duplicated and transmitted. In quantum computers the information is recorded and processed at a microscopical level using a basic two-level quantum system, called qubit, that can be found in any quantum superposition of states corresponding to two classical bits. This fact allows one to compute the function f at N points "in one shot", so to speak, so that the computational time grows only polynomiacally with the number of steps. Quantum information cannot, in general, be read or duplicated without disturbing the physical system that supports it, but can be encoded in quantum entangled states and even teleported.

Consequently, an adequate characterization of quantum entangled states is crucial for the development of the most important processes studied by quantum information [2-5]. i.e., as quantum teleportation [6], quantum cryptography [1], superdense coding [7], and quantum computation.

It is well known that, given a finite dimensional Hilbert space $H_{AB} = H_A \otimes H_B$

of a bipartite quantum system of dimension $N_1 \times N_2$, where N_1 is the dimension of H_A and N_2 the dimension of H_B, a state belonging to the composite system H_{AB} is called *separable* or classically correlated if the density matrix can be represented as

$$\hat{\rho}_{AB} = \sum_{i=1}^{n} \lambda_i \rho_i^{(A)} \otimes \rho_i^{(B)} \ , \tag{1}$$

with $0 \leq \lambda_i \leq 1$ and $\sum_{i=1}^{n} \lambda_i = 1$. Otherwise the state is *entangled* or quantum correlated. The most simple quantum system that exhibits entanglement is the two-qubits system for which $N_1 = N_2 = 2$, and a common example of a maximum entangled states is the singlet one.

The separability of a composite system can also be related with the entropy or with the information measures appropriate for the system under scrutiny. As it is well known, the information measure of a classical composite system $A \oplus B$ considered as a whole is always greater or equal than that pertaining to its subsystems. This is also the case for separable states of a composite quantum system, but apparently there are some entangled states such that the entropy of the complete system is smaller than the entropy of each individual subsystems and some others for which the entropy of the system is larger than the entropy of each subsystem. Only for pure states the entropy provide a measure of entanglement, because a pure quantum state is entangled if and only if one of its subsystems possesses an entropy larger than zero. As a consequence of the behaviour of composite quantum mixed states, the classical entropic inequalities provide only necessary but not sufficient conditions for quantum separability. This situation holds for the well known von Neumann entropy and for more general q-entropic measures such as the Rényi's or Tsallis' families, both characterized by a real parameter q.

Several approaches have been developed in order to obtain practical separability criteria for density matrices. Only the Peres-Horodecki criterion (PPT) [8] provides a necessary and sufficient condition for quantum separability in the case of Hilbert spaces of dimension 2×2 (two-qubits) and 2×3 (qubit-qutrit). The PPT criterion assert's that a density matrix $\hat{\rho}$ of a bipartite system is separable if and only if its partial transpose is positive defined. This criterion holds for systems of dimension 2×2 and 2×3, but in the more general case it only provides a necessary condition because there are some entangled states for which the partial transpose of $\hat{\rho}$ is positive defined.

In this paper, by means of a systematic numerical simulation, we try to elucidate the best value of the q parameter so that we can establish some correlations between entanglement and the q-information measures. The same numerical simulation allows us to define some relations among the separability criteria existing so far.

The paper is organized as follows. In section 2 we present the systematic numerical study of pure and mixed states of a quantum system of dimension $N = N_1 \times N_2$ and the relation of the degree of entanglement with the q-parameter of the q-information entropies. In section 3 we analyze the different separability criteria and their inclusion relations and finally in section 4 we present some conclusions.

2. Entanglement and q-information measures

In order to perform a systematic numerical survey of the state space $\mathcal{S}$ of pure and mixed states, we introduce an appropriate measure μ on this space [9-11]. An arbitrary state $\hat{\rho}$ of a quantum system described by a N-dimensional Hilbert space can be expressed as

$$\hat{\rho} = UD[\{\lambda_i\}]U^\dagger, \tag{2}$$

where $U(N)$ is an $N \times N$ unitary matrix and $D[\{\lambda_i\}]$ is a $N \times N$ diagonal matrix whose diagonal elements are $\{\lambda_1, \ldots, \lambda_N\}$, with $0 \leq \lambda_i \leq 1$, and $\sum_i \lambda_i = 1$. In the group of unitary matrices we use the uniform Haar measure [11]. In the N-simplex Δ provided by $D[\{\lambda_i\}]$ we use the Lebesgue measure $\mathcal{L}_{N-1}$ on $\mathcal{R}^{N-1}$. The above measures lead in turn to a measure μ on the set $\mathcal{S}$ of all quantum states

$$\mu = \nu \times \mathcal{L}_{N-1}. \tag{3}$$

In our numerical simulation we randomly generate pure and mixed states according to (3). This measure converges rapidly even for high dimensional systems. and provides a simple procedure to compare different separability criteria.

In order to study the relation between the entanglement properties of the generated states and the parameter q of the particular q-information measure, we have used

a) the Tsallis q-entropy

$$T_q = \frac{1}{q-1}\left(1 - \omega_q\right) \text{ with } \omega_{\rm q} = \mathrm{Tr}\left(\rho^{\rm q}\right), \tag{4}$$

b) the Rényi q-entropy

$$R_q = \frac{1}{1-q} \ln(\omega_q), \tag{5}$$

and the corresponding conditional entropies

$$T_q(A|B) = \frac{T_q(\rho_{AB}) - T_q(\rho_B)}{1 + (1-q)T_q(\rho_B)}, \tag{6}$$

for the Tsallis case, its Rényi's counterpart being

$$R_q(A|B) = R_q(\rho_{AB}) - R_q(\rho_B), \tag{7}$$

where ρ_{AB} is the density matrix of the composite system $A \oplus B$ and $\rho_B = Tr_A(\rho_{AB})$. The conditional q-entropy $T_q(B|A)$ is defined in a similar way as (6), replacing ρ_B by $\rho_A = Tr_B(\rho_{AB})$.

For separable states, we have

$$
\begin{aligned}
T_q(A|B) &\geq 0 \\
T_q(B|A) &\geq 0
\end{aligned}
\tag{8}
$$

and the same condition holds for Rényi's case.

For the sake of establishing some connections between entanglement and total q-entropies of bipartite quantum systems, we restrict ourselves to the case of two-qubits systems. For this particular instance, Wootters obtained an explicit expression for the entanglement of formation $E[\hat{\rho}]$. The entanglement of formation [12] quantifies the resources needed to create a given entangled state $\hat{\rho}$. Wootters's formula reads [13]

$$
E(\hat{\rho}) = h\left(\frac{1+\sqrt{1-C^2}}{2}\right) , \tag{9}
$$

where $h(x) = -x\log_2 x - (1-x)\log_2(1-x)$, and $C(\hat{\rho})$ is the so called concurrence given by $C(\hat{\rho}) = max(0, \lambda_1 - \lambda_2 - \lambda_3 - \lambda_4)$, where the λ_i's are the square roots, in decreasing order, of the eigenvalues of the non-hermitian matrix $\hat{\rho}\tilde{\rho}$, with $\tilde{\rho} = (\sigma_y \otimes \sigma_y)\rho^\star(\sigma_y \otimes \sigma_y)$, and $\rho^\star$ are the complex conjugate of $\hat{\rho}$. The entanglement of formation $E[\hat{\rho}]$ is a monotonous function of the concurrence squared C^2 and both provide a measure of the degree of entanglement.

We use C^2 to establish the connection between the degree of entanglement of the generated two qubits states and the Rényi entropy R_q. We have computed the dispersions of R_q

$$
\sigma_q^{(R)} = [< R_q^2 > - < R_q >^2]^{1/2} , \tag{10}
$$

and the derivatives of the average q-entropy with respect to C^2

$$
d < R_q > /d(C^2) , \tag{11}
$$

A given q value would lead to a good entropic "indicator" if it corresponds to a large value of $d < R_q > /d(C^2)$ and a small value of σ_q. The two factors are appropriately taken into account in the ratio r

$$
r = \left| \frac{\sigma_q^{(R)}}{d < R_q > /d(C^2)} \right| , \tag{12}
$$

The value of r as a function of C^2 is plotted in Fig. 1 for $q = 1$ and $q = \infty$ and provides a quantitative measure for the strength of the entropic entanglement correlations. In fact we can consider that r estimates the smallest increment ΔC^2 in the square of concurrence which produces a change in R_q [14]. Consequently, small values of r indicate that the q value considered is a better indicator of the degree of entanglement measured by means of C^2. The two upper curves in Fig. 1 correspond to the r values obtained by considering all two-qubits states generated by means of (3). The lower curves are the results obtained considering only states diagonal in the Bell basis. In both cases the values of r associated with $q = \infty$ can be considered better indicators of the entanglement than the q information measures associated

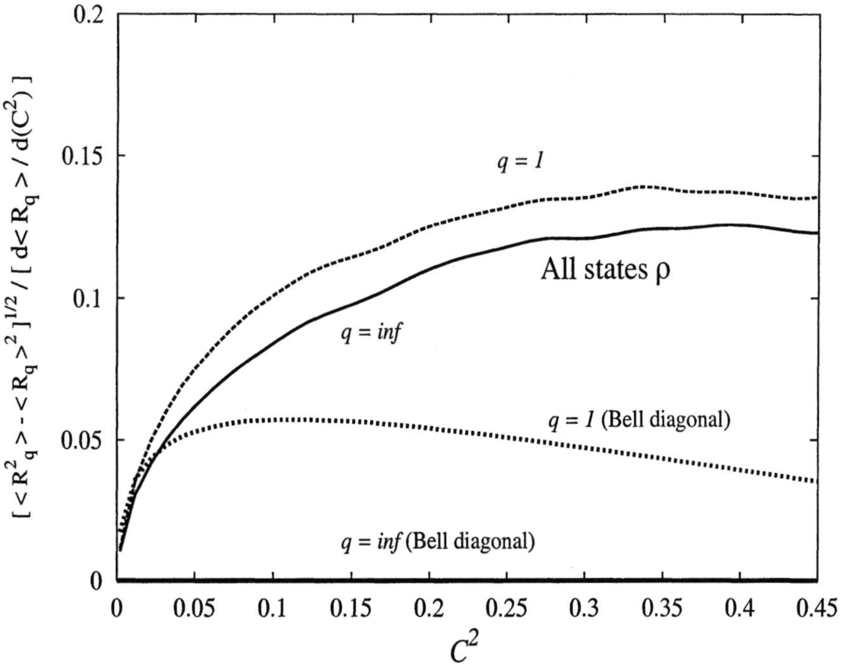

Figure 1. Absolute value of $r = \left|\frac{\sigma_q^{(R)}}{d<R_q>/d(C^2)}\right|$ as a function of the squared concurrence C^2 for $q = 1$ and $q = \infty$. The lower curves are obtained using the set of states diagonal in the Bell basis and the upper ones with the set of all generated two qubits states.

with other q values. Nevertheless the improvement when we use all two-qubits states is smaller in comparison with the results obtained using only states diagonal in the Bell basis, because for these states there is a perfect correlation between C^2 and the Rényi entropy for $q = \infty$, and consequently r vanishes. In reefs. [15,16] the authors, by using only states diagonal in the Bell basis, suggested that the q-information measures with $q = \infty$ are better indicators of the entanglement. Fig. 1 shows, that even if the conjecture is correct, the results obtained using only the set of states diagonal in the Bell basis, cannot be extrapolated in general to the complete state-space of two qubits.

Using the conditional entropies (6) and (7) we have analyzed the volume in state space corresponding to those states complying with the classical q-entropic inequalities (8). We have shown that the volume of states complying with (8) in the case $q = \infty$ is the closest one to the set of states with positive partial transpose (PPT)[17]. For any Hilbert space of dimension $N_1 \times N_2$ the volume of states with positive conditional q-entropies ($q = \infty$) is larger than the volume associated with states complying with PPT (see Fig. 2), because it has been proved that there is no necessary and sufficient criteria for quantum separability based only on the eigenvalues ρ_{AB}, ρ_A and ρ_B.

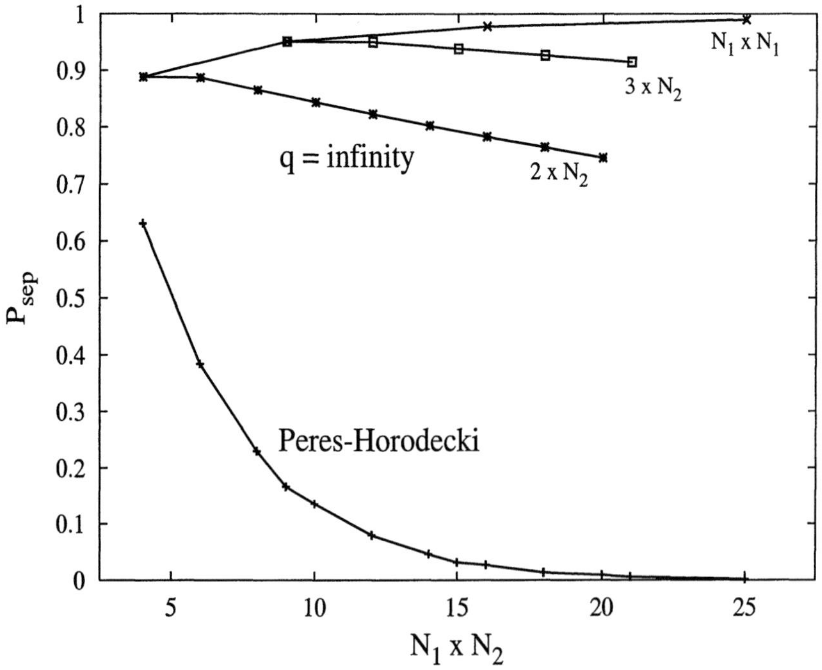

Figure 2. Probability of separability obtained by means of the classical entropic inequalities with $q = \infty$ for systems of dimension $2 \times N_2$, $3 \times N_2$ and $N_1 \times N_1$. For comparison the results of the Peres-Horodecki (PPT) criterion are also shown.

We also shown [17] that the volume of states associated with positive valued conditional q-entropies behave in a monotonous way in spite of the fact that the monotonicity property does not hold for every state.

3. Relations between different separability criteria

Horodecki *et al.* [18] have shown that a density matrix $\rho \equiv \rho_{AB}$ is entangled if and only if there exists an entanglement witness (a hermitian super-operator $\hat{W} = \hat{W}^\dagger$) such that

$$\begin{aligned} &Tr\,\hat{W}\,\rho \leq 0, \quad \text{while} \\ &Tr\,\hat{W}\,\rho \geq 0, \quad \text{for all separable states} \end{aligned} \tag{13}$$

The positive partial transpose (PPT) provides a necessary and sufficient condition for Hilbert spaces of dimension up to 2×3. For Hilbert spaces of higher dimensions the PPT criterion is only necessary but not sufficient, nevertheless as we have found by means of our numerical simulation it is the most restrictive condition.

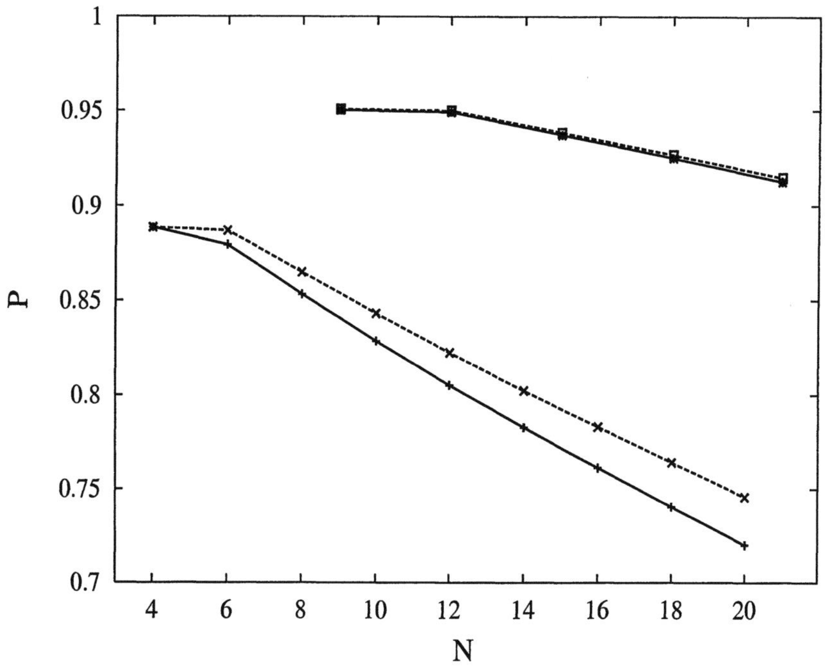

Figure 3. Dashed line: Probability of finding a state with two conditional q-entropies positive ($q = \infty$). The result obtained by means of the majorization criterion is shown by the solid line. Top curves represent a Hilbert space of dimension $3 \times N_2$ and bottom a system of dimension $2 \times N_2$.

Let T stand for matrix transposition. The PPT requires that

$$[\hat{1} \otimes \hat{T}](\rho) \geq 0., \tag{14}$$

Another operational criterion is called the *reduction* criterion, that is satisfied, for a given state $\rho \equiv \rho_{AB}$, when both [19]

$$\begin{aligned} \hat{1} \otimes \rho_B - \rho &\geq 0 \\ \rho_A \otimes \hat{1} - \rho &\geq 0 \end{aligned} \tag{15}$$

If a state satisfies the PPT criterion, it automatically verifies the reduction criterion [19] and, using the numerical simulation (3), we have proved that the converse is also true for systems of dimension $2 \times N_2$. Intuitively, the distillable entanglement is the maximum asymptotic yield of singleton states that can be obtained, via LOCC, from a given mixed state. Horodecki *et al.* [20] demonstrated that any entangled mixed state of two qubits can be distilled to obtain the singleton. This is not true in general. There are entangled mixed states of two qutrits, for instance, that cannot be distilled, so that they are useless for quantum communication. In our scenario an important fact is that all states that violate the reduction criterion are distillable [21].

The most restrictive criterion based on the eigenvalues of ρ_{AB}, ρ_A and ρ_B is majorization. Let $\{\lambda_i\}$ be the set of eigenvalues of the matrix ξ_1 and $\{\gamma_i\}$ be the set of eigenvalues of the matrix ξ_2. We assert that the ordered set of eigenvalues $\vec{\lambda}$ of ξ_1 *majorizes* the ordered set of eigenvalues $\vec{\gamma}$ of ξ_2 (and write $\vec{\lambda} \succ \vec{\gamma}$) when $\sum_{i=1}^{k} \lambda_i \geq \sum_{i=1}^{k} \gamma_i$ for all k. It has been shown [22] that, for all separable states $\rho_{AB} \equiv \rho$,

$$\begin{aligned} \vec{\lambda}_{\rho_A} &\succ \vec{\lambda}_{\rho}, \text{ and} \\ \vec{\lambda}_{\rho_B} &\succ \vec{\lambda}_{\rho} \end{aligned} \tag{16}$$

By means of our numerical simulation we have shown that all states that verify reduction and PPT also verify majorization strictures [23]. There is an intimate relation between this majorization criterion and the entropic inequalities. Majorization probabilities are lower bounds for relative q-entropic inequalities and both criteria coincide for two-qubits systems when we take $q = \infty$ (see Fig. 3). Notice that the two approaches give similar results for $N = 3 \times N_2$.

Concerning the probability of distillability we shown in Fig. 4 the relative number of states that violate the reduction criterion for $N = 2 \times N_2$ (upper solid line) and $N = 3 \times N_2$ (lower line). Notice that as N grows the probability of finding distillable states also grows. These results are upper bounds to the ones encountered by the majorization criterion.

5. CONCLUSIONS

By recourse of a Monte Carlo simulation we have established that the q-entropies with the parameter $q = \infty$ are better indicators of the degree of entanglement of a bipartite quantum state in comparison with the ones obtained using other q finite values. However when consider the whole state space the advantage of the value $q = \infty$ turns out to be much smaller than the one we can infer from the study of the set of states diagonal in the Bell basis.

Concerning the classical entropic inequalities, also the value $q = \infty$ provides the most restrictive separability criterion, i.e. the one most closely to the PPT criterion in comparison with the results obtained with other q-values.

The same Monte Carlo simulation allows us to perform a systematic comparison between different separability criteria.

Following the work of B. Terhal [19] we have numerically proved that for a system of dimension $2 \times N_2$ the PPT and the reduction separability criteria coincide. For systems with larger dimension the reduction criteria is less restrictive than PPT.

The separability probabilities given by the majorization criteria are a lower bound to the results obtained by the q-entropic inequalities for $q = \infty$, the two criteria coincide only for two qubits systems. For dimension larger than $3 \times N_2$ the two criteria give almost the same results.

Majorization criterion is also less restrictive than reduction criterion and the

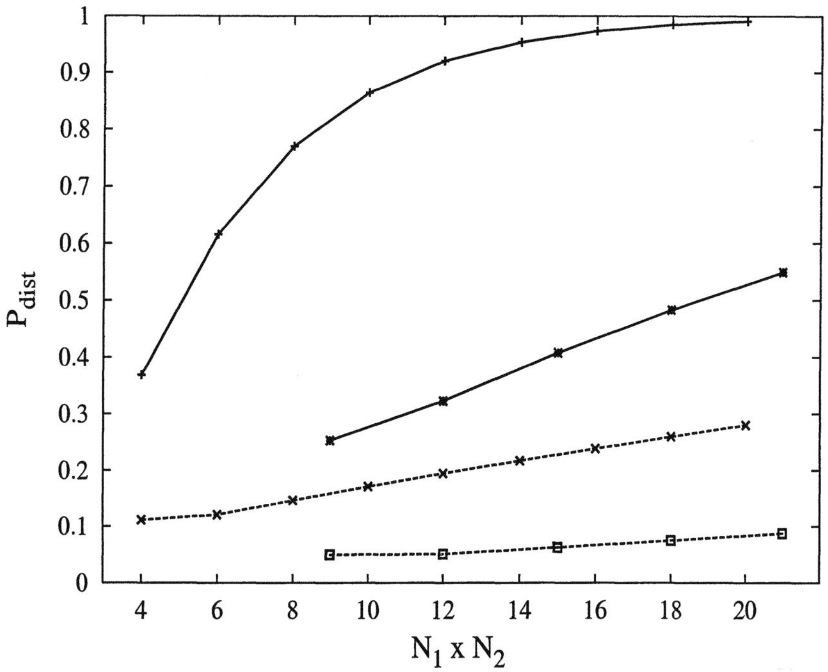

Figure 4. Probability that a state violates the reduction criterion (solid line). Top corresponds to systems of dimension $N = 2 \times N_2$ and bottom to systems of dimension $N = 3 \times N_2$. The same violation obtained by the majorization criterion is given by the dashed lines (crosses $N = 2 \times N_2$ and squares $N = 3 \times N_2$).

violation of the last one gives a better lower bound to the volume of distillable states in comparison with the results obtained by means of the majorization criteria.

ACKNOWLEDGMENTS

This work was partially supported by the MCYT grant BFM2002-0341 and SAB2001-0006 (Spain), by the Government of Balearic Islands and by CONICET (Argentine Agency).

REFERENCES

[1] M.A. Nielsen and I.L. Chuang, *Quantum Computation and Quantum Information*, Cambridge University Press, Cambridge (2000).

[2] Hoi-Kwong Lo, S. Popescu, T. Spiller (ed.), *Introduction to Quantum Computation and Information*, World Scientific, River Edge (1998).

[3] C.P. Williams (ed.), *Quantum Computing and Quantum Communications*, Springer,

Berlin (1998).

[4] D. Bouwmeester, A. Ekert, A. Zeilinger (ed.), *The Physics of Quantum Information*, Springer, Berlin, Heidelberg (1998).

[5] G. Alber, T. Beth, P. Horodecki, R. Horodecki, M. Röttler, H. Weinfurter, R. Werner, A. Zeilinger, *Quantum Information*, Springer Tracts in Modern Physics 173, Springer, Berlin (2001).

[6] C.H. Bennett, G. Brassard, C. Crepeau, R. Jozsa, A. Peres, W.K. Wootters, *Phys. Rev. Lett.* **70**, 1895 (1993).

[7] C.H. Bennett, S.J. Wiesner, *Phys. Rev. Lett.* **69**, 2881 (1993).

[8] A. Peres, *Quantum Theory: Concepts and Methods*, Kluwer, Dordrecht (1993).

[9] K. Zyczkowski, P. Horodecki, A. Sanpera, M. Lewenstein, *Phys. Rev. A* **58**, 883 (1998).

[10] K. Zyczkowski, *Phys. Rev. A* **60**, 3496 (1999).

[11] M. Pozniak, K. Zyczkowski, M. Kus, *J. Phys A: Math. Gen.* **31**, 1059 (1998).

[12] C. H. Bennett, D. P. DiVicenzo, J. Smolin, W. K. Wootters, *Phys. Rev A* **54**, 3824 (1996).

[13] W. K. Wootters *Phys. Rev. Lett.* **80**, 2245 (1998).

[14] J. Batle, M. Casas, A. Plastino, A. R. Plastino *Phys. Lett. A* **318**, 506 (2003).

[15] F. Giraldi, P. Gringolini, *Phys. Rev. E* **64**, 2310 (2001).

[16] N. Canosa, R. Rossignoli, *Phys. Rev. Lett.* **88**, 170401 (2001).

[17] J. Batle, A. R. Plastino, M. Casas, A. Plastino, *Eur. Phys. J. B* **35**, 391 (2003).

[18] M. Horodecki, P. Horodecki, R. Horodecki, *Phys. Lett. A* **223**, 1 (1996).

[19] B.M. Terhal, *Theor. Comput. Sci.* **287**, 313 (2002).

[20] M. Horodecki, P. Horodecki, R. Horodecki, *Phys. Rev. Lett.* **78**, 574 (1997).

[21] M. Horodecki, P. Horodecki, *Phys. Rev. A* **59**, 4206 (1999).

[22] M.A. Nielsen, J. Kempe, *Phys. Rev. Lett.* **86**, 5184 (2001).

[23] J. Batle, A.R. Plastino, M. Casas, A. Plastino, *J. Phys A: Math. Gen.* (in press) (2003).

Appendix

THE SMALL WORLD OF THE NOBEL NEMATODE CAENORHABDITIS ELEGANS

J. W. Clark and A. T. Eggebrecht
Department of Physics, Washington University
St. Louis, Missouri 63130, USA

1. INTRODUCTION

Many complex networks, consisting of nodes connected by directed or undirected links, display a "small-world" character [1-4]. Like a randomly connected network, they exhibit short global separations between nodes, yet like a regular lattice, they show high local connectivity. Well-known examples include the web of human acquaintances ("six degrees of separation"), the network of movie actors linked by shared billing, the internet, and food webs in ecological systems. In this contribution, key concepts of the statistical physics of complex networks will be illustrated by studying the connectivity of the 302-neuron "brain" of the nematode *C. Elegans*, a tiny worm that has been the subject of a huge body of scientific work recognized in the 2002 Nobel Prize in Physiology or Medicine.

Our successes in understanding the behavior of the systems studied traditionally by condensed-matter physicists and many-body theorists can be largely attributed to the simplicity of the operant pairwise interactions between the constituents [4]. There is no ambiguity or irregularity in the topology of interactions; it is clear what is connected to (or affected by) what. In many cases, the strength of the interaction is uniquely determined by the ordinary physical 3-space distance between the constituents (together, perhaps, with their spin configurations). Indeed, the interactions are commonly local, in the usual 3-space sense. However, scientists are increasingly confronted with more complex systems – or, more specifically, complex networks of nodes or agents and their connections or interactions – in which ordinary physical distance loses its meaning, and the existence of an interaction between any two constituents becomes ambiguous. One faces situations (as in the airline system) where local or near-neighbor actions – whether in the conventional sense or more abstractly – can produce striking global effects, in a manner that depends sensitively on network structure. The last few years have seen a great surge of interest in the development of an effective statistical physics of complex networks as well as an improved mechanistic understanding of their topological properties [2–4].

In Section 2, we focus on neural nets as a prime example of complex networks. We propose, as a primitive yet apt measure of the distance between two neurons, the smallest number of synaptic jumps needed to get from the one to the other. Following Ref. [1], we proceed to develop a theory of this measure for randomly connected neural nets. In Section 3, we present results for the average distance and distance distributions in two simple models of networks that deviate from the random paradigm and display varying degrees of local order. Section 4 enlarges our view and introduces, in addition to distance and its distribution, the further concepts of clustering coefficient and degree distribution as necessary ingredients of a statistical analysis of complex networks. Section 5 is devoted to a brief discussion of what it means to be a "small-world network" and offers numerous examples. In Section 6, we motivate the study of *C. Elegans* both as a "hydrogen atom" of multicellular animals and, through its nervous system, as a test-bed for understanding the small-world phenomenon. Section 7, the heart of our discourse, consists of a detailed analysis of the topological properties of a major portion of the nervous system of this noble worm, based on the theory and concepts provided in Sections 2 and 3 and employing connectivity data available on the world wide web. Finally, our analysis and results are compared with an earlier study [2] of the "brain" of *C. Elegans* that also served to verify the small-world nature of its topology.

2. DISTANCE IN RANDOM NEURAL NETWORKS

Consider a network of N neurons, regarded as structureless units that interact via synaptic junctions. A chemical synapse only works one way, with information flowing from the presynaptic neuron j to the postsynaptic neuron i; thus, neuron j can have a direct effect in i without the reverse being true. In other words, neural interactions are generally not symmetric. (Newton's third law is not obeyed in the nervous system: action and reaction are not equal!) The *connectivity* of such a neural network – it's "wiring diagram" or "architecture" – is conveniently specified by a $N \times N$ matrix (V_{ij}), where the matrix element $V_{ij} \in \{0, 1\}$ is nonzero if and only if unit j extends a connection to unit i.

We define the *distance* d_{ki} from generic neuron i to generic neuron k by the minimum number of synaptic junctions which information must traverse in going from i to k. The *distance matrix* (d_{ki}) is in general asymmetric.

Now imagine an ensemble of neural networks, each network being assembled randomly by the following algorithm.

(a) Consider an arbitrary neuron j and potential target neuron i, also chosen arbitrarily; with probability m, connect j to i with a synapse directed from j to i. (Thus, i is a potential postsynaptic neuron of the presynaptic neuron j.)

(b) Repeat for all j and then for all neurons i.

The parameter m is called the *connection probability* or the *connection parameter* of the ensemble of networks. Such nets define a class of *unstructured random networks*. Each neuron has, on average, $M = Nm$ outputs and the same number of inputs. It will be assumed that all distances in each sample net are finite. By this we mean that information can be transmitted from *any* neuron to *any* other neuron in the system via some sequence of neurons and across some sequence of synapses, while observing the fact that some (indeed, most) interneuronal junctions only work one way. This is the relevant case for our analysis, although it will not hold strictly for a biological nerve net because any functioning neural system must have inputs from, and outputs to, its surroundings in the organism or the world.

The above definitions and the coming analysis will actually apply just as well to the study of abstract networks composed of nodes connected by links. One may simply replace the specific terms "neuron" by "node" and "synaptic junction" by "directed link." Thus one may consider an ensemble of randomly constructed graphs with oriented edges. One may also consider the simpler case of undirected edges, in which connections between nodes work both ways. The theory of random graphs was pioneered by Erdös [5]. For a standard text, see Bollabás [6]; for an excellent recent review, see Albert and Barbási [4].

Keeping with the case of directed random nets, let us focus on a particular neuron A and find, in the ensemble average, the number $n(d)$ of neurons lying a distance d from A. Denote by $q(d)$ the number of neurons at distances from A *greater* than d; then

$$q(d) = N - \sum_{r=1}^{d} n(r)\,. \tag{1}$$

On average, each neuron has Nm output lines, so

$$n(1) = Nm\,. \tag{2}$$

The number of neurons left over is $N - Nm$, so

$$q(1) = N(1-m)\,. \tag{3}$$

Next pick, arbitrarily, one of the neurons B which receives one of the Nm outputs from A. On average, this neuron will itself have output lines going to Nm neurons. However, some of these neurons reached by B are already reached after only one step from neuron A, the rest being at a distance $d = 2$ from A. At any rate, outputs from B reach a fraction m of the $q(1)$ neurons left over after one step. This leaves a smaller pool of unreached neurons numbering

$$q(1) - mq(1) = q(1)(1-m) = N(1-m)(1-m)\,. \tag{4}$$

But neuron A has Nm target neurons like B, each of which reduces the pool of left-over neurons by a factor $(1-m)$. Hence there are

$$q(2) = q(1)(1-m)^{Nm} = q(1)(1-m)^{n(1)} \tag{5}$$

neurons unreached after two steps, making use of $Nm = n(1)$.

Continuing in this way, we may establish the following recursion relations for the function $n(d)$, where $d \geq 1$:

$$q(d+1) = q(d)(1-m)^{n(d)}\,, \tag{6a}$$

$$n(d+1) = q(d) - q(d+1) = q(d)\left[1-(1-m)^{n(d)}\right]. \tag{6b}$$

These equations are initiated by $n(1) = Nm$ and $q(1) = N(1-m)$. We immediately verify that $n(1) = N$ and $q(d) = 0$ for all d if $m = 1$.

The probability distribution $\rho(d)$ of neuron-to-neuron distances, with normalization $\sum_{d=1}^{d_{\max}} \rho(d) = 1$, is formed simply as $n(d)/N$. The average interneuronal distance is then given by

$$
\begin{aligned}
\langle d \rangle &= \sum_{d=1}^{d_{\max}} d\, n(d)/N \\
&= \{n(1) + 2n(2) + 3n(3) + 4n(4) + \cdots\}/N \\
&= \{n(1) + 2[q(1) - q(2)] + 3[q(2) - q(3)] + \cdots\}/N \\
&= \{n(1) + 2q(1) - 2q(2) + 3q(2) - 3q(3) + 4q(3) - \cdots\}/N \\
&= \{Nm + 2N(1-m) + q(2) + q(3) + \cdots q(d) + \cdots\}/N\,,
\end{aligned}
$$

$$\langle d \rangle = 2 - m + \sum_{d=2}^{d_{\max}} q(d)/N\,. \tag{7}$$

For fixed, finite m independent of N (implying that M scales like N^1), $\langle d \rangle$ saturates at $2 - m$ for large N. This follows since, when m is held constant, $q(d)$ becomes arbitrarily small compared to N for $d \geq 2$ at large enough N.

In general, it could be that M in $Nm = M$ scales like N^p instead of N^1. The case $p = 0$ means that M stays fixed at some finite value while N grows. In this case the mean distance $\langle d \rangle$ cannot saturate asymptotically, since the minimum number of steps needed to cover the net is N/M and the average distance must be greater. The lack of saturation may also be seen from the series representation of $\langle d \rangle$ on observing that the first recursion relation implies $q(d+1) = q(d) = N$ for $N \to \infty$. With $q(1) = N(1-m) = N$, all terms of the summation in Eq. (7) then contribute an equal finite amount. This second scenario (i.e., $M \sim N^0$) might correspond to considering an ever greater sample of cortical tissue, where the number of outputs (or inputs) per neuron remains roughly constant at something like 100–1000.

Figures 1 and 2 illustrate the behavior of the average distance $\langle d \rangle$ determined from Eq. (7) and the recursion relations (6) for an ensemble of randomly assembled networks, respectively as a function of the connection probability m and as a function of the average number $M = Nm$ of outputs per neuron. Figure 1 clearly demonstrates the saturation of $\langle d \rangle$ for large network sizes, in the case that m is independent of N.

3. STRUCTURED AND UNSTRUCTURED NETWORKS

Suppose we know the *connection matrix* (V_{ij}) for a particular network, which might be a member of an ensemble constructed randomly according to the algorithm of the last section, or might be a regular network with orderly connections, or might be something in between. In other words, consider a network with an arbitrary pattern of directed connections. The distribution of distances in such a network can be found from the fact that if the distance from neuron l to neuron k is d, then the klth element of the dth power of (V_{ij}) will be nonzero, while the klth element of all lower powers will vanish.

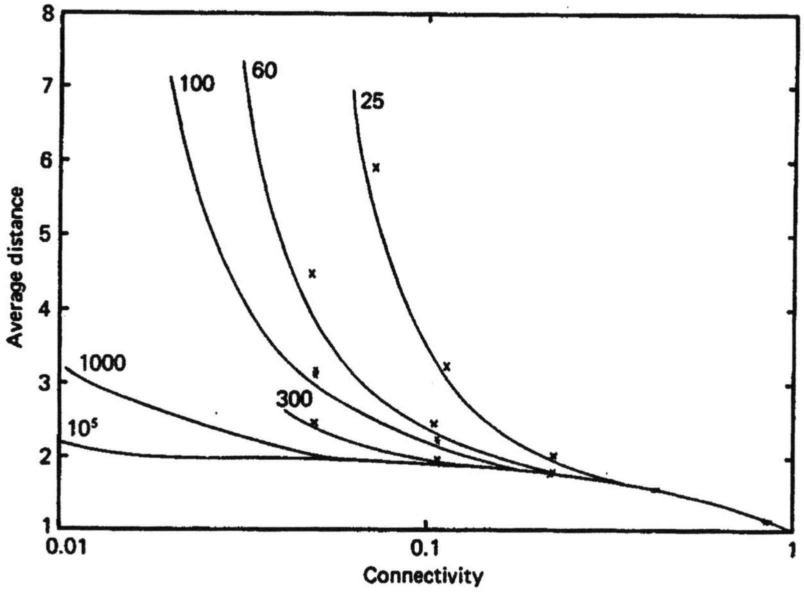

Figure 1. Average distance $\langle d \rangle$ as a function of connection probability m in an ensemble of randomly assembled networks for various sizes N. The solid curves are calculated from Eq. (7), while the crosses show actual mean distances in selected sample networks.

Thus, we have a simple recipe:

Compute successive powers of the matrix (V_{ij}) *and, by counting the number of elements that change from zero to a nonzero value at each stage, construct the distance distribution* $\rho(d)$ *of the sample net.*

Let us now consider two models for introducing order into network structure.

Collection of Weakly-Connected Netlets. Divide the set of N neurons into g groups (called netlets), each containing N/g neurons. Make *intranetlet* connections randomly, just as before, with connectivity parameter m_{int}, and form *internetlet* connections randomly with connectivity parameter $m_{\text{ext}} < m_{\text{int}}$. The ratio $l = m_{\text{int}}/m_{\text{ext}}$ serves as a measure of *local emphasis* or *clustering*. In simulations [1], the choices $N = 100$, $g = 4$, and $l = 5$, 10, and 20 have been considered.

Ring Structure. Having made an arbitrary initial labeling of the neurons, $i = 1, \ldots, N$, form the connectivity matrix according to these rules:

(i) Choose an integer L between 0 and $N-1$, and a number m satisfying $0 < m \leq 1$.

(ii) For a chosen presynaptic neuron i and postsynaptic neuron j, the matrix element V_{ij} is permitted to differ from zero *only if* $i - j \leq L$. (Hence the integral parameter L limits the number of neighbors.)

(iii) If the condition in (ii) is met, let j send a connection to i with probability m.

(iv) Repeat for all $N(N-1)$ pairs ij. In simulations [1], the choices $N = 100$, L from 3 to 20, and m from 0.2 to 0.8 have been considered.

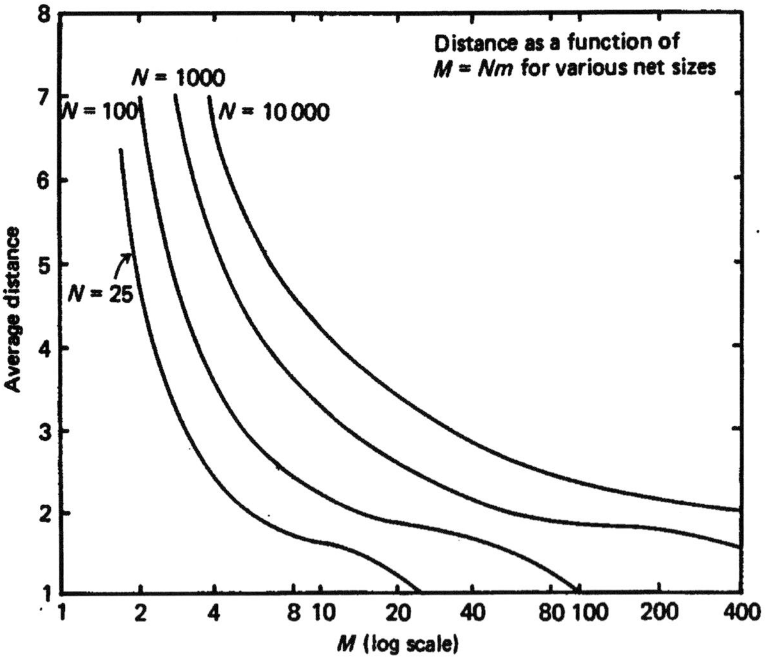

Figure 2. Average distance $\langle d \rangle$ as a function of the mean number $M = Nm$ of outputs per neuron in an ensemble of randomly assembled networks for various sizes N.

Some results for the distance distribution and average distance of structured nets of the above types are shown in Figs. 3 and 4, in comparison with results (sample or ensemble) for random networks. The most salient conclusion to be drawn from these results is that the average distance values obtained for the structured nets lie remarkably close to the curve derived for the corresponding ensemble of random nets, even for cases in which there is significant local emphasis (as measured by l or inversely by L). This feature is characteristic of systems that have come to be known as "small-world" networks.

A second observation is that the results for sample random nets, while showing satisfactory agreement with the statistical analysis of Section 2, nevertheless do evince appreciable deviations from the idealized, ensembled-averaged predictions for the distance distribution and average distance, owing to statistical fluctuations that increase with decreasing N (and fixed m) and with decreasing m (for fixed N). The fluctuations are not serious enough to obscure the small-world character of the networks studied, unless N or m is quite small. (More quantitative information on the effects of fluctuations may be found in Ref. [1].)

4. PROPERTIES OF COMPLEX NETWORKS

Let us continue to broaden our view and identify certain defining characteristics of complex networks, of whatever nature, made up of nodes or vertices connected by links or edges. We may consider networks with undirected edges, in which case a link

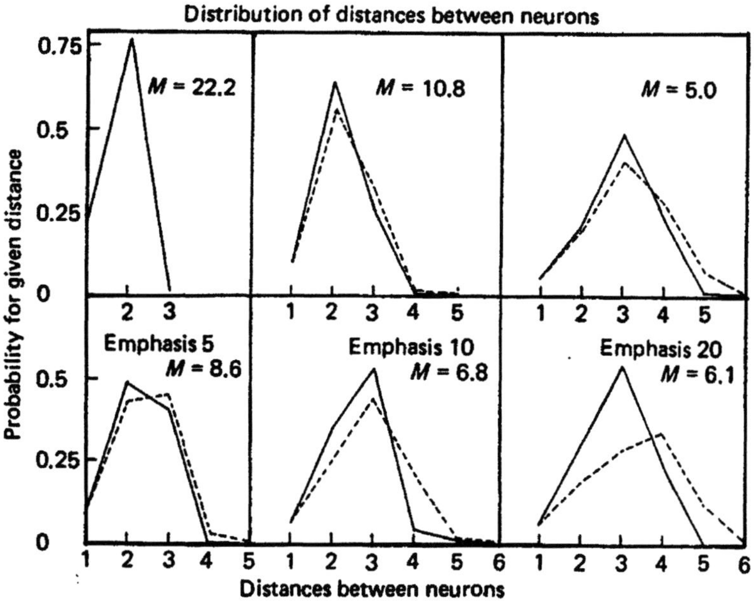

Figure 3. Dashed curves in upper triptych: actual distance distributions in three sample random networks of size $N = 100$ and respective connection probabilities $m = 0.222$, 0.108, and 0.050. Dashed curves in lower triptych: actual distance distributions in three sample networks of size $N = 100$ and respective average connection probabilities $m = 0.086$, 0.068, and 0.061, formed into $g = 4$ equal-sized netlet substructures with the indicated values of local emphasis l. Solid curves: ensemble-averaged statistical predictions for randomly assembled networks, determined from the recursion relations (6). The average number M of outputs per neuron is given for each case. The dashed and solid curves are practically coincident in the random case with $M = 22.2$.

between node j and node i establishes a one-step path from i to j as well as from j to i. This is the more common case studied in the literature. Alternatively, we may consider networks with directed, or oriented, edges; a connection directed from j to i does not imply the existence of a one-step path from i to j. This is the case relevant to neural networks. Chemical synapses are indeed directional connections; however, gap junctions (electrical synapses), which work both ways, are also present in neural systems. A gap junction between neurons i and j may be regarded either as a single undirected link or as a pair of reciprocal directed connections $j \to i$ and $i \to j$. The latter interpretation is the appropriate choice within our treatment of the model neural networks considered in the preceding sections, as well as for the nervous system of *C. Elegans*.

Def. The *distance* d_{ij} between two nodes j and i is the number of links or edges along the shortest path connecting them, with proper observance of the orientation of edges in the directed case.

Def. The *average distance* $\langle d \rangle$ is the mean of d_{ij} over all pairs ij (noting that ij and ji are regarded as different pairs in the case of directed links).

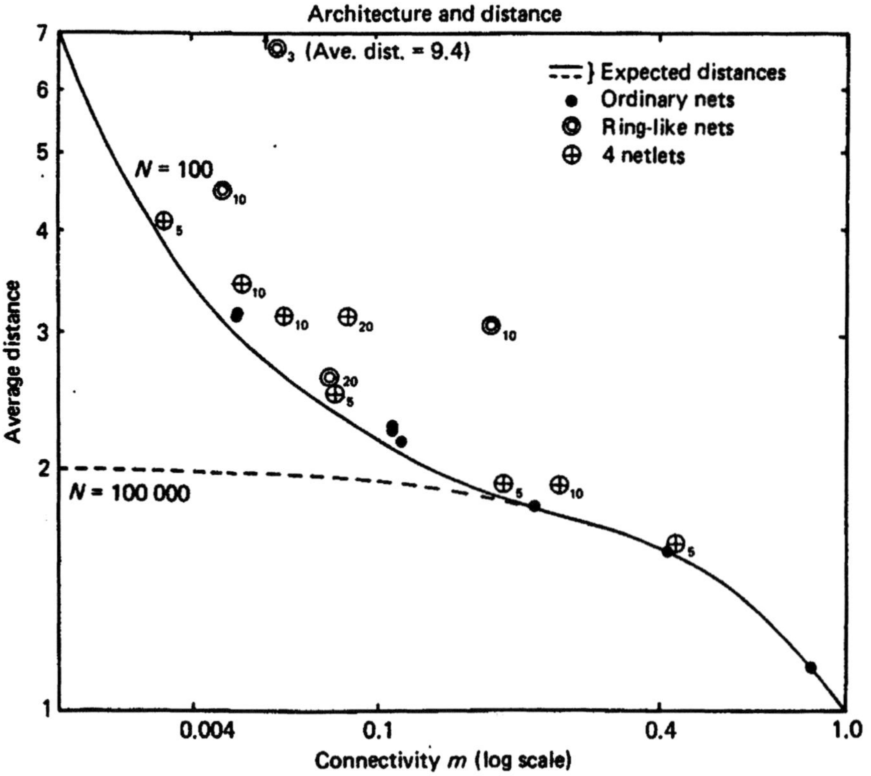

Figure 4. Average distances in randomly constructed sample nets ("ordinary nets") and in structured networks of the two types considered (group of weakly connected netlets; ring networks) are compared with ensemble-averaged distances predicted by the formulas (6)-(7) for the purely random case ("expected distances"), across the full range of the connectivity parameter m. The solid curve and the symbols for sample networks correspond to $N = 100$; the dashed curve, calculated for $N = 10^5$, is included for reference. The numbers attached to the symbols for the overtly structured networks denote the local emphasis measure L or l, as appropriate.

Def. The tendency of the nodes in a network to form clusters or cliques is frequently measured by the *clustering coefficient* C, also known as the "fraction of transitive triples." To find C, count the number of cases in which two nodes i and j that are neighbors of one another (i.e., one step apart) have a chosen node k as common neighbor. Divide by the number of directly-connected pairs i, j, thereby forming the clustering coefficient specific to node k. Then average over all k to obtain the overall clustering coefficient C. By choice (i.e., by definition), the direction of a link is irrelevant in forming the $\langle i, j, k\rangle$ triangles. For *random* networks, C coincides with the connection probability m.

Def. For the case of undirected edges, the *degree* of a node is the number of edges attached to it. In the case of directed edges, we define the *input degree* [*output degree*] of a node as the number of incoming [outgoing] connections to [from] the node.

Def. The *degree distribution* is defined by the probability $P(\mu)$ that a randomly chosen node i has exactly μ edges (undirected case). Extension to the case of directed edges is transparent.

For a random net of N nodes with connection probability m, the degree distribution is binomial,

$$P(\mu_i = \mu) = \binom{N-1}{\mu} m^{\mu}(1-m)^{N-1-\mu} \,. \tag{8}$$

The distribution therefore becomes Poisson in the limiting regime where N is asymptotically large and Nm remains finite.

In 1998, Watts and Strogatz [2] introduced a one-parameter model of complex networks, which, by tuning one parameter, allows one to study the transition from complete order to complete randomness. Their strategy was to start with order and then randomize. The specific algorithm they adopted runs as follows:

(i) Begin with a regular lattice of ring structure containing N nodes, each node being connected to its nearest K neighbors on the the ring. It is assumed that $N >> K >> \ln N >> 1$ so as to ensure that the network is sparse yet always connected.

(ii) Select a node on the ring and consider the link that connects it to its nearest neighbor, reckoned clockwise around the ring. With probability p, detach that link from the neighbor and reconnect it to a node chosen uniformly from all the nodes in the ring, subject to the provision that self-connections and duplicate connections are forbidden. Repeat this process $N-1$ times, working clockwise around the ring. In this way, some $pNK/2$ long-range connections replace the same number of short-range ones.

This model is strongly reminiscent of the ring model introduced in Ref. [1] and described in Section 3. However, there are some important differences. For one thing, the authors of Ref. [1] adopted a strategy opposite that of Watts and Strogatz, proceeding instead from randomness to order. For another thing, Watts and Strogatz do not assign directions to edges, whereas oriented links are intrinsic to the work of Ref. [1] as well as the present study.

5. WHAT IS A "SMALL-WORLD" NETWORK?

The *Nature* article [2] of Watts and Strogatz stimulated world-wide interest in the "small-world" phenomenon and a rapidly proliferating literature on this subject [3,4]. These authors found that realizations of their model could retain significant and discernible order, yet display "small-world" behavior in the sense that the average distance between nodes remains small, as in a random network. (We note that the studies of Ref. [1], carried out a decade earlier, gave evidence for the same phenomenon.)

Divorcing the discussion from any particular model, a small-world network is in general characterized topologically by (a) short separations between arbitrary nodes, as in the case of a random graph, together with (b) a high degree of local connectivity, as in a regular lattice. These seemingly contradictory properties are reflected quantitatively in a relatively small average distance $\langle d \rangle$ and a relatively large clustering coefficient C (or large local emphasis). The degree distribution can show marked differences from a Binomial or Poisson distribution (e.g., a slower tail); on the other hand it can exhibit near-random behavior in some examples.

Actually, one of the first to draw attention to the small-world phenomenon in the modern era was the social psychologist Stanley Milgram [7], whose remarkable experiment revealing the short mean distance in the web of human acquaintances was the origin of the pithy adage "six degrees of separation," also used as the title of a popular Broadway play by John Guare. Other examples include [4]: the world-wide web (site level); the internet (domain level); the network of movie actors linked by shared billing; co-authorship of scientific papers; genealogical networks; the substrate and reaction graphs of *E. Coli*; food webs in ecological systems; co-occurrence of words in text; networks of synonyms; the power grid of the U.S.; and the nervous system of *C. Elegans*. It seems reasonable to add the human brain to the list, but the analysis of its topological properties presents an awesome task at this stage of our knowledge.

6. C. ELEGANS: WHY STUDY THIS LOWLY WORM?

Let us turn now to an application of the concepts and analysis of Sections 2–4 to a real biological neural network.

First, what is *C. Elegans*? It is a tiny animal belonging to the *Phylum Nematoda*, which consists of the roundworms and threadworms, these being smooth-skinned, unsegmented worms having a long body of cylindrical shape, tapered at its ends. The Phylum includes worms that are free-living or parasitic, and worms that live in the water or on land. Our worm, *C. Elegans*, is not a parasite; it lives freely in the soil and feeds off bacteria. It is of no economic importance to mankind, and it does us no harm, but its conceptual importance is large. (This and other descriptive material on *C. Elegans* is drawn from a variety of sources on the world wide web [8-15], as well as the monograph of Achacoso and Yamamoto [16].)

The organism is only about 1 mm in length. In can be cultivated in a petri dish sprinkled with bacteria. Conveniently, it is transparent, so one can view its organs through a microscope. Its lifespan is normally only 2–3 weeks. (A curious exception is the *dauer phase*: the worm goes into a dormant larval state when food is scarce; with its mouth sealed shut, it can live for months and then revive.) There are two sexes – no, not the usual male and female, but rather a male (which is very rare, accounting for only one birth in a thousand) and a hermaphrodite. The hermaphrodite has both eggs and sperm and can reproduce either on its own or by mating with a male. Something like 300 baby worms are born after each sexual encounter (solo or pairwise). The reproductive system takes up much of the volume of the animal.

For the purposes of study, it is a remarkable and important fact that all hermaphroditic individuals are effectively identical, cell by cell. This version of the worm has 959 somatic cells, of which 302 – all identified, studied, and labeled – are neurons, these being accompanied by 56 glial support cells. (In case you are curious, the male has a larger nervous system, with 381 neurons supplemented by 92 glial cells; this in spite of the fact that it is much easier for the male to find an hermaphrodite than vice versa.)

All very amusing, but why would biologists want to study this lowly worm with such intensity? The answer is that *C. Elegans* may be the simplest and most primitive organism that shares so many of the essential biological characteristics of the human animal. For one thing, it is conceived as a single cell and undergoes a complicated process of development, embryonic cleavage and morphogenesis being followed by growth to the adult form. Second, it possesses a nervous system including a "brain" (identified with the circumpharyngeal nerve ring). It even shows adaptive behavior attributable to a simple learning mechanism. As already mentioned above, it manufactures both sperm and eggs, and it can reproduce by mating. After birth, the worm gradually ages, eventually weakens, and dies.

While exhibiting all these familiar phenomena, *C. Elegans* is only about 1 mm long and can be cultivated and studied like a microorganism. As a biological preparation, it offers a splendid compromise between complexity and tractability. Very significantly, it is the first organism for which a complete genomic sequencing was achieved (specifically, by a team including Washington University researchers). The importance of *C. Elegans* to biology was celebrated in the 2002 Nobel award in Physiology or Medicine to Sydney Brenner, H. Robert Horvitz, and John E. Sulston [10,11]. It was Brenner [11] who championed *C. Elegans* as a fundamental prototype for multicellular organisms.

Our interest is obviously focused on the nervous system of *C. Elegans*, especially the nature of its connectivity. The neural structures in the worm foreshadow those of higher animals, both in configuration and function. One finds a collection of sense organs in the head that respond to taste, smell, touch, and temperature. The creature has no eyes, but does show a slight response to light. There are 81 muscle cells stimulated by some subset of the 302 neurons making up the nervous system. An elegant swimming motion is achieved through the coordinated action of four longitudinal bands of muscle paired sub-dorsally and sub-ventrally ("dorsal" refers to the back or upper side of an animal, "ventral" to its belly).

Although it has only a small number of neurons, *C. Elegans* possesses a rich collection of neuron types. As intimated above, and according to "The Mind of the Worm" [13],

> *Each neuron has a unique combination of properties, such as morphology, connectivity and position, so that every neuron may be given a unique label. Groups of neurons that differ from each other only in position have been assigned to classes. There are 118 classes that have been made using these criteria, the class sizes ranging from 1 to 13.*

The 302 neurons interact at some 5000 chemical synapses (based on asymmetric transfer of information through transmission of neurochemicals from presynaptic terminals to receptor sites on the postsynaptic cell), at more than 600 gap junctions (where the transmission is electrical and presumed to be symmetric), and at about 2000 neuromuscular junctions (where muscle actions are stimulated by motor neurons). Most gap junctions are found between neurons of the same class; this contrasts with the case of chemical synapses, which rarely join members of the same class. The system of neurons is subserved by 56 non-excitable glial cells that provide support while separating nerve cells from each other and from non-neural body cells.

Broadly speaking, neurons may be divided into three categories: (i) *sensory neurons* (providing input to the nervous system), (ii) *interneurons* (which modulate the flow of information internally), and (iii) *motor neurons* (which contact muscle cells and generate action corresponding to the computations that have been performed by the system based on its input). These three types account respectively for (roughly) one-third, one half, and one-quarter of the excitable neural cells.

The basic body plan of the organism involves two concentric tubes: an outer tube containing the cuticle, hypodermis, neurons, and muscle cells, and an inner tube comprised of a pseudocoelom space filled with intestines and gonads. Structurally, the nervous system divides into two parts, the pharyngeal nervous system (consisting of 20 neurons for which the connectivity data is not yet fully available) and the central nervous system (consisting of the remaining 282, whose connectivity is well mapped). The pharyngeal nervous system belongs to the pharynx, a neuromuscular pump in the mouth of the worm that is responsible for feeding behavior. It is largely independent of the central nervous system and therefore will be largely irrelevant to our investigation. (A pair of cells in the central nervous system, labeled CANL and CANR, do form connections with the pharyngeal system.)

The population of neurons in the central nervous system is organized into nine distinct ganglia, which contain afferent collectors and efferent senders of information. Between the ganglia are cells with relatively few connections, thought to act as logical gates [16]. Each ganglion is a "hub" for processing information relevant to a certain function or functions. Some collect data from many sources and convey output to only a few targets; and vice versa. The nerve tracks run in parallel "process bundles" with little branching. (Here, "process" is a biological term synonymous with "axon," the extended fiber integral to a nerve cell that functions as a cable for electrical signal transmission.) The primary process bundle, called the ventral cord, is analogous to our spinal cord. Others include the nerve ring and the dorsal and lateral processes. The nerve bundles run antiposteriorly from the nerve ring and/or circumferentially. Synapses occur "en passant" in regions of dense neuropile. On average, each neuron is connected to about half of its *physical* neighbors; of course, it may also form connections with neurons at considerable physical distances.

For many purposes, it is correct to say that the neural connectivity (the "wiring diagram") of *C. Elegans* has been completely mapped out experimentally. Basically, we know who talks to whom (i.e., which neuron communicates with which), and often we know through how many channels (i.e., through how many synaptic contacts) the conversation is conducted. On the other hand, the individual strengths of the many synaptic interactions remain largely unknown. Here we are limiting our attention merely to the list of postsynaptic neurons contacted by any given presynaptic neuron, in other words, to the connectivity (or adjacency) matrix (V_{ij}).

We shall not be concerned with the multiplicity of synaptic contacts of one cell upon another; rather, we only care whether such contacts are – or are not – made. Nevertheless, some comments on the issue of multiplicity may be useful for clarification. Physically, an *individual* synaptic contact involves the conjunction of an axonal digit of the presynaptic cell with the dendritic tree or soma of the postsynaptic cell. In the *C. Elegans* system, multiplicity is found to range between 1 and 19, with an average of five [16]. Multiplicity might serve as an appropriate measure of the strength or weight of the connection from the presynaptic to the postsynaptic neuron. It can be difficult to determine, since postsynaptic partners of a given presynaptic neuron may be far away. Moreover, the presynaptic cell may well deliver different neurotransmitter chemicals at its different axon terminals, which may contain neurotransmitter vesicles of different sizes.

7. NEURAL CONNECTIVITY OF C. ELEGANS

Our study of *C. Elegans* as a potential small-world network is based on connectivity data taken from the Wormbase web site [14], and more specifically from the data on the pages [15]. This source provides us with complete connectivity information for a subset of 180 nerve cells considered to form the "main" nervous system. The data takes account of directed as well as reciprocal connections and therefore allows us to construct a connectivity matrix (V_{ij}) for this primary collection of neurons. Of the remaining 122 cells of the full nervous system, some 85 are motor neurons, which by definition have terminals outside the nervous system proper and thus might sensibly be omitted in an analysis that acknowledges the possible directionality of connections. Also omitted is the essentially independent subsystem of 20 pharyngeal neurons. The network selected for study involves 2406 outgoing connections from its neurons and 2403 incoming connections to its neurons. Of these, 340 are formed by gap junctions and 222 by other reciprocal interactions, for a total of 2×562 bi-directional connections.

Figure 5 shows the distance distribution $\rho(d)$ derived from repeated multiplication of the empirically determined matrix (V_{ij}) by itself. This matrix has a total of $180 \times 180 = 32,400$ elements and allows for the same number of connections. However, only 2406 of these elements are nonzero, corresponding to the existing interneuronal connections; this density of connections corresponds in turn to a connection probability m of 0.0742. Also shown in Figure 5 is the distance distribution for a random network with the same connection probability. We observe that the actual distribution is somewhat broader, although evaluation of the average distance $\langle d \rangle$ based on this distribution gives a value 2.50, not much larger than the result 2.26 obtained for the random case from Eqs. (6)–(7). The standard deviation associated with the former mean value is 0.732, i.e., the spread is significant.

The process of repeated self-multiplication of the connection matrix does not converge to a multiple that is free of zeros. This means that for some neuron pairs ij it is not possible to find a continuous directed pathway from one member of the pair to the other; in other words, our assumption that all interneuron distances are finite is not strictly correct. However, some violation must be expected, since any functioning nervous system must have an input interface and an output interface where its neurons interact with their environment (whether internal or external to the organism). For example, all inputs to a sensory system could originate from the

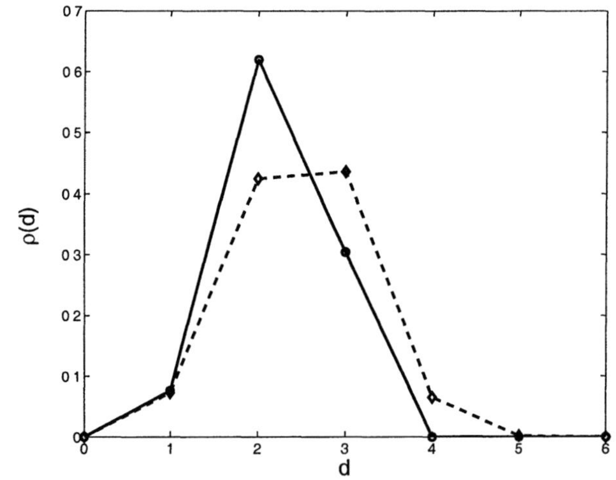

Figure 5. Distance distribution $\rho(d)$ versus distance d for the 180-neuron subnet of the nervous system of *C. Elegans* (diamonds and dashed line). Plotted for comparison is the average distance distribution obtained from Eqs. (6) and (7) for an ensemble of random networks constructed using the same connectivity parameter m (circles and solid line).

visual environment. At any rate, the violation observed in the present case is not very serious. Recall that in the 180-neuron system, there are 2406 nonzero elements in the connection matrix (V_{ij}). Raising (V_{ij}) to successive integral powers, saturation is reached at the fifth power, in the sense that no further matrix elements change from zero to nonzero values upon forming any higher power. A residue of less than 400 zero elements remains, implying that more than 98% of the 32,400 ordered (i, j) pairs are actually connected by some admissible, directed pathway.

Figures 6 and 7 provide data on two degree distributions associated with the chosen 180-neuron network of *C. Elegans.* Figure 6 refers to the distribution in the number of efferent (outgoing) connections of neurons of the system; and Figure 7, to the distribution in the number of afferent (incoming) connections. The mean number of input connections per neuron is 13.37, and the mean number of output connections per neuron is 13.35. These counts need not coincide, since some connections may terminate outside (or originate from outside) the 180-neuron network. At any rate, we may infer an empirical value $m = 0.0742$ for the connection probability introduced in Section 2.

For each of the degree distributions derived from the *C. Elegans* data, comparison is made with the corresponding Poisson distribution predicted from Eq. (8) for a random network at large N but finite Nm. Substantial deviation from the Poisson form is observed in both cases; in particular, the fall-off at large degree appears to be slower than exponential.

The clustering coefficient C determined from the connectivity data on the 180-neuron system is found to be 0.299, a value considerably larger than the result 0.0742 for the corresponding random case. Of the three broad types of neurons alluded to above, the *sensory neurons* have, on average, the highest clustering

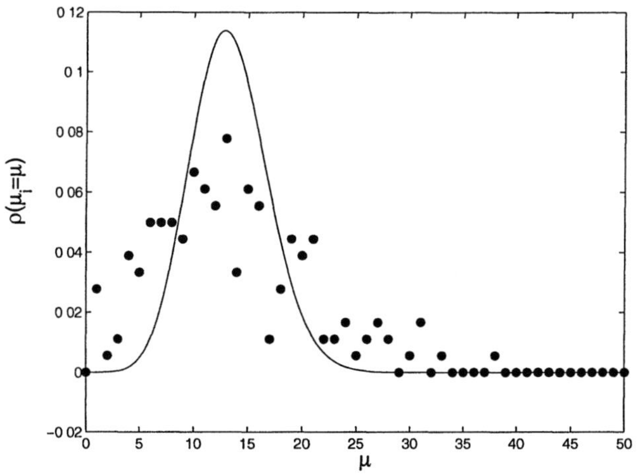

Figure 6. Degree distribution $\rho(\mu_i = \mu)$ of the *outgoing* connections of an arbitrary neuron i, versus the number μ of efferent connections emanating from the neuron. The corresponding Poisson distribution, expected for a random network in the limit of large N but finite M, is plotted for reference (solid curve).

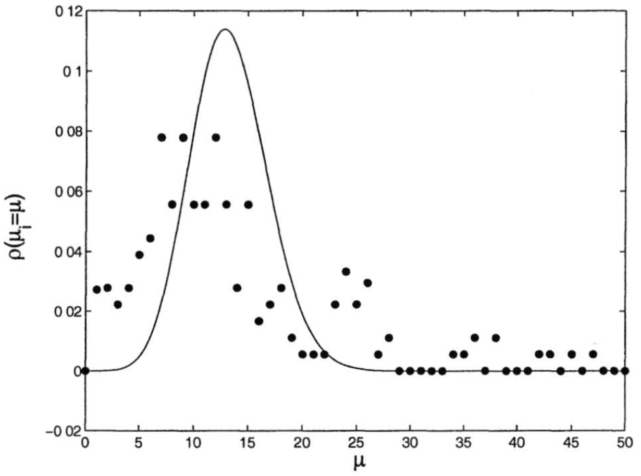

Figure 7. Degree distribution $\rho(\mu_i = \mu)$ of the *incoming* connections to an arbitrary neuron i, versus the number μ of afferent connections impinging on the neuron. The corresponding Poisson distribution, expected for a random network in the limit of large N but finite M, is plotted for reference (solid curve).

coefficients, the average over all cells of this type being 0.332. The largest clustering coefficient found was 0.6, for the sensory neuron named ASJR [15]. The strong clustering of sensory neurons is not unexpected, in view of the rapid diffusion of sensory information coming from the environment, which requires a high density of connections with the affected ganglionic cells.

The clustering coefficients for *interneurons* and *motor neurons* present in the 180-neuron system are somewhat smaller, with the respective average values 0.278 and 0.275. It is understandable that these types of neurons should participate in a smaller fraction of transitive triples. Roughly speaking, the set of interneurons serves collectively as the switchboard for communication within the worm's nervous system, providing for both positive and negative feedback. Although these cells have many physical neighbors, they connect preferentially with remote parts of a nerve bundle, or with cells in entirely different neighborhoods. In fact, the interneuron RMGR has the lowest coefficient (0.154) of any cell studied. Turning to the motor neurons, we need merely observe that their primary connections are made outside the nervous system. (It was for this very reason that not many motor neurons were included in the 180-neuron system chosen for "small-world" analysis.) Their function is to transmit signals to the muscles, usually those on the opposite side of the body, by means of axon fibers that pass through tiny holes in a ridge of skin-type cells that line the ventral side of the creature. We must note, of course, that since most of the motor neurons were disregarded in our study, the clustering coefficients we have derived for them may not be representative.

Setting aside the relatively minor differences in local connectivity found for the three categories of neurons, it is well to emphasize the high *average* clustering coefficient determined for the 180-neuron network chosen for investigation. This finding is in complete accord with the following observation quoted from "The Mind of the Worm" [13]:

> *One of the striking features of the connectivity diagrams is the high incidence of triangular connections linking three classes. These structures may occur frequently as a consequence of the organization of the neuropile. A typical neuron in C. elegans is accessible (i.e. adjacent) to a fairly limited subset of the total complement of neurons but is fairly highly locally connected within this subset. Thus, if a neuron has synaptic contacts with two partners, these two partners must be neighbours to the neuron and therefore are likely to be neighbours themselves. It is therefore quite probable, given the high level of local connectivity, that there will be a synaptic contact between them, which will close the triangle. The abundance of triangular connections in the nervous system of C. elegans may thus simply be a consequence of the high levels of connectivity that are present within neighbourhoods.*

8. CONCLUSIONS

Utilizing connectivity data available on the world wide web, we have carried out an analysis of the complex network represented by the nervous system of the nematode *C. Elegans* based on the concepts and techniques developed and reviewed in Refs. [1,4] and presented in Sections 2–4. The results of a similar analysis of the worm's nervous system were reported in the path-breaking *Nature* article [1] of Watts and Strogatz (WS). Both treatments offer clear and convincing evidence for the small-world character of this fundamental biological nerve network. Nevertheless, there are some key differences in the two treatments that deserve comment.

One significant difference is that the present analysis takes into account the intrinsic directionality of chemical synapses, whereas WS suppress directionality and regard the system as an undirected graph. Clearly, our analysis is more realistic in this sense. On the other hand, WS consider a larger portion of the full neural net of *C. Elegans*, including 282 neurons compared to our 180. Different data sources are chosen for the two studies; in particular, our data has been taken from the updated Wormbase on-line resource [15], whereas WS use the connectivity matrix provided in the invaluable book by Achacoso and Yamamoto [16]. The network analyzed by WS omits only the 20 neurons of the pharyngeal nervous system, whereas ours deletes those and most of the motor neurons of the central nervous system. On this score, the WS choice might be viewed as the more realistic.

Remarkably, the two analyses are in rather close agreement in terms of the essential measures that signal small-world behavior. For the average distance we find 2.50, compared to the WS value of 2.62 (and the random-network value 2.26). For the average clustering coefficient, our result of 0.299 is to be compared with their 0.28 (and our random-network value 0.05). One would naturally expect an increase in average distance when the directionality of connections is acknowledged, so the very small difference between the $\langle d \rangle$ values found in the two studies – with our result actually being the *smaller* – is perhaps surprising. On the other hand, the expected increase may well be largely compensated by the omission from our study of most of the motor neurons, which are by nature "less connected" than the bulk of the other neurons in the central nervous system.

The results of a repetition of our analysis for the larger data set considered in Ref. [2] will be reported in a future article.

ACKNOWLEDGMENTS

This research was supported in part by the U. S. National Science Foundation under Grant No. PHY-0140316. JWC is grateful for travel support that enabled him to participate in CMT26, jointly provided to him by the U.S. Army Research Office–Research Triangle Park (through a grant to Southern Illinois University–Carbondale) and by Fundação Luso-Americana para o Desenvolvimento (FLAD). He is also indebted to FLAD and to the Fundação para a Ciência e a Technologia (FCT) for financial support of his participation in Madeira Math Encounters XXIII at the University of Madeira, where part of this work was done. He thanks both Professor João da Providência and Professor Ludwig Streit for exceptionally generous hospitality.

REFERENCES

[1] J. W. Clark, G. C. Littlewort, and J. Rafelski, in *Computer Simulation in Brain Science*, R. M. J. Cotterill, ed. (Cambridge University Press, Cambridge, 1988), pp. 104-118.

[2] D. J. Watts and S. H. Strogatz, *Nature* **393**, 440 (1998).

[3] D. J. Watts, *Small Worlds: The Dynamics of Networks Between Order and Randomness* (Princeton University Press, Princeton, NJ, 1999).

[4] R. Albert and A.-L. Barabási, *Reviews of Modern Physics* **74**, 47 (2002).

[5] P. Erdös and A. Reńyi, *Publ. Math. Inst. Hung. Acad. Sci.* **5**, 17 (1960).

[6] B. Bollabás, *Random Graphs* (Academic Press, NY, 1985).

[7] S. Milgram, *Psychol. Today* **1**, 60 (1967).

[8] http://elegans.swmed.edu/.

[9] http://www.biotech.missouri.edu/Dauer-World/Wormintro.html; http://www.loci.wisc.edu/outreach/text/celegans.html.

[10] http://www.nobel.se/medicine/laureates/2002/press.html; http://almaz.com/nobel/medicine/2002a.html.

[11] http://elegans.swmed.edu/Sydney.html.

[12] http://www.wormatlas.org/.

[13] J. G. White, E. Southgate, J. N. Thomson, and S. Brenner, "The structure of the nervous system of the nematode *Caenorhabditis elegans*, *Phil. Trans. Royal Soc. London. Series B, Biol. Sciences* **314**, 1 (1986); this paper is easily accessed at http://www.wormatlas.org/.

[14] http://www.wormbase.org/.

[15] http://www.wormbase.org/db/searches/neuron302.cgi.

[16] T. B. Achacoso and W. S. Yamamoto, *Neuroanatomy of C. elegans for Computation* (CRC Press, Boca, Raton, FL, 1992).

INDEX